chemistry of life processes

periodic table of the elements

	IB	IIB	IIIA	IVA	VA	VIA	VIIA	0
								2 **He** 4.0026
			5 **B** 10.811	6 **C** 12.01115	7 **N** 14.0067	8 **O** 15.9994	9 **F** 18.9984	10 **Ne** 20.183
			13 **Al** 26.9815	14 **Si** 28.086	15 **P** 30.9738	16 **S** 32.064	17 **Cl** 35.453	18 **Ar** 39.948
28 **Ni** 58.71	29 **Cu** 63.54	30 **Zn** 65.37	31 **Ga** 69.72	32 **Ge** 72.59	33 **As** 74.9216	34 **Se** 78.96	35 **Br** 79.909	36 **Kr** 83.80
46 **Pd** 106.4	47 **Ag** 107.870	48 **Cd** 112.40	49 **In** 114.82	50 **Sn** 118.69	51 **Sb** 121.75	52 **Te** 127.60	53 **I** 126.9044	54 **Xe** 131.30
78 **Pt** 195.09	79 **Au** 196.967	80 **Hg** 200.59	81 **Tl** 204.37	82 **Pb** 207.19	83 **Bi** 208.980	84 **Po** (210)	85 **At** (210)	86 **Rn** (222)

63 **Eu** 151.96	64 **Gd** 157.25	65 **Tb** 158.924	66 **Dy** 162.50	67 **Ho** 164.930	68 **Er** 167.26	69 **Tm** 168.934	70 **Yb** 173.04	71 **Lu** 174.97
95 **Am** (243)	96 **Cm** (247)	97 **Bk** (247)	98 **Cf** (249)	99 **Es** (254)	100 **Fm** (253)	101 **Md** (256)	102 **No** (256)	103 **Lw** (257)

chemistry of life processes

raymond p. mariella

Loyola University

rose ann blau

Loyola University

harcourt, brace & world, inc.

New York / Chicago / San Francisco / Atlanta

Photograph from "Molecular Model for Protein Synthesis," G. Zubay, *Science,* Vol. 140, pp. 1092–1095, 7 June 1963.

Library of Congress Catalog Card Number: 68-12975

Printed in the United States of America

preface

This book is designed for the many students—for example, nurses, home economists, and medical technologists—who require a course in elementary physiological chemistry.

To understand physiological chemistry, students need some knowledge of organic chemistry and biochemistry. This need is not adequately met in most textbooks, which contain much inorganic chemistry but very little organic chemistry and biochemistry. In such books, the inorganic material tends to be a review of high-school chemistry, while organic chemistry and biochemistry are treated in a condensed fashion, omitting many important topics.

To meet the needs of the students, we restrict the inorganic chemistry in this book to the fundamental principles essential to an understanding of organic chemistry and biochemistry. In our discussion of organic chemistry, we stress the functional groups and the nomenclature of compounds. To stimulate the student's interest, we also discuss the pharmacological and industrial uses of many compounds. The biochemistry is introduced on an elementary level, but without sacrificing accuracy; most body processes are quite complex and we try to present them in a comprehensible style without resorting to oversimplification.

To cover the entire book adequately requires a year's course. However, we have used this material at Loyola University in teaching a one-semester course by omitting the last three chapters and many of the details of the other chapters. This book may also be used in a very elementary biochemistry course for students who have some background in organic chemistry. In this case, the instructor may wish to begin with Chapter 10.

We wish to acknowledge, with deep gratitude and sincere thanks, the following people who have been so helpful in discussing and reviewing much of the material in this book: Dr. Stephen Pavkovic, Dr. James Wilt, Dr. C. D. Hurd, and Dr. M. Goldie.

We also wish to thank Margaret McCarthy and Mary Rita Coit for their help with reading proof and indexing; and Mimi Mariella and Ann Marie Mariella for typing the entire manuscript.

RAYMOND P. MARIELLA
ROSE ANN BLAU

contents

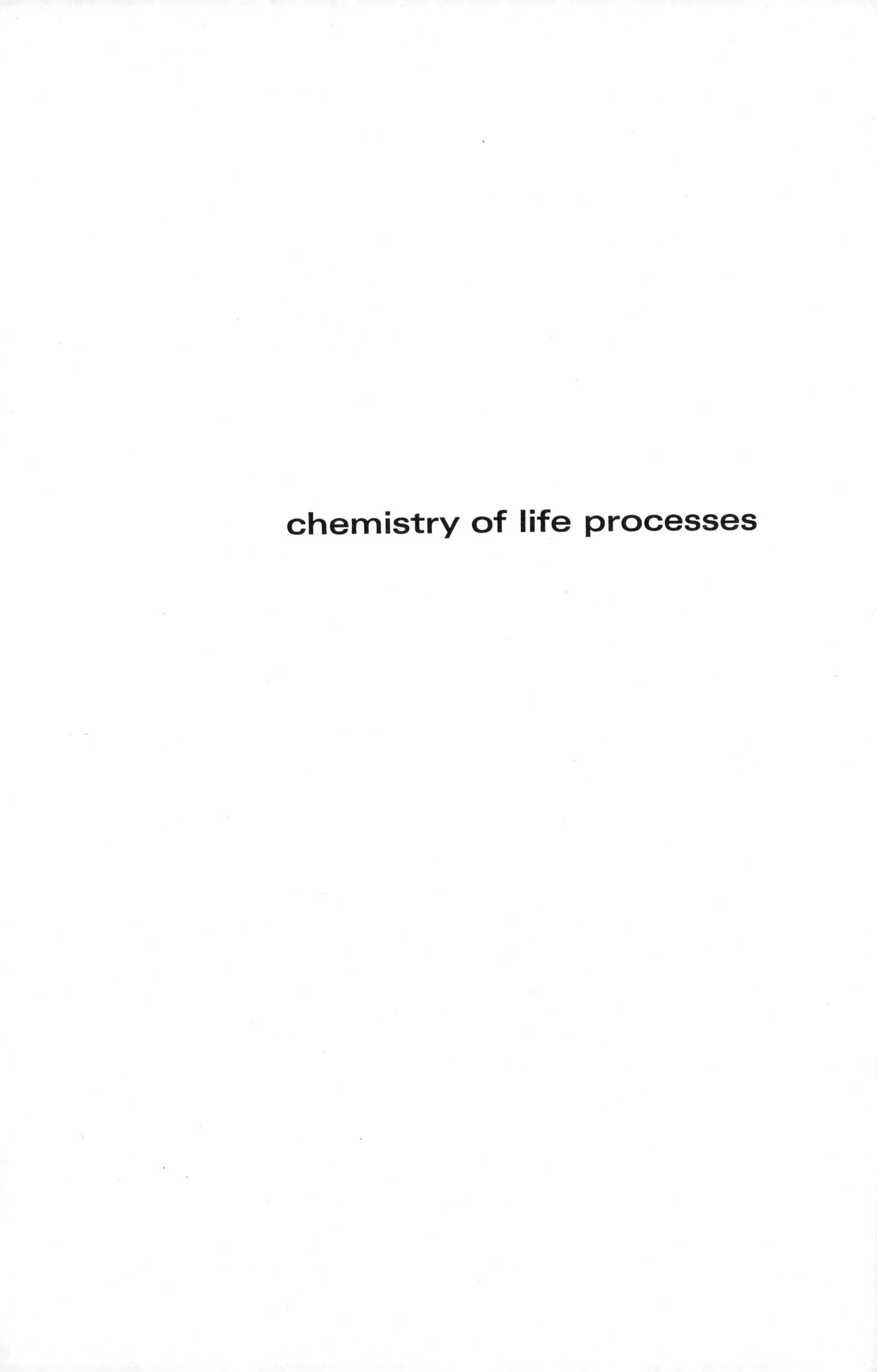

chemistry of life processes

1

fundamental principles

Chemistry is the study of matter and the changes it undergoes. To understand this definition, we must define matter. *Matter* is anything that occupies space. It may exist in three states or forms: gaseous, liquid, and solid. Water, for example, may commonly exist as a gas (steam), a liquid, or a solid (ice); oxygen is usually found as a gas; sodium chloride (table salt) is usually found as a solid.

Matter may undergo two types of changes: physical and chemical. A *physical change* is the alteration of the physical properties of the substance while the substance remains the same. For example, when ice is melted, the form of water changes, but it is still water. Boiling water changes it to steam, which will have the properties of a gas, but the substance will still be water and react like water. A *chemical change* is the alteration of the chemical properties of the substance; this changes the substance into something new. For example, burning wood changes it into gases, light, heat, and charcoal. The substance is no longer wood; it is now gases and charcoal. Exploding a firecracker changes the explosive into gases, heat, and energy; these are new substances, and the firecracker as it was no longer exists. A less destructive chemical change is photosynthesis. The plant changes carbon dioxide and water into sugar. The sugar does not have the properties of carbon dioxide or water; it has all the properties of the substance sugar.

Classification of matter

Matter may be classified as homogeneous or heterogeneous. *Homogeneous* matter is pure, that is, alike throughout. *Heterogeneous* matter, called a mixture, consists of distinctly different parts separated from one another by boundary surfaces. Parts of a mixture may be visible to the eye, such as the constituents of a granite rock, or may need magnification to be seen, such as the constituents of steel or a mixture of white sand and sugar.

Homogeneous matter may be further classified as elements, compounds, and solutions.

Elements

An *element* is a substance that cannot be decomposed into more simple substances. Elements are the fundamental units of the universe, and, at the present time, 103 elements are known to man. Each element has a name and a characteristic symbol, which is the convenient shorthand notation of the chemist. If one letter represents the element, the letter is capitalized; if two letters represent the element, the first letter is capitalized and the second is lower case. (Elements and symbols are listed on the inside back cover.) Oxygen is the most abundant element known on earth.

Suppose we divide a sample of pure gold until the particles are much smaller than can be seen either by the unaided eye or by magnification. These ultrasmall particles are still gold, and if we continue this process, we would finally obtain the smallest possible particle, which would still be gold. This particle is called an *atom.* An atom, then, is the smallest particle of an element that still possesses the properties of the element.

If we divide a sample of pure aluminum until we obtain the smallest possible particle that possessed the properties of aluminum, we would have an atom of aluminum. Gold and aluminum atoms differ in size, shape, weight, and reactivity. No one has ever actually seen atoms, but we have excellent evidence of their properties.

Elements have varying degrees of reactivity; that is, aluminum differs from sodium in its reaction with water. Because many are quite reactive, elements tend to combine with each other. In fact, some elements are so reactive that they are difficult to purify and obtain in the atomic state.

When two or more atoms combine, we obtain a substance called a *molecule*. Some elements tend to exist naturally in the molecular form. They may be diatomic, for example, H_2 (hydrogen), O_2 (oxygen), and Cl_2 (chorine); triatomic, for example, O_3 (ozone); tetratomic, for example, P_4 (phosphorus vapor), etc.

Compounds

A *compound* is a pure substance composed of two or more different elements in a definite proportion by weight, for example, HCl, hydrogen chloride gas (consisting of two elements, hydrogen and chlorine); $CHCl_3$, chloroform (three elements); $C_6H_3N_3O_7$, picric acid (four elements); etc. The smallest unit of a compound is a molecule. A molecule of hydrogen chloride gas consists of one hydrogen atom and one chlorine atom. A molecule of chloroform contains one carbon atom, one hydrogen atom, and three chlorine atoms. One molecule of picric acid consists of six carbon atoms, three hydrogen atoms, three nitrogen atoms, and seven oxygen atoms.

Although only 103 elements are known, so many different combinations exist that more than a million compounds are known today.

Structure of atoms

Fundamental Particles

Atoms are composed of particles, and it is informative to consider three of these in some detail: *proton, neutron,* and *electron.* The proton carries a positive charge, the electron carries a negative charge of the same magnitude, and the neutron is neutral and carries no net charge. Together the proton and neutron make up most of the mass of the atom, and they are located at its center in a very dense region known as the nucleus. Because the nucleus contains all the protons, it is always positively charged. In Table 1-1 are listed the symbol, charge, relative mass, and location of these fundamental atomic particles.

The number of protons determines the identity of the atom. Accord-

Table 1-1 Fundamental atomic particles

NAME	SYMBOL	CHARGE	RELATIVE MASS	LOCATION
proton	p	positive	1	nucleus
neutron	n	neutral	approx. 1	nucleus
electron	*e*	negative	approx. 1/2,000	orbitals

ingly, all hydrogen atoms contain one proton, all oxygen atoms eight protons, and all chlorine atoms 17 protons. This important feature of an atom gives rise to its *atomic number,* which is simply the number of protons contained in the nucleus. Therefore, the atomic numbers of hydrogen, oxygen, and chlorine are one, eight, and 17, respectively.

The mass of an atom is dependent on both the number and kind of particles in the atom. However, because protons and neutrons have a much greater mass than electrons, they essentially are responsible for the entire mass of the atom. Consequently, an oxygen atom with eight protons and eight neutrons will have a relative mass of 16, a nitrogen atom with atomic number seven (seven protons) and seven neutrons will have a mass of 14, and the atom of atomic number 15 having 16 neutrons will have a relative mass of 31 (phosphorus). The total mass of an atom is called its *atomic weight* or *atomic mass,* and thus the atomic weights of oxygen, nitrogen, and phosphorus are 16, 14, and 31, respectively.

An examination of the atomic weights for elements listed on the inside back cover will reveal that they are not whole numbers as the above examples might imply, but rather they are generally nonintegers. This may be attributed to three factors; (1) the masses of the proton and neutron are not exactly unity, and they differ slightly from one another; (2) the mass due to the electrons in an atom has been neglected in our consideration, although this must also contribute to the atomic weight; and (3) atoms of a given element may have different masses by virtue of containing different numbers of neutrons. Of these three factors, the last is responsible to the greatest degree for noninteger atomic weights and warrants further discussion.

Isotopes

Whereas the atomic number for all atoms of a particular element is the same and fixed, a similar restriction does not apply to their atomic weights. Atoms of the same element may differ in the number of neutrons in their nuclei and thus differ in their atomic weights as well. Such atoms are called *isotopes* of the element. They are alike in their chemical properties but differ in mass. For example, chlorine atoms exist in two isotopic forms, one with 17 protons and 18 neutrons referred to as ^{35}Cl, and the other with 17 protons and 20 neutrons referred to as ^{37}Cl. The numbers 35 and 37, written as superscripts before the symbol Cl for chlorine, are used to signify the relative masses of the individual isotopes. Atoms of chlorine, as they are found in nature, consist of more ^{35}Cl than ^{37}Cl, so that the average atomic weight of natural chlorine is a number closer to 35. Thus, the actual atomic weight of chlorine is a consequence of the relative abundances of the two isotopes. It has the value of 35.453 in atomic mass units. Similarly, the atomic weights for all the elements are based upon the number of isotopes for an element, their mass, and their relative abundances. At this point, it is worthwhile to mention two isotopes of hydrogen that are particularly useful in chemistry. Deuterium has one proton and one neutron and therefore a relative mass of two. It is called "heavy hydrogen" and is given a special symbol D. Tritium has one proton and two neutrons and a relative mass of three. It may be called "super-heavy hydrogen" and is known by the symbol T. Some other isotopes are useful in chemistry and medicine and will be discussed in the Appendix.

Electronic structure

Shells and Subshells

Now let us consider the electrons in an atom. First, they are located in a region of space about the nucleus (which they do not penetrate) and are restricted to particular segments of this region. Second, in elemental matter, the number of electrons in an atom just equals its atomic number so that there is no net charge on the atom. However, it is possible for atoms to gain, lose, or share electrons, and then they are no longer neutral species. The gain or loss of electrons results in charged species termed *ions.*

The regions of electron occupancy in an atom or ion are of great importance to the chemist because chemistry deals with those changes in matter that are most directly related to electronic changes. Electrons in atoms are described generally in terms of the energy levels they occupy. The main energy levels or shells are designated by the numbers 1, 2, 3, 4, . . . , etc., which refer to the first, second, third, fourth, . . . , etc., energy level or shell an electron may occupy relative to the nucleus. The maximum number of electrons each shell may contain is limited and follows a simple mathematical rule expressed as $2(n^2)$, where n refers to the number of the shell. The result of applying this rule for several values of n is given in Table 1-2. The first shell is completely filled with two electrons, the second may contain eight, the third eighteen, and so on.

There is much experimental evidence to indicate that each main shell is actually composed of subshells, which differ slightly in their energies.

Table 1-2 Capacity of electron shells

SHELL	n	$2(n^2)$	MAXIMUM NUMBER OF ELECTRONS
first	1	2	2
second	2	8	8
third	3	18	18
fourth	4	32	32
...	...	...	...

Table 1-3 Electron shells and subshells

SHELL	n	SUBSHELLS	MAXIMUM NUMBER OF ELECTRONS
first	1	s	2
second	2	$s + p$	$2 + 6 = 8$
third	3	$s + p + d$	$2 + 6 + 10 = 18$
fourth	4	$s + p + d + f$	$2 + 6 + 10 + 14 = 32$
...	...	$s + p + \cdots$	$2 + 6 + \cdots$

Four subshells have been distinguished, and these are of primary interest to us. They are designated as the *s, p, d,* and *f* subshells and may accommodate a maximum of 2, 6, 10, and 14 electrons, respectively. The relationship between shell and subshell is shown in Table 1-3. Note that each successive shell has one more subshell than its predecessor, and that when shells and subshells are filled, they contain even numbers of electrons (a fact that foreshadows the importance of electron pairs).

Electronic Configuration

Electrons in atoms are represented generally in terms of the principal energy level they occupy (i.e., 1, 2, 3, . . .), and the subshell in which they are contained (i.e., *s, p, d,* or *f*). Electrons of an atom or ion in its *lowest energy state,* referred to as its *ground state,* will occupy a particular set of subshells. The description of the shell and subshell arrangement for all the electrons in an atom or ion is called its electronic configuration. Electronic configurations are determined by progressively placing electrons into the unfilled subshell of lowest energy until all electrons in the atom or ion have been exhausted. A very simple illustration of this point is the hydrogen atom, which has only one electron to be placed in a subshell. The shell of lowest energy available to this electron is the first, and the subshell within the first shell is of the *s* type (refer to Table 1-3). We will specify the *s* subshell in the first shell by the notation 1*s*. Since this is the first shell and subshell an electron can occupy, the one electron of hydrogen will reside here, of course. We represent this fact by adding the superscript one to the notation 1*s*, as in $1s^1$. Electronic configurations are designated in this fashion, and we will consider some further examples to show the relative energies of subshells. Remember that the superscript indicates the number of electrons in the subshell, and that the subshell is part of the main shell whose number n appears before the letter *s, p, d,* or *f*.

Helium, with atomic number two, has two electrons, which in the ground state occupy and completely fill the 1*s* shell. (See Table 1-3.) The electronic configuration of helium is written as $1s^2$, which indicates that this atom has two electrons in the 1*s* energy level. The lithium atom has three electrons. Only two of these may occupy the 1*s* shell; the third must be contained in the next nearest available energy level—the 2*s* subshell. Thus, the electronic configuration of lithium is written as $1s^22s^1$. Beryllium, an element having one more electron than lithium, has the configuration $1s^22s^2$, with both subshells completely filled. Boron atoms have five electrons; two each may be accommodated by the 1*s* and 2*s* subshells; the fifth is required to reside in the 2*p* subshell. Boron thus has the electronic configuration $1s^22s^22p^1$. The addition of electrons to these subshells continues in a straightforward fashion, and the 2*p* subshell becomes filled in this manner with the element neon having the configuration $1s^22s^22p^6$. In neon atoms, the first and second shells are completely filled. The electronic configurations for atoms of elements from hydrogen through neon are given in Table 1-4. The 3*s* and 3*p* subshells are filled next in order. The electrons of the first eighteen elements occupy subshells in the following sequence: 1*s* first and then 2*s*, 2*p*, 3*s*, and 3*p*. At this point, you might anticipate the addition of electrons to the 3*d* subshell to complete the third main shell. However, such is not the case, and experimental evidence shows that electrons enter the 4*s* subshell after the 3*p* subshell is filled but before the 3*d* subshell begins acquiring electrons. This is an example of a smaller subshell (*s*) of a shell with a higher *n* value (4) being filled with electrons before a larger subshell (*d*) of a shell of lower *n* value (3). Restated, this means that subshells of different shells may have comparable energies, so electrons can enter a new shell before some other shell has been filled to capacity. This feature may be visualized more clearly by reference to Figure 1-1, in which the relative energies of the various subshells are represented. The 1*s* subshell, having the lowest energy, is located at the bottom of the figure. Next in energy and also order of electron occupancy is the 2*s*, followed by the 2*p*, 3*s*, and 3*p* subshells. After this, the 4*s* and 3*d*

Table 1-4 Electronic configurations of the first ten elements

ELEMENT	SYMBOL	NUMBER OF ELECTRONS	ELECTRONIC CONFIGURATION
hydrogen	H	1	$1s^1$
helium	He	2	$1s^2$
lithium	Li	3	$1s^22s^1$
beryllium	Be	4	$1s^22s^2$
boron	B	5	$1s^22s^22p^1$
carbon	C	6	$1s^22s^22p^2$
nitrogen	N	7	$1s^22s^22p^3$
oxygen	O	8	$1s^22s^22p^4$
fluorine	F	9	$1s^22s^22p^5$
neon	Ne	10	$1s^22s^22p^6$

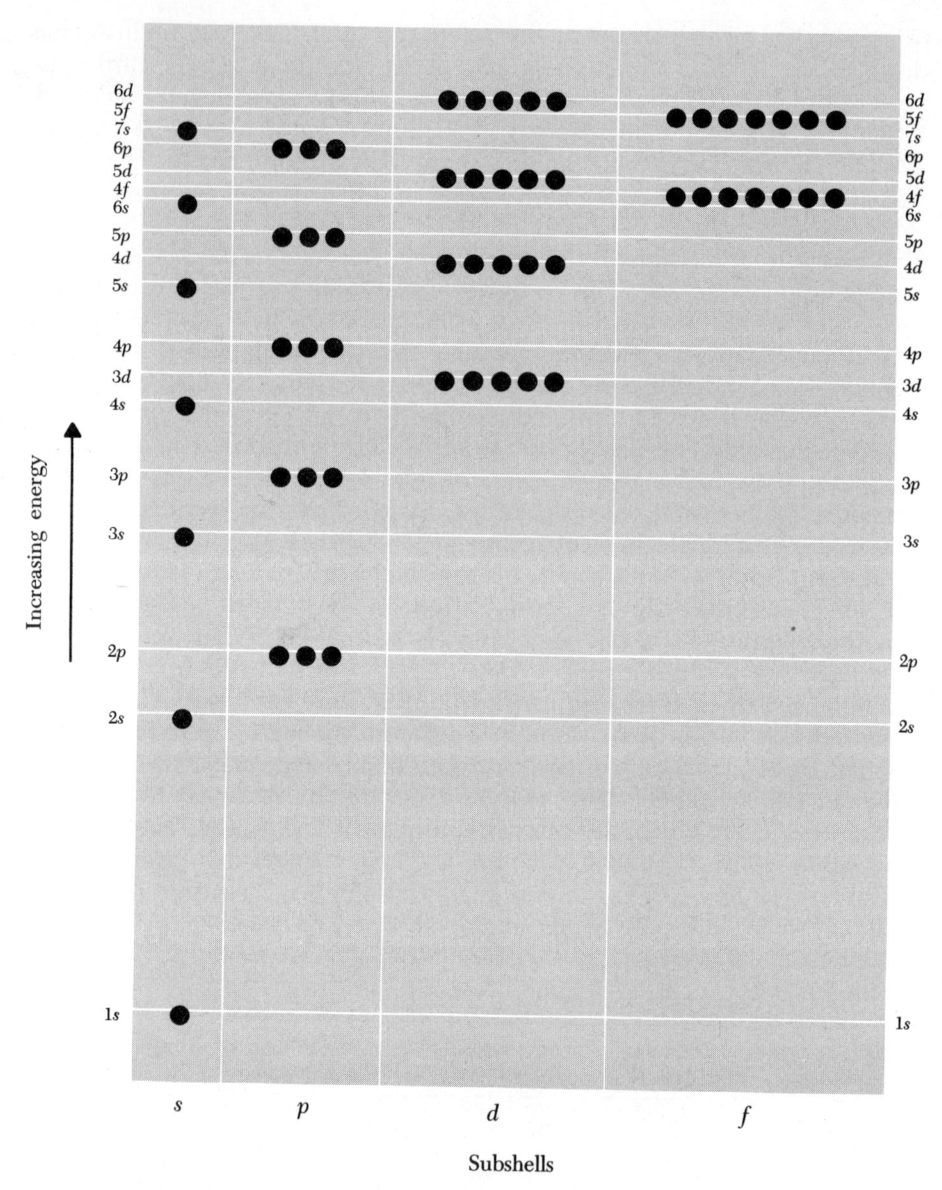

Figure 1-1 Approximate relative energy of electrons in subshells. (© 1965 by Harcourt, Brace & World, Inc. Reproduced from *The Elements of Chemistry* by Lawrence P. Eblin, p. 138.)

subshells are seen to have comparable energies, and, as mentioned previously, the electrons occupy the 4*s* subshell before the 3*d* subshell. The energy difference between the 5*p* and 4*f* subshells is seen to be even more pronounced, and electrons plainly enter the $5p$ subshell before they enter the $4f$ subshell. Similar incidents occur more frequently as the atomic number increases, so electronic configurations of the heavier elements become quite involved. The electronic configurations of the elements in their ground states are listed in Table 1-5 for reference. You should become familiar with the notation used to represent these configurations.

Periodic Properties

Since the energies normally available through chemical changes generally affect only the outer electrons in atoms (the so-called valence electrons), these are of primary concern to the chemist. Inner electrons, particularly those in filled shells or subshells, are not disturbed greatly. Because of this, atoms having similar outer-electron configurations might be expected to display some degree of similarity in their chemical properties. This expectation is indeed observed and finds expression in an instrument known as a *periodic table* of the elements. To construct such a table, the elements are entered in the order of increasing atomic number, beginning with hydrogen, and then arranged in such a fashion that those atoms with similar outer-electron configurations are contained in the same vertical column. The term *periodic* arises because as one considers each element in order of increasing atomic number, the recurrence of similar properties in other elements develops in a regular and periodic manner. The so-called long form of the periodic table is shown on the inside front cover.

Elements that compose a vertical column in the table are said to be members of a "family," because their electronic configurations are related. The alkali metals define one such column, and the electronic configurations of the first three members, lithium, sodium, and potassium, are shown in Table 1-6. The outer electrons of the members are underlined to emphasize the relationship among them.

It is seen that all of the alkali metals have one outermost electron in an s subshell. This similarity in their electronic makeup is responsible for their parallel behavior in many chemical situations. In an analogous manner, all the alkaline earth metals have identical numbers of electrons in their outermost subshells and form another family. The first three members are also listed in Table 1-6. They have chemical properties in common with the remaining family members of strontium, barium, and radium, which are gradually tempered by differences in mass. All have two electrons in an outermost s subshell. The members of the halogen family have a common feature in their electronic configuration, consisting of five electrons in an outermost subshell. The last family we will mention is known as the noble gases. After helium, which is the lightest member, all have a completely filled p subshell as their outermost electronic component. Com-

Table 1-5 Electronic configurations of the elements

ATOMIC NUMBER	ELEMENT	1	2		3			4				5				6			7
		s	*s*	*p*	*s*	*p*	*d*	*s*	*p*	*d*	*f*	*s*	*p*	*d*	*f*	*s*	*p*	*d*	*s*
1	**H**	1																	
2	**He**	2																	
3	**Li**	2	1																
4	**Be**	2	2																
5	**B**	2	2	1															
6	**C**	2	2	2															
7	**N**	2	2	3															
8	**O**	2	2	4															
9	**F**	2	2	5															
10	**Ne**	2	2	6															
11	**Na**	2	2	6	1														
12	**Mg**	2	2	6	2														
13	**Al**	2	2	6	2	1													
14	**Si**	2	2	6	2	2													
15	**P**	2	2	6	2	3													
16	**S**	2	2	6	2	4													
17	**Cl**	2	2	6	2	5													
18	**Ar**	2	2	6	2	6													
19	**K**	2	2	6	2	6		1											
20	**Ca**	2	2	6	2	6		2											
21	**Sc**	2	2	6	2	6	1	2											
22	**Ti**	2	2	6	2	6	2	2											
23	**V**	2	2	6	2	6	3	2											
24	**Cr**	2	2	6	2	6	5	1											
25	**Mn**	2	2	6	2	6	5	2											
26	**Fe**	2	2	6	2	6	6	2											
27	**Co**	2	2	6	2	6	7	2											
28	**Ni**	2	2	6	2	6	8	2											
29	**Cu**	2	2	6	2	6	10	1											
30	**Zn**	2	2	6	2	6	10	2											
31	**Ga**	2	2	6	2	6	10	2	1										
32	**Ge**	2	2	6	2	6	10	2	2										
33	**As**	2	2	6	2	6	10	2	3										
34	**Se**	2	2	6	2	6	10	2	4										
35	**Br**	2	2	6	2	6	10	2	5										
36	**Kr**	2	2	6	2	6	10	2	6										
37	**Rb**	2	2	6	2	6	10	2	6			1							
38	**Sr**	2	2	6	2	6	10	2	6			2							
39	**Y**	2	2	6	2	6	10	2	6	1		2							
40	**Zr**	2	2	6	2	6	10	2	6	2		2							
41	**Nb**	2	2	6	2	6	10	2	6	4		1							
42	**Mo**	2	2	6	2	6	10	2	6	5		1							
43	**Tc**	2	2	6	2	6	10	2	6	6		1							
44	**Ru**	2	2	6	2	6	10	2	6	7		1							
45	**Rh**	2	2	6	2	6	10	2	6	8		1							
46	**Pd**	2	2	6	2	6	10	2	6	10									
47	**Ag**	2	2	6	2	6	10	2	6	10		1							
48	**Cd**	2	2	6	2	6	10	2	6	10		2							
49	**In**	2	2	6	2	6	10	2	6	10		2	1						
50	**Sn**	2	2	6	2	6	10	2	6	10		2	2						
51	**Sb**	2	2	6	2	6	10	2	6	10		2	3						
52	**Te**	2	2	6	2	6	10	2	6	10		2	4						

Table 1-5 (Continued)

ATOMIC NUMBER	ELEMENT	1	2		3			4				5				6			7
		s	*s*	*p*	*s*	*p*	*d*	*s*	*p*	*d*	*f*	*s*	*p*	*d*	*f*	*s*	*p*	*d*	*s*
53	**I**	2	2	6	2	6	10	2	6	10		2	5						
54	**Xe**	2	2	6	2	6	10	2	6	10		2	6						
55	**Cs**	2	2	6	2	6	10	2	6	10		2	6			1			
56	**Ba**	2	2	6	2	6	10	2	6	10		2	6			2			
57	**La**	2	2	6	2	6	10	2	6	10		2	6	1		2			
58	**Ce**	2	2	6	2	6	10	2	6	10	1	2	6	1		2			
59	**Pr**	2	2	6	2	6	10	2	6	10	3	2	6			2			
60	**Nd**	2	2	6	2	6	10	2	6	10	4	2	6			2			
61	**Pm**	2	2	6	2	6	10	2	6	10	5	2	6			2			
62	**Sm**	2	2	6	2	6	10	2	6	10	6	2	6			2			
63	**Eu**	2	2	6	2	6	10	2	6	10	7	2	6			2			
64	**Gd**	2	2	6	2	6	10	2	6	10	7	2	6	1		2			
65	**Tb**	2	2	6	2	6	10	2	6	10	9	2	6			2			
66	**Dy**	2	2	6	2	6	10	2	6	10	10	2	6			2			
67	**Ho**	2	2	6	2	6	10	2	6	10	11	2	6			2			
68	**Er**	2	2	6	2	6	10	2	6	10	12	2	6			2			
69	**Tm**	2	2	6	2	6	10	2	6	10	13	2	6			2			
70	**Yb**	2	2	6	2	6	10	2	6	10	14	2	6			2			
71	**Lu**	2	2	6	2	6	10	2	6	10	14	2	6	1		2			
72	**Hf**	2	2	6	2	6	10	2	6	10	14	2	6	2		2			
73	**Ta**	2	2	6	2	6	10	2	6	10	14	2	6	3		2			
74	**W**	2	2	6	2	6	10	2	6	10	14	2	6	4		2			
75	**Re**	2	2	6	2	6	10	2	6	10	14	2	6	5		2			
76	**Os**	2	2	6	2	6	10	2	6	10	14	2	6	6		2			
77	**Ir**	2	2	6	2	6	10	2	6	10	14	2	6	7		2			
78	**Pt**	2	2	6	2	6	10	2	6	10	14	2	6	9		1			
79	**Au**	2	2	6	2	6	10	2	6	10	14	2	6	10		1			
80	**Hg**	2	2	6	2	6	10	2	6	10	14	2	6	10		2			
81	**Tl**	2	2	6	2	6	10	2	6	10	14	2	6	10		2	1		
82	**Pb**	2	2	6	2	6	10	2	6	10	14	2	6	10		2	2		
83	**Bi**	2	2	6	2	6	10	2	6	10	14	2	6	10		2	3		
84	**Po**	2	2	6	2	6	10	2	6	10	14	2	6	10		2	4		
85	**At**	2	2	6	2	6	10	2	6	10	14	2	6	10		2	5		
86	**Rn**	2	2	6	2	6	10	2	6	10	14	2	6	10		2	6		
87	**Fr**	2	2	6	2	6	10	2	6	10	14	2	6	10		2	6		1
88	**Ra**	2	2	6	2	6	10	2	6	10	14	2	6	10		2	6		2
89	**Ac**	2	2	6	2	6	10	2	6	10	14	2	6	10		2	6	1	2
90	**Th**	2	2	6	2	6	10	2	6	10	14	2	6	10		2	6	2	2
91	**Pa**	2	2	6	2	6	10	2	6	10	14	2	6	10	2	2	6	1	2
92	**U**	2	2	6	2	6	10	2	6	10	14	2	6	10	3	2	6	1	2
93	**Np**	2	2	6	2	6	10	2	6	10	14	2	6	10	4	2	6	1	2
94	**Pu**	2	2	6	2	6	10	2	6	10	14	2	6	10	6	2	6		2
95	**Am**	2	2	6	2	6	10	2	6	10	14	2	6	10	7	2	6		2
96	**Cm**	2	2	6	2	6	10	2	6	10	14	2	6	10	7	2	6	1	2
97	**Bk**	2	2	6	2	6	10	2	6	10	14	2	6	10	9	2	6		2
98	**Cf**	2	2	6	2	6	10	2	6	10	14	2	6	10	10	2	6		2
99	**Es**	2	2	6	2	6	10	2	6	10	14	2	6	10	11	2	6		2
100	**Fm**	2	2	6	2	6	10	2	6	10	14	2	6	10	12	2	6		2
101	**Md**	2	2	6	2	6	10	2	6	10	14	2	6	10	13	2	6		2
102	**No**	2	2	6	2	6	10	2	6	10	14	2	6	10	14	2	6		2
103	**Lw**	2	2	6	2	6	10	2	6	10	14	2	6	10	14	2	6	1	2

Table 1-6 Selected periodic families and their electronic configurations

FAMILY NAME AND SOME MEMBERS	ELECTRONIC CONFIGURATION
Alkali Metals	
lithium (**Li**)	$1s^2\underline{2s^1}$
sodium (**Na**)	$1s^22s^22p^6\underline{3s^1}$
potassium (**K**)	$1s^22s^22p^63s^23p^6\underline{4s^1}$
Alkaline Earth Metals	
beryllium (**Be**)	$1s^2\underline{2s^2}$
magnesium (**Mg**)	$1s^22s^22p^6\underline{3s^2}$
calcium (**Ca**)	$1s^22s^22p^63s^23p^6\underline{4s^2}$
Halogens	
fluorine (**F**)	$1s^22s^2\underline{2p^5}$
chlorine (**Cl**)	$1s^22s^22p^63s^2\underline{3p^5}$
bromine (**Br**)	$1s^22s^22p^63s^23p^64s^23d^{10}\underline{4p^5}$
Noble Gases	
helium (**He**)	$1s^2$
neon (**Ne**)	$1s^22s^2\underline{2p^6}$
argon (**Ar**)	$1s^22s^22p^63s^2\underline{3p^6}$ = (**Ar**)
krypton (**Kr**)	(**Ar**)$4s^23d^{10}\underline{4p^6}$

pounds recently have been prepared for some of the noble gases, long considered to be chemically inert. The periodic table is of great assistance to the chemist for correlating or predicting properties of elements and compounds, from considerations based upon the electronic configuration of the constituent atoms or ions. Note that in the long form of the periodic table, metals occupy the left portion, and nonmetals are grouped in the upper right-hand corner; a diagonal line separates these two elemental types.

Atomic Orbitals

Now let us return to the observation that shells and subshells are filled by even numbers of electrons. Recall that the *s, p, d,* and *f* subshells may contain a maximum of 2, 6, 10, and 14 electrons. This may be restated in terms of electron pairs; thus, the *s, p, d,* and *f* subshells may contain a maximum of 1, 3, 5, and 7 *pairs* of electrons. Within a subshell, electrons may congregate in pairs (actually, it is the electron spins that become paired). The region occupied by an electron pair in a subshell is called an *atomic orbital.* It then follows that an *s* subshell, which can accommodate one pair of electrons, is also an *s* atomic orbital. In each *p* subshell, three electron pairs may be present, and this means that the *p* subshell is actually composed of three *p* atomic orbitals. Likewise, in any *d* subshell, five electron pairs require five *d* atomic orbitals, and the fourteen electrons in an *f* subshell need seven *f* atomic orbitals. Each type of atomic orbital has

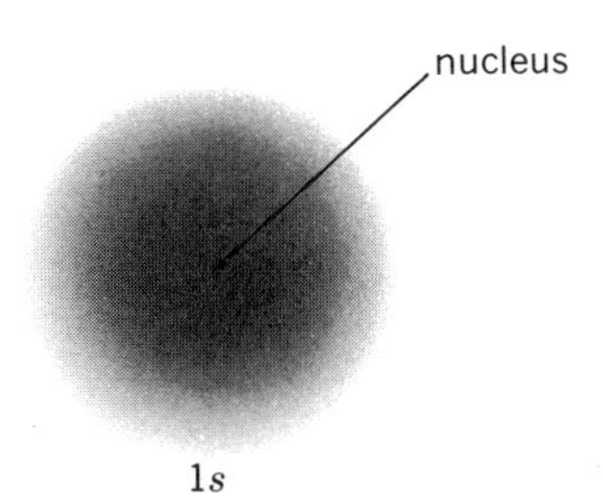

Figure 1-2 An *s* orbital.

a unique shape and a well-defined spacial relationship to the other orbitals in an atom. These shapes are useful for describing some aspects of chemical bonding, and we will consider them in more detail.

Atomic orbitals of the *s* type are spherical in shape with the nucleus at the center. A diagram of an *s* orbital is depicted in Figure 1-2. The interpretation usually given to such a diagram is that an electron or electron pair occupying this orbital will spend the greatest amount of its time in the regions having the darkest shading in the sphere. A *p* atomic orbital has two lobes, which lie on a line with the nucleus at their center. There are three *p* orbitals in each *p* subshell, and these are at right angles to each other and share a common center. The lobes lie on the axes of an ordinary *x*, *y*, and *z* coordinate system. On this basis, they may be referred to as the p_x, p_y, and p_z atomic orbitals. The shapes of the three individual *p* atomic orbitals are shown in Figure 1-3, and in Figure 1-4 they are depicted together as they exist in the atom. The surface boundaries of the five *d* orbitals are more complex and are generally represented separately, as in Figure 1-5, rather than in a collective manner. The seven *f* atomic orbitals have even more involved shapes, and because examples of bonds to *f* orbitals are met less frequently, we will not include their diagrams here.

Electrons are added to a subshell so as to occupy the atomic orbitals singly. Placing two electrons in a given atomic orbital is avoided until absolutely necessary. For example, a nitrogen atom with the electronic

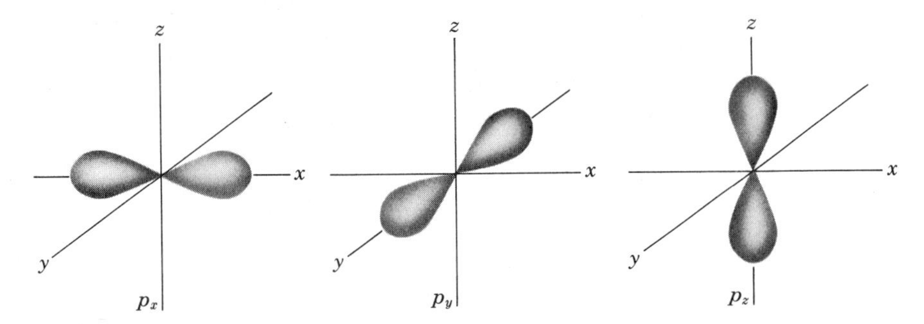

Figure 1-3 The shapes of the three *p* atomic orbitals.

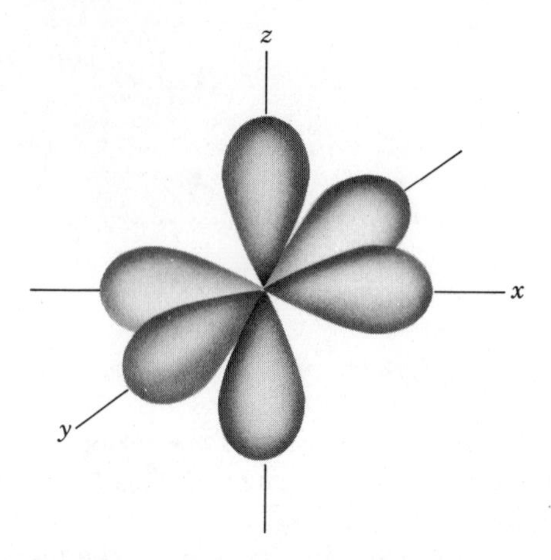

Figure 1-4 The p atomic orbitals as they exist in an atom.

configuration $1s^22s^22p^3$ will have each of its electrons in the $2p$ subshell occupy one $2p$ atomic orbital. Therefore, it would be more complete and correct to write its electron configuration as $1s^22s^22p_x{}^12p_y{}^12p_z{}^1$, indicating the exact distribution of electrons in the $2p$ subshell. An oxygen atom has one more electron in the $2p$ subshell than nitrogen, and, therefore, one electron pair must be present. Oxygen's electronic configuration may be written more completely as $1s^22s^22p_x{}^22p_y{}^12p_z{}^1$, rather than as $1s^22s^22p^4$. Which

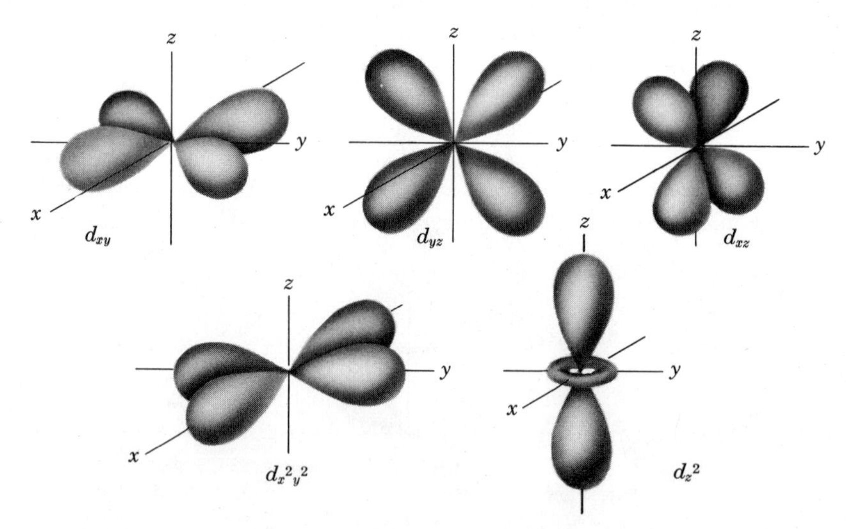

Figure 1-5 The five possible orientations in space of a d orbital. (© 1966 by Harcourt, Brace & World, Inc. Reproduced from *Principles of Chemistry* by Keith J. Laidler, p. 90.)

of the three *p* atomic orbitals in oxygen actually contains the electron pair is not critical for our purposes.

Ground-state electrons in atoms of the first twenty elements reside only in *s* and *p* orbitals. Since these elements are quite common and form so many compounds, it is particularly desirable to acquaint yourself with all aspects of the *s* and *p* atomic orbitals. The *d* orbitals are of primary interest for the transition metals represented by the symbols Sc, Ti, V, Cr, Mn, Fe, Co, Ni, Cu, and Zn and the families they head. Many of these metals and their ions appear only as trace amounts in systems of biological importance, but here they are believed to play very significant roles. In this respect, it may be mentioned that the cobalt in vitamin B_{12} and iron in hemoglobin are functional centers in these vital molecules.

Chemical bonding

Ionic bonds

Atoms of elements, or their ions, can combine with each other to form compounds that have properties generally quite different from those of the original components. The smallest representative part of a compound is called a *molecule.* The bonding forces between the members of a molecule involve electrons, and two types of bonding are commonly recognized. In *ionic bonding,* electrons are accepted or donated by an atom, resulting in the formation of ions, and in *covalent bonding,* electron pairs are shared by the bonded atoms. Compounds containing ionic bonds are generally characterized by high melting and boiling points, are soluble in water but insoluble in ether, and have the ability to conduct electrical current. This is to be contrasted with covalent compounds, which generally have low melting and boiling points, are insoluble in water but soluble in ether, and cannot conduct electrical current. Let us consider ionic bonding first.

In its simplest form, an ionic bond arises from the electrostatic attraction between ions of opposite charge. Metals have a tendency to lose electrons, forming positive ions called *cations,* whereas nonmetals have a tendency to gain electrons, forming negative ions called *anions.* Because electrostatic charges of opposite sign attract each other, an attractive force will exist between cations and anions. In reality, solid ionic compounds are composed of many cations and anions arranged in a lattice (see Figure 1-6) having definite geometrical requirements, in which the ions must be present in sufficient numbers so that the solid is electrically neutral. On the other hand, ions in solution are usually insulated from each other by molecules of the solvent, and the form of aggregation here is less well defined.

As a preliminary to the formation of an ionic bond, let us consider some examples of ion formation. The formation of sodium ions may be

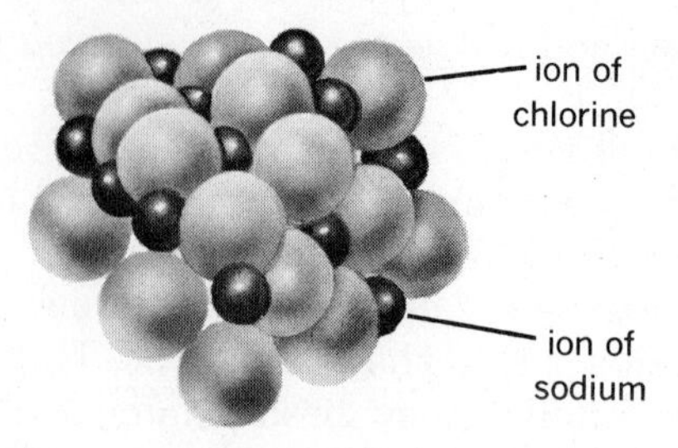

Figure 1-6 A sodium chloride crystal. (© 1966 by Harcourt, Brace & World, Inc. Reproduced from *Concepts in Chemistry* by A. W. Greenstone, F. X. Sutman and L. D. Hollingworth, p. 60.)

represented by the following equation, which employs electronic configurations:

$$\underset{\begin{pmatrix}\text{sodium atom}\\ 11\text{p}, 11e\end{pmatrix}}{\mathbf{Na}(1s^2 2s^2 2p^6 3s^1)} \longrightarrow \underset{\begin{pmatrix}\text{sodium ion}\\ 11\text{p}, 10e\end{pmatrix}}{\mathbf{Na}^+(1s^2 2s^2 2p^6)} + 1e$$

The sodium atom is electrically neutral with eleven protons and eleven electrons. A sodium ion has eleven protons, but the number of electrons is now reduced to ten, so there is a net charge of positive one. This charge appears as a superscript to the symbol for sodium Na, and this notation, that is, Na^+, is used to represent sodium ions. Formation of magnesium ions may be approached in the same manner. The magnesium atom is electrically neutral with twelve protons and twelve electrons. A magnesium ion still has twelve protons, but two electrons have been lost; thus, the net charge is positive two, as shown by the equation

$$\underset{\begin{pmatrix}\text{magnesium atom}\\ 12\text{p}, 12e\end{pmatrix}}{\mathbf{Mg}(1s^2 2s^2 2p^6 3s^2)} \longrightarrow \underset{\begin{pmatrix}\text{magnesium ion}\\ 12\text{p}, 10e\end{pmatrix}}{\mathbf{Mg}^{++}(1s^2 2s^2 2p^6)} + 2e$$

The magnesium ion is represented by the notation Mg^{++}. Anion formation by nonmetals is the result of atoms accepting electrons. Chlorine atoms have 17 protons and 17 electrons. When one electron is added to this arrangement, a chloride ion results having a net charge of negative one, as shown by the equation

$$\underset{\begin{pmatrix}\text{chlorine atom}\\ 17\text{p}, 17e\end{pmatrix}}{\mathbf{Cl}(1s^2 2s^2 2p^6 3s^2 3p^5)} + 1e \longrightarrow \underset{\begin{pmatrix}\text{chloride ion}\\ 17\text{p}, 18e\end{pmatrix}}{\mathbf{Cl}^-(1s^2 2s^2 2p^6 3s^2 3p^6)}$$

The chloride ion is written as Cl^-. The ions formed from oxygen atoms are illustrated by the equation

$$\underset{\begin{pmatrix}\text{oxygen atom}\\ 8\text{p}, 8e\end{pmatrix}}{\mathbf{O}(1s^2 2s^2 2p^4)} + 2e \longrightarrow \underset{\begin{pmatrix}\text{oxide ion}\\ 8\text{p}, 10e\end{pmatrix}}{\mathbf{O}^{--}(1s^2 2s^2 2p^6)}$$

The oxide ion has two electrons in excess of its eight protons and is written as O^{--}. Note that the ions formed in these examples have a completely filled outermost subshell. Although this is generally true for the lighter element ions, it is not an absolute guide for determining the charges of particular ions.

The electrons gained or lost by an atom to form ions are the outermost valence electrons. Because of this, the sign and magnitude of the charge on an ion is sometimes called its valency. In this manner, sodium ions are said to have a +1 valence, magnesium ions a +2 valence, chloride ions a −1 valence, and oxide ions a −2 valence. The valence charges for several common ions are listed in Table 1-7. They are grouped in terms of cations, anions, and radicals, which we will consider shortly. The headings mono-, di-, and tri-valent refer to the magnitude of the charge on the ion. The valency table is useful for determining the formulas of ionic compounds, and you should become familiar with the charges of the more common ions.

Radicals are associations of atoms having a net charge. They remain intact through many types of chemical changes and are considered a single ionic unit. For example, one sulfur atom and four oxygen atoms do not constitute a radical ion by themselves. It is necessary to add two electrons to this assemblage of atoms to complete the components present in the very stable sulfate ion. Sulfate ion is represented by the notation SO_4^{--}.

Table 1-7 Common valences

	MONOVALENT		DIVALENT		TRIVALENT	
Cations	hydrogen	H^+	magnesium	Mg^{++}	aluminum	Al^{+++}
	lithium	Li^+	calcium	Ca^{++}	chromium(III)	Cr^{+++}
	sodium	Na^+	zinc	Zn^{++}	iron(III)	Fe^{+++}
	potassium	K^+	copper(II)	Cu^{++}	arsenic	As^{+++}
	copper(I)	Cu^+	barium	Ba^{++}	bismuth	Bi^{+++}
	silver	Ag^+	mercury(II)	Hg^{++}	antimony	Sb^{+++}
	mercury(I)	Hg^+	iron(II)	Fe^{++}		
	ammonium	$(NH_4)^+$	lead(II)	Pb^{++}		
Anions	fluorine (fluoride)	F^-	oxygen (oxide)	O^{--}	nitrogen (nitride)	N^{---}
	chlorine (chloride)	Cl^-	sulfur (sulfide)	S^{--}	phosphorus (phosphide)	P^{---}
	bromine (bromide)	Br^-				
	iodine (iodide)	I^-				
Radicals	bicarbonate	$(HCO_3)^-$	carbonate	$(CO_3)^{--}$	phosphate	$(PO_4)^{---}$
	chlorate	$(ClO_3)^-$	sulfate	$(SO_4)^{--}$	arsenate	$(AsO_4)^{---}$
	hydroxide	$(OH)^-$	sulfite	$(SO_3)^{--}$		
	nitrate	$(NO_3)^-$				
	nitrite	$(NO_2)^-$				

Other radical ions include hydroxide (OH^-), bicarbonate (HCO_3^-), carbonate (CO_3^{--}), phosphate (PO_4^{---}), and several more listed in Table 1-7. Note that the names of some ions differ from those of their corresponding atoms; for example, oxygen atoms form oxide ions.

In ionic compounds, we will be interested not so much in the mechanics of bonding (which are very complex) as in recognizing the relative proportion of cations to anions required to preserve electrical neutrality in the compound. This necessary cation-anion ratio serves as the basis for the chemical formula used to describe ionic compounds. To illustrate, consider a compound formed from sodium and oxide ions. Sodium ions with a +1 charge must be present in the compound in sufficient numbers to neutralize the −2 charge on the oxide ions available. Since the magnitude of the charge on oxide ion is twice that of the sodium ion, this requires that two sodium ions be present for each oxide ion. The formula of the compound must reflect this 2:1 ratio of sodium to oxide ions, and it is written as Na_2O. The subscript (two in this case) is to be associated with the symbol of the element it follows and refers to the number of ions of that element present relative to the other members in the compound. A compound containing magnesium and oxide ions will require equal numbers of each ion, because the magnitudes of their charges are alike. Its formula would be written as MgO.

The use of a valency table allows the formulas of ionic compounds to be determined in a more direct manner. Suppose it is desired to determine the formula of the compound that contains magnesium and chloride ions. From the table, magnesium is seen to have a +2 and chloride ion a −1 valence. To illustrate the method used here, we will assume this task is so complicated that we could not possibly imagine what the correct formula should be beforehand. Let us begin by writing the symbol of the cation with its valence, and to its right writing the anion. Now simply use the valence of the anion as the subscript for the cation, and the valence of the cation as the subscript for the anion. This operation can be termed crossing valences to determine subscripts. Doing this for the magnesium and chloride ions may be depicted as follows:

$$Mg^{+(2)} + Cl^{-(1)} = Mg_1Cl_2$$

The valence of each ion becomes the subscript for the other ion in the formula. To this we should add that the subscript 1 is not employed but understood, so that Mg_1Cl_2 is more correctly represented as $MgCl_2$. The compound containing aluminum and oxide ions would have the formula Al_2O_3, obtained by crossing valences in the following manner:

$$Al^{+(3)} + O^{-(2)} = Al_2O_3$$

This represents the fact that two aluminum ions are required to neutralize the charges of three oxide ions, and, in the solid, the ratio of aluminum to oxide ions is 2:3. The same method may be applied to compounds containing radical ions. Thus, the formula of the compound that contains potassium and sulfate ions is written as K_2SO_4, obtained in the usual manner:

$$K^{+}(1) + SO_4^{--}(2) = K_2SO_4$$

When cases arise in which a subscript is associated with a radical, the radical is enclosed in parentheses to indicate that the entire radical is to be taken as many times as the value of the subscript. For example, the compound containing aluminum and sulfate ions will require two aluminum ions for every three sulfate ions to achieve neutrality. The formula is developed as follows:

$$Al^{+++}(3) + SO_4^{--}(2) = Al_2(SO_4)_3$$

Consider the formula for the compound containing calcium and sulfide ions.

$$Ca^{++}(2) + S^{--}(2) = Ca_2S_2$$

In ionic compounds of this nature, like subscripts are omitted, and the correct formula will simply be CaS. A common exception to this occurs in compounds containing the peroxide ion, as in hydrogen peroxide (H_2O_2) or sodium peroxide (Na_2O_2). In these cases, the subscripts are not dropped because the anion present in these compounds is actually composed from two oxygen atoms and exists as O_2^{--}. To be consistent with fact, then, peroxide ions (which of course differ from oxide ions) are written as they really exist in the compound.

The existence of anions and cations in the regular network of a solid lattice results in a very large amplification of energy over that available from only a single isolated anion-cation attraction. For this reason, it is more meaningful to describe ionic bonding in terms of the forces existing between large numbers of ions and their neighbors in the vast array of a crystalline solid, rather than as a separate interaction of a cation and anion pair. On the other hand, it is possible to discuss covalent bonding on a molecular scale. An important distinction between ionic and covalent types is the range over which the bonding forces are active. In ionic compounds, as we have seen, the bonding forces involve large numbers of ions and are dispersed throughout a vast network; however, in covalent molecules, only two atoms are ordinarily joined by one bond.

Covalent Bonds

Covalent bonds involve a distribution of electron pairs between atoms. They may be classified as *sigma* or *pi* bonds and are written as σ and π, respectively. It is generally true that covalent bonds consisting of only one electron pair are sigma bonds, and bonding electron pairs in excess of the first are pi bonds. The two types are actually distinguished by their general location relative to the bonded atoms, as shown in Figure 1-7. A σ-bonding electron pair is located mainly on the line joining the two nuclei of the bonded atoms or, in other words, directly on the bond axis. On the other hand, π bonds are located around the bonding axis but not directly on it. Sigma bonds are stronger than pi bonds because they are involved more directly with the bonded atoms. Sigma- and pi-bond formation is visualized more easily by reference to the atomic orbitals in which the bonding electrons originate.

Let us consider a very simple covalent molecule, molecular hydrogen, consisting of two hydrogen atoms bonded by a sigma bond and written as H_2. Each hydrogen atom possesses one electron in a 1*s* atomic orbital. As the two atoms approach bonding distances, these orbitals overlap, and a new region of electron occupancy, which encompasses both nuclei, then exists in the molecule. The resulting region is called a *molecular orbital* since its territory extends beyond one atom to include the entire molecule. A molecular orbital can accommodate one electron pair, and the electrons available from the two hydrogen atoms furnish this pair. The sequence of events in going from two hydrogen atoms to the hydrogen molecule is shown in Figure 1-8. The molecular orbital is seen to include both nuclei, and the probability of finding electrons is greater directly between the two nuclei, or on the bonding axis, than around the axis. Therefore, the bond is a σ bond.

The bond in a hydrogen molecule consists of a molecular orbital containing an electron pair. The molecular orbital in this case arises from the

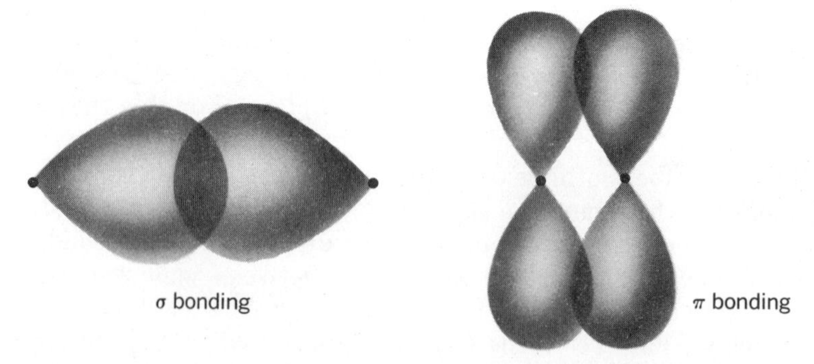

Figure 1-7 The difference between a σ bond and a π bond. (© 1966 by Harcourt, Brace & World, Inc. Reproduced from *Principles of Chemistry* by Keith J. Laidler, p. 143.)

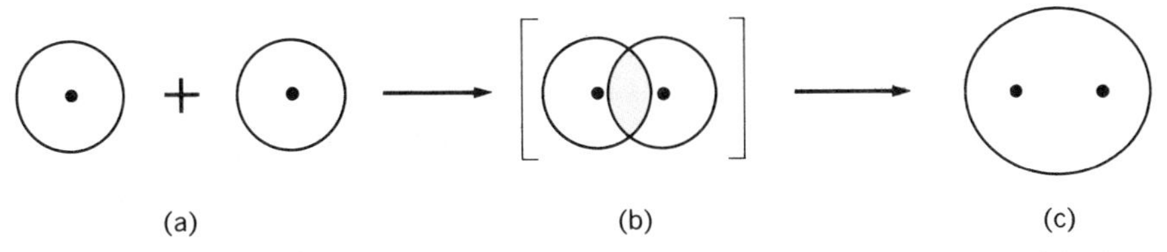

Figure 1-8 A representation of the bonding in the hydrogen molecule, H_2. (a) The original $1s$ atomic orbitals; (b) overlap of the atomic orbitals at bonding distances; (c) boundary surface of the sigma molecular orbital.

combination of two hydrogen $1s$ atomic orbitals, and each atom contributes one electron toward the pair. A molecular orbital and an electron pair are the essential components of a covalent bond.

Sigma bonds may also be formed by the combination of atomic orbitals other than the s type. For example, hydrogen fluoride, HF, has a σ-bonding electron pair in a molecular orbital formed from $1s$ (from hydrogen atom) and $2p$ (from fluorine atom) atomic orbitals. Hydrogen atom has one electron in the $1s$, and fluorine atom has the configuration $1s^22s^22p^5$ or, more correctly, $1s^22s^22p_x^{\,2}2p_y^{\,2}2p_z^{\,1}$. Fluorine has all of its atomic orbitals filled except the $2p_z$ orbital. For hydrogen to furnish its electron to the bonding pair, it can combine only with the unfilled orbital of fluorine to form the molecular orbital. Any other combination will involve electrons in excess of the one pair a molecular orbital may contain. Therefore, the filled atomic orbitals of fluorine do not participate in σ-bond formation and are not shown in Figure 1-9, which depicts the construction of the bond. Overlap occurs again between the $1s$ and $2p_z$ atomic orbitals pertinent to bond

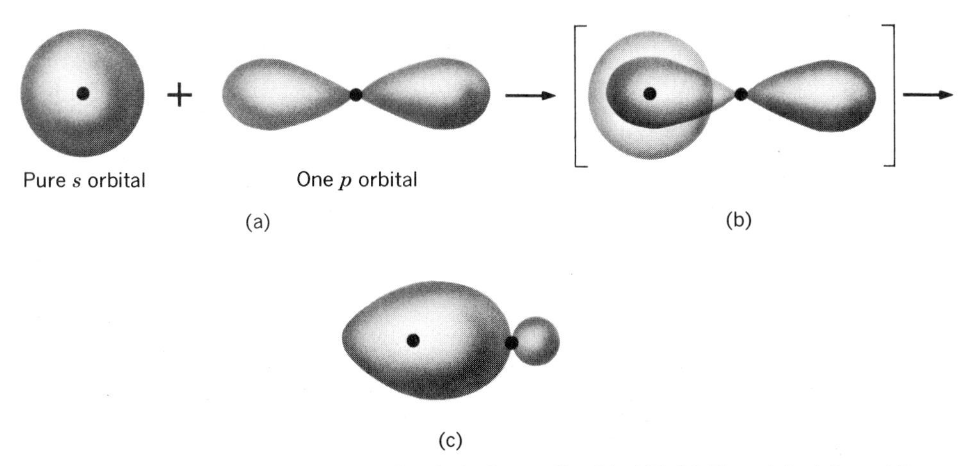

Figure 1-9 A representation of the bonding in hydrogen fluoride, HF. (a) The original $1s$ and $2p$ atomic orbitals; (b) overlap of the atomic orbitals; (c) boundary surface of the sigma molecular orbital.

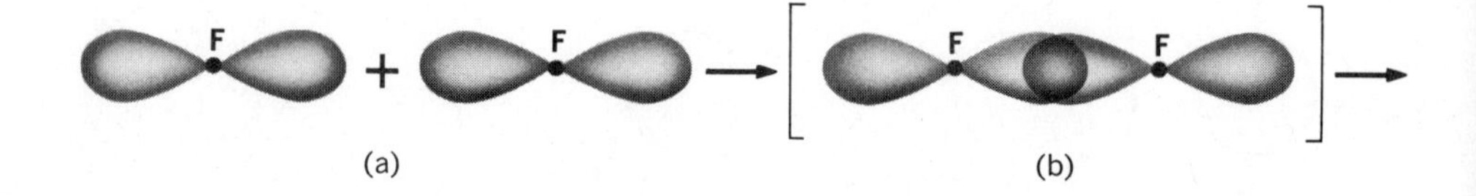

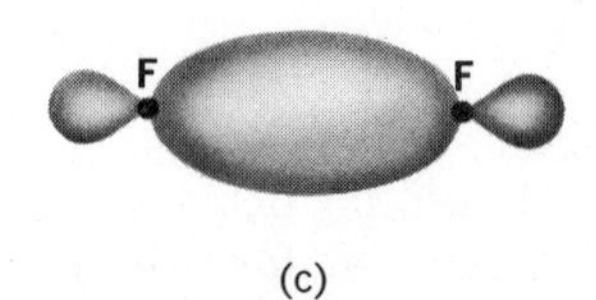

Figure 1-10 Representation of the bonding in the fluorine molecule, F_2. (a) Separate *p* orbitals; (b) overlap of *p* orbitals; (c) boundary surface of sigma molecular orbital.

formation, and a molecular orbital results that encompasses both nuclei and contains an electron pair. The shape of the molecular orbital in HF is different from that of H_2, but it lies directly on the bonding axis and is therefore classified as a σ bond again. Molecular fluorine F_2 consists of two fluorine atoms joined by a σ bond, which has its origin in two $2p_z$ atomic orbitals. The bond formation is shown in Figure 1-10. The examples used here illustrate σ-bond formation from two *s* atomic orbitals, an *s* and a *p* orbital union, and two *p* orbitals. These represent common combinations of atomic orbitals used to form molecular orbitals.

Each of the above examples contains one σ bond. This is often called a single bond. The addition of one or two π bonds to a σ bond gives rise to the terms double and triple bonds, as indicated in Table 1-8. Let us now consider some examples of atoms bonded by double and triple bonds. Recall that an oxygen atom, with electronic configuration $1s^2 2s^2 2p_x{}^2 2p_y{}^1 2p_z{}^1$, has all of its atomic orbitals filled except two $2p$ orbitals, which contain one electron each. Both of these unfilled orbitals may be used in covalent bond formation, but only one can lie on the bond axis and be classified as a σ bond. The remaining $2p$ orbital is at right angles to the first and to the bond axis as well. Therefore, any overlap this second orbital participates in must be in the region about the bond axis, and this results in a π bond. Such a bonding situation is set forth in Figure 1-11, in which each atom has two

Table 1-8 Sigma, pi, and multiple bonds

BOND TYPE	NO. OF BONDING ELECTRON PAIRS	ALTERNATE NAME FOR BOND
σ	one	single
$\sigma + \pi$	two	double
$\sigma + 2\pi$	three	triple

$2p$ orbitals available. The orbitals directed at the nuclei of the other atom form a molecular orbital lying on the bond axis, which contains one electron pair; this is a σ bond. The remaining orbitals form a molecular orbital, which lies about the bond axis and also contains one electron pair; this is a π bond. The two atoms are bonded by a σ and a π bond or, in other words, a double bond.

Elementary nitrogen exists as the diatomic molecule N_2. Each atom with the electronic configuration $1s^22s^22p_x{}^12p_y{}^12p_z{}^1$ has three $2p$ orbitals available for covalent bond formation. The bonding in this molecule may be pictured by imagining the behavior of the available orbitals as the two atoms approach each other to the limit of bonding distances. The orbitals directed at the nuclei of the other atom will overlap and form a molecular orbital lying on the bond axis, resulting in a σ bond. The two remaining $2p$ orbitals are at angles to the bonding axis and can take part only in π-bond formation. A diagrammatic representation of the bond formation in the N_2 molecule is given in Figure 1-12. The σ and two π bonds in the molecule give rise to the description of the bonding as a triple bond.

In the realm of covalently bonded atoms, compounds of the element carbon play a dominant role. Atomic carbon has the electronic configuration $1s^22s^22p_x{}^12p_y{}^12p_z{}^0$. This would indicate that carbon atoms have two $2p$ orbitals, each containing one electron and available for the kind of covalent bond formation we have been considering. In addition, there is an empty $2p$ orbital. Use of these three orbitals in some bonding mode would result in a maximum of three bonds to the carbon atom. However, many

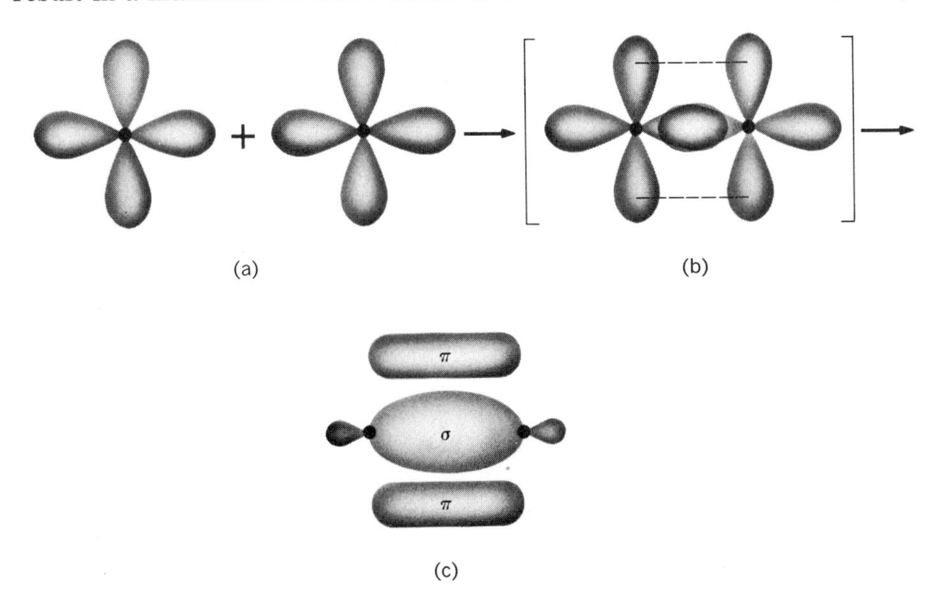

Figure 1-11 Representation of σ and π bonding by two atoms. (a) Original atomic orbitals; (b) overlap along bonding axis; (c) boundary surface of sigma and pi molecular orbitals.

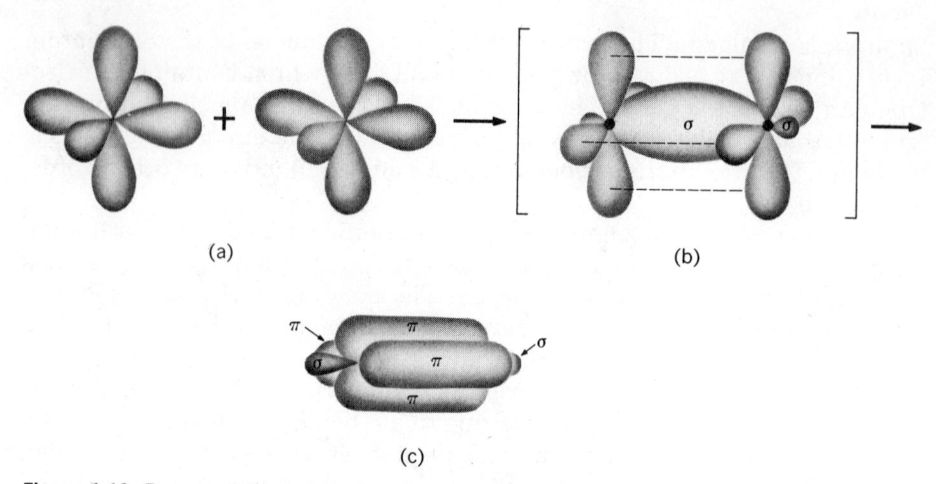

Figure 1-12 Representation of the bonding in molecular nitrogen, N_2. (a) The three half-filled $2p$ orbitals on each nitrogen atom; (b) overlap to form the sigma molecular orbital; (c) the pi bond molecular orbitals.

examples of compounds are known in which there are four bonds to the carbon atom. To explain this, it has been useful to include the concept of hybridization in the area of covalent bonding.

Hybridization

Although it is true that the ground-state electronic configuration of carbon is $1s^2 2s^2 2p_x{}^1 2p_y{}^1 2p_z{}^0$, relatively little energy is required to unpair the electrons in the $2s$ orbital and subsequently "promote" one of them to the empty $2p_z$ orbital. After such a process, the electronic configuration becomes $1s^2 2s^1 2p_x{}^1 2p_y{}^1 2p_z{}^1$. This opens up the possibility of covalent bond formation to all four orbitals of the second shell and is in accord with the many compounds that contain four atoms bonded to carbon. However, three of these orbitals are p orbitals and the fourth is an s orbital. We are aware that the s and p orbitals are quite different, particularly in their orientations in space. Therefore, it would seem reasonable to expect that three of the bonds in carbon compounds (which originate from the p orbitals) should also be quite different from the fourth bond (originating from an s orbital). However, experimental information for compounds such as methane (CH_4) and carbon tetrachloride (CCl_4) indicates that the four bonds to carbon are completely equivalent in all aspects, and one cannot be distinguished from the others. To account for such facts as four equal bonds to carbon and electron promotion, the idea that particular sets of atomic orbitals may become "hybridized" has been applied. Let us consider this in more detail.

In the framework of hybridization, one imagines that those s and p

atomic orbitals involved in σ-bond formation may combine in some fashion to create a new set of equivalent orbitals. The new orbitals are called "hybrid" orbitals because although they contain contributions from the original *s* and *p* atomic orbitals, they differ from these. One of the most interesting aspects of hybrid orbitals is the manner in which they are directed in space. For example, in carbon compounds with four σ bonds, the four hybrid orbitals are directed at the corners of a regular tetrahedron with the carbon atom at its center. The four hybrid orbitals result from the combination of a 2*s* and three 2*p* atomic orbitals from carbon, as shown in Figure 1-13. The origin of the hybrid set is also used as a label, and, in this case, the four equal bonds are referred to as an sp^3 hybrid set. The angles between the bonds of an sp^3 hybrid set are required to be 109° 28′ by the geometry of a tetrahedron, and it is indeed true that the angles between atoms in CH_4 and CCl_4 are found to have the expected tetrahedral values. It should be mentioned here that the bonding angles found in many carbon compounds indicate that the four bonds about carbon are tetrahedrally disposed. In this respect, hybridization is consistent with fact. The orbitals used in the bonding of methane are shown in Figure 1-14.

When only three of the orbitals of carbon are involved in σ bonding, another type of hybridization can take place. One *s* and two *p* orbitals may take part in forming an sp^2 hybrid set, which will have three σ bonds directed at the corners of a triangle, as shown in Figure 1-15. Because only three of the four bonding orbitals have been used in σ-bond formation, the fourth is still available for π-bond formation. A common carbon compound useful for illustrating this mode of hybridization is formaldehyde H_2CO. Three atoms are bound to carbon through σ bonds, two of hydrogen and one oxygen. This completely saturates the bonding capacity of both hydrogen atoms, but the carbon and oxygen each have one additional orbital remaining after σ-bond formation. The σ bonds in formaldehyde are depicted in Figure 1-16(a). The orbitals unused in σ bonding can overlap about the

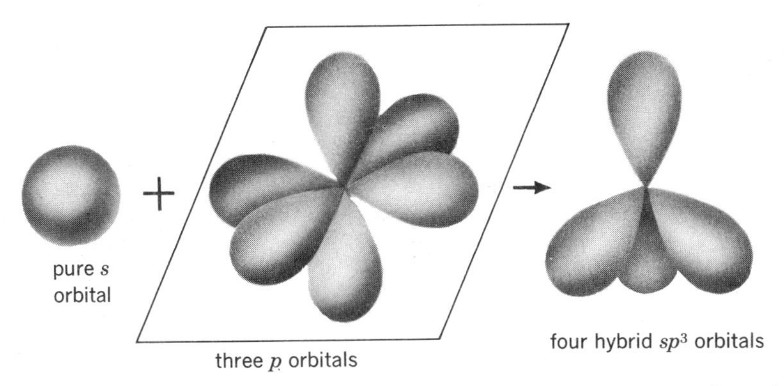

Figure 1-13 Formation of sp^3 orbitals. (© 1966 by Harcourt, Brace & World, Inc. Reproduced from *Principles of Chemistry* by Keith J. Laidler, p. 148.)

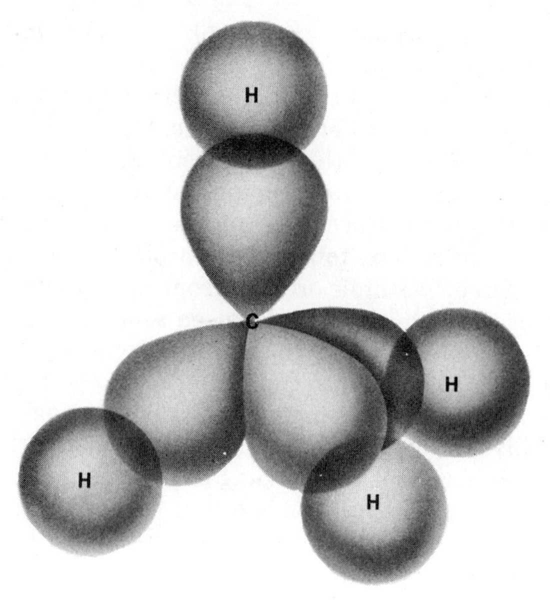

Figure 1-14 Methane molecule. (© 1966 by Harcourt, Brace & World, Inc. Reproduced from *Principles of Chemistry* by Keith J. Laidler, p. 139.)

carbon-oxygen bond axis forming a π bond, and the bonding in formaldehyde may be described as three σ bonds from carbon to one hydrogen, the second hydrogen, and oxygen, and a π bond between carbon and oxygen. Or, in other words, there are single bonds between carbon and each hydrogen but a double bond between carbon and oxygen. The complete bonding in the molecule is illustrated in Figure 1-16(b). The angles between the atoms bonded to carbon should be 120° because of the geometrical requirements of a triangle. The bonding angles as determined in the formaldehyde molecule by experimental methods are in excellent agreement with this requirement.

Another compound in which the sp^2 hybrid orbitals of carbon are

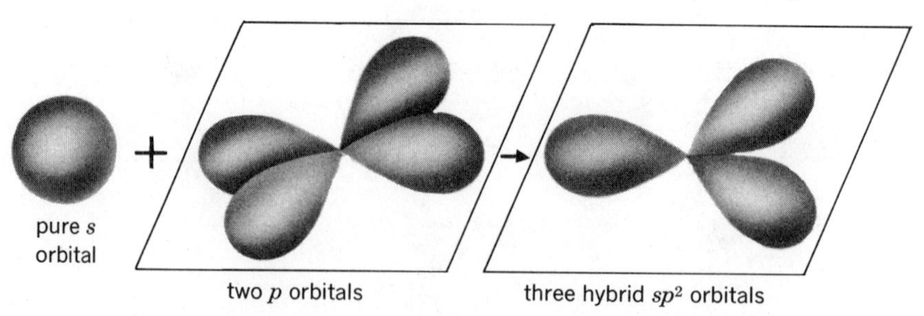

Figure 1-15 Formation of sp^2 orbitals. (© 1966 by Harcourt, Brace & World, Inc. Reproduced from *Principles of Chemistry* by Keith J. Laidler, p. 148.)

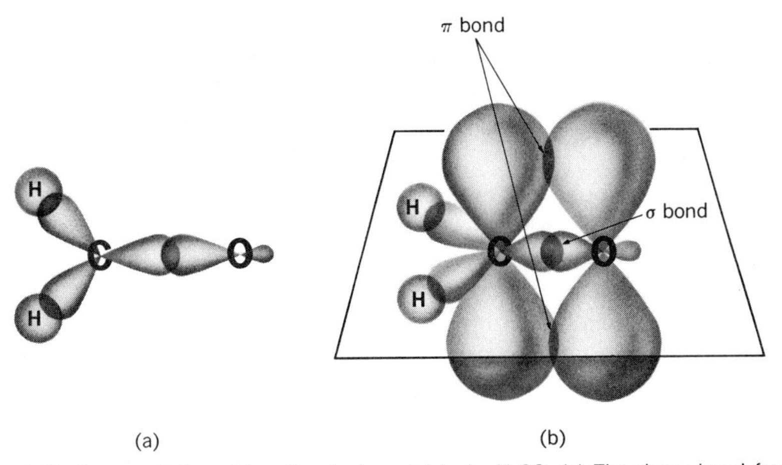

Figure 1-16 Representation of bonding in formaldehyde, H_2CO. (a) The sigma bond framework; (b) the complete bonding in the molecule.

employed in σ bonding is ethylene, H_2CCH_2. Each carbon has three σ bonds to two hydrogen atoms and the other carbon. The σ-bonding framework is shown in Figure 1-17(a). In addition, each carbon has an unused orbital that participates in π-bond formation. A description of the bonds in ethylene includes single bonds between all carbon and hydrogen atoms and a double bond between the two carbons. All the atoms in the molecule are in the same plane, and the bonding angles are in accord with that expected. The complete arrangement is shown in Figure 1-17(b). It should be mentioned here that carbon more than any other element has the ability to bind its own atoms together as in ethylene and in numerous other compounds as well. Due principally to this very property, the variety and amount of car-

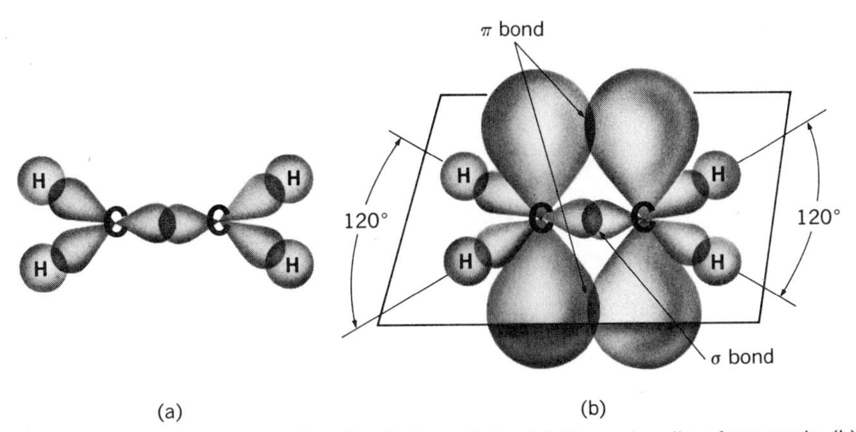

Figure 1-17 Representation of bonding in ethylene, C_2H_4. (a) Sigma bonding framework; (b) complete bonding in the molecule.

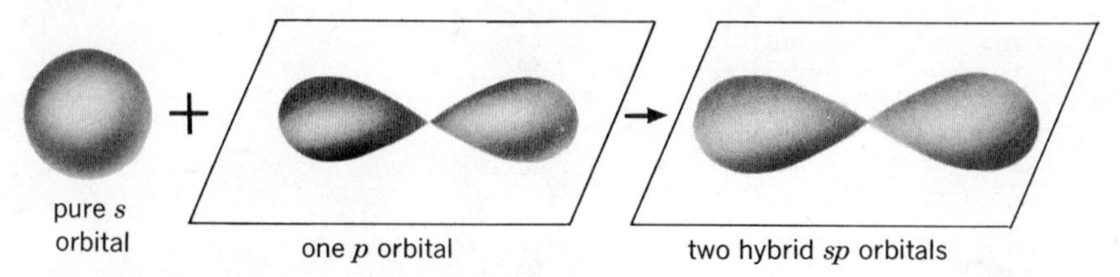

Figure 1-18 Formation of sp orbitals. (© 1966 by Harcourt, Brace & World, Inc. Reproduced from *Principles of Chemistry* by Keith J. Laidler, p. 148.)

bon compounds known is fantastically large, and a complete system, known as organic chemistry, has evolved dealing solely with carbon compounds.

We need to consider one other type of hybridization that arises when a carbon atom is σ bonded to only two other atoms. For this situation, one s and one p orbital may combine to form an sp hybrid set in which the two σ bonds lie on a straight line with carbon at its center. Formation of an sp hybrid is shown in Figure 1-18. The atoms bonded by an sp hybrid set should have a linear arrangement. An example is provided by acetylene, C_2H_2. In this compound, each carbon is σ bonded to one hydrogen and the other carbon, which permits two additional orbitals per carbon to participate in π-bond formation. The bonding in the molecule then consists of single bonds between the carbon and hydrogen atoms and a triple bond between the two carbons. This bonding development is shown in Figure 1-19. The atoms in acetylene are in fact arranged in a linear fashion, as would be expected.

The three types of hybridization we have considered, sp^3, sp^2, and sp, result from the combination of s and p orbitals. Information pertinent to these hybrid sets is displayed in Table 1-9. Combinations of atomic orbitals other than the s and p types are also quite feasible, and again this leads to

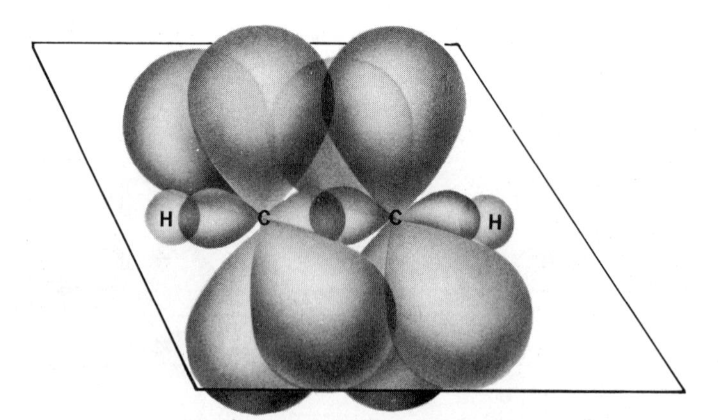

Figure 1-19 The acetylene molecule, H—C≡C—H (© 1966 by Harcourt, Brace & World, Inc. Reproduced from *Principles of Chemistry* by Keith J. Laidler, p. 146.)

Table 1-9 Some hybrid orbitals and their properties

HYBRID SET	MOLECULAR GEOMETRY	σ BONDS	EXAMPLES
sp	linear	two	as in C_2H_2
sp^2	triangular	three	as in H_2CCH_2, H_2CO
sp^3	tetrahedral	four	as in CH_4, CCl_4
dsp^2	square planar	four	as in $Cu(NH_3)_4SO_4$
d^2sp^3	octahedral	six	as in $Ni(H_2O)_6Cl_2$

hybrid sets having a definite geometrical disposition of bonds. For our purposes, however, it will be sufficient only to include several of the sets using *d* orbitals in Table 1-9, with the understanding that these sets may be utilized in the same manner as for our previous examples.

We are now in a position to utilize a method of abbreviation to indicate the bonding in a molecule. In this method, single, double, and triple bonds are simply represented by one, two, and three dashes in the formula. To illustrate, let us refer to the compounds considered above. Hydrogen molecule, H_2, has a single bond, which may be represented in this scheme by a single dash, as in H—H. Hydrogen fluoride HF also has a single bond and could be written as H—F. Fluorine F_2 would be F—F, and molecular nitrogen having a triple bond can be written as N≡N. The bonding in formaldehyde is then shown as

```
H
 \
  C=O
 /
H
```

Several further examples are given in Table 1-10. The appearance of the dotted bond in nitric acid is used to imply that the nitrogen-oxygen atoms so joined have a bond character somewhat between that of a double and a single bond. This feature can be associated with a phenomenon called resonance, but we will not pursue this principle any further here.

The concept of hybridization maintains its utility as an approach to the covalent bonding in compounds containing atoms other than carbon. For example, the bonding and structure of the ammonia molecule, NH_3, can be discussed within the framework of hybridized orbitals associated with the nitrogen atom. The electronic configuration of nitrogen is $1s^22s^22p_x{}^12p_y{}^12p_z{}^1$, which shows that there are five electrons in the second shell. Let us assume that the four orbitals of the second shell hybridize, forming an sp^3 set having a tetrahedral disposition of the four hybrid orbitals. The five electrons are distributed among this set of hybrid orbitals so that one orbital is completely filled with an electron pair (a "lone" electron pair, as it is called), and the remaining three orbitals each have one electron. Hydrogen atoms with one electron apiece form σ bonds with the

Table 1-10 Representations of the bonding in molecules

NAME OF COMPOUND	FORMULA	BONDING ARRANGEMENT
methane	CH_4	H H—C—H H
carbon tetrachloride	CCl_4	Cl Cl—C—Cl Cl
ethylene	H_2CCH_2	H H C=C H H
acetylene	C_2H_2	H—C≡C—H
sulfuric acid	H_2SO_4	O ‖ H—O—S—O—H ‖ O
phosphoric acid	H_3PO_4	O ‖ H—O—P—O—H O H
nitric acid	HNO_3	O H—O—N O

three partially filled hybrid orbitals of nitrogen, resulting in the ammonia molecule. The bonding angles in the ammonia molecule can be used as a guide for evaluating the correctness in assuming sp^3 hybridization for the nitrogen atom. Recall that the bonding angles in a tetrahedral molecule should be essentially 109°. The actual bonding angles in ammonia are found by experiment to be 107°, and the molecule has a pyramidal structure, as shown in Figure 1-20(a). This information lends support to the above bonding scheme involving sp^3 hybridization, because the difference between observed and expected bond angles is not considered to be significant. The structure suggests that the lone electron pair occupies a fourth position in space, which, in conjunction with the three hydrogen atoms, defines a tetrahedron about the nitrogen atom, as shown in Figure 1-20(b). In other words, the lone electron pair inhabits a position of geometrical importance in ammonia and one that is consistent with a tetrahedral sp^3 hybridization scheme. Indeed, evidence indicates that the spatial significance of lone electron pairs is quite a general occurrence in covalent compounds, and you

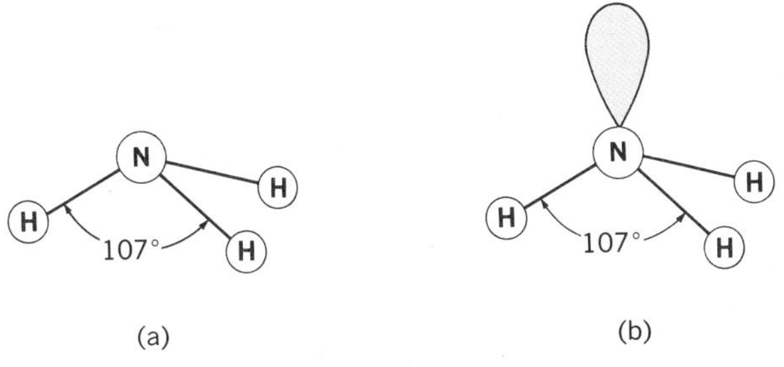

Figure 1-20 Bonding in ammonia, NH_3. (a) Location of atoms in ammonia molecule; (b) positions of hydrogen atoms and lone electron pair define a tetrahedron about the nitrogen.

should be aware of their influence on the structure and properties of a compound. Thus, the structure of ammonia may be described as a tetrahedron with a lone electron pair occupying one position and hydrogen atoms the remaining three positions about the nitrogen atom. Or alternately, when only the atoms in the molecule are viewed, they are seen to define a pyramidal structure with three hydrogen atoms forming the base and nitrogen the apex.

In a similar manner, sp^3 hybridization may be assumed for the oxygen atom in a water molecule in order to describe the bonding. Oxygen, with the electron configuration $1s^22s^22p_x^22p_y^12p_z^1$, has six electrons in the second shell. When these are distributed among the four hybrid orbitals of an sp^3 set in oxygen, two will contain lone electron pairs and two will be partially filled. Hydrogen atoms can form σ bonds with the partially filled orbitals, which results in the formation of a water molecule, H_2O. The structure of the molecule is such that the three atoms lie in a plane with an angle of 105° between the two hydrogen atoms. This is shown in Figure 1-21(a). Again, 105° is not too far from the 109° expected for a tetrahedron, which suggests that hybridization of the oxygen atomic orbitals is a useful approach to describe the bonding in a water molecule. If the two hydrogen atoms occupy tetrahedral sites about the oxygen, there is the strong possibility that the lone electron pairs are present in

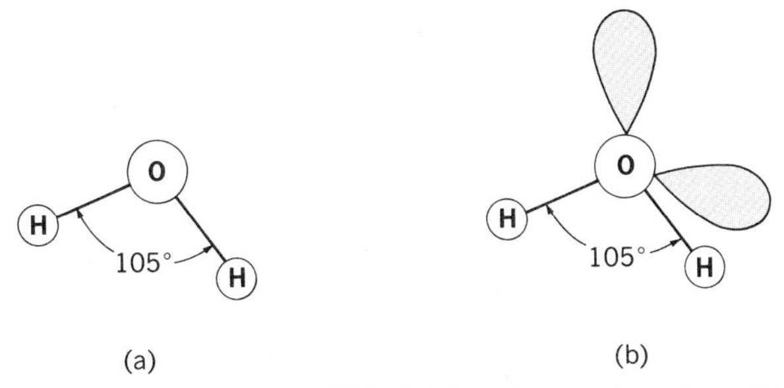

Figure 1-21 Bonding in water, H_2O. (a) Location of atoms in water molecule; (b) position of H atoms and lone electron pairs define a tetrahedron about the oxygen.

positions that complete the tetrahedron about oxygen, as shown in Figure 1-21(b). Thus, in water as well as in ammonia, the lone electron pairs seem to occupy places important to the structure of the molecule.

Let us now consider another manner in which covalent bonding may arise. Recall that the prerequisites for a covalent bond are (1) two atomic orbitals capable of generating a molecular orbital that involves both atoms more directly, and (2) an electron pair that resides in the molecular orbital. When two atoms are joined by a covalent bond, each must contribute an atomic orbital to develop the molecular orbital. However, no similar restriction applies to the origin of the electrons that make up the electron pair. Each atom may donate one electron apiece, or, equally as well, both electrons can come from one atom and none from the other. Restated, this simply means that whereas each atom must have an available orbital, the origin of the two electrons is immaterial in a covalent bond. In the examples so far used to illustrate covalent bonding, each atom involved in the bond contributed one electron to the bonding pair. Now let us consider some examples where the electrons in the bonding pair originate as a lone pair of electrons.

Ammonia, NH_3, contains a lone electron pair on the nitrogen atom available for use as a bonding pair in the proper situation. A hydrogen atom has the electron configuration $1s^1$. Upon loss of its only electron, there results a hydrogen ion, written as H^+, with the configuration $1s^0$. The agent responsible for this electron loss need not concern us here. Hydrogen ion has an empty $1s$ orbital, and ammonia possesses a lone electron pair in an sp^3 hybrid orbital; the conditions are present for covalent bond formation. The two orbitals can overlap and generate a molecular orbital, and an electron pair is available for its occupancy. The molecular orbital will lie on the bond axis and is a σ bond. In forming this bond, the charge present on the hydrogen ion is not neutralized by addition to the ammonia molecule, and the species formed retains the $+1$ charge. An equation that represents this event may be written as follows:

$$H^+ + NH_3 = NH_4^+$$

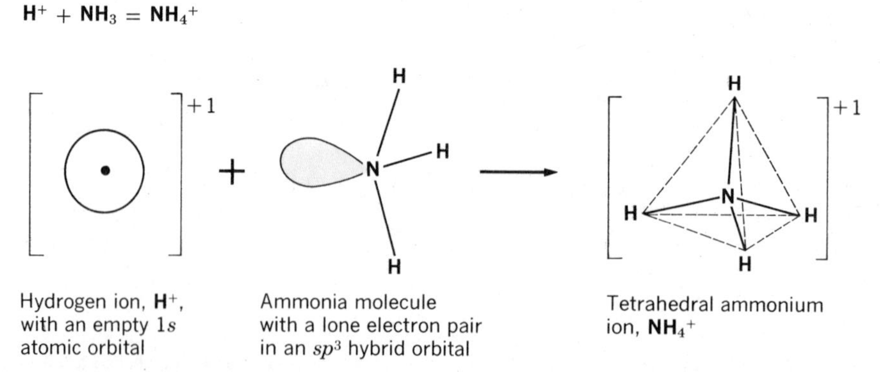

Figure 1-22 Formation of ammonium ion, NH_4^+.

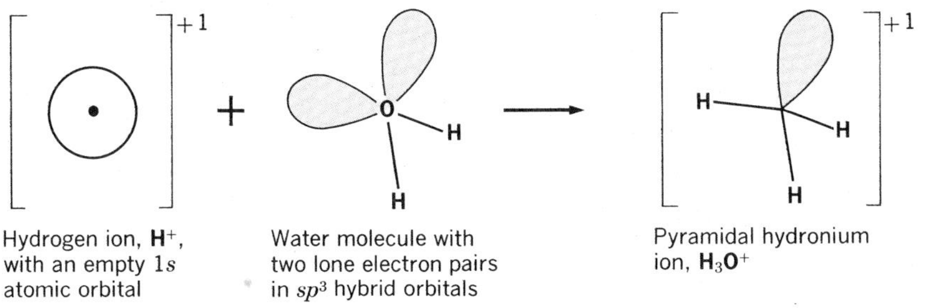

Hydrogen ion, H^+, with an empty 1*s* atomic orbital

Water molecule with two lone electron pairs in sp^3 hybrid orbitals

Pyramidal hydronium ion, H_3O^+

Figure 1-23 Formation of hydronium ion, H_3O^+.

In Figure 1-22, the orbitals involved in bond formation and their charges are depicted. The product formed is called the ammonium ion, NH_4^+. In this ion, the four σ bonds are equivalent and directed at the corners of a tetrahedron. The bond that arose from the nitrogen lone electron pair and the hydrogen ion is indistinguishable from the other nitrogen-hydrogen bonds in the ammonium ion. Since all bonds are the same, the origin of the bonding pair of electrons is seen to be insignificant.

Another such example involves bond formation between hydrogen ion and one of the lone electron pairs on oxygen in the water molecule. Again, the empty 1*s* of hydrogen ion and the sp^3 hybrid orbital on oxygen containing a lone electron pair complete the requirements for covalent bond formation. A molecular orbital forms that contains the electron pair, and the bond is a σ bond. The charge on the hydrogen ion is not extinguished by its reaction with the neutral water molecule, and that charge persists in the species formed. An equation representing this reaction is

$$H^+ + H_2O = H_3O^+$$

The ion that results is called the hydronium ion, H_3O^+. The pertinent change in orbitals is indicated in Figure 1-23. In the hydronium ion, there are three oxygen-hydrogen σ bonds that are equal in kind, and the oxygen atom still possesses one lone electron pair. The structure of the ion is essentially that of a tetrahedron, with the lone pair defining the fourth position. The hydronium ion is generally used to represent the manner in which hydrogen ions exist in water solutions. Since hydrogen ions are responsible for the characteristic properties of the group of chemical compounds known as acids, it is often said that acids in water yield hydronium ions.

Many ions and atoms contain empty orbitals available for bond formation, as does the hydrogen ion, and there are also many substances capable of donating lone electron pairs, as was true for ammonia and water molecules. Noteworthy in this respect are the transition metals, in which the *d* orbitals are available for bonding with substances having lone electron pairs. One infamous example of such bond formation is responsible for the danger of carbon monoxide poisoning. Carbon monoxide, CO, has a lone electron pair on the carbon atom, and iron ions (many of which are associated with the hemoglobin in blood) have *d* orbitals in the third shell available for bond formation. The iron-carbon bond that forms is so stable that the hemoglobin is prevented from maintaining its normal physiological activity, and poisoning results even from extremely minute concentrations of carbon monoxide in air.

Metals, nonmetals, metalloids

The known elements can be classified into four general categories: (1) metals, (2) nonmetals, (3) elements called metalloids that exhibit the characteristics of both metals and nonmetals, and (4) elements such as noble gases, which do not fit into any of the three previous classes.

Metals are generally shiny and solid at room temperature (mercury, a liquid, is an exception). Metals tend to lose electrons and become positively charged ions. Metallic oxides usually react with water to form bases.

Some examples of metals are sodium (Na), magnesium (Mg), and calcium (Ca). They all tend to form positive ions.

$$Na^0 \longrightarrow Na^+ + 1e^-$$
$$Mg^0 \longrightarrow Mg^{++} + 2e^-$$
$$Ca^0 \longrightarrow Ca^{++} + 2e^-$$

Their oxides react with water in the following manner:

$$Na_2O + H_2O \longrightarrow 2NaOH$$

sodium oxide, water, sodium hydroxide (*lye*)

$$MgO + H_2O \longrightarrow Mg(OH)_2$$

magnesium oxide, water, magnesium hydroxide (*milk of magnesia*)

$$CaO + H_2O \longrightarrow Ca(OH)_2$$

calcium oxide (*lime*), water, calcium hydroxide (*lime water*)

and, in every case, a base is formed.

Nonmetals generally have no luster, and many are gases. The oxides of nonmetals usually react with water to form acids. Some examples of nonmetals are sulfur (S), phosphorus (P), and nitrogen (N_2).

Their oxides react with water to form acids.

$$SO_3 + H_2O \longrightarrow H_2SO_4$$

sulfur trioxide, water, sulfuric acid

P_2O_5	+ $3H_2O$	$\longrightarrow$	$2H_3PO_4$
phosphorus pentoxide	water		phosphoric acid

N_2O_5	+ H_2O	$\longrightarrow$	$2HNO_3$
nitrogen pentoxide	water		nitric acid

Metalloids are elements that act either as a metal or as a nonmetal. Aluminum (Al) and chromium (Cr) are two common metalloids. The hydroxides of these elements act as an acid or a base, depending upon the conditions. A substance that can be acidic or basic is an *amphoteric compound.*

If acid is added to aluminum hydroxide or chromium hydroxide, a salt and water are formed. This justifies calling the starting compound a base.

$Al(OH)_3$ +	$3HCl$	$\longrightarrow$	$AlCl_3$	+ $3H_2O$
aluminum hydroxide	hydrochloric acid		aluminum chloride	water
base	*acid*		*salt*	*water*

$2Cr(OH)_3$ +	$3H_2SO_4$	$\longrightarrow$	$Cr_2(SO_4)_3$	+ $6H_2O$
chromium hydroxide	sulfuric acid		chromium sulfate	water
base	*acid*		*salt*	*water*

But, if a base is added to both aluminum hydroxide and chromium hydroxide, they act as if they were aluminic acid and chromous acids, respectively.

H_3AlO_3 +	$NaOH$	$\longrightarrow$	$NaAlO_2$	+ $2H_2O$
aluminic acid	sodium hydroxide		sodium aluminate	water
acid	*base*		*salt*	*water*

H_3CrO_3 +	$NaOH$	$\longrightarrow$	$NaCrO_2$	+ $2H_2O$
chromous acid	sodium hydroxide		sodium chromite	water
acid	*base*		*salt*	*water*

The *noble gases* have already been discussed.

Acids, bases, and salts

Bases are substances that form hydroxyl ions (OH^-) in solution; more generally, bases are substances that will *accept* a proton.

Sodium hydroxide ($NaOH$), magnesium hydroxide ($Mg(OH)_2$), and calcium hydroxide ($Ca(OH)_2$), for example, are bases, because in water solution they yield free hydroxyl ions.

$$NaOH \xrightarrow{H_2O} Na^+ + OH^-$$

$$Mg(OH)_2 \xrightarrow{H_2O} Mg^{++} + 2OH^-$$

$$Ca(OH)_2 \xrightarrow{H_2O} Ca^{++} + 2OH^-$$

Ammonia (NH_3) is a base because it can accept a proton to form the ammonium ion.

$$NH_3^0 + H^+ \longrightarrow NH_4^+$$

We can classify bases in two ways: strong or weak. A strong base forms a large concentration of hydroxyl ions in solution. Some common strong bases are

LiOH	lithium hydroxide
NaOH	sodium hydroxide
KOH	potassium hydroxide

Bases are generally written in the molecular form with the OH^- last. Weak bases form very few hydroxyl ions in solution. The most common weak base is ammonium hydroxide (NH_4OH). Other weak bases may be derived from ammonia, usually with various organic groups replacing one or more hydrogens. We will discuss these in Chapter 9.

Acids are substances that form hydrogen ions (H^+) in solution or, more generally, substances that *donate* a proton.

Sulfuric acid in water solution forms hydrogen ions,

$$H_2SO_4 \longrightarrow H^+ + HSO_4^-$$

as does phosphoric acid,

$$H_3PO_4 \longrightarrow H^+ + H_2PO_4^-$$

and nitric acid

$$HNO_3 \longrightarrow H^+ + NO_3^-$$

Although acids yield H^+, it appears that these hydrogen ions react with water (H_2O) to form H_3O^+, which is the *hydronium ion* (hydrated hydrogen ion). Therefore, the protons furnished by acids are solvated in water solution. However, for the sake of convenience, hydrogen ions in solution are simply represented as H^+.

Sulfuric (H_2SO_4), phosphoric (H_3PO_4), and nitric (HNO_3) acids are known as oxyacids, because they contain a nonmetal, hydrogen, and oxygen. There are also some nonoxy acids. Some examples are hydrofluoric (HF), hydrochloric (HCl), hydrobromic (HBr), hydroiodic (HI), and hydrosulfuric (H_2S) acids.

When the nonoxy acids are placed in water, they also furnish H^+ ions. For example,

$HCl \longrightarrow H^+ + Cl^-$
$HBr \longrightarrow H^+ + Br^-$
$HI \longrightarrow H^+ + I^-$

A *strong acid* furnishes a large amount of H^+; a weak acid produces very little H^+. Table 1-11 lists some common acids and their relative strengths.

Acids are generally written in the molecular form with H in front.

An acid and a base always react to give a salt and water. This is called neutralization. A *salt* is an ionic compound composed of the positive part of the base and the negative part of the acid.

HCl	+	$NaOH$	$\longrightarrow$	$NaCl$	+	H_2O
hydrochloric acid		sodium hydroxide		sodium chloride		water

H_2SO_4	+	$Ca(OH)_2$	$\longrightarrow$	$CaSO_4$	+	$2H_2O$
sulfuric acid		calcium hydroxide		calcium sulfate		water

Sodium chloride and calcium sulfate are called neutral salts because both are formed from strong acids and strong bases.

HCN	+	$NaOH$	$\longrightarrow$	$NaCN$	+	H_2O
hydrocyanic acid		sodium hydroxide		sodium cyanide		water

H_2CO_3	+	$Mg(OH)_2$	$\longrightarrow$	$MgCO_3$	+	$2H_2O$
carbonic acid		magnesium hydroxide		magnesium carbonate		water

Both sodium cyanide and magnesium carbonate are basic salts, because they are made from weak acids and strong bases.

NH_4OH	+	HCl	$\longrightarrow$	NH_4Cl	+	H_2O
ammonium hydroxide		hydrochloric acid		ammonium chloride		water

Table 1-11 Acid strength

Strong acids	HCl	hydrochloric acid
	HBr	hydrobromic acid
	HI	hydroiodic acid
	HNO_3	nitric acid
	H_2SO_4	sulfuric acid
	$HClO_4$	perchloric acid
Intermediate	H_3PO_4	phosphoric acid
Weak acids	HCN	hydrocyanic acid
	H_2S	hydrosulfuric acid
	H_2CO_3	carbonic acid
	$HC_2H_3O_2$	acetic acid
	and other related organic acids	

Ammonium chloride is an acidic salt because it is made from a strong acid and a weak base.

Inorganic Nomenclature

In naming the positive part (usually written first), the name of the metal, or hydrogen, or radical, is given first.

Na^+Cl^-	K^+Br^-	H^+I^-
sodium chloride	*potassium* bromide	*hydrogen* iodide
$(SbO)^+Cl^-$	$(UO_2)^{++}(NO_3)_2$	
antimonyl chloride	*uranyl* nitrate	

If a metal can exhibit more than one valence, the high one is usually given an -ic ending and the low one an -ous ending. A more useful method indicates the particular valence as a Roman numeral in parentheses after the metal.

$FeCl_3$	$FeCl_2$	$CuCl_2$	$CuCl$
ferr*ic* chloride [*iron*(III) *chloride*]	ferr*ous* chloride [*iron*(II) *chloride*]	cupr*ic* chloride [*copper*(II) *chloride*]	cupr*ous* chloride [*copper*(I) *chloride*]
$CoCl_3$	$CoCl_2$		
cobalt*ic* chloride [*cobalt*(III) *chloride*]	cobalt*ous* chloride [*cobalt*(II) *chloride*]		

In naming the negative part of salts, the endings must be related to the acids from which they came. A binary compound contains only two different elements. The binary acids end in -ic and use a prefix hydro-. Such binary acids form salts, which end in -ide.

HCl	$NaCl$
*hydro*chlor*ic* acid	sodium chlor*ide*
H_2S	Ag_2S
*hydro*sulfur*ic* acid	silver sulf*ide*

Examples of other binary compounds are

Mg_3N_2	Ca_3P_2	MgO
magnesium nitr*ide*	calcium phosph*ide*	magnesium ox*ide*

In naming inorganic acids with three or more elements (one of the elements is usually oxygen and these acids are called the oxyacids), the ending is -ic, and such acids form -ate salts.

H_2SO_4	Na_2SO_4
sulfur*ic* acid	sodium sulf*ate*
HNO_3	KNO_3
nitr*ic* acid	potassium nitr*ate*

H_2CO_3	$CaCO_3$
carbon*ic* acid	calcium carbon*ate*

Remember, an -ic acid always forms an -ate salt.

However, since it is not unusual for the key element of these oxyacids to exhibit more than one oxidation state, we must know which is the "regular" or "ortho" acid, as our anchor point, so that we can relate one acid to the other.

For example, if any oxyacid has *one more oxygen* than the regular acid, the prefix per- is used for both the acid and its salts.

$HClO_3$	$KClO_3$
chlor*ic* acid (*the regular or ortho acid*)	potassium chlor*ate*

but

$HClO_4$	$KClO_4$
*per*chlor*ic* acid	potassium *per*chlor*ate*
$HC_2H_3O_2$	$KC_2H_3O_2$
acet*ic* acid	potassium acet*ate*

but

$HC_2H_3O_3$	$KC_2H_3O_3$
*per*acet*ic* acid	potassium *peracetate*

If an acid can be formed with *one less oxygen* than the regular oxygen acid, we use the suffix -ous for the acid, and the suffix -ite for the salt.

H_2SO_4	$CaSO_4$
sulfur*ic* acid	calcium sulf*ate*

but

H_2SO_3	$CaSO_3$
sulfur*ous* acid	calcium sulf*ite*
HNO_3	KNO_3
nitr*ic* acid	potassium nitr*ate*

but

HNO_2	KNO_2
nitr*ous* acid	potassium nitr*ite*

If an oxyacid has *two less oxygens* than the regular acid, we use the prefix hypo- and the suffix -ous; and salts of such an acid also use the prefix hypo- and the suffix -ite.

$HClO_2$	$NaClO_2$
chlor*ous* acid	sodium chlor*ite*
$HClO$	$NaClO$
*hypo*chlor*ous* acid	sodium *hypo*chlor*ite*

A *meta* acid is formed by the removal of a molecule of water from an oxyacid.

H_3PO_4	$[HPO_3]_x$
phosphor*ic* acid	*meta*phosphor*ic* acid (*polymeric form*)
H_3PO_3	HPO_2
phosphor*ous* acid	*meta*phosphor*ous* acid

A *pyro* acid may be considered to be the acid obtained by removing a molecule of water from two molecules of the oxyacid.

$$\begin{array}{r} H_2SO_4 \\ +H_2SO_4 \\ \hline H_4S_2O_8 \\ -H_2\ \ O \\ \hline H_2S_2O_7 \end{array} \qquad \begin{array}{r} H_3PO_4 \\ +H_3PO_4 \\ \hline H_6P_2O_8 \\ -H_2\ \ O \\ \hline H_4P_2O_7 \end{array}$$

$H_2S_2O_7$ is *pyro*sulfuric acid $H_4P_2O_7$ *pyro*phosphoric acid

Solutions

In a flask of distilled water, we can easily show that the water at one part of the flask is exactly the same as the water at any other part. In other words, the water is homogeneous: it is the same throughout. If we add a small amount of sugar to the water, the sugar dissolves completely and distributes itself evenly throughout the water, making a sugar solution in water. We refer to the sugar as the *solute* and the water as the *solvent.* Again, we can show that a portion of the solution at one part of the flask contains a fixed amount of sugar. An equivalent volume of water in any other part of the flask will contain the same amount of sugar. The sugar concentration is the same everywhere in the solution; therefore, the sugar solution is homogeneous.

Our observations show that there is a limit to the amount of sugar that can be added to a definite volume of water. If we exceed the limit, the excess sugar will not dissolve. The governing factor, then, is the solubility of the sugar in water. Each substance has its own characteristic solubility in any given solvent.

We can define a solution as a *homogeneous mixture of two or more substances, the composition of which may be varied continuously within certain limits.* The concentration of solutions can be expressed in many ways, and these will be discussed later.

So-called colloidal "solutions" are not true solutions but are actually heterogeneous systems. We will discuss this topic in greater detail later in this chapter.

Expressing concentrations of solutions

Let us review some concepts of quantitative chemistry.

Molecular weight. A molecular weight is the sum of all the atomic weights of the elements in a compound.

Mole. A mole is Avogadro's number (6.023×10^{23}) of molecules of a particle. (It equals the molecular weight expressed in grams.)

$$\text{mole} = \frac{\text{grams}}{\text{molecular weight}}$$

EXAMPLE

Determine the weight of 1 mole of hydrochloric acid.

HCl atomic weights: **H** = 1.0
Cl = 35.5

$$\begin{aligned} 1 \times 1.0 &= 1.0 \\ 1 \times 35.5 &= \underline{35.5} \\ & \quad 36.5 \end{aligned}$$

Therefore, 36.5 = molecular weight of HCl, and 36.5 grams of HCl = 1 mole of HCl.

EXAMPLE

Determine the weight of 1 mole of sulfuric acid.

H_2SO_4 atomic weights: **H** = 1.0
S = 32.0
O = 16.0

$$\begin{aligned} 2 \times 1.0 &= 2.0 \\ 1 \times 32.0 &= 32.0 \\ 4 \times 16.0 &= \underline{64.0} \\ & \quad 98.0 \end{aligned}$$

Therefore, 98.0 = molecular weight of H_2SO_4, and 98.0 grams of H_2SO_4 = 1 mole of H_2SO_4.

We can readily see that if the number of grams equals the molecular weight, the number of moles is 1. It is to be realized that a formula is only a mathematical means of restating a definition.

EXAMPLE

Suppose we had 120 g of acetic acid, 4 g of sodium hydroxide, 49 g of phosphoric acid, 73 g of hydrochloric acid, and 76 g of sodium sulfate. How many moles of each would we have?

CH_3COOH mol. weight = 60 How many moles do 120 g represent?

$$\text{moles of } \mathbf{CH_3COOH} = \text{g/mol. weight} = \frac{120}{60} = 2 \text{ moles}$$

$$120 \text{ g of } \mathbf{CH_3COOH} = 2 \text{ moles}$$

NaOH mol. weight = 40 How many moles do 4 g represent?

$$\text{moles of } \mathbf{NaOH} = \text{g/mol. weight} = \frac{4}{40} = 0.1 \text{ mole } (\tfrac{1}{10})$$

$$4 \text{ g of } \mathbf{NaOH} = 0.1 \text{ mole}$$

H_3PO_4 mol. weight = 98 How many moles do 49 g represent?

$$\text{moles of } \mathbf{H_3PO_4} = \text{g/mol. weight} = \frac{49}{98} = 0.5 \text{ mole } (\tfrac{1}{2})$$

$$49 \text{ g of } \mathbf{H_3PO_4} = 0.5 \text{ mole}$$

HCl mol. weight = 36.5 How many moles do 73 g represent?

$$\text{moles of } \mathbf{HCl} = \text{g/mol. weight} = \frac{73}{36.5} = 2 \text{ moles}$$

$$73 \text{ g of } \mathbf{HCl} = 2 \text{ moles}$$

Na_2SO_4 mol. weight = 142 How many moles do 76.0 g represent?

$$\text{moles of } \mathbf{Na_2SO_4} = \text{g/mol. weight} = \frac{76.0}{142} = 0.535 \text{ mole}$$

$$76.0 \text{ g of } \mathbf{Na_2SO_4} = 0.535 \text{ mole}$$

Molarity

The concentration of a solution is often an important piece of information. One of the most common chemical ways to solve this problem is to express the concentration in moles per liter of solution. We call this expression the molarity (M) of the solution.

molarity = moles/liter

One liter equals 1,000 ml or 1,000 cm^3. If the volume is expressed in liters, this number can be used as such in solving problems. If the volume is expressed in milliliters (ml) or cubic centimeters (cm^3), the volume in liters is quickly found by dividing by 1,000.

If we have 100 ml, how many liters do we have?

100 ml = $\frac{100}{1000} = \frac{1}{10}$ liter = 0.1 liter

If we have 50 ml, how many liters do we have?

50 ml = $\frac{50}{1000} = \frac{1}{20}$ liter = 0.05 liter

Let us examine a few calculations of molarity.

EXAMPLE

Suppose we had 40 g of sodium hydroxide in 1 liter; what is the molarity of this solution?

$$\text{moles of } \mathbf{NaOH} = \frac{\text{g}}{\text{mol. weight}} = \frac{40}{40} = 1 \text{ mole}$$

$$\text{molarity} = \frac{\text{moles}}{\text{liters}} = \frac{1}{1} = 1$$

A solution containing 40 g of NaOH in 1 liter is 1 molar (written $1M$).

EXAMPLE

A solution contains 49 g of sulfuric acid in 1 liter; what is the molarity of this solution?

$$\text{moles of } \mathbf{H_2SO_4} = \frac{\text{g}}{\text{mol. weight}} = \frac{49}{98} = \frac{1}{2} \text{ mole}$$

$$\text{molarity} = \frac{\text{moles}}{\text{liters}} = \frac{\frac{1}{2}}{1} = \frac{1}{2}M = \frac{M}{2}$$

A solution of 49 g of H_2SO_4 in 1 liter is $\frac{1}{2}M$ or $0.5M$.

EXAMPLE

If we had a solution of 4 g of sodium hydroxide in 100 ml, how many moles per liter would we have?

$$\text{moles of } \mathbf{NaOH} = \frac{\text{g}}{\text{mol. weight}} = \frac{4}{40} = \frac{1}{10} \text{ mole}$$

$$\text{volume of the solution in liters} = \frac{100}{1000} = \frac{1}{10} \text{ liter}$$

$$\text{molarity} = \frac{\text{moles}}{\text{liter}} = \frac{\frac{1}{10}}{\frac{1}{10}} = 1 \text{ molar}$$

As can be easily seen, a solution containing 4 g of sodium hydroxide in 100 ml is just as strong as a solution of 40 g of sodium hydroxide in 1 liter.

EXAMPLE

If we had 120 g of acetic acid in 4 liters, what would be the molarity of this solution?

$$\text{moles of acetic acid} = \frac{\text{g}}{\text{mol. weight}} = \frac{120}{60} = 2 \text{ moles}$$

$$\text{molarity} = \frac{\text{moles}}{\text{liter}} = \frac{2}{4} = \frac{1}{2}M$$

Normality

Often the concentration of the ions in a solution of ionizing compounds is more important than the number of moles of the compound. This concentration of ions is expressed as *gram-equivalents per liter* and is called *normality* (N). Normality considers the valence of the ions, whereas molarity does not.

A gram-equivalent of a compound is the equivalent weight expressed in grams. For acids or bases, the equivalent weight is equal to the molecular weight divided by the number of H^+ or OH^- that are furnished by the molecule in the reaction. For all acids or bases containing one H^+ or OH^-, the equivalent weight equals the molecular weight. For all other ionizing compounds, the normality will be a multiple of the molarity.

EXAMPLE

Calculate the equivalent weight of H_2SO_4.

mol. weight of $H_2SO_4 = 98$

Since there are two hydrogens, the equivalent weight is

$$\frac{98}{2} = 49$$

EXAMPLE

What is the equivalent weight of H_3PO_4?

mol. weight of $H_3PO_4 = 98$

When the three hydrogen ions are furnished in a reaction, the equivalent weight is

$$\frac{98}{3} = 32.67$$

EXAMPLE

Determine the equivalent weight of $Ca(OH)_2$.

mol. weight of $Ca(OH)_2 = 74$

Since there are 2 OH^-, the equivalent weight is

$$\frac{74}{2} = 37$$

In compounds such as HCl, NaOH, NaCl, and KCl, which contain only univalent ions, the equivalent weight is equal to the molecular weight.

If we had 98 g of sulfuric acid in 1 liter, we would have a 1 molar solution (1 mole in 1 liter of solution). However, 98 g represents 2 gram-equivalents, and so we would have two gram-equivalents per liter, which represents a $2N$ solution (2 gram-equivalent weights in 1 liter of solution).

If we had 133.5 g of $AlCl_3$ in 1 liter of solution, we would have a $1M$ solution. However, since 133.5 of $AlCl_3$ is 3 gram-equivalents, we would have a $3N$ solution.

The determination of normality of a solution is the same as the determination of the molarity of the solution, except that the gram-equivalent weight replaces the molecular weight.

EXAMPLE

If 49 g of sulfuric acid is dissolved in 500 ml of water, what is the normality of the solution?

$$\text{g-equivalents of } H_2SO_4 = \frac{\text{g}}{\text{eq. wt}} = \frac{49}{49} = 1 \text{ g-equivalent}$$

$$500 \text{ ml} = \tfrac{1}{2} \text{ liter}$$

$$\text{normality} = \frac{\text{g-equivalent}}{\text{liter}} = \frac{1}{\frac{1}{2}} = 2 \text{ g-equivalent/liter} = 2N$$

One of the chief uses of normal solution is in titrations.

TITRATION

Often it is important to learn the concentration of acid or base in a certain solution. In medicine, we may want to know the alkaline reserve of the blood, or the acidity of the stomach, or the acidity or basicity of the urine. This is conveniently done by a process known as titration. In titration, we add a measured volume of known concentration of a substance to a measured volume of unknown concentration of another substance. We generally use an indicator that changes color at a certain pH (see following section) to tell us when the titration is complete.

If we know the substance involved and can write the balanced equation, then we can calculate the unknown concentration of the solution measured.

EXAMPLE

Suppose we had a beaker containing 100 ml of HCl of unknown concentration, titrated this with $\frac{1}{10}M$ NaOH, and had to use 100 ml of the NaOH. What is the concentration of the HCl?

We know in advance that NaOH and HCl react to give salt and water.

$$NaOH + HCl \longrightarrow NaCl + H_2O$$

We see quickly that one mole of NaOH reacts with one mole of HCl. The value of having the balanced equation is that we know the ratio, in moles, of the substance involved in the equation and in the titration. Because the same number of moles of NaOH and HCl are involved, we can write

$$\text{moles } \mathbf{NaOH} = \text{moles } \mathbf{HCl}$$

Our definition was

$$\text{molarity} = \text{moles/liter}$$

This can be restated, by solving for moles, as

$$\text{moles} = \text{molarity} \times \text{liters}$$

so

$$\text{moles } \mathbf{NaOH} = \text{molarity } \mathbf{NaOH} \times \text{liters } \mathbf{NaOH}$$

and

$$\text{moles } \mathbf{HCl} = \text{molarity } \mathbf{HCl} \times \text{liters } \mathbf{HCl}$$

To work the problem (for HCl),

$$\text{moles} = \frac{1}{10} M \times \frac{100}{1000} \text{ liter} = \frac{1}{100} \text{ mole}$$

Therefore, $\frac{1}{100}$ mole of HCl was involved, since moles HCl = moles NaOH.

$$\text{moles } \mathbf{HCl} = \text{molarity } \mathbf{HCl} \times \text{liters } \mathbf{HCl}$$

$$\frac{1}{100} = \text{molarity } \mathbf{HCl} \times \frac{100}{1000}$$

The only unknown quantity is the molarity of the HCl. Solving for this we obtain

$$\text{molarity } \mathbf{HCl} = \frac{\frac{1}{100}}{\frac{1}{10}} = \frac{1}{10} M$$

The HCl is $\frac{1}{10}M$.

Let us illustrate another problem.

EXAMPLE

Suppose we titrate sulfuric acid with sodium hydroxide and use an indicator so that the following equation is valid.

$$\mathbf{2NaOH + H_2SO_4 \longrightarrow Na_2SO_4 + 2H_2O}$$

Suppose we had 25 ml of the sulfuric acid of unknown concentration and had to use 80 ml of $0.07M$ NaOH. What is the concentration of the sulfuric acid?

From the equation, we see that

$$2 \text{ moles } \mathbf{NaOH} = \text{moles } \mathbf{H_2SO_4} \text{ or moles } \mathbf{NaOH} = \frac{1}{2} \text{ mole } \mathbf{H_2SO_4}$$

since twice as many moles of NaOH are involved as moles of H_2SO_4. Then

$$\text{moles } \mathbf{NaOH} = \text{molarity } \mathbf{NaOH} \times \text{liters } \mathbf{NaOH}$$

or

$$\text{moles } \mathbf{NaOH} = 0.07M \times \frac{80}{1000} \text{ liter} = 0.0056 \text{ mole of } \mathbf{NaOH}$$

Because moles $H_2SO_4 = \frac{1}{2}$ mole of NaOH $= \frac{1}{2}(0.0056) = 0.0028$ mole

$$\text{moles } \mathbf{H_2SO_4} = \text{molarity } \mathbf{H_2SO_4} \times \text{liters } \mathbf{H_2SO_4}$$

$$0.0028 = \text{molarity } \mathbf{H_2SO_4} \times \frac{25}{1000}$$

$$\text{molarity } \mathbf{H_2SO_4} = \frac{0.0028}{0.025} = 0.112M$$

The H_2SO_4 is $0.112M$.

This same problem can be solved using normalities.

EXAMPLE

25 ml of H_2SO_4 of unknown concentration required 80 ml of $0.07M$ NaOH to neutralize it. What is the normality of the H_2SO_4?

As we stated, the gram-equivalents of acid are equal to the gram equivalents of base.

Sodium hydroxide has one OH^-; therefore, 1 gram-equivalent is equal to 1 mole.

$$0.07M = 0.07N$$

$$\text{normality} = \frac{\text{gram-equivalent}}{\text{liter}}$$

$$\text{normality } \mathbf{NaOH} \times \text{liters } \mathbf{NaOH} = \text{gram-equivalents } \mathbf{NaOH}$$

$$0.07 \times \frac{80}{1000} = 0.0056 \text{ gram-equivalents of } \mathbf{NaOH}$$

Because gram-equivalents NaOH = gram-equivalents H_2SO_4,

$$0.0056 \text{ gram-equivalents of } \mathbf{H_2SO_4} = \text{normality } \mathbf{H_2SO_4} \times \frac{25}{1000} \text{ liter } \mathbf{H_2SO_4}$$

$$\frac{0.0056}{0.025} = 0.224N \ \mathbf{H_2SO_4}$$

Since 1 gram-equivalent of H_2SO_4 = moles of $H_2SO_4/2$, the sulfuric acid solution is $0.224N$ or $0.112M$.

EXAMPLE

25 ml of $\frac{1}{10}N$ H_3PO_4 is used to neutralize 75 ml of KOH of unknown concentration. Calculate the normality of the KOH.

$$\text{normality} = \frac{\text{gram-equivalents}}{\text{liter}}$$

$$\text{normality } \mathbf{H_3PO_4} \times \text{liter } \mathbf{H_3PO_4} = \text{gram-equivalents } \mathbf{H_3PO_4}$$

$$\frac{1}{10} \times \frac{25}{1000} = 0.0025 \text{ g-equivalents of } \mathbf{H_3PO_4}$$

Since g-equivalents of acid = g-equivalents of base,

$$0.0025 \text{ g-equivalents of } \mathbf{H_3PO_4} = 0.0025 \text{ g-equivalents of } \mathbf{KOH}$$

$$\text{normality of } \mathbf{KOH} = \frac{0.0025 \text{ g-equivalents}}{0.075 \text{ liter}}$$

$$N = 0.033$$

The KOH solution is $0.033N$.

EXAMPLE

What is the normality of an HCl solution if 50 ml of $0.01N$ NaOH is needed to neutralize 75 ml of the acid?

$$\text{liters} \times \text{normality} = \text{g-equivalents}$$

$$50 \text{ ml} = 0.05 \text{ liter}_{\text{NaOH}}$$

$$0.05 \text{ liter}_{\text{NaOH}} \times 0.01N_{\text{NaOH}} = 0.0005 \text{ g-equivalents of } \mathbf{NaOH}$$

Therefore, 0.0005 g-equivalents of HCl were used.

$$\frac{0.0005 \text{ g-equivalents}}{0.075 \text{ liter}} = 0.0067N$$

The HCl solution is $0.0067N$.

Aqueous solutions of acids and bases

pH

pH is a method of expressing the acidity or basicity of a solution. We define pH as $-\log [H^+]$, where $[H^+]$ is hydrogen ion concentration.

Let us review at this time some concepts of acidity and basicity.

One of the serviceable definitions of an acid is a substance that furnishes hydrogen ions (H^+), and a base is a substance that furnishes hydroxyl ions (OH^-).

Water is an interesting substance to consider first since it furnishes both hydrogen and hydroxyl ions.

$$\mathbf{HOH = H^+ + OH^-}$$

The amount of ions present in a sample of pure water is very small, but these quantities are known to a great degree of accuracy. Using the symbols $[H^+]$ and $[OH^-]$ to represent the molar concentrations of hydrogen and hydroxyl ions, respectively, it has been found that in pure water at room temperature,

$$[H^+] = 0.0000001 \text{ mole/liter}$$

and

$$[OH^-] = 0.0000001 \text{ mole/liter}$$

At room temperature, we see that the concentration of the hydrogen and hydroxyl ions is very low, but note that the hydrogen ions equal the hydroxyl ions. This is our definition of neutrality, and water is the perfectly neutral substance. It is, of course, logical that the $[H^+] = [OH^-]$, because each time a water molecule ionizes to form a H^+, it also must form one OH^-.

The disadvantage of discussing acidity and basicity of weak acids and bases in terms of the numbers mentioned above is apparent, because they are so unwieldy and cumbersome. For this reason, we invoke the powers of ten system.

The powers of ten system is a convenient way of expressing all numbers, particularly very large and very small numbers, as a one-digit number times ten to some power.

For expressing large numbers,

$$\begin{aligned}
1 &= 1 \\
10 &= 1 \times 10 \\
100 &= 1 \times (10 \times 10) = 1 \times 10^2 \\
1{,}000 &= 1 \times (10 \times 10 \times 10) = 1 \times 10^3 \\
10{,}000 &= 1 \times (10 \times 10 \times 10 \times 10) = 1 \times 10^4 \\
100{,}000 &= 1 \times (10 \times 10 \times 10 \times 10 \times 10) = 1 \times 10^5 \\
1{,}000{,}000 &= 1 \times (10 \times 10 \times 10 \times 10 \times 10 \times 10) = 1 \times 10^6 \\
10{,}000{,}000 &= 1 \times (10 \times 10 \times 10 \times 10 \times 10 \times 10 \times 10) = 1 \times 10^7
\end{aligned}$$

If we say 10^2 = ten squared or ten times ten, the 2 is called the *exponent;* the exponent tells us how many tens are involved.

For expressing small numbers,

$$\begin{aligned}
1 &= 1 \\
0.1 &= \frac{1}{10} = \frac{1}{1 \times 10} = 1 \times 10^{-1} \\
0.01 &= \frac{1}{100} = \frac{1}{1 \times (10 \times 10)} = \frac{1}{1 \times 10^2} = 1 \times 10^{-2} \\
0.001 &= \frac{1}{1{,}000} = \frac{1}{1 \times (10 \times 10 \times 10)} = \frac{1}{1 \times 10^3} = 1 \times 10^{-3} \\
0.0001 &= \frac{1}{10{,}000} = \frac{1}{1 \times (10 \times 10 \times 10 \times 10)} = \frac{1}{1 \times 10^4} = 1 \times 10^{-4} \\
0.00001 &= \frac{1}{100{,}000} = \frac{1}{1 \times (10 \times 10 \times 10 \times 10 \times 10)} = \frac{1}{1 \times 10^5} = 1 \times 10^{-5} \\
0.000001 &= \frac{1}{1{,}000{,}000} = \frac{1}{1 \times (10 \times 10 \times 10 \times 10 \times 10 \times 10)} = \frac{1}{1 \times 10^6} = 1 \times 10^{-6} \\
0.0000001 &= \frac{1}{10{,}000{,}000} = \frac{1}{1 \times (10 \times 10 \times 10 \times 10 \times 10 \times 10 \times 10)} = \frac{1}{1 \times 10^7} = 1 \times 10^{-7}
\end{aligned}$$

When a number is changed from the bottom of a fraction to the top, the sign of the exponent is changed.

EXAMPLE

Express the following numbers as powers of ten.

$$0.000023 = 2.3 \times 10^{-5}$$
$$0.0000000000175 = 1.75 \times 10^{-11}$$
$$23{,}000{,}000 = 2.3 \times 10^{7}$$
$$186{,}000{,}000{,}000 = 1.86 \times 10^{11}$$

Let us return to pH. We have shown that for water the $[H^+] =$ 0.0000001 moles per liter, which expressed as a power of ten equals 1×10^{-7} moles per liter. We are now in a position to calculate the pH of a pure water solution.

$$pH = -\log [H^+],\ [H^+] = 1 \times 10^{-7} \text{ mole per liter}$$
$$pH = -\log [1 \times 10^{-7}]$$

When two numbers are multiplied together we add their logs.

$$pH = -[\log 1 + \log 10^{-7}]$$

By definition, $\log [1] = 0$. This expression now reduces to

$$\text{pH of a pure water solution} = -\log [10^{-7}]$$

Again, *by definition,* the logarithm of ten to a certain power is that particular power, so

$$-[\log 10^{-7}] = -(-7) = 7.$$

The pH of a neutral solution is 7.

We define K_w as the ionization constant of water, and this figure is constant for a particular temperature.

$$K_w = [H^+] \times [OH^-]$$

In pure water,

$$[H^+] = [OH^-] = 1 \times 10^{-7}$$

So

$$K_w = [1 \times 10^{-7}] \times [1 \times 10^{-7}] = 1 \times 10^{-14} \text{ (at room temperature)}$$

(When two numbers are multiplied, we add their exponents.)

Since a constant, by its very name, does not change, if the $[H^+]$ changes, the $[OH^-]$ must change correspondingly so that the product always equals 1×10^{-14}. If the $[H^+]$ increases, the $[OH^-]$ decreases, and if the $[H^+]$ decreases, the $[OH^-]$ increases.

For pure water, we have stated that the solution is neutral and that $[H^+] = [OH^-]$.

We redefine an acid solution as one in which the $[H^+]$ is greater than the $[OH^-]$ concentration, and a basic solution as one in which the $[OH^-]$ is greater than the $[H^+]$.

EXAMPLE

Suppose the hydrogen ion concentration of a solution were ten times greater than that of pure water; $[H^+] = 0.000001$. What would be the pH of such a solution?

$$[H^+] = 0.000001 = 1 \times 10^{-6}$$

Therefore,

$$pH = -\log [1 \times 10^{-6}]$$
$$pH = -(-6) = 6.$$

If $[H^+] = 1 \times 10^{-6}$, $[OH^-]$ must equal 1×10^{-8}, because $[H^+]$ times $[OH^-]$ must equal 1×10^{-14}. Therefore, since the hydrogen ion concentration is greater than the hydroxyl ion concentration, a pH of 6 would represent an *acidic* solution.

EXAMPLE

What is the pH of a solution with $[H^+] = 0.01$? If $[H^+] = 0.01$,

$$pH = -\log [1 \times 10^{-2}]$$
$$pH = -(-2) = 2$$

If $[H^+] = 10^{-2}$, $[OH^-] = 1 \times 10^{-12}$.

A pH of 2 must represent an *acidic* solution, because the hydrogen ion concentration is greater than the hydroxyl ion concentration.

EXAMPLE

What is the pH of a solution with $[H^+] = 1 \times 10^{-8}$?

$$pH = -\log [1 \times 10^{-8}]$$
$$pH = -(-8) = 8$$

If $[H^+] = 1 \times 10^{-8}$, $[OH^-] = 1 \times 10^{-6}$. Thus, a pH of 8 represents a *basic* solution, because the $[OH^-]$ is greater than the $[H^+]$.

EXAMPLE

If $[H^+] = 1 \times 10^{-12}$, what is the pH of the solution?

$$pH = -\log [1 \times 10^{-12}]$$
$$pH = -(-12) = 12$$

If $[H^+] = 1 \times 10^{-12}$, $[OH^-] = 1 \times 10^{-2}$. Thus, a pH of 12 represents a *basic* solution, because the $[OH^-]$ is greater than the $[H^+]$.

In the examples so far, we have purposely picked numbers that would be illustrated easily. We have always chosen a number of 1 times a power of ten, because the logarithm of 1 is zero; more frequently the number is not 1. Under these conditions, we would have to look up the logarithm of this number.

EXAMPLE

If the $[H^+] = 0.0002$, what is the pH of the solution? (Use logarithm tables.)

$$pH = -\log [2 \times 10^{-4}]$$
$$pH = -[\log 2 + \log 10^{-4}]$$
$$pH = -[0.30 + (-4)]$$
$$pH = -[0.30 - 4]$$
$$pH = -[-3.70]$$
$$pH = 3.7$$

EXAMPLE

If the $[H^+] = 0.000000000005$, what is the pH of the solution?

$$pH = -\log [5 \times 10^{-12}]$$
$$pH = -[\log 5 + \log 10^{-12}]$$
$$pH = -[0.70 + (-12)]$$
$$pH = -[0.70 - 12]$$
$$pH = -[-11.30]$$
$$pH = 11.30$$

Indicators

An indicator is an organic dye that changes color at a certain pH. Each indicator is different; that is, each indicator has its own characteristic pH at which the color changes. The endpoint of a titration is reached when the indicator changes color and remains permanently changed. In actual titration, as one solution is added from the buret to the other solution, which is contained in a beaker or Erlenmeyer flask and which also contains the indicator, it is noticed that as one nears the endpoint, the color seems to change and then return to original. As one approaches the endpoint, the known solution should be added drop by drop. When properly conducted, as the endpoint is reached one drop will completely change the color of the entire solution permanently.

Indicators must be chosen with care. Only after a consideration of the acid-base system involved can one properly choose an indicator.

In general, it may be stated that the *proper indicator is one that changes color at the pH of the salt that is formed.* Table 1-12 lists some useful indicators.

Table 1-12 Indicators

	COLOR		pH RANGE
	in acid	*in base*	
acid cresol red	orange	yellow	0.2–1.8
thymol blue	red	yellow	1.2–2.8
meta-cresol purple	red	yellow	1.2–2.8
methyl orange	red	yellow	2.9–4.0
bromophenol blue	yellow	blue	3.0–4.6
congo red	blue	red	3.0–5.0
bromocresol green	yellow	blue	3.8–5.4
methyl red	red	yellow	4.4–6.0
chlorophenol red	yellow	red	4.8–6.4
alizarin red	yellow	purple	5.5–6.8
bromophenol red	yellow	red	5.2–6.8
bromothymol blue	yellow	blue	6.0–7.0
phenol red	yellow	red	6.8–8.4
litmus	red	blue	7.0
cresol red	yellow	red	7.2–8.8
meta-cresol purple	yellow	purple	7.4–9.0
thymol blue	yellow	blue	8.0–9.6
phenolphthalein	colorless	red	8.3–10.0
cresolphthalein	colorless	red	8.0–10.0

Let us briefly review salts in the light of what we have just mentioned about pH. NaCl is a neutral salt. When NaCl is placed in water, the pH is 7. Why?

When NaCl is placed in water, we may picture that a hydrolysis reaction is at work. *Hydrolysis* may be considered the reaction of a salt with water to form an acid and a base. This is the reverse of neutralization. For example, one may imagine that the ions of a salt combine with the hydrogen and hydroxyl ions from water and that an acid and base are formed. Depending on the ionizing character of the acid and base, it is possible to predict whether the solution will be acidic, basic, or neutral as a result of the hydrolysis of the salt. In this manner, if the ions of sodium chloride (Na^+, Cl^-) combine with the ions of water (H^+, OH^-), the acid formed would be hydrochloric acid (HCl) and the base would be sodium hydroxide (NaOH). Both of these would be present in equal amounts, and both are strong in their ionizing character. Therefore, the net result for the hydrolysis of sodium chloride is a neutral solution, as represented by the equation:

$$Na^+, Cl^- + H^+, OH^- \rightleftharpoons \underset{\displaystyle H^+, Cl^-}{\underset{\downarrow}{HCl}} + \underset{\displaystyle Na^+, OH^-}{\underset{\downarrow}{NaOH}}$$

The nature of the salt determines the direction in which the pH of a solution will change.

Ammonium chloride, NH_4Cl, is called an acidic salt, because its aqueous solutions turn litmus red. If the ions of this salt (NH_4^+, Cl^-) combine with the ions of water (H^+, OH^-) the acid and base formed would be hydrochloric acid and ammonium hydroxide. The ionizing character of the acid is strong, but this is not true for the base; ammonium hydroxide is only partially ionized. Therefore, its formation will reduce the concentration of hydroxyl ions so that an excess of hydrogen ions are present and the solution will be acidic, as shown by the equation

$$NH^+_4, Cl^- + H^+, OH^- \rightleftharpoons \underset{\underset{H^+,\ Cl^-}{\downarrow}}{HCl} + \underset{\underset{NH_4^+,\ OH^-}{\upharpoonleft\downharpoonright}}{NH_4OH}$$

The pH of such a solution is between 5 and 6.

Sodium bicarbonate, $NaHCO_3$, is a basic salt. When it is placed in water, the hydrolysis reaction produces a basic solution that will turn litmus blue. If the ions of this salt (Na^+, HCO_3^-) are combined with the ions of water (H^+, OH^-), carbonic acid (H_2CO_3) and sodium hydroxide ($NaOH$) are the result. For this case, the acid is only partially ionized, and the hydrogen ion concentration will be decreased for this reason. In conjunction with the completely ionized base, NaOH, the overall effect is to produce a basic solution.

$$Na^+, HCO_3^- + H^+, OH^- \rightleftharpoons \underset{\underset{H^+,\ HCO_3^-}{\upharpoonleft\downharpoonright}}{H_2CO_3} + \underset{\underset{Na^+,\ OH^-}{\downarrow}}{NaOH}$$

The pH of such a solution may be greater than seven (e.g., 8).

To illustrate the proper choice of an indicator, let us look at the titration of H_3PO_4 with sodium hydroxide. This titration may be regarded to go in a stepwise fashion, since H_3PO_4 has three replaceable hydrogens and they are removed one at a time.

1. $NaOH + H_3PO_4 = NaH_2PO_4 + H_2O$
   $pH = 4.5$

2. $NaH_2PO_4 + NaOH = Na_2HPO_4 + H_2O$
   $pH = 8.0$

3. $Na_2HPO_4 + NaOH = Na_3PO_4 + H_2O$
   $pH = 12$

Phosphoric acid is a moderately strong acid, NaH_2PO_4 (sodium dihydrogen phosphate) is a moderately acidic salt, Na_2HPO_4 (disodium hydrogen phosphate) is a weakly basic salt, and Na_3PO_4 (sodium phosphate) is a fairly basic salt.

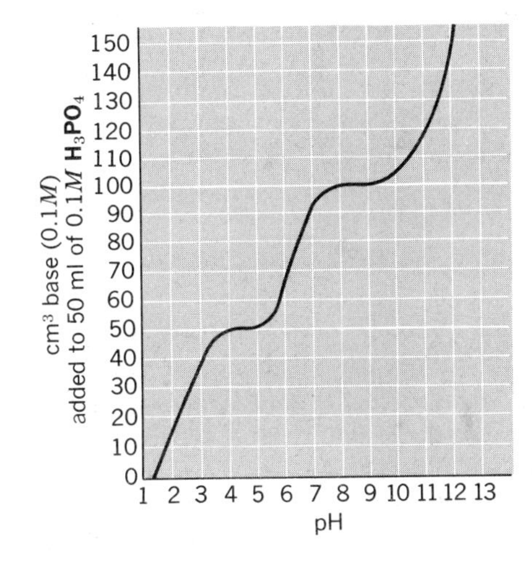

Figure 1-24 Graph of pH.

We see that as we start with a beaker containing H_3PO_4 and slowly add NaOH to it, the pH changes from 2 to approximately 12. See Figure 1-24.

The indicator chosen is important because it tells us how much NaOH to add. If we use an indicator that changes color at pH = 4.5, we would use one mole of NaOH for one mole of H_3PO_4 (Eq. 1). If we use an indicator that changes color at pH = 8, we would use two moles of NaOH for one mole of H_3PO_4 (Eqs. 1 and 2). If we use an indicator that changes color at pH = 12, we would use three moles of NaOH for one mole of H_3PO_4 (Eqs. 1, 2, and 3).

Sometimes the improper indicator furnishes results that may be meaningless. For example, when titrating acetic acid with sodium hydroxide, one gets sodium acetate and water:

$$NaOH + CH_3COOH = \underset{\text{a basic salt}}{CH_3COONa} + H_2O$$

Sodium acetate is a basic salt because by hydrolysis we get a weak acid and a strong base, and consequently the $[OH^-]$ is greater than the $[H^+]$.

$$CH_3COONa + H_2O \rightleftharpoons CH_3COOH + NaOH$$

$$CH_3COOH \rightleftharpoons CH_3COO^- + H^+ \qquad NaOH \rightarrow Na^+ + OH^-$$

One mole of acetic acid will react with one mole of sodium hydroxide, as shown in the equation, but one mole of acetic acid furnishes very few H^+, since it is a weak acid. In contrast, one mole of sodium hydroxide in dilute solution furnishes a mole of OH^-, because it is a strong base and is completely ionized. The pH of a 0.1M acetic acid solution is about 3–4. Sodium acetate is a basic salt that in water would register a pH of about 8–9.

Therefore, in titrating acetic acid with sodium hydroxide, a proper indicator would be one like phenolphthalein, which changes color at pH = 8–10 (i.e., use an indicator that registers near the pH of the salt formed).

If methyl orange, which changes color at pH of 2.9–4.0, is used as the indicator, it is almost ready to change to its basic color in pure dilute acetic acid. As soon as a little NaOH is added to the acetic acid, the pH rises to about 5, and the methyl orange changes color, telling us incorrectly that we are finished with the titration.

In titrating a weak base, such as NH_4OH, with a strong acid, such as HCl, we get an acidic salt, NH_4Cl. Here we should use an indicator that changes color on the acidic side of neutrality. Methyl orange would be acceptable in this case, and phenolphthalein would give erroneous results.

Determination of pH

The pH of a solution can be quickly determined by means of a pH meter, an instrument that registers the pH on a dial. These results are accurate to a fraction of a pH unit.

The pH of a solution may also be determined by a combination of indicators. Suppose a solution turns litmus red and methyl orange yellow. What is its pH? If litmus is red, we know the pH must be between 1–7. If methyl orange is yellow, we know that the pH must be between 4–13. Therefore, the pH of this solution must be between 4–7.

Suppose a solution turns litmus blue and also turns phenolphthalein colorless. What is its pH? If litmus is blue, the pH must be between 7–13. If phenolphthalein is colorless, the pH must be between 1–8.3. Therefore, the pH must be between 7–8.3.

You can use this technique to obtain the pH to within a pH unit.

Various kinds of pH paper are available from supply houses. The pH paper changes color depending on the pH. This paper also is accompanied by a standard color chart for comparison purposes. By simply dipping the pH paper into the solution to be tested and comparing the color produced with the standard chart, the pH is immediately estimated to within a pH unit.

Nitrazine paper, which is yellow at a pH of 4.5 and blue at a pH of 7.5, is used in hospitals to test the pH of urine. Acidic urine, that is, a pH of 4.5, is an indication of a serious body disorder. Nitrazine paper is frequently used to test the urine of patients receiving sulfa drug therapy.

Buffers

Buffers are substances that when present in solution prevent a sudden or large change in the pH, even when strong acids or strong bases are added.

Buffer action is of particular importance in living matter. For example, the pH of blood must be kept within a very narrow region, pH = 7.1–7.4; this is accomplished by the buffers in the blood. The buffer systems are the life-saving devices of the body. It can be stated, in general, that all reactions of living protoplasm take place in buffered media.

The best buffers are weak acids and salts of these weak acids and a strong base; and weak bases and salts of these weak bases and a strong acid.

Acetic acid is a weak acid. Sodium acetate, CH_3COONa, is the corresponding salt of this weak acid and a strong base.

$$\left.\begin{array}{l} CH_3COOH \\ CH_3COONa \end{array}\right\} \text{buffer pair}$$

Carbonic acid is a weak acid, and sodium bicarbonate, $NaHCO_3$, is the corresponding salt of this weak acid and a strong base.

$$\left.\begin{array}{l} H_2CO_3 \\ NaHCO_3 \end{array}\right\} \text{buffer pair}$$

Sodium dihydrogen phosphate, NaH_2PO_4, is a weakly acidic substance of about the same strength as acetic acid. Disodium hydrogen phosphate is the corresponding salt of this weak acid and a strong base.

$$\left.\begin{array}{l} NaH_2PO_4 \\ Na_2HPO_4 \end{array}\right\} \text{buffer pair}$$

Ammonium hydroxide, NH_4OH, is a weak base, and ammonium chloride, NH_4Cl, is the corresponding salt of this weak base and a strong acid.

$$\left.\begin{array}{l} NH_4OH \\ NH_4Cl \end{array}\right\} \text{buffer pair}$$

Proteins and their salts also may be regarded as buffer systems (see Chapter 19). You can, of course, select a pair to buffer at any desired pH.

To illustrate how a buffer works, suppose we have four beakers. In two of these beakers, we put distilled water, pH = 7; in the other two beakers, we put solutions buffered at pH = 7. Now add a *little* strong base as indicated. Figure 1-25 illustrates a possible result.

We see that if strong acid is added to distilled water, the solution immediately becomes very acidic. If strong base is added to distilled water, the solution immediately becomes very basic. However, if either strong acid or strong base is added to a buffered solution, the pH changes very little.

Since the bicarbonate and phosphate buffers are the two principal buffers encountered in biological processes, we shall discuss them in detail. The proteins are relatively efficient buffers, but their discussion will be deferred until later.

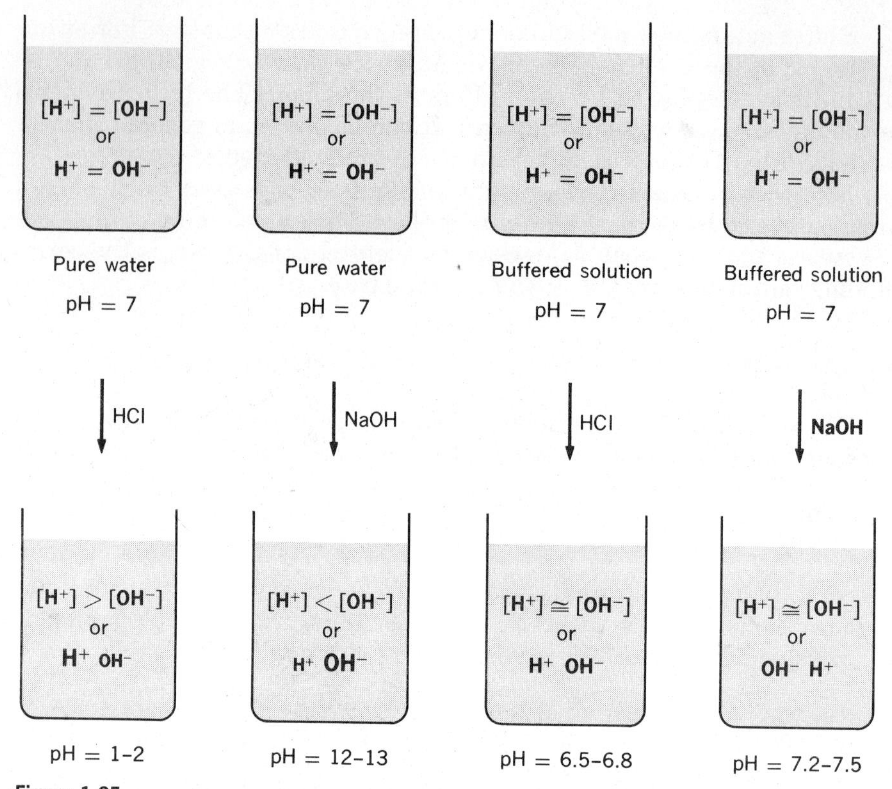

Figure 1-25

Let us consider the H_2CO_3-$NaHCO_3$ system. Carbonic acid is the acidic component (pH = 6–6.5), and $NaHCO_3$ is the basic component (pH = approx. 8).

If an acid is added to this system, the basic component immediately reacts with the added acid; if a base is added to the system, the acidic component immediately reacts with the added base.

When a strong acid, such as HCl, is added to the carbonate buffer system, the $NaHCO_3$ reacts immediately with the HCl to form H_2CO_3 and sodium chloride.

$$HCl + NaHCO_3 \longrightarrow H_2CO_3 + NaCl$$

We know that NaCl is neutral and that carbonic acid is almost neutral. In addition, carbonic acid is unstable and, if present in too large quantities, decomposes to form water and carbon dioxide:

$$H_2CO_3 \rightleftharpoons H_2O + CO_2$$

Although we add a strong acid, the products from the reaction of this strong acid and the buffer system are essentially neutral, and the pH hardly changes. This is indeed what occurs in the body. If too much acid is formed and it reaches the blood, the carbonate buffers react with the acid, increasing the amount of carbonic acid in the blood. This usually stimulates the respiration and causes us to exhale the excess carbon dioxide as a gas. If great amounts of acids are formed in the body (e.g., during an illness or for some other metabolic reason), the $NaHCO_3$ supply in the blood is greatly diminished as the strong acids are neutralized. The basic units of the blood, such as $NaHCO_3$, are known as the alkali reserve; when these units are diminished, a condition known as acidosis results. This means that the blood is about pH = 7.1–7.2. If the pH of the blood ever gets below 7 (i.e., 6.9), this would be fatal. It is for this reason that the buffers are so important.

During a typical illness resulting in an acidosis condition, foods with a high alkaline ash may be recommended. The alkaline ash tends to replace the depleted alkali reserve of the blood. Beans, fruits, and vegetables are high in alkaline ash.

When a strong base, such as NaOH, is added to the carbonate buffer system, the carbonic acid immediately reacts with this base to form sodium bicarbonate:

$$NaOH + H_2CO_3 \rightleftharpoons NaHCO_3 + H_2O$$

Instead of becoming very basic, only a weak base is formed, and the pH changes only slightly. If a large amount of alkali is liberated in the blood stream, the pH may rise to 7.4–7.5. This condition is known as alkalosis and is not as common as acidosis. If large amounts of $NaHCO_3$ are formed, the excess bicarbonate is eliminated in the urine.

Let us consider the phosphate buffer system. If a strong acid, for example, HCl, is added to this system, the basic Na_2HPO_4 will react immediately with the added acid to form the weakly acidic NaH_2PO_4 and the neutral NaCl; the pH will not change much.

$$HCl + Na_2HPO_4 \rightleftharpoons NaH_2PO_4 + NaCl$$

A large amount of NaH_2PO_4 would also contribute to an acidosis condition, and the excess NaH_2PO_4 would be eliminated in urine, thereby making urine acidic in these cases.

If a strong base, for example, NaOH, is added to the phosphate buffer system, the acidic component reacts immediately with the added base to form the weakly basic salt Na_2HPO_4; the pH is not significantly altered.

$$NaOH + NaH_2PO_4 \rightleftharpoons Na_2HPO_4 + H_2O$$

Increased quantities of Na_2HPO_4 would also contribute to an alkalosis condition, and the excess Na_2HPO_4 would be excreted in the urine.

In the chapters on putrefaction and metabolism, we shall learn that many acids and bases may be formed in the body and that these substances represent a constant threat to our health and lives. It is chiefly through the buffers that we prevent the body pH from changing significantly when these acids and bases are formed.

Pseudo-solutions

Colloids

Colloidal matter is a state of matter whose chief characteristic is the size of the particles. Particles larger than colloids may be considered as coarse or massive matter, and particles smaller than colloidal matter are the actual molecules and ions themselves (crystalloids).

There are no sharp boundaries between these three classes, but we arbitrarily set certain limits.

Let us review some length measurements.

1 inch = 2.54 centimeters (cm)
1 millimeter (mm) = $\frac{1}{10}$ cm
$\frac{1}{1000}$ mm = 1 micron (μ)
$\frac{1}{1000}$ micron = 1 millimicron (mμ)
$\frac{1}{10}$ millimicron = 1 A (Angstrom Unit)

Units such as A and mμ are so small that they can be conveniently used to express distances between atoms in molecules, diameters of atoms and molecules, and similar small distances.

Crystalloids of crystalline matter	Colloidal matter	Massive matter
	1 mμ or 10 A	100 mμ or 0.1 μ

Particles between 1 mμ and 100 mμ in size are in the colloidal range. Particles larger than 100 mμ are in the massive matter range, and crystalloids of crystalline matter are composed of particles smaller than 1 mμ.

When crystalline matter is dissolved in a solvent, such as water, we get a true solution. True solutions are homogeneous. One cannot detect any lack of homogeneity in a solution of glucose (body sugar) in water or sodium chloride in water.

When massive matter is placed in a solvent, the result is a suspension. This is clearly heterogeneous, as can be detected visually. In the case of suspensions, the suspended massive particles usually settle out, giving further evidence of the heterogeneity. The rate of settling is a function of the particle size. Large particles settle out quickly, and small particles settle out very slowly. This is evident in a solution of mud or clay in water (muddy water).

When colloidal material is placed in a solvent, we get a colloidal solution, which may be stable and will not settle out of its own accord. Although this may appear to be homogeneous, it is actually heterogeneous, as can be revealed in several ways. Because colloidal systems are heterogeneous, we must differentiate between the solvent and the colloidal particles. We call the solvent the dispersing medium and the colloidal matter the dispersed medium.

The limit of visibility of an ordinary microscope, even when using the oil immersion objective, is about 0.1 μ. This means we can see massive matter, but we cannot see colloidal matter by means of an ordinary microscope.

The Tyndall Effect

We are all familiar with the phenomenon that occurs when a beam of light enters a somewhat darkened room (e.g., light beam from a movie projector in a movie theater, or sunbeam through a window shutter). In this situation, we see myriads of dust particles darting about in the light beam. Actually, we are not seeing the dust particles, because they are too small to be seen with the naked eye, but we are seeing the *reflection of the light from these particles.* Theoretically, if there were no dust particles in the air, we would not see the actual beam at all. However, this is an impractical situation, because there always are dust particles floating in the air. The dust particles are colloidal in nature and are in the air (which is the dispersing medium); thus, we have a colloidal solution of dust in the air.

In a similar way, we can have a colloidal solution of dust in a liquid dispersing medium. Such a solution would look homogeneous, but if we shine a beam of light into this solution, we would see the actual path of the light beam, because we are seeing the reflection of the light by the colloidal dust particles. This is known as the Tyndall effect. If a light beam were to shine through a true solution, free of dust, the solution would remain clear and we would not see the path of the beam. The ions and molecules in true solutions are so small that we cannot see any reflection by them of the light. This is another proof that crystalline particles are smaller than colloidal particles.

The ultra microscope makes use of the Tyndall effect. Instead of looking directly at the particles, as in an ordinary microscope, we look at the reflected light and can see the colloidal particles in the solution. The limit of visibility of the ultra microscope is about 1 mμ, which means that this apparatus is useful in working with colloidal solutions over the entire colloidal range. The ultra microscope is usually equipped with an electrical device, which shows us what the protective charge is on the colloidal particles. If the colloidal particles move toward the $-$ pole, the protective charge is $+$. If the colloidal particles move toward the $+$ pole, the protective charge is $-$.

The electron microscope utilizes an electron beam instead of a light beam. Instead of focusing the light beam by means of glass lenses, the electron microscope focuses the electron beam by means of magnets. In some cases, this enables us to see colloidal particles in great detail. The contours and shape of some colloidal protein molecules have been observed quite accurately by means of the electron microscope.

Table 1-13 summarizes some of the properties we have mentioned.

Colloids may be conveniently classified into eight groups, by noting the dispersed medium in the dispersing medium.

Solid in solid: Colored glasses. This system is important in metallurgy.
Solids in liquids: Gelatine in water and proteins in general in water. This is the most important in biological systems.
Solids in gas: Dust and smoke in the air.
Liquid in solids: Found mostly in minerals and gems, for example, water in opals and pearls.
Liquid in liquids: Emulsions. Mayonnaise, homogenized milk, egg yolk. Protoplasm is referred to as an emulsion.
Liquid in gas: Fog, mist in the air.
Gas in solids: Many solids both natural and artificial can absorb gases (principle of the gas mask). Artificial activated charcoal is a powerful absorbent.
Gas in liquids: This type is not very common.
Gas in gas: Are miscible in all proportions and so cannot form colloidal systems. They form true solution.

We refer to liquid colloidal systems as sols and to more or less rigid systems as gels (jelly, custards, jams, etc.).

Table 1-13

	CRYSTALLOIDS OF CRYSTALLINE MATTER	COLLOIDAL MATTER	MASSIVE MATTER
size	less than 1 mμ	from 1 mμ to 100 mμ	greater than 100 mμ
visibility	invisible	visible in the ultra microscope and electron microscope	visible by ordinary microscope or by naked eye
optical properties	transparent, will not exhibit Tyndall effect	transparent, will exhibit Tyndall effect	opaque
diffusibility and filterability	will pass through filters and membranes	will pass through filter paper but not through membranes	will not pass through either filter paper or membranes

PREPARATION AND MEANS OF DESTROYING COLLOIDS

Colloids may be prepared by breaking large massive particles down in size until they are in the colloidal range (process known as peptization).

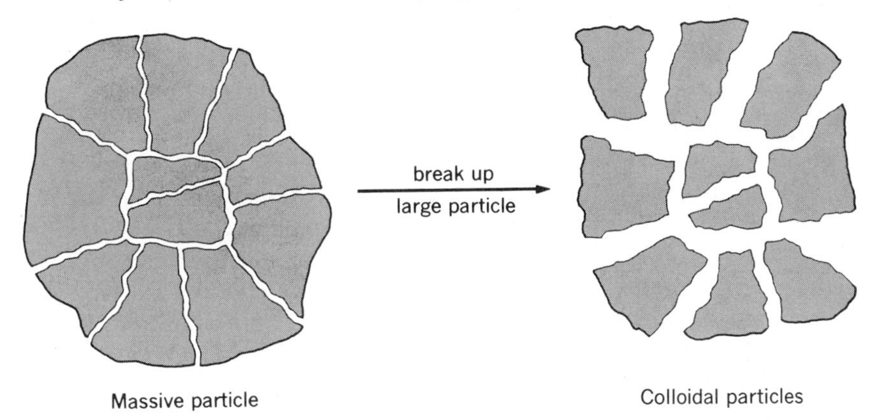

Peptization

Colloids also may be prepared by combining many small crystalloids into a unit that is in the colloidal range (process known as condensation).

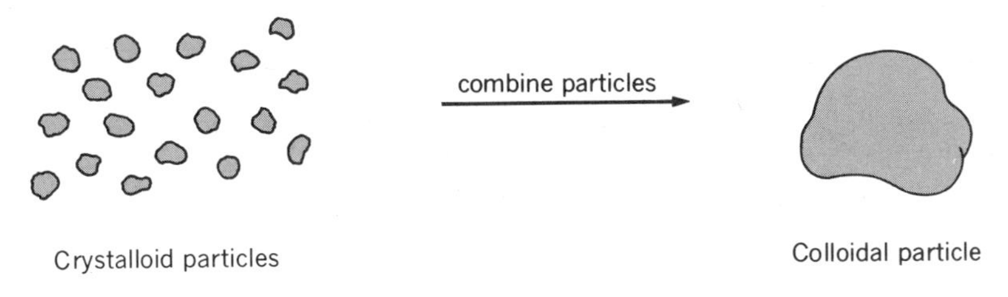

Condensation

Once colloidal particles are formed, why do they not combine by bumping against one another, coalescing to form a large massive particle, and precipitating? This is a very likely occurrence, and so colloidal particles must be protected in order to survive as colloids.

Colloids may be protected or stabilized either by electrical charges, by solvent molecules, or by a combination of both.

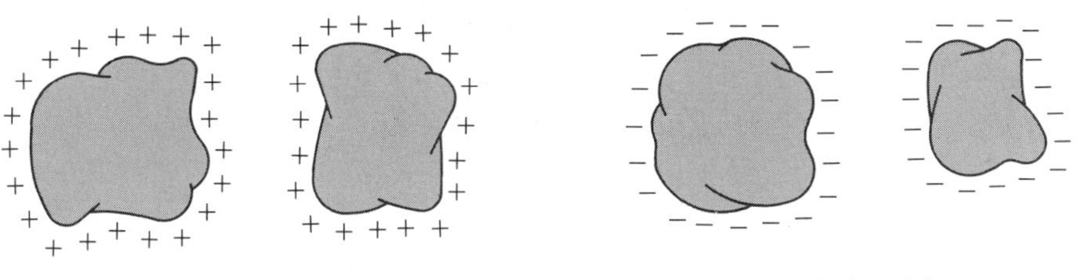

Colloidal particles protected by + charges

Colloidal particles protected by – charges

The charges on the peripheral surface of the colloidal particles may be either + or −, depending on the pH. The proteins are an important group of colloids in the body and usually have a net overall − charge. These charges stabilize the colloidal particles because like signs repel each other, and there is much less tendency for the particles to come together and coalesce.

To destroy the protective charge on the colloidal particle, you can neutralize the charge by adding particles with the opposite charge. If a − charge colloidal particle is mixed with certain + ions, the charge is removed by neutralization. If a + charged colloidal particle is placed in contact with certain − ions, the charge is also removed by neutralization. In both cases, the tendency to precipitate is increased. When the colloidal particle is brought to electrical neutrality, we call this the *isoelectric point.* At the isoelectric point, the colloid is most likely to precipitate.

Neutralization may also be accomplished by means of an electrode. Thus, in the Cottrell process, we may remove dust particles from the air by passing the smoke through an electrical field maintained between a wire and plates on the smoke stack. The dust particles are precipitated, and essentially no smoke enters the atmosphere. This has played a tremendous role in cleansing the air over many cities.

The solvent may stabilize the colloidal particles by acting like a protective coating and preventing the particles from coming together, coalescing, and precipitating.

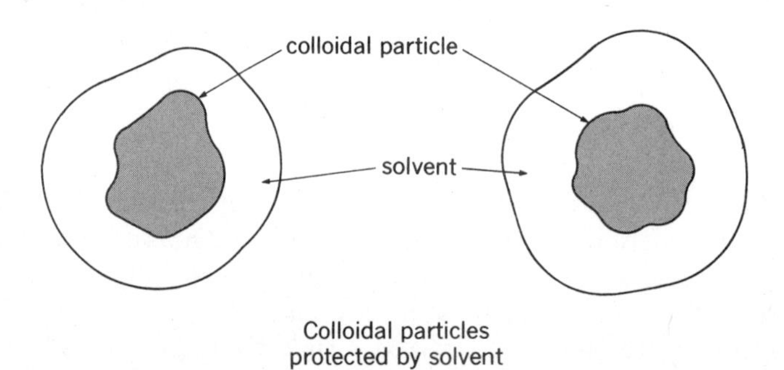

Colloidal particles
protected by solvent

The protective coat can be destroyed by simply removing the solvent. This may be done by heating, changing the solvent by adding another solvent, or salting out (i.e., by adding a salt that absorbs the protective coating).

It is possible to have a double protective arrangement of both solvent and charges.

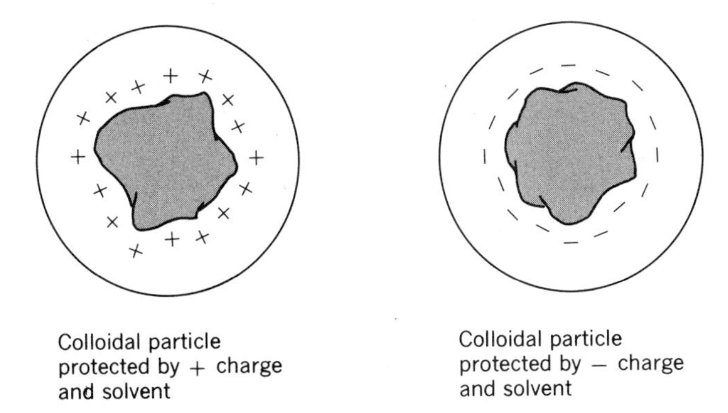

Colloidal particle protected by + charge and solvent

Colloidal particle protected by − charge and solvent

The various types of protective devices are interrelated and are summarized on Figure 1-26.

Other solution phenomena

Diffusion

Diffusion is the distribution of particles by simple thermochemical agitation. There are no membranes or barriers. All atomic and molecular particles are in a state of constant agitated motion, and the only barrier a particle may have is to strike another particle and bounce off. In the diffusion of a particle from one side of a vessel to the other, the path may be

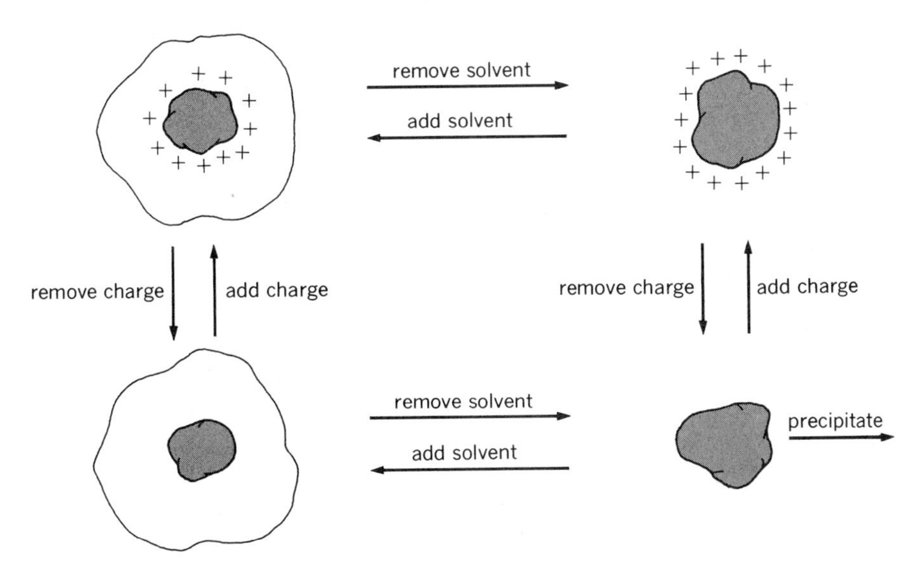

Figure 1-26

long, complicated, roundabout, reversed, or twisted, but finally the other side is reached.

Diffusion is affected by heat, concentration, physical state, and molecular size. Gases diffuse faster than liquids, and liquids diffuse faster than solids. Gases in gases diffuse rapidly, liquids in liquids diffuse with much less rapidity, and solids diffuse very slowly in solids. This is reasonable because, in gases, the molecules are relatively far apart and the gas particles have a better chance of traveling a certain distance before striking another particle. Molecules are much closer in the liquid phase than in a gas phase, and so there are more collisions. In solids, the particles are quite close together, and their movement is very restricted.

To illustrate, we mix hydrogen gas and oxygen gas together in a vessel that can be sealed. In a matter of seconds, both gases have diffused completely throughout the vessel, and the gas phase is homogeneous. In general, the smaller the molecules, the faster the rate of diffusion (e.g., hydrogen diffuses faster than nitrogen). This is reasonable since the smaller particles have less chance to collide than large particles.

If two solutions, such as $1M$ sodium chloride and $1M$ potassium sulfate, are poured together without stirring, the resulting solution will be homogeneous before hours have elapsed.

If a sheet of gold is placed on top of a sheet of lead, the two will start to diffuse, and eventually a sharp boundary between the two will cease to exist. In this case, the process of diffusion is almost too slow to measure (i.e., it takes many years).

The more concentrated the phase, the longer the time required to complete the diffusion process. This means that there are more particles to be struck by any one particle, and this hinders the diffusion process.

The higher the temperature the faster the diffusion. As the temperature is increased, we increase the agitation of the molecules, and they move faster and with more energy, and the homogeneity is achieved more rapidly.

Osmosis

Osmosis is the passage of water through a semipermeable membrane, of such a nature that it allows only water to pass through it in the direction of the most concentrated solution. It is not clearly understood how the membrane selectively accomplishes this, but osmosis is a phenomenon easily demonstrated. Concentration is expressed as moles per liter of solution (if we refer to nonionizing substances) or gram-equivalents per liter of solution (if we refer to an ionizing solution).

For example, if we separate a dilute sugar solution from a concentrated sugar solution by means of an osmotic membrane, then water will flow from the dilute solution into the more concentrated solution in an attempt

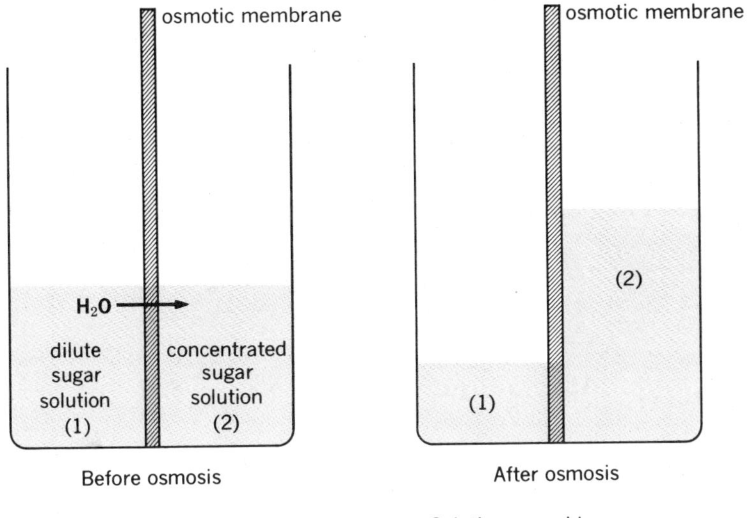

Figure 1-27 Osmosis.

to make the two concentrations equal. In doing this, the dilute solution becomes more concentrated and the concentrated solution becomes more dilute, until the solutions are essentially equal in concentration. See Figure 1-27.

The passage of water in and out of cells is an important biological function. The usual concentration of ions in the body fluids is about 0.150 gram-equivalents per liter of solution, or 0.150*N*. This is referred to as the physiological saline solution or isotonic solution. A solution more concentrated than physiological saline is known as a hypertonic solution, and a solution less concentrated than physiological saline is known as a hypotonic solution.

If a normal cell is placed in hypertonic solution, it loses water by osmosis to the concentrated solution and shrinks in size. We call this plasmolysis.

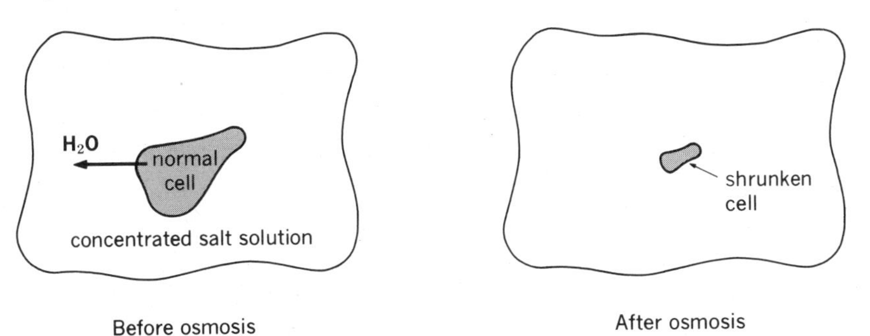

If a normal cell is placed in a diluted solution (hypotonic), water enters the cell by osmosis, and the cell expands and may even burst. We call this plasmoptysis.

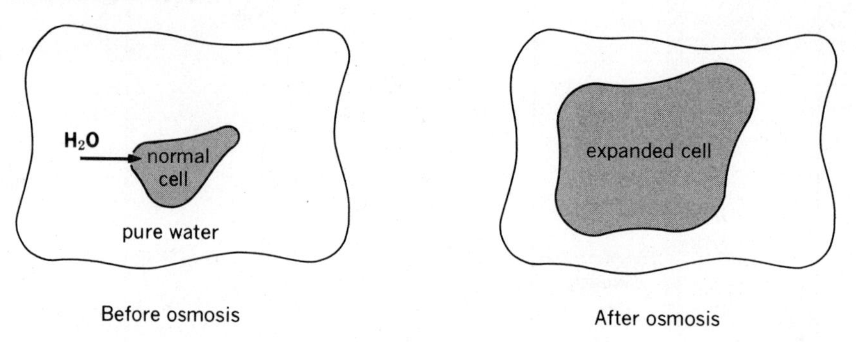

From the foregoing, it should be clear that the salt concentrations are of paramount importance in determining the distribution of body water.

Dialysis

Dialysis is the separation of crystalline material from colloidal material by a selective semipermeable membrane. In some respects, this may be regarded as a function of the pore size. The large colloidal particles are too big to pass through the small holes of the membrane, and the crystalline

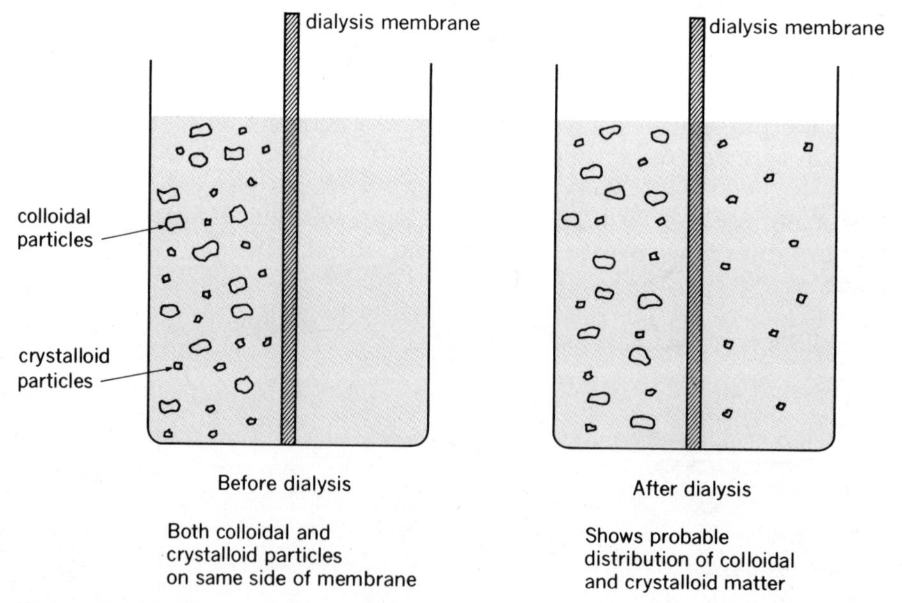

Figure 1-28 Dialysis.

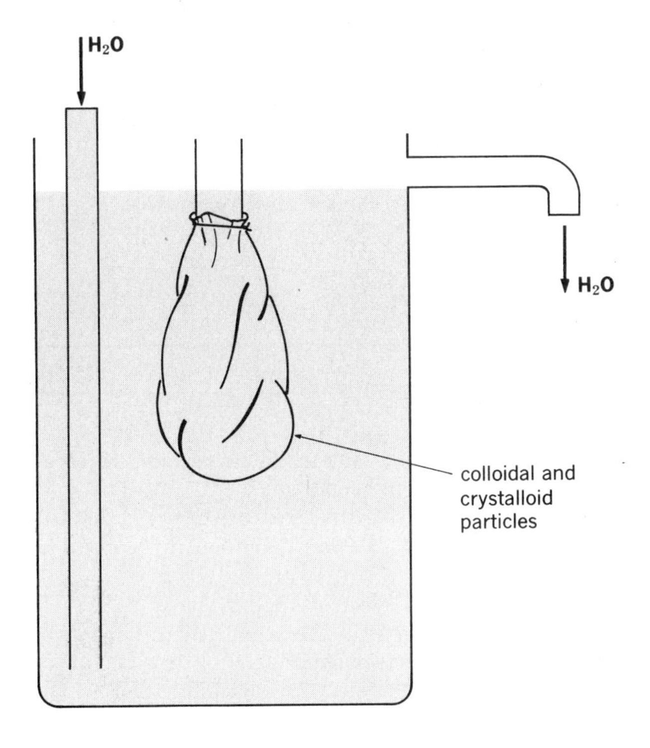

Figure 1-29 Dialysis against running water.

matter is composed of very small particles and can easily pass through. The crystalline matter moves through the membrane and distributes itself *equally* on both sides of the membrane as equilibrium is reached. See Figure 1-28.

To completely separate a crystalline substance from a colloidal substance, we need to destroy the equilibrium so that the crystalline material will *continue* to flow through the membrane. This is done by dialysis against running water. See Figure 1-29. A solution containing the crystalline and colloidal material to be separated is placed in a dialysis sac in a stream of running water. In this way, the crystalline material is washed away as soon as it passes out of the sac, and no equilibrium can be reached. The crystalline material keeps passing out of the sac until none is left.

This is a very practical method and is frequently used to separate colloidal proteins from inorganic salts. The commercial production of antitoxins involves the removal of inorganic material from the larger colloidal material.

A word of caution may be interjected here concerning the semipermeable membrane. We may encounter some cases of superselectivity. For example, some membranes will allow K^+ to pass in and out but will not allow Na^+ to pass through, and yet the Na^+ is smaller than the K^+. This unusual selectivity may be concerned with the preferential binding of certain ions by proteins or perhaps be involved in some other fundamental energy consideration not as yet clearly understood. At any rate, in some cases, the permeability of cell membranes is still a mysterious phenomenon.

REVIEW QUESTIONS

1. Define chemistry.
2. Identify the following terms: substance, matter, homogeneous, heterogeneous, true solution, element, molecule, atom, and compound.
3. What are the principal particles comprising the structure of the atom? How may these be designated? What is meant by an electrically neutral atom? a negative ion? a positive ion?
4. Identify the atomic nucleus; identify the electron shell in the atom.
5. How many electron shells may be present in the atom? What is the maximum number of electrons possible in each electron shell?
6. Discuss the nuclear composition and the electronic configuration of the noble gases. Correlate their electronic configurations with chemical reactivity.
7. Diagram the electronic configurations of several cations and anions.
8. What is an isotope? Give several examples.
9. What are some of the characteristics of compounds possessing electrovalent bonds? of compounds possessing only covalent bonds?
10. What is unique about the electronic configuration of the carbon atom?
11. Discuss the nature of the ionic, single covalent, double covalent, and triple covalent bonds.
12. Discuss the *s*, *p*, *d*, and *f* atomic orbitals, and clearly define their roles in chemical bonding.
13. Draw electron-bonding diagrams for methane, ethylene, acetylene, and ammonia. Name each bond.
14. What are some of the properties of metals and nonmetals?
15. Give some examples of strong acids, weak acids, strong bases, and weak bases.
16. Indicate which of the following are chemical changes and which are physical changes.
    (a) dissolving sugar in water
    (b) burning gasoline
    (c) melting snow
    (d) liquefying air
    (e) burning a match
    (f) gas heat
17. Write formulas for hydrochloric acid, hydrobromic acid, sulfuric acid, nitric acid, phosphoric acid, ammonium hydroxide, ferric sulfate, cuprous bromide, acetic acid, carbonic acid, sodium nitrate, hydrogen sulfide, calcium oxide.

18. Define a metalloid. Define an amphoteric compound. Give an example of each.
19. Draw bonding diagrams of carbonic acid, hydrochloric acid, and perchloric acid.
20. Define a mole.
21. Define molarity and normality.
22. Suppose we have 20 g of glucose ($C_6H_{12}O_6$) in 100 cm^3 of water solution. What is the normality of the solution? What is its molarity?
23. Suppose we have 5 g of urea (CH_4N_2O) in 50 cm^3 of water solution. What is the molarity and the normality of the solution?
24. If we have 20 cm^3 of 5M NaOH, how many grams of NaOH do we have?
25. If we have 100 cm^3 of 2N H_2SO_4, how many grams of H_2SO_4 do we have?
26. How many grams of NaOH are required to react with 10 cm^3 of 0.1M HCl?
27. How many grams of H_2SO_4 are required to react with 100 cm^3 of 0.1N NaOH?
28. How many cm^3 of 5M NaOH are required to react with 50 cm^3 of 3M H_2SO_4?
29. Define pH. What is the pH of a solution $1 \times 10^{-10}M$ in hydrogen ions, $1 \times 10^{-10}M$ in hydroxyl ions? $1 \times 10^{-5}M$ in hydrogen ions, $1 \times 10^{-3}M$ in hydroxyl ions? Is there any relationship between the hydrogen ion concentration and the hydroxyl ion concentration in water solution?
30. What is an indicator? Of what use are indicators? How are indicators chosen for various titrations? What is the color of litmus in acidic and basic solutions? If a certain solution turned litmus blue and phenolphthalein colorless, what can you say about its pH?
31. What is the normality of an H_3PO_4 solution if 75 ml of 0.01N KOH is needed to neutralize 150 ml of it?
32. What is the normality of an H_2SO_4 solution if 80 ml of 0.1N NaOH is needed to neutralize 120 ml of the acid?
33. What is meant by hydrolysis? What is the difference between an acid salt, a neutral salt, and a basic salt? Give examples of each.
34. How may the pH of a solution be determined?
35. What is meant by a buffer system? Give several examples. What buffer systems are present in the blood stream? Discuss in detail the functioning of the carbonic acid-sodium bicarbonate system and the NaH_2PO_4 and Na_2HPO_4 system.
36. What is meant by acidosis? alkalosis?
37. Discuss colloids from the point of size, stability, and means of destroying stability.
38. What is the Tyndall effect?
39. How does the ultra microscope function? How does the electron microscope function?
40. Compare colloidal matter with crystalline matter and massive matter with respect to size, visibility, optical properties, and filterability.
41. Discuss the various types of colloidal systems that can occur in nature, and give several examples of each.
42. What is meant by peptization and condensation with respect to colloidal particles?
43. What is meant by diffusion, osmosis, and dialysis? Discuss an example of each in detail.

2

introduction to organic chemistry

Organic chemistry is the chemistry of carbon compounds. Some of the most important compounds in living and growing organisms are organic. At the turn of the nineteenth century, chemists thought that organic compounds possessed a "vital force" and that the lack of this mysterious force prevented them from preparing organic compounds in the laboratory. Chemists felt that only living organisms could create such materials as urea, uric acid, and sugar.

Modern organic chemistry began in 1828, when Friedrich Wöhler (see Figure 2-1), in his famous experiment, mixed ammonium chloride ($NH_4^+Cl^-$) with sodium cyanate (Na^+CNO^-) hoping to obtain sodium chloride (Na^+Cl^-) and ammonium cyanate ($NH_4^+CNO^-$). He obtained the sodium chloride, but instead of ammonium cyanate he obtained urea [$CO(NH_2)_2$]. Ammonium cyanate and urea have exactly the same number of atoms (one carbon, one oxygen, two nitrogens, and four hydrogens). He therefore concluded correctly that the ammonium cyanate had rearranged itself into urea. Because urea was an organic product found in urine and ammonium cyanate was a salt

Figure 2-1 Friedrich Wöhler.

and regarded as inorganic, the idea of a "vital force" was apparently refuted. Numerous other examples were necessary to remove this deep-rooted concept of a mysterious force. It was not until about 1850–1860 that chemists dismissed this concept. Today, it is quite clear that the organic chemist can prepare in the laboratory just about any chemical structure he wishes.

Because so many carbon compounds exist, we study their chemistry as a separate field. Approximately 50,000 inorganic compounds (i.e., compounds containing any of the 101 elements other than carbon and hydrogen[1]) have been made, and this number is not rapidly increasing. Over 1 million different organic compounds (i.e., compounds containing at least one carbon atom) are known. Chemists synthesize thousands of new organic compounds daily, but only a very small fraction of the possible organic compounds have been prepared.

The total number of possible carbon compounds is infinite. The unusual covalency of the carbon atom accounts for the very large number of carbon compounds. Carbon atoms combine with other carbon atoms in almost every way possible.

At first glance, you might be hesitant about studying the properties of 1 million different organic compounds. Fortunately, the task is simplified because one quickly discovers that many organic compounds have similar properties and can be classified into certain similar groups or series. Consequently, we customarily consider the chemistry of a particular group. This approach tells us much about the properties of *all* the members of the group. Then, we select important members of the series and study them in more detail. For instance, compounds with the hydroxyl (—OH) group are called alcohols. The alcohol group (—OH) is called a *functional group.* Functional groups are the atoms that define the structure and determine the properties of a particular series of organic compounds. If you know the

[1]Almost all the carbon compounds contain hydrogen.

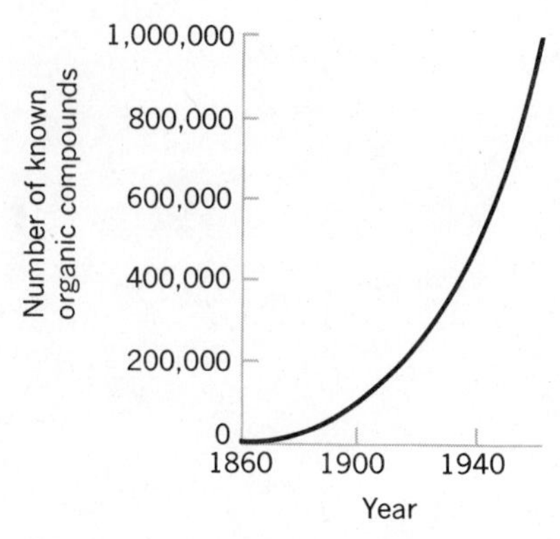

Figure 2-2 Growth of organic chemistry. (© 1967 by Harcourt, Brace & World, Inc. Reproduced from *General Chemistry* by M. A. Paul, E. J. King, and L. H. Farinholt, by permission of the publishers.)

reactions and properties of one typical alcohol, you know, in general, the reactions and properties of all alcohols (some exceptions always exist). Thus, we limit our study to the reactions and properties of the various series, rather than to particular, individual molecules.

Many organic molecules have sites of reactivity or functional groups that change during a reaction, whereas the rest of the molecule is essentially unchanged. Table 2-1 gives the names and structures of a few functional groups.

The concept of formula is important. The *empirical formula* is the simplest formula consistent with chemical analysis.[2] It gives the relative number of atoms of each element in the molecule. The *molecular formula* is the simplest formula consistent with chemical and molecular analyses (molecular weight).[3] It gives the actual number of atoms of each element in the molecule. The *structural formula* shows the arrangement of the atoms in space. Since it is usually written on paper, the structural formula represents a two-dimensional view of the three-dimensional molecule. The structural formula usually completely describes and identifies the molecule.

Formaldehyde, acetic acid, lactic acid, and dextrose all have the same analysis: C, 40%; H, 6.7%; and O, 53.3%. From these data, we can calculate the empirical formula to be CH_2O. The molecular formula should be writ-

[2] We can analyze organic chemicals by burning them in an atmosphere of pure oxygen. Under these conditions, the carbon is converted into carbon dioxide, which can be absorbed and weighed, and the hydrogen is converted into water, which can also be absorbed and weighed. The oxygen percentage is usually determined by difference (i.e., if the carbon and hydrogen percentages total 80%, and the compound otherwise contains only oxygen, then the oxygen is the remaining 20%). We can use other procedures to analyze for nitrogen, sulfur, chlorine, etc.

[3] We can conveniently determine the molecular weight by a depression of the freezing point or an elevation of the boiling point of some solvent. If you mix salt with water, the solution does not freeze at 0°C but at a lower temperature. This lowering of the freezing point is proportional to the number of moles of the dissolved substance. Knowing the moles, we can easily calculate the molecular weight.

Table 2-1 A few functional groups

GROUP	NAME	GROUP	NAME
—OH	alcohol	—C(=O)—O—C—	ester
—C(=O)—H	aldehyde	—C(—H)(—O—C—)(—O—C—)	acetal
—C—C(=O)—C—	ketone	—C(=O)—N—	amide
—C(=O)—OH	acid	—C—N—	amine
—C—O—C—	ether		

ten as $(CH_2O)_n$, because n (an integer) will have different values for the compounds mentioned. To find n, the molecular weights of the four substances are determined. Molecular weight determinations show that formaldehyde has a molecular weight of 30, acetic acid 60, lactic acid 90, and dextrose 180. The exact molecular formulas can now be written: formaldehyde CH_2O, acetic acid $(CH_2O)_2$ or $C_2H_4O_2$, lactic acid $(CH_2O)_3$ or $C_3H_6O_3$, and dextrose $(CH_2O)_6$ or $C_6H_{12}O_6$. As a check, the atomic weight of each atom is added to calculate the molecular weight. Carbon has an atomic weight of 12, hydrogen 1, and oxygen 16.

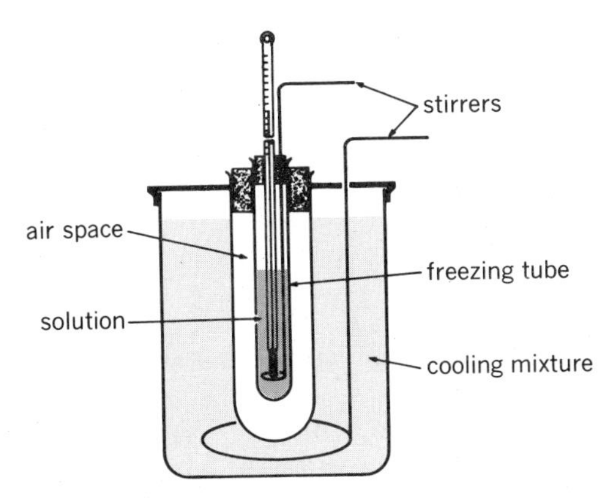

Figure 2-3 Apparatus for determination of molecular weight by freezing point depression. (Reprinted from S. Nussenbaum, *Organic Chemistry,* Boston: Allyn and Bacon, 1963, p. 74.)

formaldehyde $\mathbf{CH_2O}$

$1\ C = 1 \times 12 = 12$
$1\ O = 1 \times 16 = 16$
$2\ H = 2 \times 1 = 2$
30 (molecular weight)

acetic acid $\mathbf{C_2H_4O_2}$

$2\ C = 2 \times 12 = 24$
$2\ O = 2 \times 16 = 32$
$4\ H = 4 \times 1 = 4$
60 (molecular weight)

lactic acid $\mathbf{C_3H_6O_3}$

$3\ C = 3 \times 12 = 36$
$3\ O = 3 \times 16 = 48$
$6\ H = 6 \times 1 = 6$
90 (molecular weight)

dextrose $\mathbf{C_6H_{12}O_6}$

$6\ C = 6 \times 12 = 72$
$6\ O = 6 \times 16 = 96$
$12\ H = 12 \times 1 = 12$
180 (molecular weight)

The next step is to determine the arrangement of the atoms (structural formula). At this point, a chemist performs many reactions and tests on the compounds to determine which functional groups are present and in what order these groups are arranged. He does all the chemical tests that may be helpful and often relies heavily on measurements of the physical properties, that is, color, solubility, melting point, boiling point, density, refractive index, absorption of ultraviolet light, absorption of infrared light, absorption of energy in a magnetic field, etc. These facts are then fitted together to give the most logical structure from the viewpoint of all the data accumulated. We must postpone a discussion of these tests and the reasoning used until you have a working knowledge of the elements of organic chemistry. The structural formulas can now be written:

```
   O
   ‖
H—C—H
```

formaldehyde ($\mathbf{CH_2O}$)

```
   H  O
   |  ‖
H—C—C—O—H
   |
   H
```

acetic acid [$\mathbf{(CH_2O)_2}$ or $\mathbf{C_2H_4O_2}$]

```
   H  O—H   O
   |  |     ‖
H—C—C——————C—O—H
   |  |
   H  H
```

lactic acid [$\mathbf{(CH_2O)_3}$ or $\mathbf{C_3H_6O_3}$]

```
       H
       |
       C=O
       |
    H—C—OH
       |
   HO—C—H
       |
    H—C—OH
       |
    H—C—OH
       |
    H—C—OH
       |
       H
```

glucose or dextrose [$\mathbf{(CH_2O)_6}$ or $\mathbf{C_6H_{12}O_6}$]

The spatial configuration of the carbon atom is of interest. Each of four valence bonds is directed to the corners of a tetrahedron. You should keep in mind at all times that a covalent bond represents two shared electrons. Naturally, since electrons are negatively charged, these electrons would tend to *repel other pairs of electrons* (like charges repel). This means that the most stable carbon bonds are those that are geometrically as far from one another as possible.

In the case of a carbon with four single bonds, the bonds are best pictured by imagining that the carbon atom is in the center of a tetrahedron (i.e., a four-sided figure with four equal sides, each side an equilateral triangle), and that the four bonds are directed out through the apexes of the tetrahedron. The angle between any two bonds is about 109.5° (it is not an even number) ($A = B = C = D$).

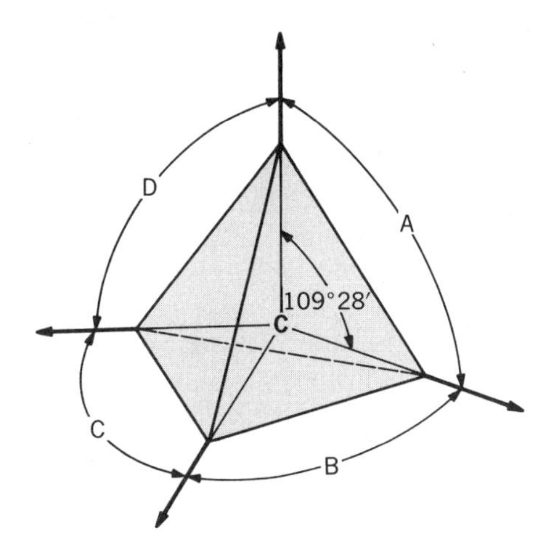

The above drawing is done in perspective to show the three-dimensional character of the carbon atoms. In the case of a carbon with a double bond, the bonds can get as far from one another as possible (and therefore be most stable) by remaining in one plane and making an angle of 120°.

120° 120°
120° C═C 120°
120° 120°

In the case of a carbon with a triple bond, the bonds can get as far from one another as possible (and therefore be most stable) by remaining in a straight line and making an angle of 180°.

180° 180°
←C≡C→

Because it is difficult to draw all organic compounds in perspective, we usually write the structures in two-dimensional form, which is only a simplified way of expressing the true structure.

For example, instead of

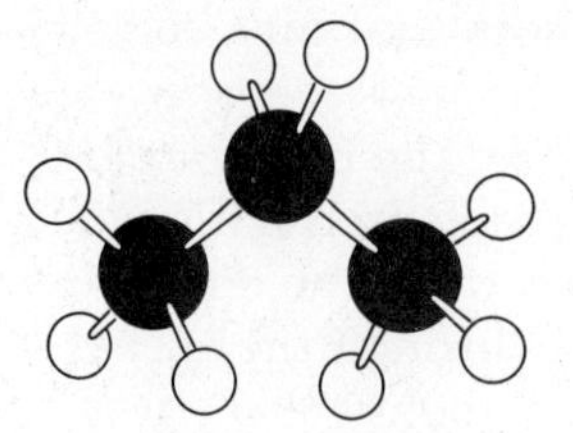

we write

```
    H   H   H
    |   |   |
H — C — C — C — H
    |   |   |
    H   H   H
```

Homologous series

A homologous series consists of structurally and chemically similar compounds, so related that if the individual compounds are arranged in the order of increasing carbon content, adjacent members differ by one carbon and two hydrogens (CH_2). The series shows consistent changes in

Table 2-2 Homologous series

MOLECULAR FORMULA	STRUCTURAL FORMULA	BOILING POINT (°C)	FORMULA DIFFERENCE
CH_4	H | H—C—H | H	−161.5	
C_2H_6	H H | | H—C—C—H | | H H	−88.3	CH_2
C_3H_8	H H H | | | H—C—C—C—H | | | H H H	−42.17	CH_2
C_4H_{10}	H H H H | | | | H—C—C—C—C—H | | | | H H H H	−0.6−−0.3	CH_2
C_5H_{12}	H H H H H | | | | | H—C—C—C—C—C—H | | | | | H H H H H	36.2	CH_2

General Formula: C_nH_{2n+2} (where n = number of **C** atoms)

Table 2-3

MOLECULAR FORMULA	STRUCTURAL FORMULA	BOILING POINT (°C)	FORMULA DIFFERENCE
CH_3OH	CH_3—OH (H—C—OH with 3 H on C)	64	
C_2H_5OH	H—C—C—OH (each C bearing 2 H)	78	CH_2
n-C_3H_7OH	H—C—C—C—OH (each C bearing 2 H)	87	CH_2
n-C_4H_9OH	H—C—C—C—C—OH (each C bearing 2 H)	117	CH_2
n-$C_5H_{11}OH$	H—C—C—C—C—C—OH (each C bearing 2 H)	138	CH_2

General Formula: $C_nH_{2n+1}OH$ (where n = number of **C** atoms)

physical properties as the carbon content increases or decreases. (See Table 2-2.)

From Table 2-2 it is evident that

1. The compounds are all structurally alike.
2. The compounds are all chemically alike (this will be substantiated later).
3. There is a constant homologous difference (CH_2).
4. Physical properties change consistently as the carbon content increases (other examples such as melting point or specific gravity could have been given).
5. A general formula can be written.

Table 2-3 gives another example of a homologous series. Here again, the five requirements for a homologous series are satisfied. A homologous series is very valuable. For example, if the boiling point of a particular compound C_4H_9OH is known, it is immediately evident that $C_5H_{11}OH$ will have a somewhat higher boiling point and that C_3H_7OH will have a somewhat lower boiling point. The compounds will have chemical properties so similar that, in general, one can reasonably be substituted for the other.

Classification of organic compounds

If a carbon compound has the maximum number of hydrogens, or other groups, attached to it, we say the molecule is *saturated.* If a compound has two carbon atoms connected by a covalent bond, each carbon atom has one of its four valence electrons in use and three valence electrons left.

```
  |  |
—C—C—
  |  |
```

If these three remaining valences were taken up by hydrogen, the structure would be

```
   H  H
   |  |           H H
H—C—C—H         H:C:C:H
   |  |           H H
   H  H
```

The molecular formula of this compound would be C_2H_6. The student of organic chemistry should always remember that each carbon atom can have a maximum of four covalent bonds.

Two carbon atoms cannot have more than six hydrogen atoms attached to them (saturated); any number less than six hydrogens indicates an *unsaturated* compound. A molecular formula of such a compound is C_2H_4. The structural formula is

```
   H  H
   |  |            H  H
H—C=C—H          H:C::C:H
```

Note that this compound contains a double bond. In general, any compound that contains a double bond is unsaturated. A double bond indicates two pairs of shared electrons. It is also possible to have a compound containing two carbon atoms and only two hydrogen atoms. This would also be an unsaturated compound. C_2H_2 is such a compound. Its structural formula is

```
H—C≡C—H          H:C:::C:H
```

Thus, any compound that contains a triple bond is unsaturated. The classification into saturated and unsaturated compounds is a very significant and useful one, since it tells us much about chemical reactivity. (Unsaturated compounds are usually much more reactive than saturated compounds.)

Organic compounds can contain any number of carbon atoms. The arrangement of these atoms enables us to classify carbon compounds as shown in Table 2-4.

Table 2-4 Classification of carbon compounds

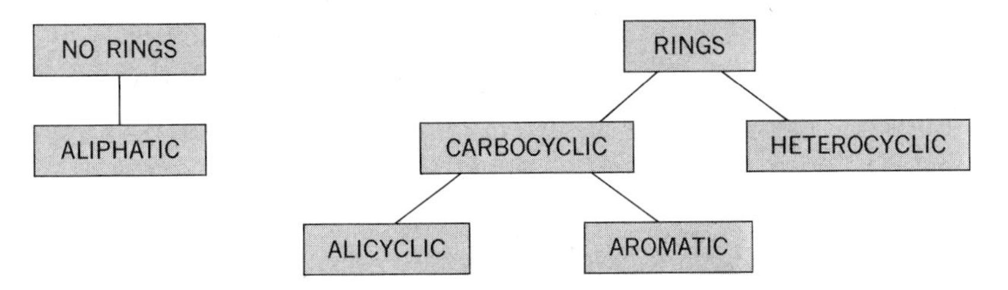

Branched or open-chain carbon compounds are aliphatic. For example,

```
   H  H  H  H
   |  |  |  |
H--C--C--C--C--H
   |  |  |  |
   H  H  H  H
```

```
        H           H
        |           |
     H--C--H  H  H--C--H  H
        |     |     |     |
H-------C-----C-----C-----C--H
        |     |     |     |
     H--C--H  H  H--C--H  H
        |           |
        H           H
```

```
              H
              |
           H--C--H
              |
   H  H    H--C--H   H  H
   |  |       |      |  |
H--C--C-------C------C--C--H
   |  |       |      |  |
   H  H    H--C--H   H  H
              |
           H--C--H
              |
              H
```

```
        H                  H
        |                  |
     H--C--H  H  H  H   H--C--H  H
        |     |  |  |      |     |
H-------C-----C--C--C------C-----C--H
        |     |  |  |      |     |
     H--C--H  H  H  H   H--C--H  H
        |                  |
        H                  H
```

Some unsaturated aliphatic compounds are

```
        H
        |
   H H--C--H         H
   |    |            |
H--C----C-----C≡C----C--H
   |    |            |
   H    H            H
```

```
   H  H  H  H
   |  |  |  |
H--C--C==C--C--H
   |        |
   H        H
```

```
   H        H
   |        |
H--C--H  H--C--H
      \    /
       C==C
      /    \
H--C--H  H--C--H
   |        |
   H        H
```

```
                            H
                            |
   H  H  H  H  H  H      H--C--H
   |  |  |  |  |  |         |
H--C--C--C==C--C--C---------C------H
   |  |        |  |         |
   H  H        H  H      H--C--H
                            |
                            H
```

If the carbon atoms are arranged in a ring, the compound is alicyclic. Alicyclic compounds usually have chemical properties resembling the aliphatic series. Some saturated alicyclic compounds are

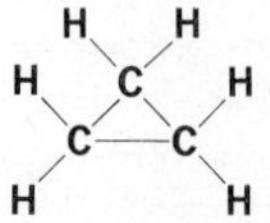

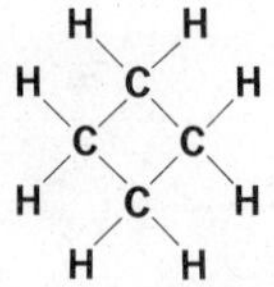

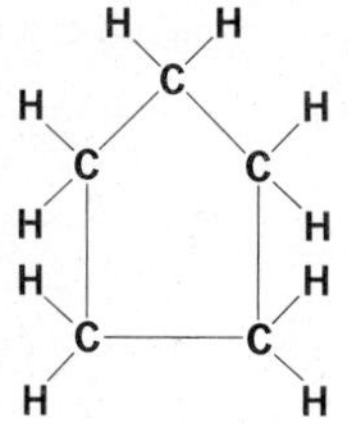

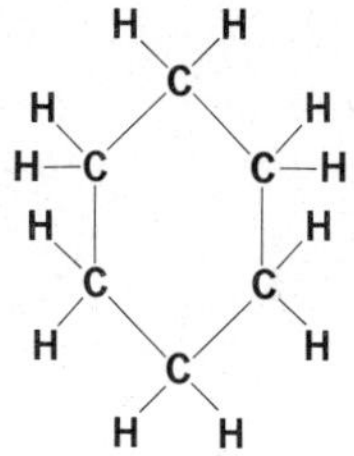

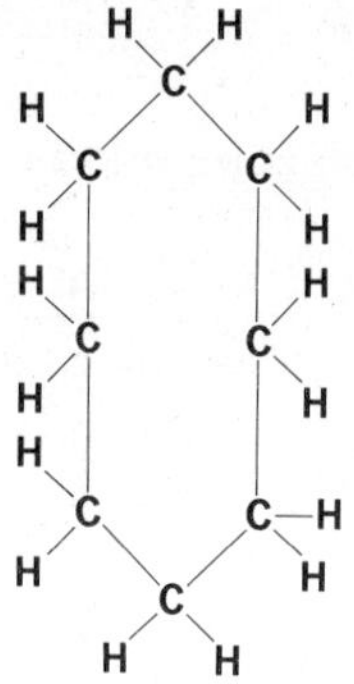

Some unsaturated alicyclic compounds are

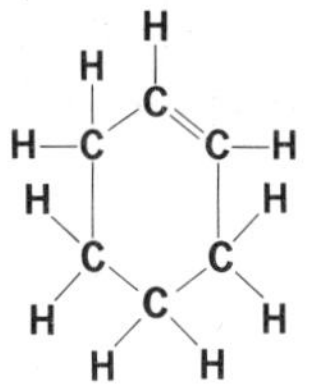

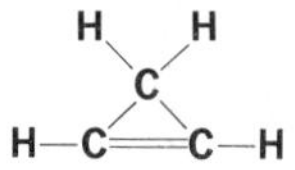

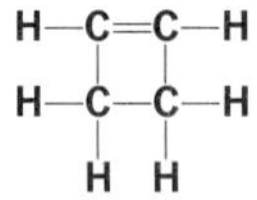

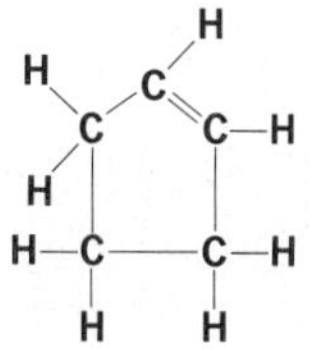

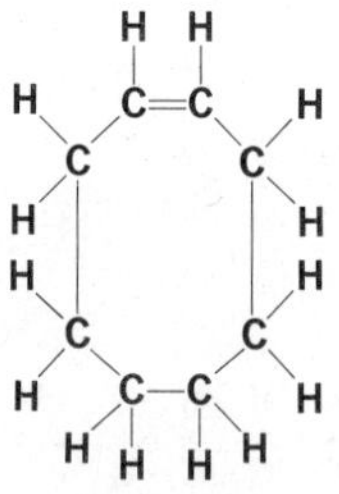

It is difficult to get a triple bond into the ring unless there are many carbon atoms (eight or more).

Aromatic carbon compounds consist of a six-carbon-atom ring system presumably containing alternating double and single bonds. Aromatic compounds always contain groups such as or combinations of these groups, such as

In all these examples, the perfect system of alternating single and double bonds is evident. Such a system is *conjugated.*

In shorthand notation we leave out the symbols for the carbon and hydrogen atoms, and we draw a regular polygon to show the number of carbon atoms in the ring. Because the formula

does not adequately express the structure of an aromatic system, the modern trend is to write

which immediately indicates the aromatic system. In this book, we shall always use this structure to indicate the aromatic ring system. For example,

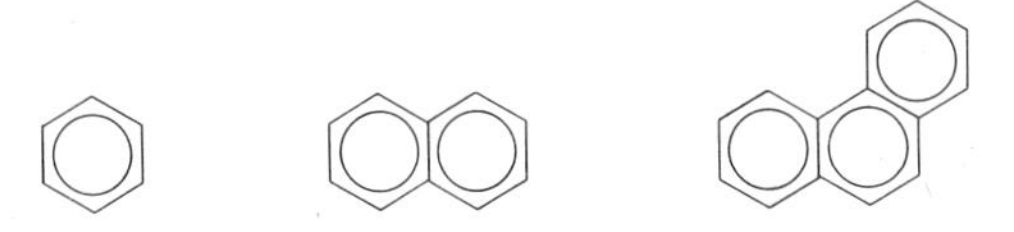

It is also possible to have a series of compounds called *heterocycles.* Hetero- means different. A heterocycle is a compound containing atoms in a ring (cycle) with at least one atom *other than carbon* in the ring (e.g., S, O, N, etc.). Some heterocyclic compounds are

```
     H                                                                     H
     |                                                                     |
     C          H         H                                                C
   //  \         \       /                                               /  \\
H—C     C—H       C=====C        H—C=====C—H       H—C=====N          H—C     N
  |     ||        |     |          ||    ||          ||    ||            ||    |
H—C     C—H     H—C     C—H      H—C     C—H       H—C     C—H        H—C     C—H
   \\  /            \  /             \  /              \  /              \  //
     N                S                O                 S                 N
```

Isomerism

When two or more compounds have the same molecular formula but differ in the arrangement of the atoms and in at least one chemical or physical property, the different compounds are called *isomers*. Organic chemistry is complicated not only by the vast number of isomers, but also by the many types of isomerism.

Simple Structural Isomerism

CARBON CHAIN ISOMERISM

Chain isomers result from the different ways in which a chain of carbon atoms can be arranged. For example, four carbon atoms can be arranged two different ways. (We use only the carbon skeleton to simplify the point.)

```
C—C—C—C     or     C—C—C
                     |
                     C
```

Five carbon atoms can be arranged three ways:

```
                                              C
                                              |
C—C—C—C—C          C—C—C—C                  C—C—C
                     |                        |
                     C                        C
```

An increase in carbon atoms results in an increase in possible variations (isomers).

POSITION ISOMERISM

Position isomers are due to the position of an atom or group of atoms with reference to any *particular arrangement of carbon atoms.* For example, there is more than one way to arrange a bromine atom on one of the carbon atoms of a three-carbon chain. (Again, we use only the carbon skeleton and the bromine atom.)

Given arrangement of carbon atoms: C—C—C

```
C—C—C     or     C—C—C
    |              |
    Br             Br
```

In an open chain, four carbon atoms can be arranged two ways.

```
C—C—C—C      or      C—C—C
                       |
                       C
  (A)                 (B)
```

When a bromine atom is placed on one of the carbon atoms, there are two places the bromine atom can be with respect to the particular arrangement in A and two places it can be with respect to the particular arrangement in B. For example,

```
C—C—C—C      or      C—C—C—C
    |                      |
    Br                     Br
            (A)

                       Br
                       |
C—C—C—Br     or      C—C—C
  |                    |
  C                    C
            (B)
```

Note that *each of these four bromine-containing isomers has the same molecular formula,* but each differs from the others. The student should personally investigate these four isomers to prove that they really differ and that no others exist. For example,

```
C—C—C—C      and      C—C—C—C
    |                   |
    Br                  Br
```

are the same;

```
C—C—C—C      and      C—C—C—C
|                           |
Br                          Br
```

are also the same. Position isomers also occur in aromatic compounds.

(We will use the carbon skeleton ⌬.)

In the unique aromatic ring (C_6H_6), two hydrogens can be replaced by two bromine atoms in three possible ways:

ortho (*o*-) meta (*m*-) para (*p*-)

When the two groups are on adjacent carbon atoms, the molecule is referred to as an ortho (*o*-) compound; when the two groups are across the

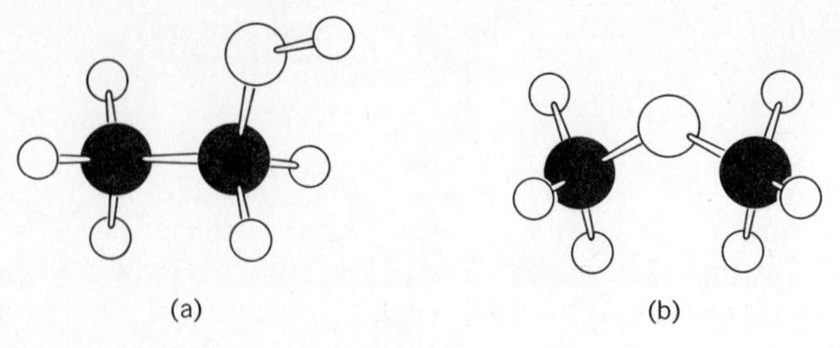

Figure 2-4 (a) Ethyl alcohol; (b) dimethyl ether.

ring (separated by two carbon atoms), the compound is para (*p*-); and when the groups are separated by one carbon atom, the compound is meta (*m*-). These names do not identify the compounds but merely indicate the position of the bromines.

FUNCTIONAL GROUP ISOMERISM

These isomers are compounds having the same molecular formula but differing in the functional group (belonging to different homologous series). This case is perhaps the easiest to differentiate. For example (see Figure 2-4),

```
    H  H                      H       H
    |  |                      |       |
 H—C—C—OH        and       H—C—O—C—H
    |  |                      |       |
    H  H                      H       H
              (C2H6O)

    H  H     O                H   O   H
    |  |    //                |   ||  |
 H—C—C—C         and       H—C—C—C—H
    |  |    \                 |       |
    H  H     H                H       H
              (C3H6O)
```

The above compounds differ structurally even though they have the same formula. They can also be easily identified chemically, which makes them the most easily distinguishable groups of isomers.

Stereoisomerism or Space Isomerism

Stereoisomers are compounds possessing the same molecular formulas and the same functional groups but differing in the three-dimensional spatial arrangement of the atoms or groups within the molecule.

OPTICAL ISOMERISM

Optical isomers are compounds with asymmetry (no symmetry) in the molecule (i.e., all four atoms or groups attached to a carbon atom in the molecule are different).

```
   H  H  Br H               Cl
   |  |  |  |               |
H—C—C—C—C—H          Br—C—H
   |  |  |  |               |
   H  H  H  H            H—C—H
                            |
                            H
```

Compounds are optically active if they can rotate a plane of polarized light either to the right (dextro) or to the left (levo). This is a large and important topic and will be discussed in some detail under carbohydrates.

GEOMETRIC ISOMERISM (*cis-trans isomerism*)

Geometric isomers occur when two atoms are attached to two carbon atoms that are not free to rotate (carbon in a double bond, or carbons in a ring). The atoms can be on the same side (i.e., *cis*) of the double bond or ring or on opposite sides (i.e., *trans*). For example,

```
Br      Br        H       Br
  \    /            \    /
   C=C               C=C
  /    \            /    \
H       H         Br      H
   cis               trans
```

Here the *cis* and *trans* isomers are distinctly different compounds although they have the same formulas. *Cis-trans* isomerism cannot exist in a case such as

```
 Br Br        Br
 |  |           \ |  |
—C—C—            C—C
 |  |             |  | \
                         Br
```

because a carbon-carbon single bond is free to rotate and can assume any configuration, as indicated by the arrows. Thus, the two forms are indistinguishable.

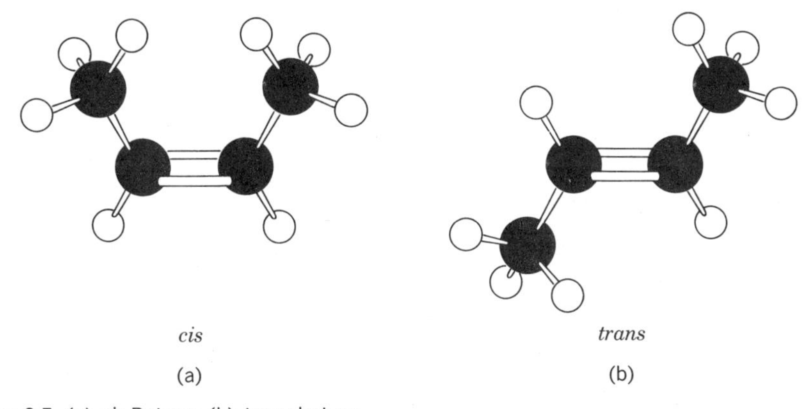

cis (a) *trans* (b)

Figure 2-5 (a) *cis*-Butene; (b) *trans*-butene.

An example of *cis* and *trans* isomerism in ring compounds is

cis *trans*

REVIEW QUESTIONS

1. With what is organic chemistry concerned? Why is organic chemistry a separate field from inorganic chemistry?
2. Write the structures of eight different functional groups.
3. Discuss the difference between an empirical formula, a molecular formula, and a structural formula.
4. Define a homologous series. Write the structures for several members of two different homologous series.
5. What is the difference between saturated and unsaturated compounds?
6. Write several structural formulas of compounds containing only single bonds, compounds containing a double bond, and compounds containing a triple bond.
7. How do aliphatic, alicyclic, aromatic, and heterocyclic compounds differ?
8. Define the term conjugated.
9. Discuss the concept of isomers in organic chemistry.
10. Outline the various kinds of isomerism and give examples of each.
11. Indicate whether the following compounds are aliphatic, aromatic, alicyclic, or heterocyclic.

(a) alicyclic (b) aromatic (c) heterocyclic

(d) alicyclic (e) aromatic (f) heterocyclic

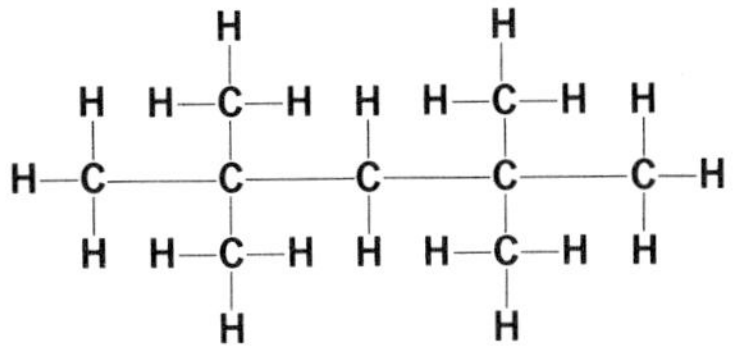

(g) aliphatic

12. Indicate which of the following pairs are isomers and which are not. If they are isomers, indicate the type.

A. (a) 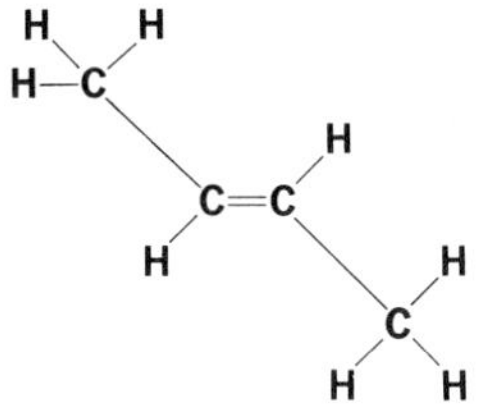 (b) cis-trans

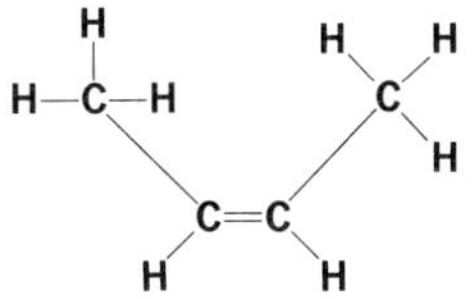

B. (a) 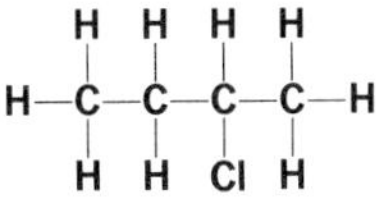 (b) position

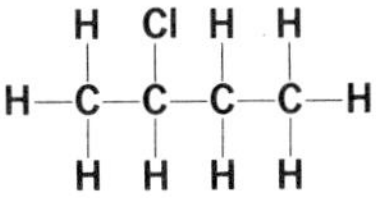

C. (a) 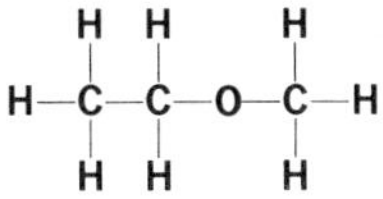 (b) NO

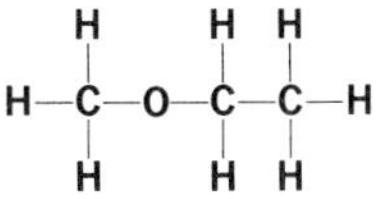

D. (a) 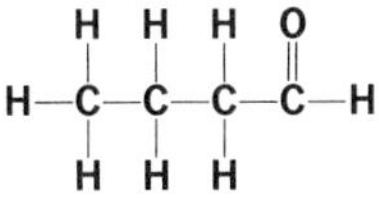 (b) functional group

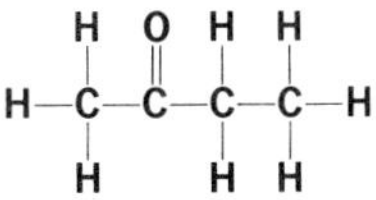

E. (a) 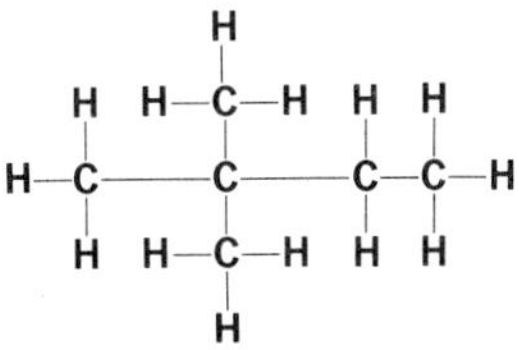 (b) chain

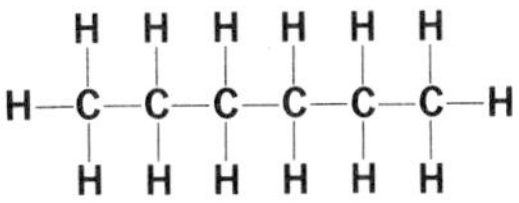

13. Which of the following are conjugated?

```
           H
           |
H—C=C—C—C=C—H
  |  |  |  |  |
  H  H  H  H  H
       (a)
```

```
    H  H  H  H  H  H
    |  |  |  |  |  |
H—C—C=C—C—C=C—H
    |        |
    H        H
         (b)
```

```
  H  H  H  H  H  H
  |  |  |  |  |  |
H—C=C—C=C—C=C—H
       (c)
```

14. Indicate which of the following are saturated and which are unsaturated.

```
          H
          |
  H  H  H—C—H  H  H
  |  |    |    |  |
H—C—C—————C————C—C—H
  |  |    |    |  |
  H  H  H—C—H  H  H
          |
          H
        (a) sat
```

```
    H  H     H
    |  |     |
H—C—C=C—C—H
    |     |  |
    H     H  H
      (b) unsat
```

```
          H  H
          |  |
H—C≡C—C—C—H
          |  |
          H  H
      (c) unsat
```

```
H     H
|   C/
C <  \\C—H
|
H
      (d) unsat
```

```
    H
    |
H—C———C===C—H
    |     |     |
    |     |     H
H—C———C—H
    |     |
    H     H
      (e) unsat
```

3

hydrocarbons

Hydrocarbons are compounds containing only carbon and hydrogen. As indicated in Chapter 2, hydrocarbons may be either saturated or unsaturated, and aliphatic, alicyclic, or aromatic.

The saturated hydrocarbons are characterized by being very *unreactive*, whereas the unsaturated hydrocarbons are generally very *reactive*. The aromatic hydrocarbons, though unsaturated, do not show the reactions typical of unsaturated hydrocarbons.

Paraffins (alkanes)

The saturated aliphatic hydrocarbons are called *alkanes* or *paraffins*. The general formula for the series is C_nH_{2n+2}, where n is the number of carbon atoms. According to the International Union of Pure and Applied Chemistry (IUPAC) system, each series has a characteristic ending. The common ending for the alkanes is the suffix -ane. By examining the paraffin

Table 3-1 Prefixes in nomenclature

NO. OF CARBONS	PREFIX	NO. OF CARBONS	PREFIX
1	meth-	11	undec-
2	eth-	12	dodec-
3	prop-	13	tridec-
4	but-	14	tetradec-
5	pent-	15	pentadec-
6	hex-	16	hexadec-
7	hept-	17	heptadec-
8	oct-	18	octadec-
9	non-	19	nonadec-
10	dec-	20	eicos-

series closely, we can learn much about the similarities of nomenclature and of members of a series, and we can acquire a working knowledge of isomerism.

Table 3-1 lists the prefixes used in organic chemistry to denote the number of carbons in a compound. The first four prefixes are unique and require memorization; the remaining prefixes, however, are in common usage in many words today.

The simplest paraffins have all the carbons in a row. We call these the straight-chain paraffins (see Figure 3-1). To name a straight-chain paraffin, we tell how many carbon atoms it has (prefix) and use the proper ending (suffix). For example,

```
   H          H H          H H H            H H H H             H H H H H
   |          | |          | | |            | | | |             | | | | |
 H-C-H      H-C-C-H      H-C-C-C-H        H-C-C-C-C-H         H-C-C-C-C-C-H
   |          | |          | | |            | | | |             | | | | |
   H          H H          H H H            H H H H             H H H H H
methane     ethane       propane           butane              pentane
```

Note, for example, that it makes no difference how butane is drawn. We see that

```
                 C      C           C C      C-C
                 |      |           | |      | |
C-C-C-C        C-C      C-C-C       C-C      C C
               |
               C
```

are all the same thing, and are all the butane carbon skeleton.

A primary carbon atom is attached to only one other carbon atom; a secondary to two; a tertiary to three; and a quaternary is attached to four other carbon atoms. A straight-chain hydrocarbon contains only primary and secondary carbons, whereas a branched compound contains either one tertiary or one quaternary carbon atom. We shall discuss their nomenclature shortly.

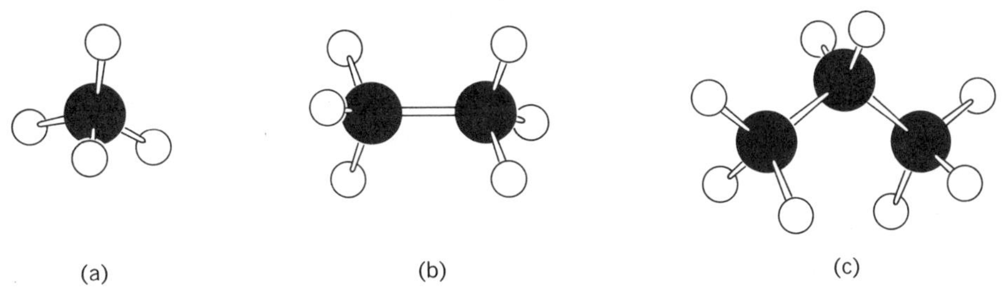

Figure 3-1 (a) Methane; (b) ethane; (c) propane.

Some examples of branched hydrocarbon skeletons are

```
                      C            C
                      |            |
C—C—C           C—C—C        C—C—C—C—C
  |                   |            |       |
  C                   C            C       C
```

Nomenclature (IUPAC)

If we have a straight-chain paraffin, we count the number of carbon atoms, write the corresponding prefix, and add the suffix -ane (see Table 3-2). If we have a branched saturated hydrocarbon, we number each carbon in the *longest chain* and then use these numbers to locate the addi-

Table 3-2 Some straight-chain hydrocarbons

NAME	MOLECULAR FORMULA	MELTING POINT (°C)	BOILING POINT (°C)	NORMAL STATE
methane	CH_4	−182.48	−161.49	gas
ethane	C_2H_6	−183.27	−88.63	gas
propane	C_3H_8	−189.9	−44.5	gas
butane	C_4H_{10}	−138.3	−0.5	gas
pentane	C_5H_{12}	−129.72	+36	liquid
hexane	C_6H_{14}	−95	+68	liquid
heptane	C_7H_{16}	−91	+98.42	liquid
octane	C_8H_{18}	−56.5	+125–126	liquid
nonane	C_9H_{20}	−51	+150.798	liquid
decane	$C_{10}H_{22}$	−29.7	+174.1	liquid
undecane	$C_{11}H_{24}$	−25	+195	liquid
dodecane	$C_{12}H_{26}$	−9.6	+216.3	liquid
tridecane	$C_{13}H_{28}$	−5.5	+243	liquid
tetradecane	$C_{14}H_{30}$	+6	+253.5	liquid
pentadecane	$C_{15}H_{32}$	+10	+270.5	liquid
hexadecane	$C_{16}H_{34}$	+18	+287	liquid
heptadecane	$C_{17}H_{36}$	+22	+303	liquid-solid
octadecane	$C_{18}H_{38}$	+28	+305–307	solid
nonadecane	$C_{19}H_{40}$	+32	+330	solid
eicosane	$C_{20}H_{42}$	+36.8	+343	solid

tional groups attached to the chain. Choose numbers so that the groups are given the lowest numbers possible.

When a group of atoms (or radicals) is attached to something, the prefix denoting the proper number of carbon atoms is still used, but the new ending is -yl.

Table 3-3 lists some frequently used radicals. Remember, a radical must be attached to something!

Table 3-3 Common radicals

RADICAL		NAME
H H—C— H	CH_3—	methyl
H H H—C—C— H H	CH_3CH_2—	ethyl
H H H H—C—C—C— H H H	$CH_3CH_2CH_2$—	*n*-propyl
H H H H—C—C—C—H H | H	CH_3CHCH_3 |	isopropyl (*i*-propyl)
H H H H H—C—C—C—C— H H H H	$CH_3CH_2CH_2CH_2$—	*n*-butyl
H H H H H—C—C—C—C—H H H | H	$CH_3CH_2CHCH_3$ |	secondary-butyl (*sec*-butyl, also *s*-butyl)
H H H H—C—C—C— H H—C—H H H	CH_3CHCH_2— | CH_3	isobutyl
H H H—C—H H—C—C— H H—C—H H	CH_3 | CH_3—C— | CH_3	tertiary-butyl (*tert*-butyl, also *t*-butyl)

The *n*-radical is always the one formed from a straight-chain hydrocarbon with the terminal (end) hydrogen removed; that is,

$CH_3CH_2CH_2CH_2CH_2CH_2CH_2CH_2—$

n-octyl

Other radicals will be discussed as they are encountered.

We refer to any radical formed from an aliphatic group as an *alkyl* radical. The general symbol for an alkyl radical is R. We refer to the radical formed from an aromatic group as an *aromatic* radical, and its general symbol is Ar. The general radicals R and Ar are used to save time and space.

SOME EXAMPLES OF IUPAC NOMENCLATURE

Suppose we were asked to name the following compound:

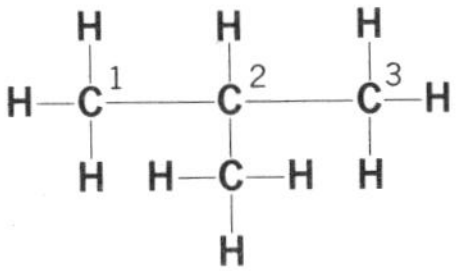

```
    H      H      H
    |1     |2     |3
H—C———C———C—H
    |      |      |
    H  H—C—H  H
           |
           H
```

The longest carbon atom chain has three atoms. We number each atom in this chain. Note that a methyl group

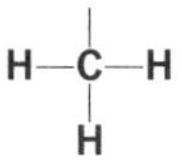

```
    |
H—C—H
    |
    H
```

methyl radical

is attached to the number 2 carbon atom. From the list given in Table 3-3, we should be able to recognize all the simple radicals.

We now proceed as follows:

1. Write the prefix that gives the number of carbons in the chain:

   prop-

2. Add the ending to denote the particular series (here, because it is a paraffin, we use the ending -ane):

   propane

3. Before this name, write the radical attached to the chain:

   methylpropane

4. Add the number of the carbon atom to which the radical is attached:

   2-methylpropane

Note that methylpropane is all one word, and that the hyphen (-) always separates a number from the name.

Although methane, ethane, and propane have only one possible structure, butane exists in two forms (both have the formula C_4H_{10}):

```
    H H H H              H     H     H
    | | | |              |     |     |
  H-C-C-C-C-H          H-C-----C-----C-H
    | | | |              |     |     |
    H H H H              H   H-C-H   H
                               |
                               H
    butane              2-methylpropane
```

Compounds often have a common name in addition to the IUPAC name. The common name for butane is *n*-butane. The compound 2-methylpropane is commonly called isobutane. The prefix iso- usually denotes the simplest possible branched system with that number of carbon atoms. Isobutane and *n*-butane are examples of carbon-chain isomerism. The *common* name for any straight-chain paraffin has an *n* (normal) in front of the name.

When five carbon atoms are present in the paraffin series, how many ways can they be arranged? First, we have the straight-chain compound pentane,

```
    H H H H H
    | | | | |
  H-C-C-C-C-C-H
    | | | | |
    H H H H H
```

pentane (C_5H_{12}) (IUPAC name)
n-pentane (common name)

which we have already encountered in the series of normal saturated paraffins. The next isomer would have a simple branched system such as

```
    H     H     H H
    |1    |2    |3|4
  H-C-----C-----C-C-H
    |     |     | |
    H   H-C-H   H H
          |
          H
```

2-methylbutane (C_5H_{12})

which, commonly called isopentane, has the IUPAC name 2-methylbutane. Note that whether the formula is drawn as above or as

```
    H H     H     H
    |4|3    |2    |1
  H-C-C-----C-----C-H
    | |     |     |
    H H   H-C-H   H
            |
            H
```

it is still 2-methylbutane. It would be *incorrect* to number the carbon atoms as

```
  H     H     H  H                       H
  |4    |3    |2 |1                      |
H-C-----C-----C--C-H         H  H  H-----C-----H  H
  |     |     |  |           |1 |2       |3       |4
  H  H--C--H  H  H         H-C--C--------C--------C-H
        |                    |  |        |        |
        H                    H  H        H        H
```

incorrect *incorrect*

because the methyl radical would be attached to the third carbon atom. In general, we number the carbon chain so that the radical or group attached will have the lowest number possible.

Another hydrocarbon with the formula C_5H_{12} is

```
        H
        |
  H  H--C--H  H
  |     |     |
H-C-----C-----C-H
  |     |     |
  H  H--C--H  H
        |
        H
```

2,2-dimethylpropane (C_5H_{12})

This isomer is commonly called neopentane. As we consider its IUPAC name, we see that no matter how we look at the molecule, the longest chain numbers three carbon atoms.

```
        H
        |
  H  H--C3-H  H
  |1    |2    |3
H-C-----C-----C-H
  |     |     |
  H  H--C1-H  H
        |
        H
```

Here, two methyl groups are attached to the same carbon atom: carbon 2. If the two groups are the same, as in this case, we can use the prefix di- to designate two of the same thing. In similar cases, tri- would designate three, tetra- four, penta- five, etc.

Every time a group is attached to a carbon-atom chain, a number is used to designate its position on the chain. Because we have two groups in this compound, we must have two numbers. Here we use the same number twice. The IUPAC name of neopentane is 2,2-dimethylpropane. When two or more numbers follow each other, they are separated by a comma.

From what we have just discussed, we see that the formula C_5H_{12} has three chain isomers: pentane (b.p. 36.1°), 2-methylbutane (b.p. 27.9°), and 2,2-dimethylpropane (b.p. 9.5°). In general, branching in the compound results in a lowering of its boiling point.

Let us examine the isomers of C_6H_{14}. (We use the carbon skeleton only.)

```
                                         C
                                         |
C—C—C—C—C—C      C—C—C—C—C         C—C—C—C—C
                   |
                   C
  hexane        2-methylpentane    3-methylpentane

    C              C C
    |              | |
  C—C—C—C        C—C—C—C
    |
    C
2,2-dimethylbutane  2,3-dimethylbutane
```

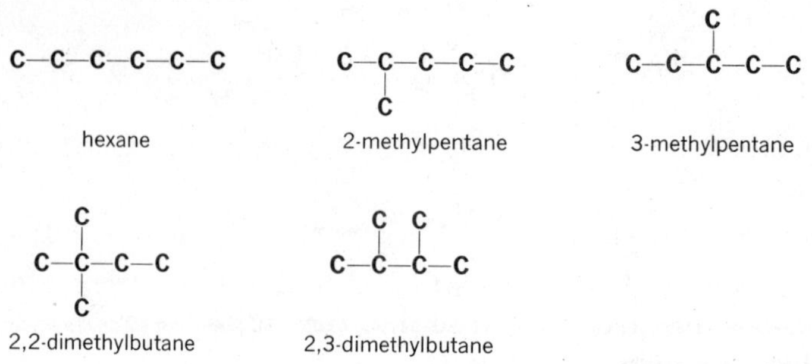

We see that there are five chain isomers of the formula C_6H_{14}.

There are nine chain isomers of the formula C_7H_{16}. (We use the carbon skeleton only.)

```
                      C                     C
                      |                     |
C—C—C—C—C—C—C       C—C—C—C—C—C         C—C—C—C—C—C
    heptane          2-methylhexane       3-methylhexane

    C C              C   C                C
    | |              |   |                |
C—C—C—C—C          C—C—C—C—C              C—C—C—C—C
                                          |
                                          C
2,3-dimethylpentane  2,4-dimethylpentane  2,2-dimethylpentane

                                              C
                                              |
    C                C C                      C
    |                | |                      |
C—C—C—C—C          C—C—C—C                C—C—C—C—C
    |                |
    C                C
3,3-dimethylpentane  2,2,3-trimethylbutane  3-ethylpentane
```

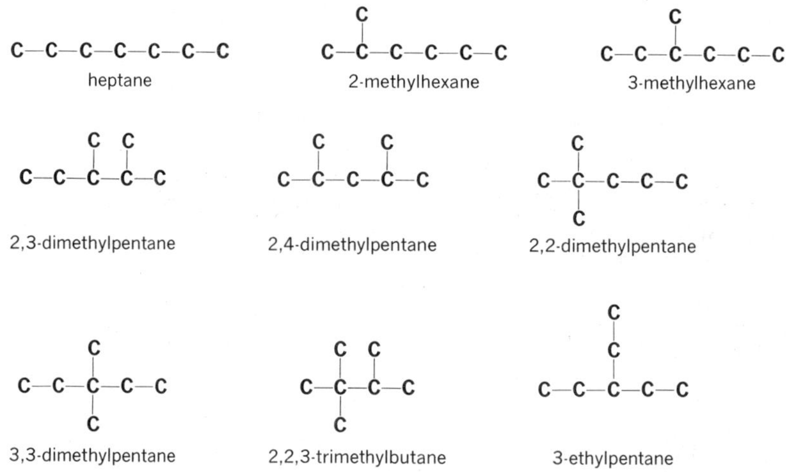

From what we have shown, it is evident that the number of isomers increases rapidly as the number of carbons increases. This can be seen from Table 3-4.

Preparation

Most of the paraffins are readily available from natural sources, such as petroleum, and do not require synthesis. However, petroleum is such a complicated mixture that it is not feasible to separate this abundant natural material into all of its components. If a chemist desires a particular isomer in a very high state of purity, synthesis methods, such as catalytic reduction and the Grignard reaction, are available.

Table 3-4 Isomers

NUMBER OF CARBONS	ISOMERS[a]
1	1
2	1
3	1
4	2
5	3
6	5
7	9
8	18
9	35
10	75
11	159
12	355
13	802
14	1,858
15	4,347
20	366,319
25	36,797,588
30	4,111,846,763
40	62,491,178,805,831

[a] Excluding stereoisomers.

CATALYTIC REDUCTION

Reduction is a general term (the opposite of oxidation). *Without exception, oxidation and reduction occur simultaneously.* When something is oxidized, something must be reduced. One is the exact opposite of the other.

Oxidation is the loss of electrons, and reduction is the gain of electrons. For example, when the hydrogen atom (one proton and one electron) loses an electron to become the hydrogen ion, oxidation occurs.

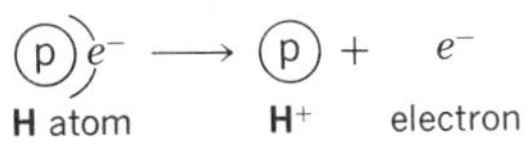

$$(p)e^- \longrightarrow (p) + e^-$$

H atom H^+ electron

When the hydrogen ion gains an electron to become the hydrogen atom, reduction occurs.

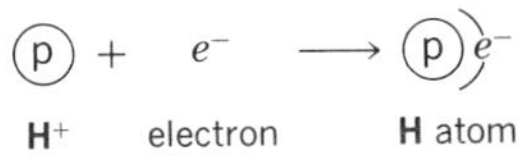

$$(p) + e^- \longrightarrow (p)e^-$$

H^+ electron H atom

The oxidation state of an element depends on the available electrons. Therefore, oxidation occurs when an element's oxidation state is increased, and reduction occurs when an element's oxidation state is lowered.

A useful rule in organic chemistry is that oxidation occurs when

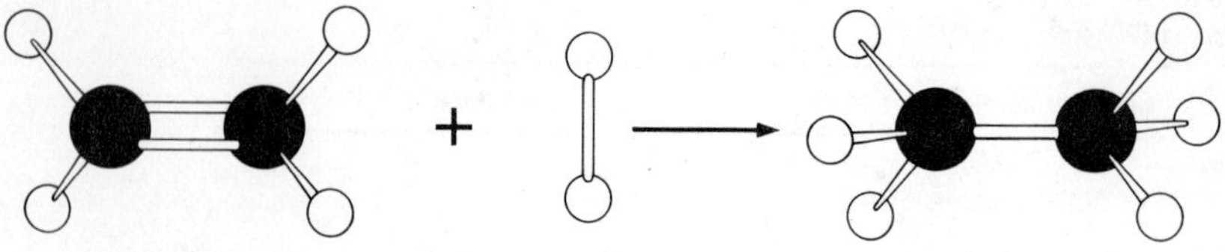

Figure 3-2 Hydrogenation of ethene.

oxygen is added to or hydrogen is removed from a compound. Reduction occurs when *oxygen is removed from or hydrogen is added to a compound.* Reduction using hydrogen is called *hydrogenation.* Hydrogen may be added to an olefin (one double bond), an acetylene (one triple bond), a diolefin (two double bonds), or any other normal unsaturation in the presence of a proper metal catalyst. Catalysts change the speed of a chemical reaction (they usually hasten the reaction), and the catalyst remains unaffected by the reaction. In practice, the catalyst does not last forever because it becomes "poisoned" by impurities or extraneous chemicals and so loses its potency. The catalyst may be platinum, palladium, nickel, or other metals. In this addition reaction, the double bond or triple bond reacts with the hydrogen to form a single bond (see Figure 3-2). Some sample reactions are

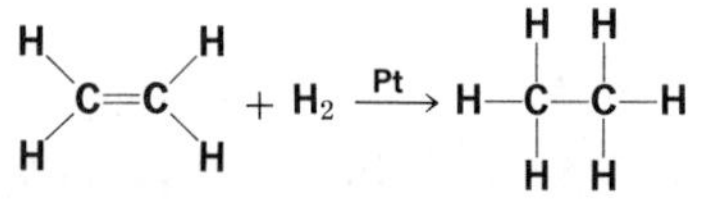

$$H_2C{=}CH_2 + H_2 \xrightarrow{Pt} H_3C{-}CH_3$$

ethene → ethane

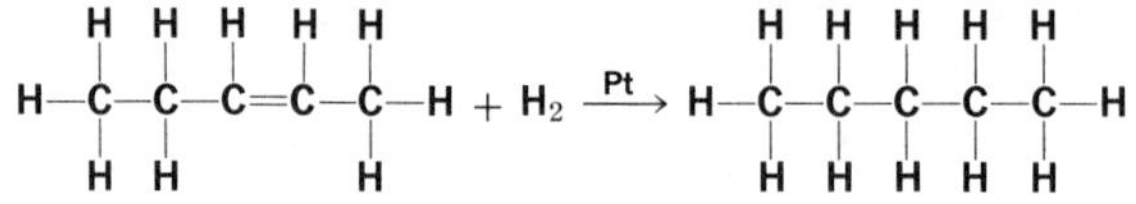

$$H_3C{-}CH_2{-}CH{=}CH{-}CH_3 + H_2 \xrightarrow{Pt} H_3C{-}CH_2{-}CH_2{-}CH_2{-}CH_3$$

2-pentene → pentane

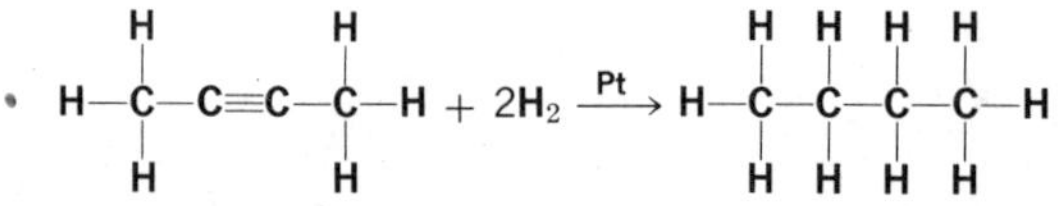

$$H_3C{-}C{\equiv}C{-}CH_3 + 2H_2 \xrightarrow{Pt} H_3C{-}CH_2{-}CH_2{-}CH_3$$

2-butyne → butane

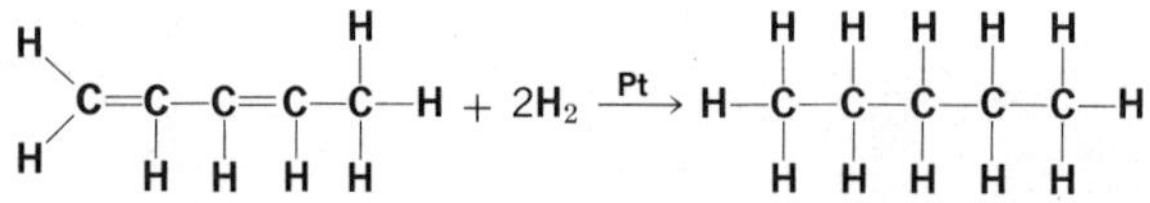

$$H_2C{=}CH{-}CH{=}CH{-}CH_3 + 2H_2 \xrightarrow{Pt} H_3C{-}CH_2{-}CH_2{-}CH_2{-}CH_3$$

1,3-pentadiene → pentane

$$H_2C{=}CH{-}C{\equiv}C{-}H + 3H_2 \xrightarrow{Pt} H_3C{-}CH_2{-}CH_2{-}CH_3$$

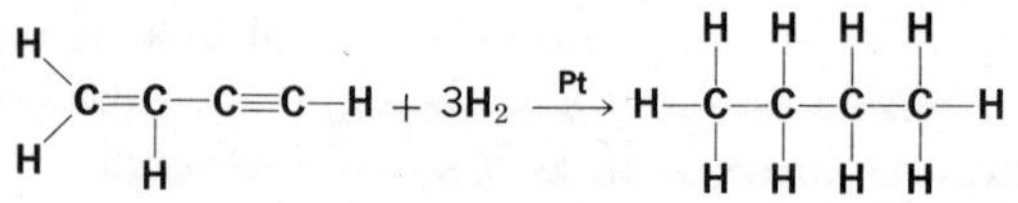

butenyne → butane

The properties, preparation, and nomenclature of compounds with double and triple bonds will be discussed later in this chapter.

THE GRIGNARD REACTION

Victor Grignard found that if an alkyl halide (RX) (X = Cl, Br, or I) and magnesium metal are placed in a dry ether solution, a lively reaction occurs. The magnesium dissolves to form an ether-soluble alkyl magnesium halide (Grignard reagent), represented for convenience by RMgX.

$$CH_3{-}I + Mg^0 \xrightarrow[\text{ether}]{\text{dry}} \underset{\text{methylmagnesium iodide}}{CH_3{-}Mg{-}I}$$

$$CH_3{-}CH_2{-}Br + Mg^0 \xrightarrow[\text{ether}]{\text{dry}} \underset{\text{ethyl magnesium bromide}}{CH_3{-}CH_2{-}Mg{-}Br}$$

The Grignard reagent is very sensitive to water and will react vigorously with moisture to form the corresponding hydrocarbon. The general equation for this reaction is

$$2RMgX + 2H_2O \longrightarrow 2RH + MgX_2 + Mg(OH)_2$$

Two specific examples are

$$\underset{n\text{-butyl magnesium bromide}}{2CH_3CH_2CH_2CH_2MgBr} + 2H_2O \longrightarrow \underset{\text{butane}}{2CH_3CH_2CH_2CH_3} + MgBr_2 + Mg(OH)_2$$

$$\underset{n\text{-hexadecyl magnesium iodide}}{2n\text{-}C_{16}H_{33}MgI} + 2H_2O \longrightarrow \underset{\text{hexadecane}}{2n\text{-}C_{16}H_{34}} + MgI_2 + Mg(OH)_2$$

Brown Brothers

Figure 3-3 Victor Grignard.

Chemical Properties and Reactions

The saturated hydrocarbons are *inert.* Reagents such as concentrated nitric acid, molten sodium hydroxide, potassium dichromate, potassium permanganate, and concentrated sulfuric acid leave a hydrocarbon such as hexane completely untouched. As we shall soon see, these reagents usually have a drastic effect on most organic compounds.

HALOGENATION[1]

The paraffins again show their inert character by *failing to react with chlorine in the dark.* However, in the presence of ultraviolet light, these hydrocarbons do react, sometimes explosively, to form *complicated mixtures.* The ultraviolet light acts as a booster to start the reaction.

The classic chlorination of methane, which gives us four different products, is a good example of the chlorination of a paraffin.

$$\begin{array}{c} \mathrm{H} \\ | \\ \mathrm{H{-}C{-}H} \\ | \\ \mathrm{H} \end{array} + \mathrm{Cl_2} \xrightarrow[\text{light}]{\text{uv}} \begin{array}{c} \mathrm{H} \\ | \\ \mathrm{H{-}C{-}Cl} \\ | \\ \mathrm{H} \end{array} + \mathrm{HCl}$$

methane — chloromethane (*methyl chloride*)

$$\begin{array}{c} \mathrm{H} \\ | \\ \mathrm{H{-}C{-}Cl} \\ | \\ \mathrm{H} \end{array} + \mathrm{Cl_2} \xrightarrow[\text{light}]{\text{uv}} \begin{array}{c} \mathrm{H} \\ | \\ \mathrm{Cl{-}C{-}Cl} \\ | \\ \mathrm{H} \end{array} + \mathrm{HCl}$$

methyl chloride — dichloromethane (*methylene chloride*)

$$\begin{array}{c} \mathrm{H} \\ | \\ \mathrm{Cl{-}C{-}Cl} \\ | \\ \mathrm{H} \end{array} + \mathrm{Cl_2} \xrightarrow[\text{light}]{\text{uv}} \begin{array}{c} \mathrm{Cl} \\ | \\ \mathrm{Cl{-}C{-}Cl} \\ | \\ \mathrm{H} \end{array} + \mathrm{HCl}$$

methylene chloride — trichloromethane (*chloroform*)

$$\begin{array}{c} \mathrm{Cl} \\ | \\ \mathrm{Cl{-}C{-}Cl} \\ | \\ \mathrm{H} \end{array} + \mathrm{Cl_2} \xrightarrow[\text{light}]{\text{uv}} \begin{array}{c} \mathrm{Cl} \\ | \\ \mathrm{Cl{-}C{-}Cl} \\ | \\ \mathrm{Cl} \end{array} + \mathrm{HCl}$$

chloroform — tetrachloromethane (*carbon tetrachloride*)

[1] Fluorine gas is exceptionally reactive, and organic fluorine compounds have special properties and characteristics. The preparations of organic fluorine compounds always require special reactions and techniques. In this text our discussions will usually not include fluorine.

We have shown the common names in addition to the IUPAC names. As we see above, the reaction yields a variety of products. Because they are excellent solvents and cleaning fluids, chlorinated hydrocarbons are used in the dry-cleaning business. Chlorinated hydrocarbons possess the added attraction of being nonflammable. In general, a compound that possesses as many halogens as or more halogens than hydrogens will not burn. Carbona cleaner contains carbon tetrachloride. The explosive chlorination of organic hydrocarbons is not usually a practical reaction because of the difficulty in separating all the isomers; thus, it has a limited application.

Bromine reacts similarly to chlorine but with much diminished intensity; and iodine is too inert to react with inert hydrocarbons.

Occurrence and Uses

Natural gas is largely a mixture of saturated hydrocarbons. Natural gas contains 80–90% methane, 5–10% ethane, 1–3% propane, and about 1% butane and higher hydrocarbons. Small amounts of nitrogen and, in some cases (e.g., natural gas found in Texas, Oklahoma, and Louisiana), small amounts of helium are also found. The gas is used mainly for heating and cooking, because burning the gas liberates heat. Marsh gas is predominately methane. Compounds related to the methane series possess varying degrees of anesthetic properties.

Petroleum consists chiefly of an elaborate mixture of paraffins ranging from low to very high carbon content (thirty or more carbon atoms). Fractional distillation is the simplest way to treat this complicated natural mixture. In fractional distillation, the various constituents of a mixture are separated by utilizing the differences in the boiling points of the various compounds. Petroleum contains so many substances that it is not practical to isolate all of them, and fractions are taken over a wide boiling range. The products of these boiling ranges have familiar names and important uses. The fraction boiling between 20–60°C is known as petroleum ether, and the fraction boiling between 60–100°C is known as naphtha or ligroine. Gasoline itself boils over a very wide range, 40–200°C. Kerosene usually boils between 200–300°C. Material boiling over 300°C is known as fuel oil or gas oil. The very heavy residual oil, known as lubricating oil, can also be obtained, as well as a residue of asphalt or petroleum coke, depending on the origin of the petroleum. Note that some of the ranges overlap, and the desired product can often determine the range.

Gasoline is a complex fluid of tremendous industrial importance. Gasoline can be obtained by fractional distillation and also by other processes (cracking, etc.) Cracking is the thermal decomposition or pyrolysis of the organic substance by means of a great amount of heat, about 700°C; in this process, the original substance is split up into many smaller fragments.

Universal Oil Products Company

Figure 3-4 Cracking tower.

For example, it has been shown that, at 700°C,

$$CH_3{-}CH_2{-}CH_2{-}CH_3 \xrightarrow{700^\circ C}$$
butane

Products	Yield
CH_4 (methane) + $CH_3{-}CH{=}CH_2$ (propene)	44%
$CH_3{-}CH_3$ (ethane) + $CH_2{=}CH_2$ (ethene)	46%
$CH_3{-}CH{=}CH{-}CH_3$ (2-butene) + H_2 (hydrogen)	5%
$CH_2{=}CH{-}CH{=}CH_2$ (1,3-butadiene) + $2H_2$ (hydrogen)	4%

By pyrolyzing a hydrocarbon of large molecular weight (i.e., 16 carbons) we can obtain fragments in the gasoline range (i.e., 8 carbons) that are therefore of greatly increased financial value. By using special catalysts, the cracking temperature may be lowered.

Octane number is a useful method of classifying gasoline. The octane number is an arbitrarily chosen number that rates the useful characteristics of the fluid in question. Knocking is a phenomenon involved in the burning of the gasoline in the combustion chamber. Heptane (which is particularly prone to knock and is not a good fuel, has octane number 0. Isooctane,

$$CH_3-\overset{\displaystyle CH_3}{\underset{\displaystyle CH_3}{\overset{|}{\underset{|}{C}}}}-CH_2-\underset{\displaystyle CH_3}{\underset{|}{CH}}-CH_3$$

2,2,4-trimethylpentane
(*isooctane*)

which does not knock and is an excellent fuel, has octane number 100. In determining octane numbers, the unknown fuel is compared to mixtures of heptane and isooctane. Premium gasoline in this country has an octane rating of approximately 80–90. Thus, a premium gasoline with a rating of 90 is comparable to a mixture of 90% isooctane and 10% heptane. There are hydrocarbons with octane ratings greater than 100 (special aviation gasoline).

Hydrocarbons are versatile solvents, but they are flammable, a decided disadvantage. *Petroleum ether,* for example, is a useful cleansing agent, which, due to its low boiling point range, quickly evaporates and is removed. It is also used extensively as a defatting agent for natural products and drugs. *Naphtha* (ligroine) is similarly useful and, because of its somewhat higher boiling range, has a slightly decreased tendency to catch on fire, although it is still flammable. *Kerosene* can be used as a solvent and fuel and, because of its yellow sooty flame, is also used as a source of illumination.

White mineral oil, or liquid petroleum, can be used as a cathartic. It is a mixture of liquid hydrocarbons obtained from petroleum. The oily mixture, indigestible and unabsorbable in the intestines, lubricates the fecal matter and prevents excessive dehydration in the colon. It is also used in many cosmetic preparations and as a solvent of many oil sprays.

Vaseline (petroleum jelly) is a semisolid mixture of paraffins of high carbon content. Although it is an excellent lubricant, Vaseline is also a good solvent and is useful in removing tape residues from skin.

Paraffin wax, a mixture of saturated solid hydrocarbons in the melting point range 45–55°C, is used mainly to make candles, but it is also an effective sealing agent in preserving food.

The chlorinated hydrocarbons are excellent solvents and are usually nonflammable. In fact, carbon tetrachloride is the liquid used in some fire extinguishers.

Chloroform is the most potent inhalation anesthetic known; it is about three times as effective as ether per unit concentration in the blood. Unfortunately, chloroform causes the patient's blood pressure to decrease continuously during an operation and, for this reason, cannot be used more than an hour, even under the most favorable circumstances. Chloroform, somewhat slow in action, takes approximately 4–10 minutes to prepare a patient for the surgical stage. Because of its heart depressant action, possible damage to the liver, and other side effects, chloroform is not used to any appreciable extent in this country. It is used more frequently in Europe and South America.

Ethyl chloride is a flammable and very volatile liquid (b.p. 13°C) that can be used as a local or general anesthetic. It is marketed in a sealed container with a special metallic cap. By releasing the spring on the cap, liquid emerges as a fine spray with some force. When the liquid hits the skin, evaporation occurs immediately, and heat is abstracted from the surrounding area, thereby cooling the skin to a temperature as low as −20°C. At this temperature the tissues are frozen, and the sensation of pain ceases at that localized area. It is used as a local anesthetic for minor surgery. Ethyl chloride can be used also as an inhalant anesthetic, and as such it is used mostly as an inductive agent, because anesthesia occurs in 1–4 minutes. After the patient is "down," the anesthetic is changed to one with a greater safety margin. Much ethyl chloride is produced in this country. The greatest portion is used in the production of tetraethyl lead, which is used as an antiknock in gasoline.

Halothane ($CF_3CHClBr$, fluothane, 2-bromo-2-chloro-1,1,1-trifluoroethane) is a very interesting halogenated paraffin. In the United States, the nonflammable compound is widely used as an inhalation anesthetic. This sweetish, highly volatile liquid is used mostly for operations of short duration. Its greatest advantage is its nonexplosive nature. It is also very easy to administer alone or with other agents, such as nitrous oxide (N_2O). When Halothane is used with care, side reactions are minimal.

Olefins (alkenes)

The hydrocarbons that contain one double bond are called *alkenes* or *olefins*. The general formula is C_nH_{2n}. The ending that denotes the presence of a double bond is -ene.

Nomenclature

In naming alkenes we must locate the double bond. We number the carbon atoms, as is the case with the paraffins. Before the name we give the lower of the two numbers containing the double bond. We number the carbon atoms so that the double bond gets the lowest possible number.

$$H_2C{=}CH_2$$

ethene

$$H_2C{=}CH{-}CH_3$$

propene

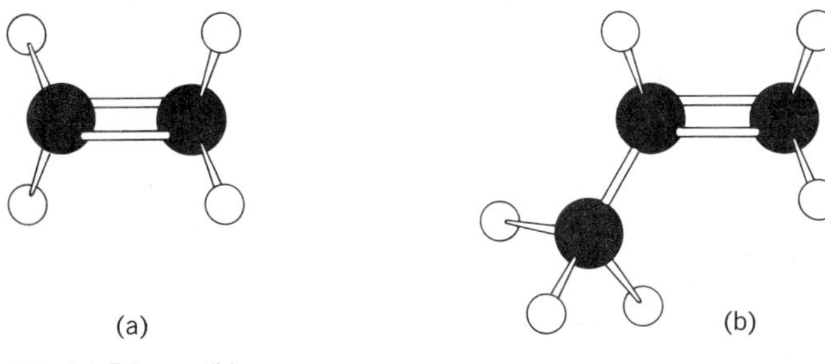

Figure 3-5 (a) Ethene; (b) propene.

We do not need numbers in ethene and propene (see Figure 3-5), because there is no question about the double bond's location. Ethene is commonly called ethylene; propene is usually referred to as propylene.

In C_4H_8 we have

```
   H  H  H  H                    H  H  H  H
   |1 |2 |3 |4                   |1 |2 |3 |4
H—C═C—C—C—H      and      H—C—C═C—C—H
         |  |                    |        |
         H  H                    H        H
   1-butene                     2-butene
```

However, we do *not* have

```
   H  H  H  H
   |1 |2 |3 |
H—C—C—C═C—H
   |  |
   H  H
```

The name 3-butene would be incorrect, because the double bond is not given the lowest possible number.

Another C_4H_8 containing a double bond is

```
   H           H
   |           |
H—C————C═════C—H
   |     |
   H  H—C—H
         |
         H
```

In naming this molecule and similar branched-chain alkenes, we use the following procedure. Choose the longest chain of carbon atoms containing the double bond, and, by numbering the atoms in the chain, locate the double bond and any group or radical attached to the chain. For example,

```
   H           H
   |3     2    |1
H—C————C═════C—H
   |     |
   H  H—C—H
         |
         H
```

1. The longest chain containing the double bond has three carbon atoms; therefore, the molecule is a prop:

    prop-

2. The molecule is an olefin; therefore, the ending is -ene:

    propene

3. The double bond is between the first and second carbon atoms; therefore, we have

    1-propene

4. The methyl group is attached to the second carbon atom; therefore, the complete name is

    2-methyl-1-propene

Some common names follow: 1-butene is called alpha-butylene or α-butylene, 2-butene is called beta-butylene or β-butylene, and 2-methyl-1-propene is called isobutylene.

Some other examples of nomenclature are

2,3-dimethyl-2-butene

2,3,4-trimethyl-2-hexene

3,3-dimethyl-1-butene

2,3,4,6-tetramethyl-1-octene

Table 3-5 Olefin isomers

CARBON CONTENT	ISOMERS[a]
2	1
3	1
4	3
5	5
6	13
7	27

[a] Excluding stereoisomers.

In the olefin series, the number of isomers increases very rapidly as the carbon content increases. See Table 3-5.

Actually, the number of isomers increases faster in the olefin series than in the saturated series, because we can vary the arrangement not only of the carbon atoms, but also of the double bond.

Preparation of Olefins

DEHYDRATION

Olefins can be produced by dehydration of alcohols by means of a dehydrating catalyst (and sometimes heat). In the dehydration reaction, the —OH comes from one carbon atom and the —H comes from the *adjacent* carbon atom.

The general reaction is

$$\begin{array}{c}\begin{array}{ccccc} & H & & H & \\ & | & & | & \\ R- & C & - & C & -H \\ & | & & | & \\ & H & & O-H & \end{array} \\ \text{alcohol}\end{array} \xrightarrow{P_2O_5} \begin{array}{c}\begin{array}{ccccc} & H & & H & \\ & | & & | & \\ R- & C & = & C & -H \end{array} \\ \text{olefin}\end{array} + H_2O$$

Some specific examples are

$$\begin{array}{c}\begin{array}{ccccc} & H & & H & \\ & | & & | & \\ H- & C & - & C & -H \\ & | & & | & \\ & H & & O-H & \end{array} \\ \text{ethyl alcohol}\end{array} \xrightarrow{P_2O_5} \begin{array}{c}\begin{array}{ccccc} & H & & H & \\ & | & & | & \\ H- & C & = & C & -H \end{array} \\ \text{ethylene}\end{array} + H_2O$$

$$\begin{array}{c}\begin{array}{ccccccc} & H & & H & & H & \\ & | & & | & & | & \\ H- & C & - & C & - & C & -H \\ & | & & | & & | & \\ & H & & H & & O-H & \end{array} \\ n\text{-propyl alcohol}\end{array} \xrightarrow{P_2O_5} \begin{array}{c}\begin{array}{ccccccc} & H & & H & & H & \\ & | & & | & & | & \\ H- & C & - & C & = & C & -H \\ & | & & & & & \\ & H & & & & & \end{array} \\ \text{propylene}\end{array} + H_2O$$

$$\begin{array}{c}\begin{array}{ccccccc} & H & & H & & H & \\ & | & & | & & | & \\ H- & C & - & C & - & C & -H \\ & | & & | & & | & \\ & H & & O-H & & H & \end{array} \\ \text{isopropyl alcohol}\end{array} \xrightarrow{P_2O_5} \text{propylene}$$

$$\begin{array}{c}\begin{array}{ccccccc} & & & H & & & \\ & & & | & & & \\ & H & & H-C-H & & H & \\ & | & & | & & | & \\ H- & C & - & C & - & C & -H \\ & | & & | & & | & \\ & H & & O-H & & H & \end{array} \\ tert\text{-butyl alcohol}\end{array} \xrightarrow{P_2O_5} \begin{array}{c}\begin{array}{ccccccc} & & & H & & & \\ & & & | & & & \\ & & & H-C-H & & H & \\ & & & | & & | & \\ H- & C & = & C & - & C & -H \\ & | & & & & | & \\ & H & & & & H & \end{array} \\ \text{2-methyl-1-propene} \\ (isobutylene)\end{array} + H_2O$$

If there is a possibility of splitting out water in more than one way, a mixture of products is usually obtained.

```
     H  H       H  H              H  H  H  H
     |  |       |  |              |  |  |  |
  H—C—C———————C—C—H  --P2O5-->  C—C=C—C—H
     |  |       |  |    −H2O      |        |
     H (O—H    H) H               H        H

      2-butanol                    2-butene
 (secondary hydrogen)
```

but

```
     H  H       H  H              H  H  H  H
     |  |       |  |              |  |  |  |
  H—C—C———————C—C—H  --P2O5-->  C=C—C—C—H
     |  |       |  |    −H2O      |     |  |
    (H  O—H)    H  H              H     H  H

  (primary hydrogen)               1-butene
```

is also possible. We obtain both products, but one usually predominates. If there is a choice of how the reaction will proceed, the following general rule is helpful: The tertiary hydrogen comes off easiest, the secondary hydrogen next, and the primary hydrogen the least readily. Thus, in the above example, 2-butene is produced in the greatest amount.

DEHYDROHALOGENATION

Olefins can also be produced by the elimination of hydrogen halide (HCl, HBr, and HI) from alkyl halides by means of an alcoholic base. This reaction is called *dehydrohalogenation,* and the H— and X— always come from *adjacent* carbon atoms. Some specific examples are

```
     H  H                        H  H
     |  |                        |  |
  H—C—C—H  --alcoholic-->  H—C=C—H + HCl
     |  |        base
    (H  Cl)

  ethyl chloride               ethylene


     H  H  H
     |  |  |
  H—C—C—C—H
     |  |  |
     H (Br H)
                    alcoholic
  isopropyl bromide   base  ↘       H  H  H
                                     |  |  |
                                     C=C—C—H + HBr
     H  H  H                         |     |
     |  |  |        alcoholic  ↗     H     H
  H—C—C—C—H          base
     |  |  |                        propylene
    (Br H) H

  n-propyl bromide
```

```
  I  H  H  H                     H  H  H  H
  |  |  |  |                     |  |  |  |
H—C——C——C——C—H   alcoholic →     C═C——C——C—H + HI
  |  |  |  |        base         |     |  |
  H  H  H  H                     H     H  H
```

n-butyl iodide → 1-butene

Bases such as sodium hydroxide NaOH and potassium hydroxide KOH are soluble in water but are usually insoluble in organic solvents. Alkyl halides are usually soluble in organic solvents but are usually insoluble in water. In this regard, alcohol is very useful in this reaction. The alkyl halides are soluble in alcohol, and the strong bases (particularly KOH) are also reasonably soluble in alcohol; thus, alcohol is a good medium in which both reactants will dissolve so that reaction can proceed. In the splitting off of HX by an alcoholic base, as in the splitting off of HOH by dehydrating agents (preceding section), if there is a possibility of getting more than one olefin, a mixture of products is obtained (same rules as in preceding section).

DEHALOGENATION

Olefins can be produced by the elimination of two halogen atoms (Cl_2 and Br_2) from a 1,2-dihalogen compound by treatment with zinc metal. For example,

```
   H  H                  H  H
   |  |                  |  |
H—C——C—H  + Zn⁰ ⟶  H—C═C—H + ZnBr₂
   |  |
   Br Br
```

1,2-dibromoethane → ethylene

```
   H  H  H  H                    H  H  H  H
   |  |  |  |                    |  |  |  |
H—C——C——C——C—H + Zn⁰ ⟶  H—C——C═C——C—H + ZnCl₂
   |  |  |  |                    |        |
   H  Cl Cl H                    H        H
```

2,3-dichlorobutane → 2-butene

```
   H  H  H  H  H                       H  H  H  H  H
   |  |  |  |  |                       |  |  |  |  |
H—C——C——C——C——C—H + Zn⁰ ⟶  H—C═C——C——C——C—H + ZnCl₂
   |  |  |  |  |                             |  |  |
   Cl Cl H  H  H                             H  H  H
```

1,2-dichloropentane → 1-pentene

Iodine atoms are so large that they cannot readily remain attached to adjacent carbons:

```
 |  |
—C——C—
 |  |
 I  I
```

unstable

If the iodine atoms could momentarily get next to one another, the molecule would decompose to yield an olefin and I_2 (iodine).

$$\left[-\underset{I}{\overset{|}{C}}-\underset{I}{\overset{|}{C}}- \right] \longrightarrow \;>C{=}C< \; + I_2$$

olefin

Commercially, many olefins are produced by a cracking technique.

Reactions

ADDITION

Olefins readily add halogens (chlorine and bromine, but not iodine). For example,

$$H_2C{=}CH_2 + Br_2 \longrightarrow H-\underset{H}{\overset{Br}{C}}-\underset{H}{\overset{Br}{C}}-H$$

ethylene — 1,2-dibromoethane

$$H-\overset{H}{C}{=}\overset{H}{C}-\underset{H}{\overset{H}{C}}-\underset{H}{\overset{H}{C}}-H + Br_2 \longrightarrow H-\underset{Br}{\overset{H}{C}}-\underset{Br}{\overset{H}{C}}-\underset{H}{\overset{H}{C}}-\underset{H}{\overset{H}{C}}-H$$

1-butene — 1,2-dibromobutane

In an addition reaction involving a double bond, as we have stated before, the adding atoms become attached to the two carbon atoms originally involved with the double bond, and the double bond changes to a single bond. This reaction is very sensitive and can be used to detect the presence of unsaturation in a molecule, because bromine is red-brown and the dibromides are colorless. An unknown that decolorizes a bromine solution may contain some unsaturation.

Olefins can be made to add hydrogen halide (HCl and HBr).

$$H-\overset{H}{C}{=}\overset{H}{C}-H + HCl \longrightarrow H-\underset{Cl}{\overset{H}{C}}-\underset{H}{\overset{H}{C}}-H$$

ethylene — ethyl chloride

$$H-\underset{H}{\overset{H}{C}}-\overset{H}{C}{=}\overset{H}{C}-\underset{H}{\overset{H}{C}}-H + HBr \longrightarrow H-\underset{H}{\overset{H}{C}}-\underset{Br}{\overset{H}{C}}-\underset{H}{\overset{H}{C}}-\underset{H}{\overset{H}{C}}-H$$

2-butene — *sec*-butyl bromide

Note that propylene and hydrogen chloride form isopropyl chloride:

```
   H  H  H                    H  H  H
   |  |  |                    |  |  |
H—C—C=C  + HCl  ——→  H—C—C—C—H
   |     |                    |  |  |
   H     H                    H  Cl H
  propylene              isopropyl chloride
```

They do *not* form

```
   H  H  H
   |  |  |
H—C—C—C—Cl
   |  |  |
   H  H  H
 n-propyl chloride
```

This is a manifestation of Markownikoff 's rule, which states: If an unsymmetrical reagent (e.g., HX) is added to an unsaturated linkage, and there are two different ways to do this, then the positive part of the reagent (e.g., H) will tend to appear on the carbon bonded to the more hydrogens, and the negative part (e.g., X) will tend to appear on the carbon bonded to the fewer hydrogens.

Olefins can add sulfuric acid H_2SO_4 or $HOSO_2OH$. For example,

```
H       H                              H  H
 \     /                               |  |
  C=C      + H—OSO₂OH  ——→        H—C—C—H
 /     \                               |  |
H       H                              O  H
                                       |
                                  HO—SO₂
ethylene      sulfuric acid       ethyl sulfuric acid
                                  (ethyl hydrogen sulfate)
```

In the preceding reaction, Markownikoff 's rule is not involved, but the rule does hold in the following:

```
   H  H  H                               H  H      H H
   |  |  |                               |  |      |/
H—C—C=C—H + H—OSO₂OH  ——→  H—C—C———C
   |                                     |  |        \
   H                                     H  OSO₂OH    H
  propylene        sulfuric acid       isopropyl sulfuric acid
                                       (isopropyl hydrogen sulfate)
```

The alkyl sulfuric acids are very important compounds because they can be treated in different ways to make very common and useful chemicals. The alkyl sulfuric acids can be hydrolyzed with water at a certain temperature to produce alcohols and regenerate the sulfuric acid.

```
   H  H                          H  H
   |  |                          |  |
H—C—C—OSO₂OH + H₂O  ——→  H—C—C—OH  +  HOSO₂OH
   |  |                          |  |
   H  H                          H  H
 ethyl sulfuric acid          ethyl alcohol    sulfuric acid
```

$$\begin{array}{ccccc} & H & H & H & H \\ H- & C- & C- & C & \\ & H & OSO_2OH & & H \end{array} + H_2O \longrightarrow \begin{array}{ccccc} & H & H & H & \\ H- & C- & C- & C- & H \\ & H & OH & H & \end{array} + HOSO_2OH$$

isopropyl sulfuric acid — isopropyl alcohol — sulfuric acid

The alkyl sulfuric acids can also react at a certain temperature with another molecule of an alcohol to produce an ether (see Chapter 5 for a discussion of ethers). For example,

$$\begin{array}{cccc} & H & H & \\ H- & C- & C- & H \\ & H & OSO_2OH & \end{array} + \begin{array}{cccc} & H & H & \\ HO- & C- & C- & H \\ & H & H & \end{array} \longrightarrow \begin{array}{cccccccc} & H & H & & H & H & \\ H- & C- & C- & O- & C- & C- & H \\ & H & H & & H & H & \end{array} + H_2SO_4$$

ethyl sulfuric acid — ethyl alcohol — diethyl ether — sulfuric acid

$$\begin{array}{ccccc} & H & H & H & \\ H- & C- & C- & C- & H \\ & H & O & H & \\ & & SO_2OH & & \end{array} + \begin{array}{ccccc} & H & H & H & \\ H- & C- & C- & C- & H \\ & H & OH & H & \end{array} \longrightarrow \begin{array}{cccccccc} & H & H & & H & H & \\ H- & C- & C- & O- & C- & C- & H \\ & H & H-C-H & & H-C-H & H & \\ & & H & & H & & \end{array} + H_2SO_4$$

isopropyl sulfuric acid — isopropyl alcohol — diisopropyl ether — sulfuric acid

HYDROGENATION

We have already discussed the addition of hydrogen to double bonds in the preparation of paraffins. To review, several reactions can be made to go in either direction, depending on the chemical circumstances:

$$CH_3CH_2OH \underset{+H_2O}{\overset{-H_2O}{\rightleftharpoons}} H_2C{=}CH_2$$

$$CH_3CH_2Br \underset{+HBr}{\overset{-HBr}{\rightleftharpoons}} H_2C{=}CH_2$$

$$\underset{\text{Br}\ \ \text{Br}}{CH_2CH_2} \underset{+Br_2}{\overset{-Br_2}{\rightleftharpoons}} H_2C{=}CH_2$$

$$CH_3\underset{\text{OH}}{C}HCH_3 \underset{+H_2O}{\overset{-H_2O}{\rightleftharpoons}} CH_3CH{=}CH_2$$

$$CH_3\underset{\text{Br}}{C}HCH_3 \underset{+HBr}{\overset{-HBr}{\rightleftharpoons}} CH_3CH{=}CH_2$$

$$CH_3\underset{\text{Br}}{C}H\underset{\text{Br}}{C}H_2 \underset{+Br_2}{\overset{-Br_2}{\rightleftharpoons}} CH_3CH{=}CH_2$$

However, if Markownikoff's rule applies, we may obtain isomers other than the one with which we started.

$$CH_3CH_2\underset{\displaystyle OH}{\underset{|}{CH_2}} \xrightarrow{-H_2O} CH_3CH{=}CH_2 \xrightarrow{+H_2O} CH_3\underset{\displaystyle OH}{\underset{|}{C}}HCH_3$$

$$CH_3CH_2\underset{\displaystyle Br}{\underset{|}{CH_2}} \xrightarrow{-HBr} CH_3CH{=}CH_2 \xrightarrow{HBr} CH_3\underset{\displaystyle Br}{\underset{|}{C}}HCH_3$$

OXIDATION

Olefins are so susceptible to oxidation that we can devise very simple tests to detect their presence. Potassium permanganate (which contains manganese in the +7 oxidation state) is deep purple. Manganese in the +2 oxidation state is pale pink or colorless, and manganese in the +4 oxidation state (MnO_2) is a brown precipitate. Olefins will react readily with potassium permanganate to create manganese compounds of lower valence, and this is easily seen by the changes in color. In acid solution, Mn (+7) is reduced to Mn (+2), and in neutral or basic solution, Mn (+7) is reduced to Mn (+4).

In acid solution,

$$5H{-}\overset{\displaystyle H}{\overset{|}{C}}{=}\overset{\displaystyle H}{\overset{|}{C}}{-}H + 2KMnO_4 + 2H_2O + 3H_2SO_4 \longrightarrow 5H{-}\underset{\displaystyle OH}{\underset{|}{\overset{\displaystyle H}{\overset{|}{C}}}}{-}\underset{\displaystyle OH}{\underset{|}{\overset{\displaystyle H}{\overset{|}{C}}}}{-}H + K_2SO_4 + 2MnSO_4$$

ethylene	potassium permanganate (*purple*)	sulfuric acid	glycol (*colorless*)	potassium sulfate	manganese sulfate (*pale pink*)

In neutral or basic solution,

$$3\underset{\displaystyle H}{\underset{|}{\overset{\displaystyle H}{\overset{|}{C}}}}{=}\overset{\displaystyle H}{\overset{|}{C}}{-}H + 2KMnO_4 + 4H_2O \longrightarrow 3H{-}\underset{\displaystyle OH}{\underset{|}{\overset{\displaystyle H}{\overset{|}{C}}}}{-}\underset{\displaystyle OH}{\underset{|}{\overset{\displaystyle H}{\overset{|}{C}}}}{-}H + 2KOH + 2MnO_2$$

ethylene	potassium permanganate (*purple*)	glycol	potassium hydroxide	manganese dioxide (*brown, insoluble*)

Since the glycols are themselves easily susceptible to oxidation by permanganate, this is not a particularly good way to prepare glycols.

Ozone is a very reactive chemical and will readily react with unsaturated linkages (such as a double bond). The reaction with ozone ultimately results in the destruction of the double bond, breaking the molecule into fragments.

POLYMERIZATION OF THE DOUBLE BOND

As indicated before, the double bond is quite reactive and can undergo many chemical reactions. Note that a double bond can react with itself. This type of reaction is referred to as *polymerization*.

It is convenient to introduce two radicals, each containing a double bond:

$CH_2{=}CH{-}$ vinyl radical

$CH_2{=}CHCH_2{-}$ allyl radical

When a double bond polymerizes, the process is called double bond-type polymerization, ethylene-type polymerization, or vinyl-type polymerization (all these expressions may be used).

Customarily, an unreacted molecule containing a double bond is called a *monomer* (one unit or one measure).

If two single units combine, the product is a *dimer* (two units or two measures). Three units would be a *trimer,* and a *polymer* contains many units.

When a double bond polymerizes, it becomes a single bond, and the two carbon atoms involved in the organic double bond become attached to other molecules. For example,

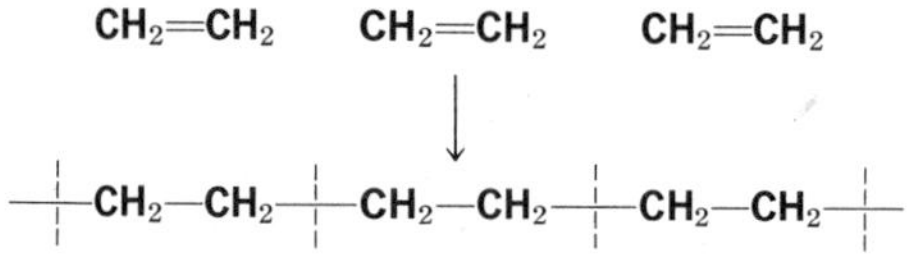

$$CH_2{=}CH_2 \quad CH_2{=}CH_2 \quad CH_2{=}CH_2$$
$$\downarrow$$
$$-|-CH_2-CH_2-|-CH_2-CH_2-|-CH_2-CH_2-|-$$

polyethylene

It is customary to represent this as

$$CH_2{=}CH_2 \longrightarrow (CH_2-CH_2)_x$$

where x may be in the thousands.

The vinyl-type plastics may be prepared by polymerizing vinyl compounds, that is, $CH_2{=}CHCl$ vinyl chloride:

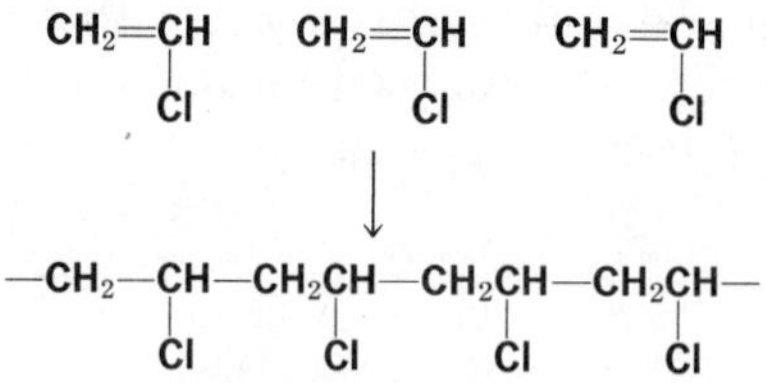

$$CH_2{=}CHCl \quad CH_2{=}CHCl \quad CH_2{=}CHCl$$
$$\downarrow$$
$$-CH_2-CH(Cl)-CH_2CH(Cl)-CH_2CH(Cl)-CH_2CH(Cl)-$$

polyvinyl chloride

To describe the polymer, we use the prefix poly- in front of the name of the monomer. For example,

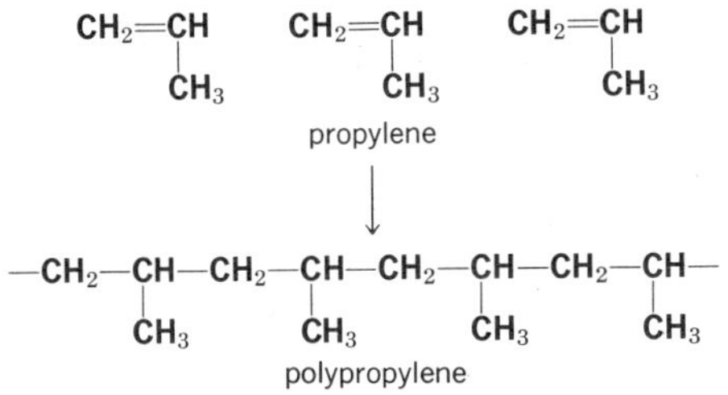

$$CH_2{=}\underset{\displaystyle CH_3}{\underset{|}{CH}} \quad CH_2{=}\underset{\displaystyle CH_3}{\underset{|}{CH}} \quad CH_2{=}\underset{\displaystyle CH_3}{\underset{|}{CH}}$$

propylene

$$\downarrow$$

$$-CH_2-\underset{\displaystyle CH_3}{\underset{|}{CH}}-CH_2-\underset{\displaystyle CH_3}{\underset{|}{CH}}-CH_2-\underset{\displaystyle CH_3}{\underset{|}{CH}}-CH_2-\underset{\displaystyle CH_3}{\underset{|}{CH}}-$$

polypropylene

Polyethylene, polypropylene, and the vinyl polymers are items of great industrial importance. They are used to fabricate so many common apparel items, household goods, automobile parts, and airplane parts, etc., that young people accept them as normal materials without realizing, perhaps, that these synthetics are substitutes for natural things such as wood, metal, silk, and cotton.

The polymer of tetrafluoroethylene has many interesting properties.

$$CF_2{=}CF_2 \quad CF_2{=}CF_2 \quad CF_2{=}CF_2 \quad CF_2{=}CF_2$$

$$\downarrow \text{polymerize}$$

$$-CF_2-CF_2-CF_2-CF_2-CF_2-CF_2-CF_2-CF_2-$$

polytetrafluoroethylene
(*Teflon*)

Polytetrafluoroethylene is very valuable because of its unusual properties. Teflon has no hydrogens, and the many carbon-fluorine bonds are quite stable. Thus, Teflon is remarkably stable, inert, chemically resistant, and an excellent electrical insulator that will not fume.

Uses

Ethylene is a flammable anesthetic gas boiling at $-104°C$. With certain mixtures of oxygen, ethylene can be quite explosive; this is one of the great dangers in its use. Its decided nontoxicity for tissues, even in high concentration, is its greatest advantage. Ethylene is a rapid, efficient anesthetic that brings the patient to the surgical plane in 2–4 minutes; thus, it is used mostly as an inductive agent.

Ethylene is used by citrus fruit growers to hasten the ripening of fruit. When a green fruit is exposed to ethylene gas, its color changes to yellow or orange.

Propylene has been reported to be twice as effective as ethylene as an anesthetic gas. Induction (2 minutes) and recovery are rapid, and postoperative nausea is at a minimum. Propylene, like ethylene, forms explosive mixtures with oxygen.

Although the three isomeric butenes have been reported to be remarkably potent anesthetics, they are not used much, because the patient goes through a very pronounced excitement stage.

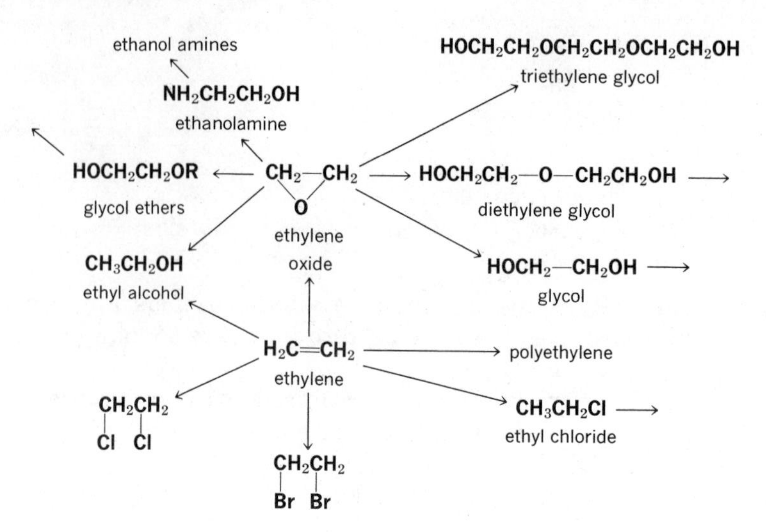

Figure 3-6 Simple flow chart of important compounds made from ethylene.

Because they are so reactive, the olefins can be used to make many other compounds. Thus, their production is an important backbone of the chemical industry and is vitally essential to the economy of the country. Ethylene and propylene production probably exceeds 10 billion pounds a year.

An important product produced by the reaction of ethylene and oxygen under special conditions is ethylene oxide.

$$CH_2{=}CH_2 + O_2 \xrightarrow[\text{silver metal catalyst}]{\text{finely powdered}} \underset{\text{O}}{CH_2{-}CH_2}$$

ethylene oxide
(gas, b.p. 10.7°C)

The oxidation reaction is carried out at 150–500°C, at atmospheric or subatmospheric pressure, with *nonexplosive* mixtures of ethylene, oxygen, and diluent. The reaction liberates much heat, most of which arises from the *formation of* CO_2 *as a byproduct.* An important step in the process is to cool efficiently the gaseous products formed. Ethylene oxide is a valuable intermediate in the chemical industry. Figure 3-6 illustrates some of the products produced from ethylene.

These simple compounds are used, in turn, to make many other compounds.

Trichloroethylene is an excellent nonflammable solvent that finds extensive use in the dry-cleaning industry. Although it possesses certain anesthetic properties, trichloroethylene has limited use as an anesthetic in this country.

trichloroethylene
(*trichloroethene*)

It is reported to be nonexplosive, relatively nontoxic, and nonnauseating, and it contributes to an uneventful recovery. It is used as an adjunct to nitrous oxide-oxygen therapy. Trichloroethylene must be used with caution because, if it is used in a closed system and passed over a strong base, the possibility of forming the toxic dichloroacetylene exists.

$$\mathrm{ClHC{=}CCl_2} \xrightarrow[-\mathrm{HCl}]{\text{strong base}} \mathrm{Cl{-}C{\equiv}C{-}Cl}$$

dichloroacetylene

Trichloroethylene has some therapeutic value in treatment of trigeminal neuralgia.

Diolefins

Diolefins are compounds containing two double bonds. Since a compound with one double bond has the ending -ene, a compound with two double bonds has the ending -diene. Dienes can be conjugated or nonconjugated. In conjugated dienes, the two double bonds are separated by an intervening single bond. Any other case is nonconjugated. The conjugated members are important in nature because of their wide occurrence in living systems.

$\mathrm{H{-}CH{=}CH{-}CH{=}CH{-}H}$

conjugated

$\mathrm{H_3C{-}CH{=}C{=}CH_2}$ $\quad$ $\mathrm{HC{=}CH{-}CH_2{-}CH{=}CH{-}H}$

nonconjugated

The rules for naming the diolefins are the same as those for naming the olefins, except that we must indicate the positions of two double bonds.

$\mathrm{H{-}\overset{1}{C}H{=}\overset{2}{C}H{-}\overset{3}{C}H{=}\overset{4}{C}H{-}H}$

1,3-butadiene

$\mathrm{H{-}\overset{1}{C}H{=}\overset{2}{C}{=}\overset{3}{C}H{-}\overset{4}{C}H_2{-}H}$

1,2-butadiene

$\mathrm{H{-}\overset{1}{C}H{=}\overset{2}{C}H{-}\overset{3}{C}H_2{-}\overset{4}{C}H{=}\overset{5}{C}H{-}H}$

1,4-pentadiene

An important diolefin (naturally occurring) is isoprene:

$\mathrm{H{-}\overset{1}{C}H{=}\overset{2}{C}(CH_3){-}\overset{3}{C}H{=}\overset{4}{C}H{-}H}$

isoprene
(*2-methyl-1,3-butadiene*)

POLYENES

Compounds with three or more double bonds are possible. The molecule with three double bonds would be a triene, with four double bonds would be a tetraene, with five double bonds would be a pentaene, etc.

Some Common Diolefins

CRUDE RUBBER

One of the most important chemical commodities is rubber. Although rubber is found in many plants, about 95% of it is obtained from the plant *Hevea brasiliensis.* When an incision is made in the bark of this plant, a milky fluid called latex oozes out. This is a dispersion of rubber particles in water. The addition of acid coagulates the rubber, and this "curdled" sticky material is the crude rubber shipped to this country from tropical areas. Crude rubber contains the rubber hydrocarbon (90–95%), fatty acids (3%), and small amounts of sugar, resins, and nitrogen-containing substances of protein character.

Crude rubber is sticky, soft, and gummy and has many undesirable properties. It will not wear well, does not lend itself easily to fabrication, and does not last long. Charles Goodyear discovered that heating crude rubber with sulfur produces a product with superior lasting and wearing qualities. This process is known as vulcanization.

Chemical investigation has shown that rubber is a large molecule with a molecular weight of approximately 300,000; its empirical formula is $(C_5H_8)_n$, where n = approximately 4,500. This means that approximately 4,500 molecules of formula C_5H_8 are attached to one another to form this large molecule. This unit has been identified as the conjugated diolefin, isoprene.

```
    H     H  H
    |     |  |
H—C=C—C=C—H
       |
    H—C—H
       |
       H
```

isoprene
(2-methyl-1,3-butadiene)

It appears that isoprene, an unstable liquid, polymerizes (reacts with itself many times) to produce natural rubber. We shall illustrate this reaction by using three isoprene molecules. Note that we are indicating only a small fragment of the molecule. (Only carbon skeletons are shown.)

```
+  C=C—C=C  +  C=C—C=C  +  C=C—C=C  +
     |            |            |
     C            C            C
                  ↓
+ [—C—C=C—C—] + [—C—C=C—C—] + [—C—C=C—C—] +
      |              |              |
      C              C              C
                  ↓
··· —C—C=C—C—C—C=C—C—C—C=C—C— ···
       |         |         |
       C         C         C
```

natural rubber

The bracketed formulas are used to show how the double bonds go to the middle of the isoprene molecule, leaving the ends free to react with other free ends of isoprene molecules.

From the above formula, we see that natural rubber still contains many double bonds and has many undesirable properties. The double bonds, sensitive to oxidation, will react with the oxygen of the air to change the natural rubber to a useless substance. Rubber owes its elasticity to the fact that it is coiled, like a huge spring, and not a straight molecule as indicated above. Pulling the rubber tends to uncoil the spring, causing stretching, and releasing the rubber causes it to snap back to the original preferred coil position. In the vulcanization process, which is still not clearly understood, sulfur atoms become attached to the molecule in cross-linking positions, thereby decreasing the sensitivity of the molecule and producing a material that is stable and more elastic and that possesses good wearing qualities.

SYNTHETIC RUBBER

Because isoprene could polymerize to give natural rubber, logically other conjugated diolefins could also be used to produce synthetic rubbers. Because isoprene is not easily made, and we cannot readily duplicate nature's polymerization process, scientists have devoted much time trying to imitate as closely as possible nature's handiwork. Periods of war often place special demands on certain countries. During World War I, for example, Germany, cut off from its supply of natural rubber, was forced to make rubber synthetically and thus polymerized 2,3-dimethyl-1,3-butadiene

```
        H
        |
      H—C—H  H
        |    |
   H—C=C—C=C—H
     |    |
     H  H—C—H
          |
          H
```

2,3-dimethyl-1,3-butadiene

to make methyl rubber. This was not very satisfactory, but it helped relieve an acute shortage. In the United States in 1931, chloroprene,

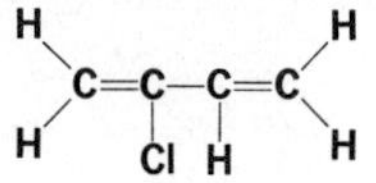

```
H               H
 \             /
  C=C——C=C
 /  |    |   \
H   Cl   H    H
```

chloroprene

produced from acetylene, was polymerized to produce Neoprene.

Butadiene rubbers became important about 1930. Germany was making many synthetic rubbers by polymerizing butadiene using sodium (Buna rubbers),

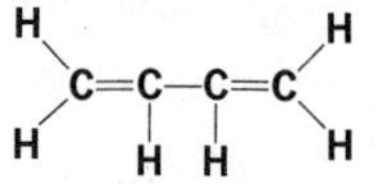

```
H               H
 \             /
  C=C——C=C
 /  |    |   \
H   H    H    H
```

1,3-butadiene

but these rubbers had a limited usefulness.

Later work showed that when two different polymerizable substances are polymerized together (copolymerization), a material with very interesting properties is obtained. Such an important copolymer is GRS or Buna-S. Butadiene (75%) and styrene (25%) copolymerize to form GRS, an excellent substitute for tires and mechanical rubber goods.

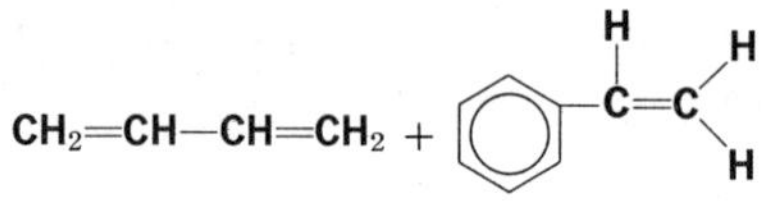

$CH_2{=}CH{-}CH{=}CH_2$ + $C_6H_5{-}CH{=}CH_2$

butadiene (*3 parts*)

styrene (C_8H_8) (*one part*)

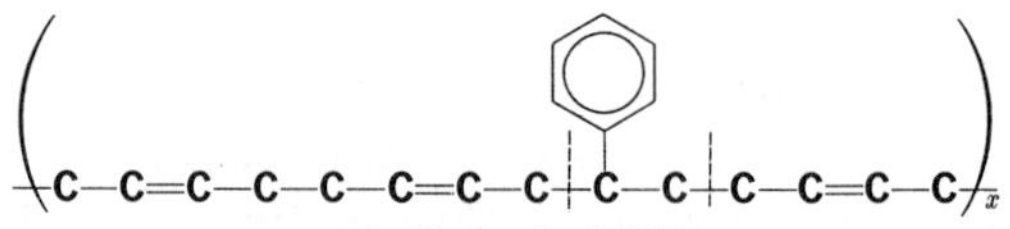

$\left({-}C{-}C{=}C{-}C{-}C{-}C{=}C{-}C{-}C(C_6H_5){-}C{-}C{-}C{=}C{-}C{-} \right)_x$

repeating unit of GRS

During World War II, the United States produced enough GRS to supply its mechanized armed forces and civilian population. The big bottleneck was the supply of styrene and butadiene. The problem was solved by producing the butadiene from ethyl alcohol and the styrene from benzene and ethylene. Thus, by using very cheap and easily available compounds, we solved a problem of great need. The synthetic rubber business has survived the war, and synthetic rubber is still produced today.

The diolefins are usually more potent anesthetics than the corresponding olefin with the same number of carbon atoms, but the diolefin's decided toxicity, flammability, and instability preclude its use in medicine.

Acetylenes

Acetylenes are compounds containing a triple bond (see Figure 3-7). The name is derived from the simplest member of the series, acetylene. The general formula is C_nH_{2n-2}. The proper ending for an acetylene-type compound is -yne, and the nomenclature rules used for olefins apply.

```
                          H
                          |
H—C≡C—H                H—C—C≡C—H
                          |
                          H
```

acetylene (C_2H_2)
(ethyne)

propyne (C_3H_4)

The two isomers of the formula C_4H_6 are

```
  H H                   H       H
  | |                   |       |
H—C—C—C≡C—H           H—C—C≡C—C—H
  | |                   |       |
  H H                   H       H
  1-butyne               2-butyne
```

The three isomers of the formula C_5H_8 are

```
  H H H                 H H       H           H     H
  | | |                 | |       |           |     |
H—C—C—C—C≡C—H         H—C—C—C≡C—C—H         H—C-----C—C≡C—H
  | | |                 | |       |           |     |
  H H H                 H H       H           H   H—C—H
                                                    |
                                                    H
   1-pentyne              2-pentyne          3-methyl-1-butyne
```

The seven isomers of the formula C_6H_{10} (only carbon skeletons are used) are

```
C—C—C—C—C≡C          C—C—C—C≡C—C          C—C—C≡C—C—C
  1-hexyne              2-hexyne             3-hexyne

C—C—C—C≡C            C—C—C—C≡C            C—C—C≡C—C
    |                  |                    |
    C                  C                    C
3-methyl-1-pentyne   4-methyl-1-pentyne   4-methyl-2-pentyne

    C
    |
  C—C—C≡C
    |
    C
3,3-dimethyl-1-butyne
```

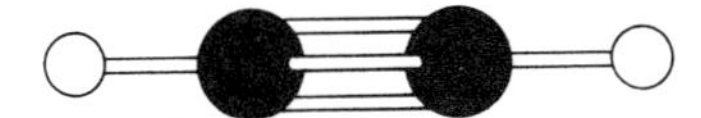

Figure 3-7 Acetylene.

Table 3-6 Isomers[a]

NO. OF CARBONS	PARAFFIN ISOMERS	OLEFIN ISOMERS	ACETYLENE ISOMERS
1	1	0	0
2	1	1	1
3	1	1	1
4	2	3	2
5	3	5	3
6	5	13	7
7	9	27	14
8	18	68	32

[a] Excluding stereoisomers.

Table 3-6 compares the number of isomers in the three series.

From this table we see that the acetylene isomers tend to be more numerous than the paraffin isomers but less numerous than the olefin isomers.

It is possible for a compound to have two triple bonds. Such a compound would be a diyne (two triple bonds). For example,

$$H{-}C{\equiv}C{-}C{\equiv}C{-}H$$

1,3-butadiyne

Another example is

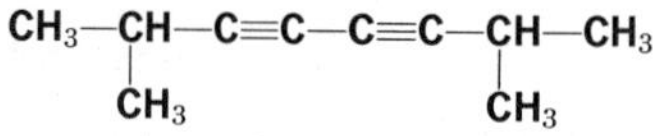

$$CH_3{-}\underset{\displaystyle CH_3}{\underset{|}{CH}}{-}C{\equiv}C{-}C{\equiv}C{-}\underset{\displaystyle CH_3}{\underset{|}{CH}}{-}CH_3$$

2,7-dimethyl-3,5-octadiyne

It is also possible to have a double and triple bond in the same molecule. In naming these compounds, the triple bond gets preference for the lowest number. For example,

$$\overset{6}{CH_3}{-}\overset{5}{CH}{=}\overset{4}{CH}{-}\overset{3}{CH_2}{-}\overset{2}{C}{\equiv}\overset{1}{C}{-}H$$

4-hexene-1-yne

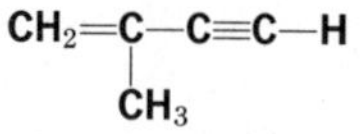

$$CH_2{=}\underset{\displaystyle CH_3}{\underset{|}{C}}{-}C{\equiv}C{-}H$$

3-methyl-3-butene-1-yne

Preparation

Acetylene itself is prepared in a special manner. Limestone ($CaCO_3$) is heated to a high temperature and lime (CaO) is formed.

$$CaCO_3 \xrightarrow{900°C} CaO + CO_2\uparrow$$

When this lime is heated with carbon at an exceedingly high temperature, calcium carbide CaC_2 is formed.

$$CaO + 3C \xrightarrow{3,000°C} CaC_2 + CO\uparrow$$

When calcium carbide is placed in water, acetylene and lime water are formed.

$$CaC_2 + 2H_2O \longrightarrow \underset{\substack{\text{calcium hydroxide} \\ (\textit{lime water})}}{Ca(OH)_2} + H{-}C{\equiv}C{-}H\uparrow$$

The acetylene is an insoluble gas that bubbles out of the reaction mixture. The calcium hydroxide is a reasonably strong base and can be easily detected by means of litmus paper. Acetylene has a distinctive odor, and it burns in the air with a sooty flame. The acetylene synthesis is particularly attractive because the ingredients ($CaCO_3$, C, and H_2O) are readily available throughout the world.

Acetylene is an acidic substance, and one or both hydrogens can be replaced by metals. In fact, any hydrogen attached to a carbon atom involved in a triple bond is acidic.

$$(H){-}C{\equiv}C{-}(H)$$
acidic

$$R{-}C{\equiv}C{-}(H) \quad \text{acidic}$$

If acetylene gas is passed into a solution of sodamide in liquid ammonia, sodium acetylide is formed.

$$H{-}C{\equiv}C{-}H + \underset{\text{sodamide}}{NaNH_2} \longrightarrow \underset{\text{sodium acetylide}}{H{-}C{\equiv}C{-}Na} + NH_3$$

If this acetylide is allowed to react with alkyl halides (RX), sodium halide is formed, and a substituted acetylene is produced.

$$H{-}C{\equiv}C{-}Na + RX \longrightarrow NaX + H{-}C{\equiv}C{-}R$$

that is,

$$\underset{\text{sodium acetylide}}{H{-}C{\equiv}C{-}Na} + \underset{\text{ethyl bromide}}{Br{-}CH_2{-}CH_3} \longrightarrow \underset{\text{1-butyne}}{H{-}C{\equiv}C{-}CH_2{-}CH_3} + NaBr$$

$$\underset{n\text{-octyl bromide}}{n\text{-}C_8H_{17}Br} + HC{\equiv}C{-}Na \longrightarrow \underset{\text{1-decyne}}{H{-}C{\equiv}C{-}C_8H_{17}} + NaBr$$

This substituted acetylene still has one acidic hydrogen that can be replaced by sodium:

$$R{-}C{\equiv}C{-}H + NaNH_2 \longrightarrow R{-}C{\equiv}C{-}Na + NH_3$$

that is,

$$CH_3{-}CH_2C{\equiv}C{-}H + NaNH_2 \longrightarrow CH_3{-}CH_2C{\equiv}C{-}Na + NH_3$$

or

$$H{-}C{\equiv}C{-}C_8H_{17} + NaNH_2 \longrightarrow NaC{\equiv}C{-}C_8H_{17} + NH_3$$

The sodium salts of the substituted acetylides can also react with alkyl halides (RX) to form a salt and disubstituted acetylenes:

$$R{-}C{\equiv}C{-}Na + R'X \longrightarrow R{-}C{\equiv}C{-}R' + NaX$$

$$\underset{\text{sodium salt of 1-butyne}}{CH_3{-}CH_2{-}C{\equiv}C{-}Na} + CH_3Br \longrightarrow \underset{\text{2-pentyne}}{CH_3{-}CH_2{-}C{\equiv}C{-}CH_3} + NaBr$$

$$\underset{\text{sodium salt of 1-decyne}}{Na{-}C{\equiv}C{-}C_8H_{17}} + \underset{\text{isopropyl iodide}}{CH_3{-}\underset{\displaystyle CH_3}{\underset{|}{CH}}{-}I} \longrightarrow NaI + \underset{\text{2-methyl-3-dodecyne}}{CH_3{-}\underset{\displaystyle CH_3}{\underset{|}{CH}}{-}C{\equiv}C{-}C_8H_{17}}$$

By the techniques shown above, almost every type of acetylene compound can be conveniently prepared. Since the triple bond can be readily reduced to the double bond (see following section), and since the double bond has been shown to be exceedingly useful, the acetylene compounds are among the most versatile of all chemistry. Compounds in which a metal such as sodium is attached to a carbon atom are called *organometallics*. The sodium carbon bond is quite electrochemical, or ionic, in nature.

Reactions

ADDITION OF HYDROGEN

Acetylene compounds can be reduced selectively with one mole of hydrogen under carefully controlled conditions to produce olefins, or acetylenes can be made to react with two moles of hydrogen to produce paraffins.

$$\underset{\text{propyne}}{CH_3{-}C{\equiv}C{-}H} + H_2 \xrightarrow[\text{conditions}]{\text{controlled}} \underset{\text{propylene}}{CH_3{-}CH{=}CH_2}$$

or

$$\underset{\text{propyne}}{CH_3{-}C{\equiv}C{-}H} + 2H_2 \xrightarrow{\text{Pt}} \underset{\text{propane}}{CH_3{-}CH_2{-}CH_3}$$

By using regular hydrogenation catalysts like Pt, the triple bond is reduced to the single bond. However, if catalytic conditions are such that the reduction of the double bond to the single bond is prevented, the triple bond is reduced to the double bond and the reaction stops.

ADDITION OF HALOGEN

Two moles of halogen can be added to the triple bond to produce a tetrasubstituted paraffin. Very probably the reaction proceeds in steps:

$$H{-}C{\equiv}C{-}H + Br_2 \longrightarrow \left[H{-}\underset{Br}{\underset{|}{C}}{=}\underset{Br}{\underset{|}{C}}{-}H \right]$$

nonisolable intermediate

$$\left[H{-}\underset{Br}{\underset{|}{C}}{=}\underset{Br}{\underset{|}{C}}{-}H + Br_2 \right] \longrightarrow H{-}\overset{Br}{\overset{|}{\underset{Br}{\underset{|}{C}}}}{-}\overset{Br}{\overset{|}{\underset{Br}{\underset{|}{C}}}}{-}H$$

1,1,2,2-tetrabromoethane

or, as another example,

$$\underset{\text{2-pentyne}}{CH_3{-}CH_2{-}C{\equiv}C{-}CH_3} + 2Br_2 \longrightarrow \underset{\text{2,2,3,3-tetrabromopentane}}{CH_3{-}CH_2{-}CBr_2{-}CBr_2{-}CH_3}$$

We can consider the reaction of bromine with a triple bond a test for unsaturation, because the tetrabromo compounds are colorless, and the original bromine solution is red-brown.

ADDITION OF HX

Acetylenes add two moles of HX (both obey Markownikoff's rule):

$$CH{\equiv}CH + 2HX \longrightarrow CH_3{-}CHX_2$$

$$\underset{\text{propyne}}{CH_3{-}C{\equiv}C{-}H} + 2HCl \longrightarrow \underset{\text{2,2-dichloropropane}}{CH_3{-}\overset{Cl}{\overset{|}{\underset{Cl}{\underset{|}{C}}}}{-}CH_3}$$

OXIDATION OF THE TRIPLE BOND

The triple bond, similar to the double bond, is readily oxidized. For example,

$$\underset{\text{acetylene}}{3HC{\equiv}CH} + \underset{\substack{\text{potassium}\\\text{permanganate}\\(\textit{purple})}}{4KMnO_4} + 2H_2O \longrightarrow \underset{(\textit{brown})}{4MnO_2} + 4KOH + \underset{\text{glyoxal}}{3H{-}\overset{O}{\overset{\|}{C}}{-}\overset{O}{\overset{\|}{C}}{-}H}$$

or

$$3CH_3{-}C{\equiv}C{-}H + 4KMnO_4 + 2H_2O \longrightarrow 4MnO_2 + 4KOH + \underset{\substack{\text{methylglyoxal}\\(\textit{pyruvaldehyde})}}{3CH_3{-}\overset{O}{\overset{\|}{C}}{-}\overset{O}{\overset{\|}{C}}{-}H}$$

Glyoxal and compounds similar to glyoxal under these conditions are somewhat unstable and are probably further oxidized to organic acids or even ultimately to CO_2 and H_2O.

Uses

Acetylene is a gas (b.p. $-83.4°C$) that is both flammable and explosive. Commercial acetylene contains impurities and possesses a distinctive odor. Even purified acetylene has a strong odor. Acetylene exhibits anesthetic properties, but it is more toxic and less efficient than ethylene and has never been used much in this country.

Acetylene burns with a highly luminous flame and can be used conveniently for illumination purposes. Burning acetylene in oxygen is a highly exothermic reaction (i.e., heat-liberating reaction); the oxyacetylene torch, for example, reaches temperatures of 2,700°C and is useful for cutting and welding metals.

Acetylene is such a remarkably reactive substance that almost every simple organic compound can be prepared from it. During World War II, Germany became chemically independent of the rest of the world by preparing large quantities of all the standard organic chemicals from acetylene. For example, it can be used to prepare ethyl alcohol, ethyl chloride, acetaldehyde, acetic acid, butadiene, and many other important starting compounds. Acetone can be prepared from methyl acetylene (propyne).

Cycloparaffins (alicycles)

Cycloparaffins have the carbon atoms in a ring. In naming these compounds, we use the prefix cyclo- to denote the cyclic structure and also the proper prefix to denote the number of carbon atoms, followed by the proper ending (e.g., -ane if it is saturated). The general formula for a cyclic saturated hydrocarbon is C_nH_{2n}. Some saturated cycloparaffins are

CH_2
$CH_2—CH_2$
cyclopropane

$CH_2—CH_2$
$CH_2—CH_2$
cyclobutane

CH_2
CH_2 CH_2
$CH_2—CH_2$
cyclopentane

CH_2
CH_2 CH_2
CH_2 CH_2
CH_2
cyclohexane

CH_2
$CH_2—CH—CH_3$
methylcyclopropane

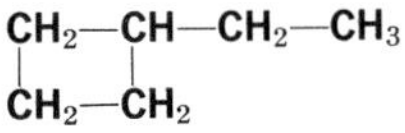

$$\begin{array}{l} CH_2-CH-CH_2-CH_3 \\ | \quad\quad\;\; | \\ CH_2-CH_2 \end{array}$$

ethylcyclobutane

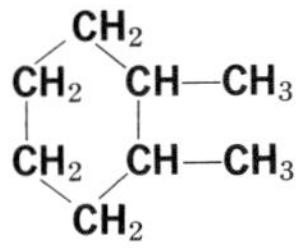

$$\begin{array}{c} CH_2 \\ CH_2 \quad CH-CH_3 \\ | \quad\quad\; | \\ CH_2 \quad CH-CH_3 \\ CH_2 \end{array}$$

1,2-dimethylcyclohexane

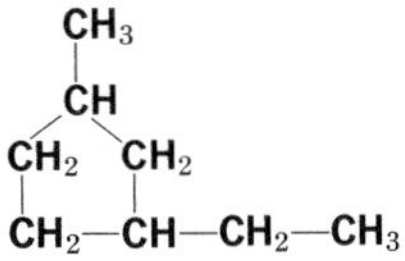

$$\begin{array}{l} CH_3 \\ | \\ CH \\ CH_2 \quad CH_2 \\ | \quad\quad\; | \\ CH_2-CH-CH_2-CH_3 \end{array}$$

1-methyl-3-ethylcyclopentane

Some unsaturated cycloparaffins are

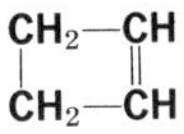

$$\begin{array}{l} CH_2-CH \\ | \quad\quad\; \| \\ CH_2-CH \end{array}$$

cyclobutene

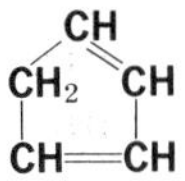

$$\begin{array}{c} CH \\ CH_2 \quad CH \\ | \quad\quad | \\ CH=CH \end{array}$$

1,3-cyclopentadiene

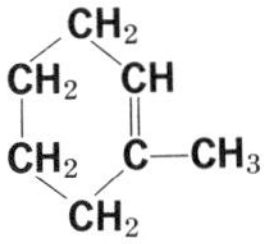

$$\begin{array}{c} CH_2 \\ CH_2 \quad CH \\ | \quad\quad \| \\ CH_2 \quad C-CH_3 \\ CH_2 \end{array}$$

1-methyl-1-cyclohexene

$$\begin{array}{c} CH_2-C\equiv C-CH_2 \\ (CH_2)_8 \end{array}$$

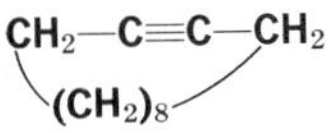

cyclododecyne

The cyclododecyne contains twelve carbon atoms in a ring, which has one triple bond. We refer to such a drawing as the condensed way of drawing organic structures. It is obviously a chemical shorthand to write $-(CH_2)_8-$ instead of drawing all eight CH_2's in a row.

Preparation

Many cycloparaffins occur as such in petroleum. Cyclopentane and cyclohexane derivatives may usually be identified from this natural source, but they are not easily isolated in a very pure state.

Many special methods and techniques are used to prepare alicycles, and most of these methods are beyond the scope of this book.

Cyclopropane itself is prepared by the reaction of zinc dust on 1,3-dichloropropane. The reaction is carried out in aqueous alcohol containing sodium iodide and sodium carbonate.

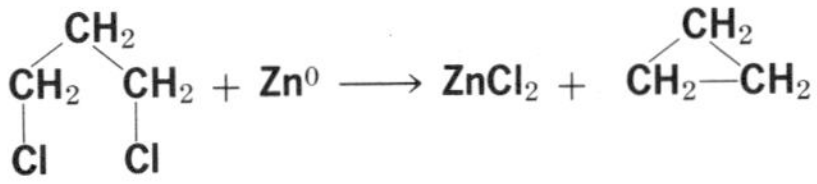

$$\begin{array}{c} CH_2 \\ CH_2 \quad CH_2 \\ | \quad\quad\; | \\ Cl \quad\quad Cl \end{array} + Zn^0 \longrightarrow ZnCl_2 + \begin{array}{c} CH_2 \\ CH_2-CH_2 \end{array}$$

cyclopropane

The cyclopropanes and cyclobutanes have somewhat unusual properties due to the ring strain. The usual angle of the carbon-carbon bond is about 110°.

CH_2
60°
CH_2—CH_2
cyclopropane

CH_2—CH_2
90°
CH_2—CH_2

From the above formulas, it can be seen that the carbon-carbon angles have been shortened and strained. For this reason, the chemistry of cyclobutane and cyclopropane compounds (the chemistry of small rings) is distinctive and is often related to the strain in the molecules.

In cyclopentane compounds, the carbon-carbon angle is 108°, which is so close to the normal angle that it presents no obvious strain. The cyclohexane and higher rings present no strain because the rings are not planar and the atoms can adjust to relieve any strain. Two possible nonplanar structures (see Figure 3-8) of cyclohexane are

C
C—C
C—C
C
chair form

C C
C—C
C—C
boat form

Uses

Cyclopropane is important because it is the most potent anesthetic gas. It is heavier than air, is sweetish in odor, and has a boiling point of −33°C. In anesthetic conditions it is odorless. It is conveniently stored in metallic cylinders; care must be exercised in handling the gas, because it

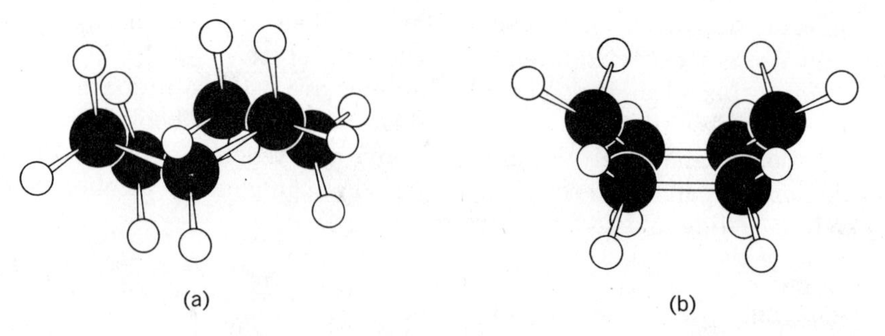

Figure 3-8 Chair (a) and boat (b) forms of cyclohexane.

is both flammable and explosive. Cyclopropane is enjoying increasing popularity in this country because of its wide margin of safety. When morphine is given as a preliminary medication, a concentration of 13% of cyclopropane in the lungs is needed to produce anesthesia, whereas 43% is the toxic concentration.

Cyclobutane is an exceedingly difficult and expensive substance to obtain. Preliminary tests have shown that cyclobutane may be superior to cyclopropane in anesthetic properties.

Many substituted cyclopentanes and cyclohexanes occur in petroleum and possess good gasoline properties.

The terpenes are a large group of naturally occurring compounds composed of multiple units of isoprene C_5H_8. A regular terpene contains two isoprene units ($C_{10}H_{16}$). Some oxygenated terpenes are called camphors ($C_{10}H_{16}O$). The C_{15} compounds (three units of isoprene) are called sesquiterpenes, the C_{20} compounds (four units of isoprene) are called diterpenes, and the C_{30} compounds (six units of isoprene) are called triterpenes. The various terpene structures may exist in open-chain forms or as alicyclic structures.

Many terpenes contain the cyclopropane, cyclobutane, and cyclopentane rings; the cyclohexane ring is also very common. *Camphane* is a molecule containing a cyclohexane ring and two cyclopentane rings, fused together in an interesting fashion. Camphane is the parent hydrocarbon of camphor.

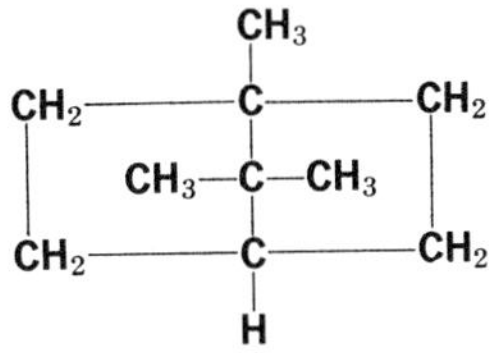

camphane　　or　　camphane

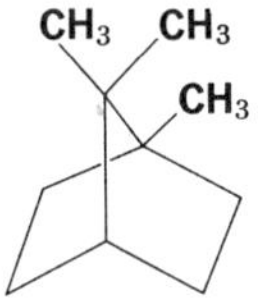

Menthane is the parent hydrocarbon of menthol and contains the cyclohexane ring.

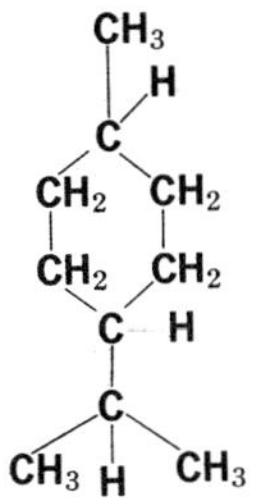

menthane　　or　　menthane

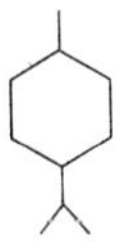

α-Thujene and *d-sabinene* are found in natural oils. They contain the cyclopropane ring (only carbon skeletons are shown).

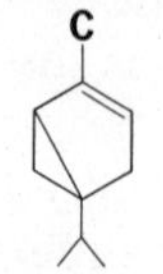

α-thujene 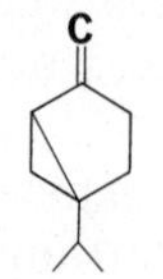 d-sabinene

α-Pinene, widely distributed in nature and found in the oils of the *coniferae,* is the chief constituent of the oil of turpentine. α-pinene contains the cyclobutane ring (only the carbon skeleton is shown).

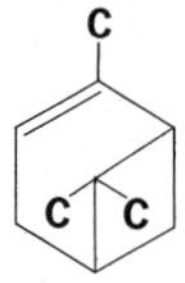

α-pinene

The carotenes are a group of naturally occurring cyclic hydrocarbons containing the cyclohexane ring. There are three forms, α, β, and γ. The β-form is the most important, since it is the provitamin A. Upon fission, the molecule is split into essentially two equal parts, each one being vitamin A. The carotene molecules are highly conjugated (only the carbon skeleton is shown).

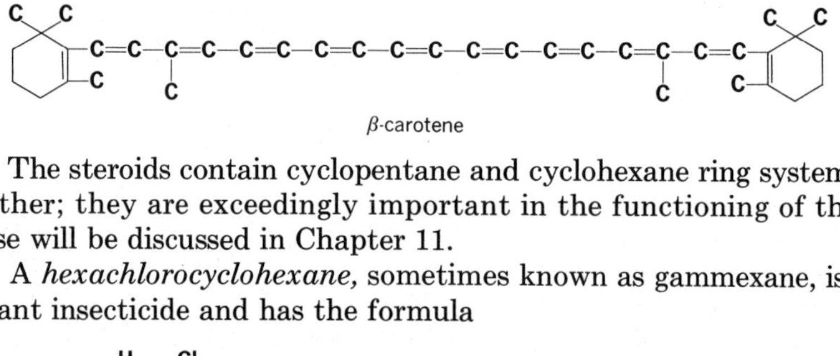

β-carotene

The steroids contain cyclopentane and cyclohexane ring systems fused together; they are exceedingly important in the functioning of the body. These will be discussed in Chapter 11.

A *hexachlorocyclohexane,* sometimes known as gammexane, is an important insecticide and has the formula

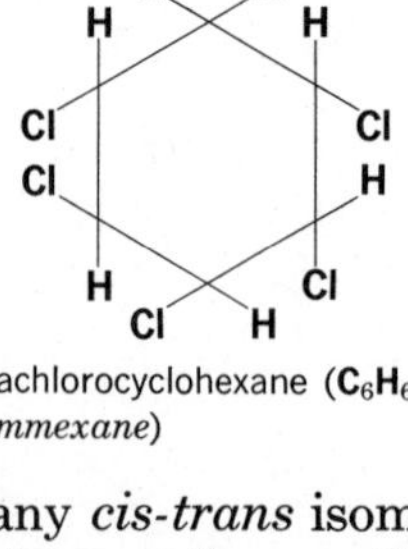

hexachlorocyclohexane ($C_6H_6Cl_6$)
(*gammexane*)

Many *cis-trans* isomers of this molecule are possible, and the so-called gamma isomer (hence, the name gammexane) is the most potent. It is excellent in killing cockroaches. Gammexane is also known as benzene hexachloride (*BHC*).

Aromatic hydrocarbons

The most common aromatic compound is benzene. Its molecular formula is C_6H_6. Experiments have shown that the six carbon atoms are in a ring and that each carbon has one attached hydrogen atom.

Since each carbon atom is attached to two other carbon atoms and to one hydrogen atom, three of the four bonding electrons are already involved in bond formation. This leaves the fourth electron [called the pi (π) electron] to be placed in bond formation.

The placement of this fourth electron and the actual structure of benzene is one of the oldest problems in organic chemistry. The following structure of benzene shows all the carbon atoms with their three sigma bonds in proper places and with the fourth electron in an unassigned position:

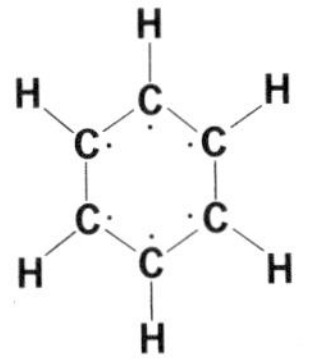

Let us first number the carbon atoms and then follow the obvious assumption that the extra electrons pair up between carbon atoms to form alternating single and double bonds (conjugated) as shown in structure I.

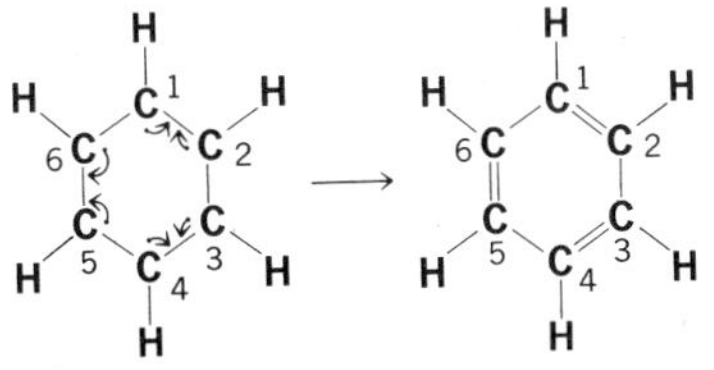

(I)

However, the electrons could also pair up to give structure II.

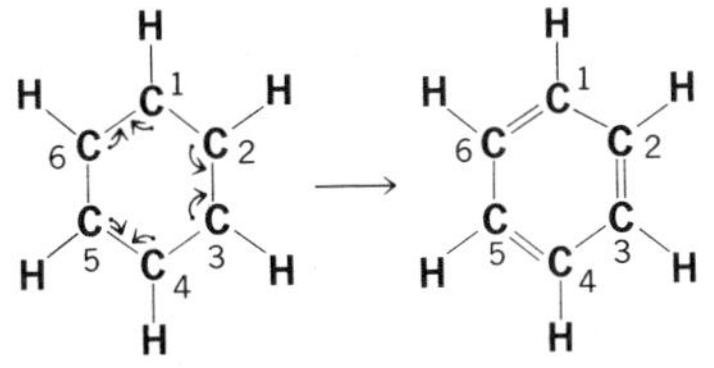

(II)

At first glance, structures I and II look identical (which is true), even though, for example, in structure I, there is a double bond between carbons 1 and 2, and in structure II, there is a single bond between carbons 1 and 2.

However, if two chlorine atoms, for example, are on adjacent carbons, that is,

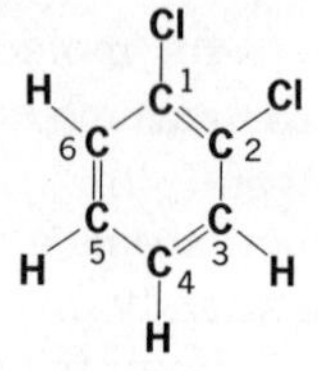

(III) 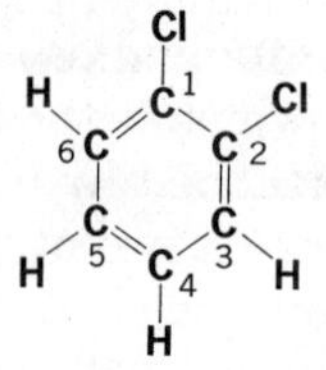 (IV)

$C_6H_4Cl_2$

it should make a difference whether there is a double bond between atoms 1 and 2 (structure III) or a single bond between atoms 1 and 2 (structure IV). If structures III and IV are possible and correct, the structures will indeed be different. *In fact, there is only one structure* $C_6H_4Cl_2$, *and neither of the above structures (III and IV) is correct.*

In addition, evidence shows that I, II, III, and IV are not correct structures. For example, if there are indeed double bonds in benzene, then it should react like an unsaturated compound. The double bonds of benzene should react readily by addition with Br_2 and H_2SO_4, should be readily oxidized by $KMnO_4$, and should be readily reduced by hydrogen in the presence of platinum catalyst. However, benzene does *not* react by addition with bromine, does *not* react by addition with sulfuric acid, is *not* oxidized by $KMnO_4$, and is not readily reduced by hydrogen in the presence of platinum catalyst. Thus, benzene seems to have no double bonds.

Other evidence concerning bond distances is of value. Table 3-7 shows the distances between carbon atoms as a function of the type of bond.

The data in Table 3-7 indicate that the greater the number of electrons involved in bond formation between two carbon atoms, the shorter the distance between the two atoms. In benzene, all carbon-carbon bond distances equal 1.39 A.

Table 3-7 Bond distances

TYPES OF BOND	DISTANCE BETWEEN CARBON ATOMS (A)[a]
carbon—carbon (single bond)	1.54
carbon═carbon (double bond)	1.33
carbon≡carbon (triple bond)	1.20

[a] The A is the Angstrom unit, which is one hundred-millionth of a centimeter, or one ten-billionth of a meter.

Figure 3-9 Benzene.

If benzene had double and single bonds, it could be represented as follows:

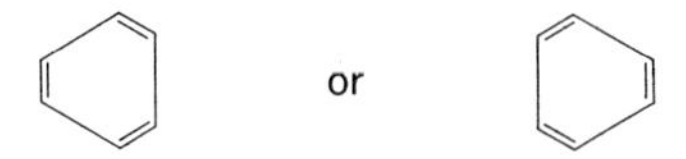

However, benzene is a perfectly symmetrical planar molecule, a per-

fect hexagon, with the carbon-carbon bond distances approximately one-and-a-half bonds in length (see Figure 3-9).

In reality, there is no correct classic manner of drawing the benzene ring. Modern theory indicates that the fourth electron of each carbon atom interacts with the fourth electron of all the other carbon atoms to form an electronic cloud or pathway, which mathematically depicts the probability of the positions of these six pi (π) electrons. See Figure 3-10. The two doughnuts, one below and one above the planar ring, are the pathways traversed by these π electrons.

Since there is only one benzene, we conveniently illustrate this unique structure as

benzene (C_6H_6)

Note that the hydrogens are not usually drawn in the molecule.

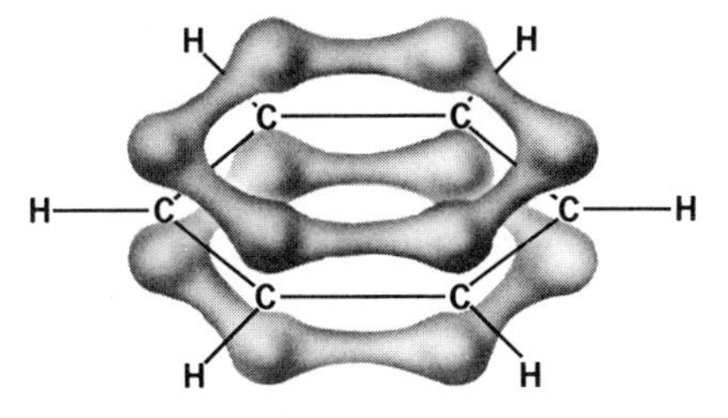

Figure 3-10 The π molecular orbital of benzene.

Resonance is the phenomenon that occurs when two or more possible electronic structures have somewhat equal probability. Under these circumstances, the actual final structure is determined by the number of electronic possibilities; that is, the final structure is none of the individual structures but seems to partake of all of them. Most important, however, is the great stability exhibited by the final structure. The increased stability is a measure of the resonance energy.

We shall indicate some members of the benzene series, whose general formula is C_nH_{2n-6}. Benzene itself is C_6H_6.

Toluene is the next homolog, C_7H_8:

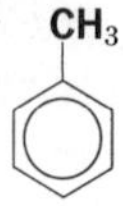
CH3

toluene
(*methylbenzene*)

There are four isomers of the formula C_8H_{10}:

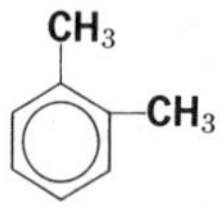
CH3
CH3

1,2-dimethylbenzene
(*o-xylene*)

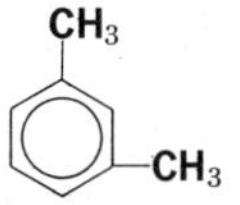
CH3
CH3

1,3-dimethylbenzene
(*m-xylene*)

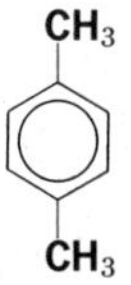
CH3
CH3

1,4-dimethylbenzene
(*p-xylene*)

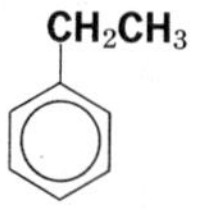
CH2CH3

ethylbenzene

The *o*-, *m*-, and *p*-isomers are examples of position isomerism.

There are eight isomers of the aromatic structure C_9H_{12}:

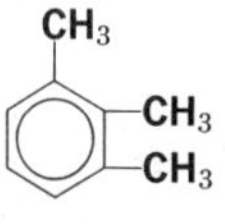
CH3
CH3
CH3

1,2,3-trimethylbenzene

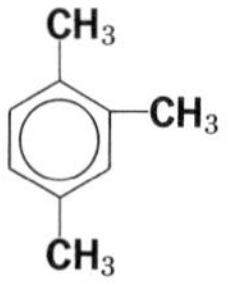
CH3
CH3
CH3

1,2,4-trimethylbenzene

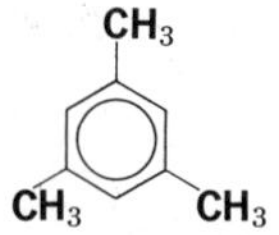
CH3
CH3
CH3

1,3,5-trimethylbenzene

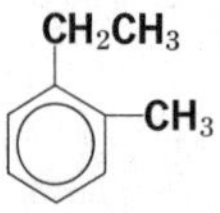
CH2CH3
CH3

1-ethyl-2-methylbenzene

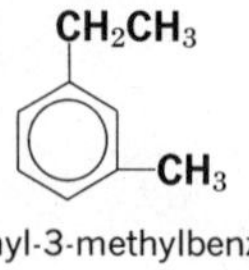
CH2CH3
CH3

1-ethyl-3-methylbenzene

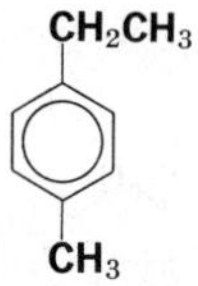
CH2CH3
CH3

1-ethyl-4-methylbenzene

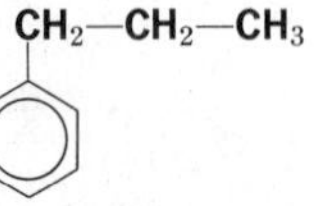
CH2—CH2—CH3

n-propylbenzene

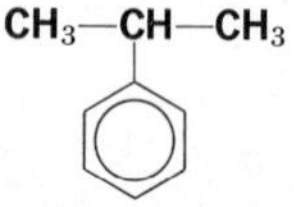
CH3—CH—CH3

isopropylbenzene

The radical formed by removing one hydrogen from the benzene ring is called the *phenyl* radical:

phenyl radical (C_6H_5—)

When two phenyl radicals are attached, we have a new aromatic system called diphenyl.

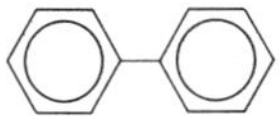

diphenyl ($C_{12}H_{10}$)

Another important radical is benzyl.

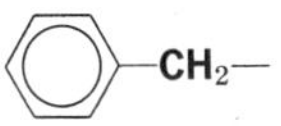

—CH_2—

benzyl radical

The naphthalene system is also important.

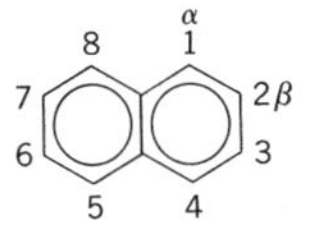

naphthalene ($C_{10}H_8$)

Some examples of nomenclature are

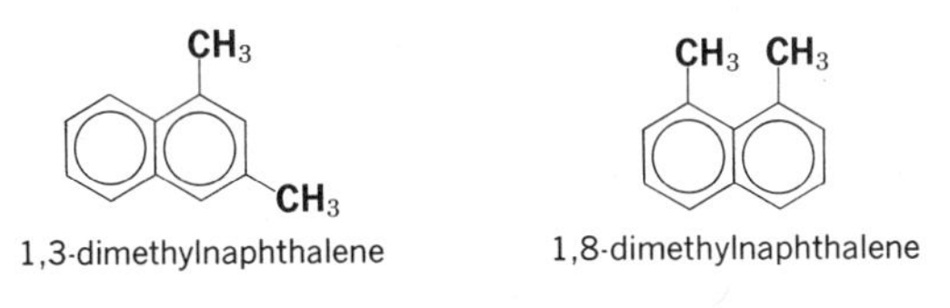

1,3-dimethylnaphthalene

1,8-dimethylnaphthalene

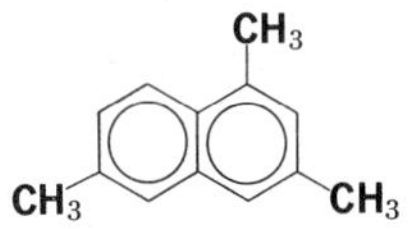

1,3,6-trimethylnaphthalene

The anthracene system is encountered many times, and its unusual numbering system is shown.

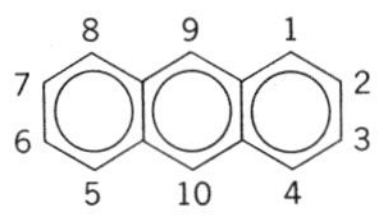

anthracene ($C_{14}H_{10}$)

Some substituted anthracenes are

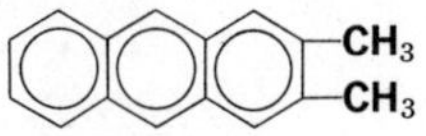

2,3-dimethylanthracene

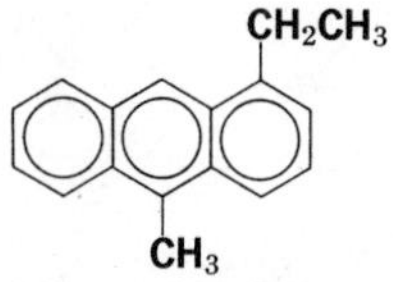

1-ethyl-10-methylanthracene

One of the most important large ring systems is that of phenanthrene.

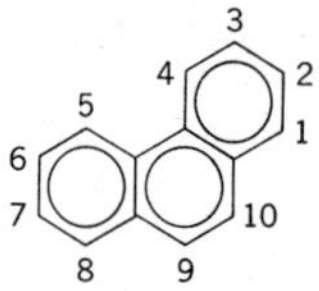

phenanthrene ($C_{14}H_{10}$)

When the cyclopentane ring is attached to the phenanthrene system in the following way, we get the basic unit for the steroids. This cyclopentanophenanthrene system is very important.

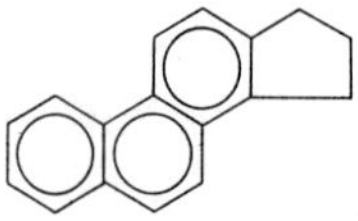

cyclopentanophenanthrene

Steroids are usually *hydrogenated* cyclopentanophenanthrenes.

Preparation

If coal is heated in the air, the coal will burn. However, if coal is heated in the absence of air (coking oven), many complex reactions occur, and gas and liquids distill out of the coal.

The liquids from the coal tar are mostly aromatic hydrocarbons and have been used for many years as the source of aromatics. In the last several decades, however, it has been possible to crack and cyclize aliphatics from petroleum and to form aromatics by using special catalysts and conditions.

Because many of the desired aromatic hydrocarbons are obtained from either coal tar or petroleum, the problem of synthesis is often of only an academic nature. It is possible to synthesize the aromatic ring, but it is common *to start with some simple compounds containing the benzene ring.*

For example, aromatic hydrocarbons can be prepared by means of the Wurtz-Fittig reaction. The general equation is

$$ArX + RX + 2Na^0 \longrightarrow ArR + 2NaX$$

Specific examples are

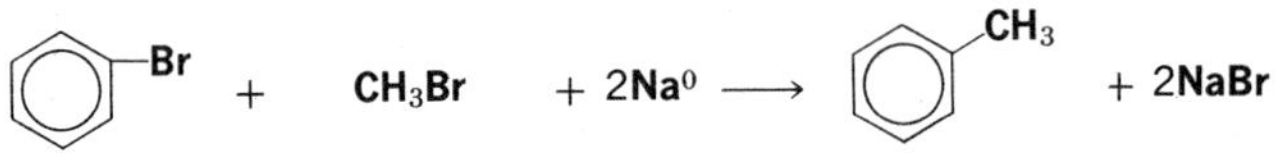

$$C_6H_5Br + CH_3Br + 2Na^0 \longrightarrow C_6H_5CH_3 + 2NaBr$$

bromobenzene methyl bromide toluene (*methylbenzene*)

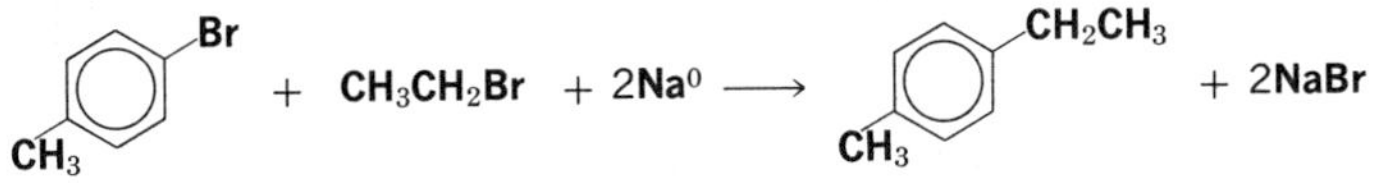

$$p\text{-}CH_3C_6H_4Br + CH_3CH_2Br + 2Na^0 \longrightarrow p\text{-}CH_3C_6H_4CH_2CH_3 + 2NaBr$$

p-bromotoluene ethyl bromide *p*-methylethylbenzene

The Grignard method could also be used to synthesize aromatic hydrocarbons. For example,

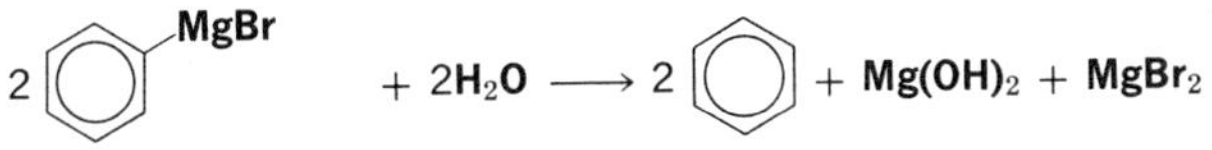

$$2\,C_6H_5MgBr + 2H_2O \longrightarrow 2\,C_6H_6 + Mg(OH)_2 + MgBr_2$$

phenyl magnesium bromide benzene

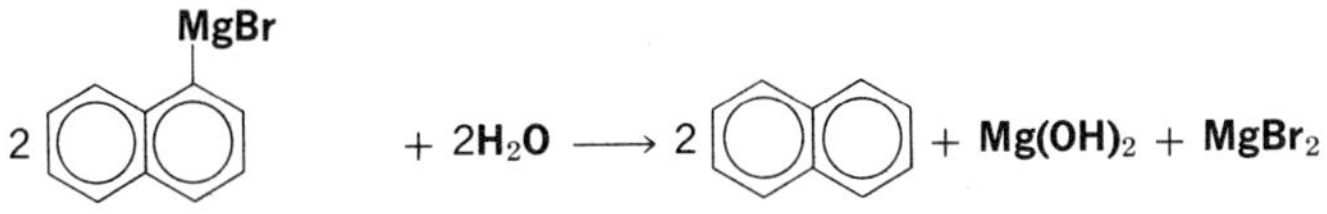

$$2\,C_{10}H_7MgBr + 2H_2O \longrightarrow 2\,C_{10}H_8 + Mg(OH)_2 + MgBr_2$$

α-naphthyl magnesium bromide naphthalene

Other methods of preparing aromatic hydrocarbons exist, but they are beyond the scope of this book.

Reactions

REDUCTION

Aromatic compounds can be reduced to saturated alicyclic compounds by reaction with hydrogen in the presence of certain catalysts. However, it is much more difficult to reduce aromatic compounds than to reduce olefins. For example, relatively strenuous conditions are necessary to reduce benzene to cyclohexane and toluene to methylcyclohexane.

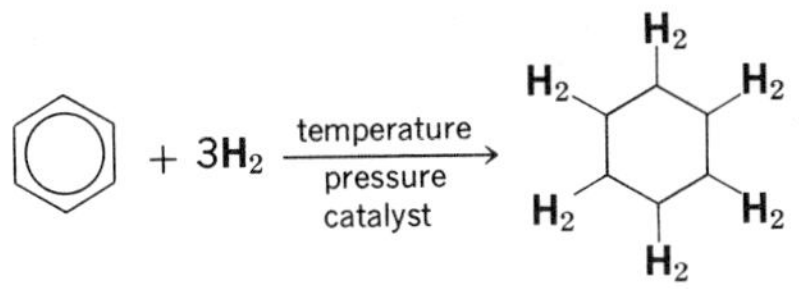

$$C_6H_6 + 3H_2 \xrightarrow[\text{pressure, catalyst}]{\text{temperature}} C_6H_{12}$$

benzene cyclohexane

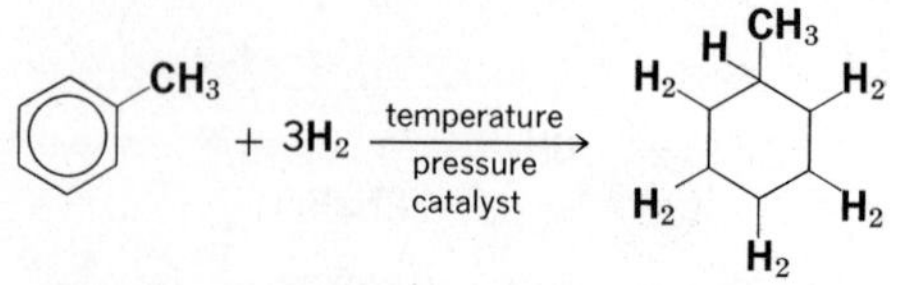

$$C_6H_5CH_3 + 3H_2 \xrightarrow[\text{pressure, catalyst}]{\text{temperature}} C_6H_{11}CH_3$$

toluene → methylcyclohexane

Butadiene is relatively easily converted to butane.

$$CH_2{=}CH{-}CH{=}CH_2 + 2H_2 \xrightarrow[\text{room temperature, low pressure}]{Pt^0} CH_3CH_2CH_2CH_3$$

1,3-butadiene → butane

1,3,5-Hexatriene is easily converted into hexane.

$$CH_2{=}CH{-}CH{=}CH{-}CH{=}CH_2 + 3H_2 \xrightarrow[\text{room temperature, low pressure}]{Pt^0} CH_3CH_2CH_2CH_2CH_2CH_3$$

1,3,5-hexatriene → hexane

The above reactions illustrate the stability of the benzene ring.

HALOGENATION

The aromatic ring is generally inert to halogens. In other words, chlorine may be passed into benzene and bromine may be dissolved in benzene with no rapid reaction. This is in marked contrast to the reaction of bromine with olefins, which occurs immediately. Again we have an example of the stability of the aromatic ring. Benzene can be made to react with bromine and chlorine, but we need a special catalyst (e.g., iron), and we obtain a compound that differs from that obtained in the bromination of an olefin. For example,

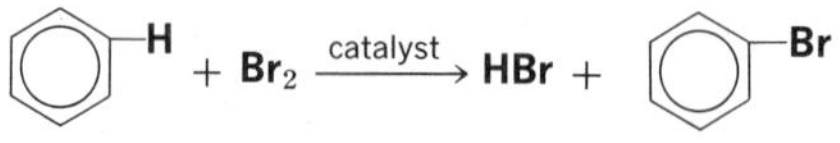

$$C_6H_5{-}H + Br_2 \xrightarrow{\text{catalyst}} HBr + C_6H_5{-}Br$$

benzene → bromobenzene

We see that the ring is still *intact* and that only *one* bromine atom has been introduced (two were added in the reaction of bromine with an olefin). The above reaction is called a *substitution* reaction; that is, a hydrogen atom on the benzene ring has been replaced by a bromine atom.

OXIDIZING AGENTS

Oxidizing agents, such as potassium permanganate and potassium dichromate, leave the aromatic ring untouched.

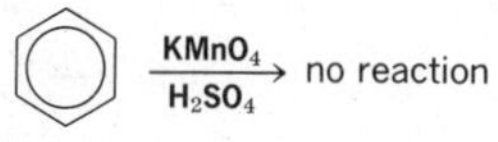

$$C_6H_6 \xrightarrow[H_2SO_4]{KMnO_4} \text{no reaction}$$

benzene

However, an aliphatic group attached to the benzene ring may be oxidized, demonstrating again the marked preferential stability of the aromatic ring as compared to an aliphatic group. For example, toluene can be oxidized with $KMnO_4$ to form benzoic acid (see Chapter 7), a compound with the benzene ring intact.

$$C_6H_5CH_3 \xrightarrow[H_2SO_4 \; [O]]{KMnO_4} C_6H_5COOH$$

toluene → benzoic acid

ACTION OF STRONG ACIDS

Cold concentrated hydrochloric, nitric, and sulfuric acids do not ordinarily react with benzene; but nitric and sulfuric acids *can* react with benzene under certain forcing conditions. When this reaction is so forced, it does not give the type of product encountered in the reaction of ethylene and sulfuric acid.

$$C_6H_5\text{—}H + HO\text{—}NO_2 \xrightarrow{\text{concentrated nitric acid}} C_6H_5NO_2 + H_2O$$

benzene → nitrobenzene

$$C_6H_5\text{—}H + HO\text{—}SO_2OH \xrightarrow{\text{concentrated sulfuric acid}} C_6H_5SO_2OH + H_2O$$

benzene → benzene sulfonic acid

We see that benzene can be made to react with nitric and sulfuric acids by *substitution,* but not by *addition.*

Our discussion of the reaction of aromatic hydrocarbons must necessarily be brief. The topic is important and voluminous, however. There are many notable exceptions to the statements already made; many special and specific reactions are used, and a very large variety of compounds is known.

Occurrence, Uses, and Properties

When bituminous coal is heated to 1,200–1,300°C in the absence of air, the coal is turned into coke, coal gas is formed (mostly hydrogen and methane), and a somewhat volatile liquid, *coal tar,* is obtained (3% of the weight of the coal).

Coal tar contains many valuable chemicals. By a distillation process, the components may be separated roughly into various boiling point fractions (see Table 3-8). The fractions are highly aromatic in odor, and hence the name of the series.

Table 3-8

	TEMP. RANGE	PRODUCT
1	up to 170°C	light oil
2	170–235°C	carbolic oil
3	235–270°C	creosote oil
4	270–325°C	light anthracene oil
5	325–355°C	heavy anthrance oil
6	above 355°C	residue of pitch

The light oil contains benzene, *o*-, *m*-, *p*-xylenes, and other simple substituted benzenes in about 2% by weight of the coal tar.

Aromatics, such as benzene, toluene, and xylene, are produced in tremendous quantities (many billions of pounds a year). Not only are they excellent solvents, but they are also used widely as starting materials from which many important drugs and chemicals are produced.

Naphthalene is the most abundant single constituent by weight (11%) of coal tar. Its cheapness and mild insecticidal properties make naphthalene familiar to us in the form of moth balls.

Other hydrocarbons obtained in the various fractions are

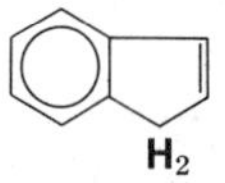

H_2
indene (C_9H_8)

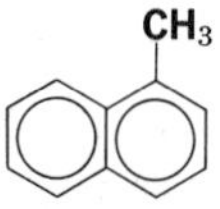

CH_3
1-methylnaphthalene ($C_{11}H_{10}$)

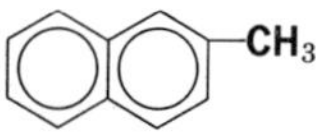

CH_3
2-methylnaphthalene ($C_{11}H_{10}$)

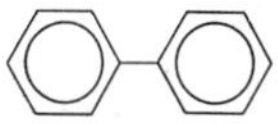

diphenyl ($C_{12}H_{10}$)

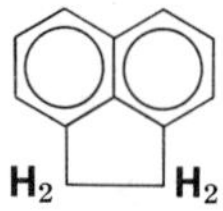

H_2 H_2
acenaphthene ($C_{12}H_{10}$)

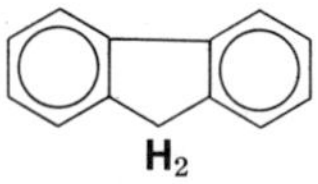

H_2
fluorene ($C_{13}H_{10}$)

Some compounds containing many benzene rings are also found in a coal tar.

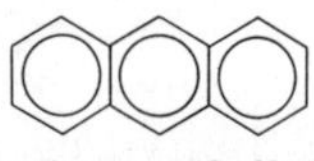

anthracene ($C_{14}H_{10}$)

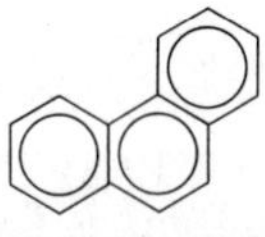

phenanthrene ($C_{14}H_{10}$)

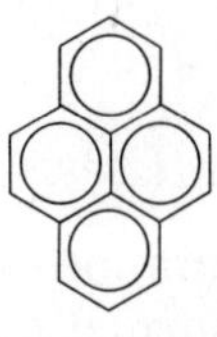

pyrene ($C_{16}H_{10}$)

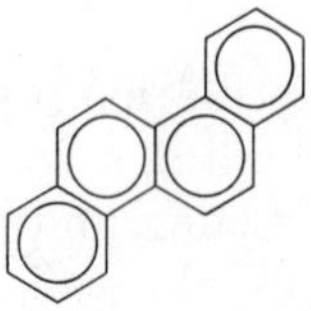

chrysene ($C_{18}H_{12}$)

The above-mentioned hydrocarbons are used to prepare many organic compounds used as medicinals, dyes, and solvents. Coal tar also has oxygen-, nitrogen-, and sulfur-containing compounds.

Carcinogenic Hydrocarbons

People working in certain coal tar plants in Europe (where safety conditions were not too strenuously enforced) had shown a higher incidence of skin cancer than other industrial workers.

In 1915, it was shown that cancer could be produced in experimental animals by rubbing certain coal tar fractions on the skin. In 1933, a small amount of 3,4-benzpyrene

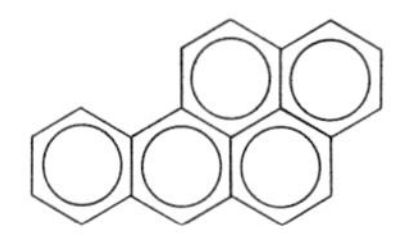

3,4-benzpyrene

was isolated from coal tar (0.003% by weight of coal tar), and this substance was capable of producing malignant growths in animal tissue (carcinogenic).

Subsequent work showed that other compounds containing many benzene rings are also carcinogenic, and many occur in minute amounts in coal tar. Some examples are

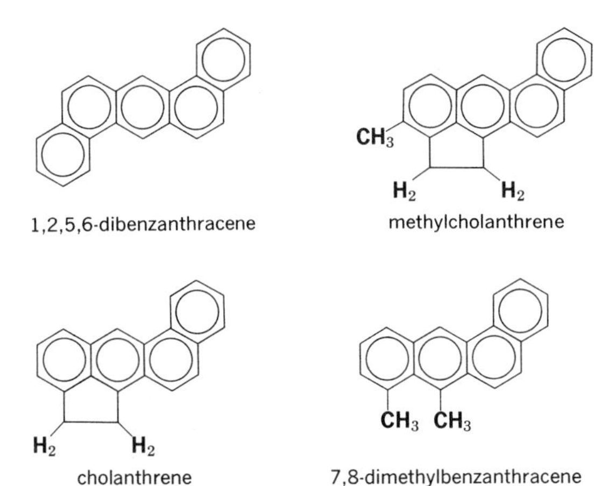

1,2,5,6-dibenzanthracene

methylcholanthrene

cholanthrene

7,8-dimethylbenzanthracene

It soon became apparent that these carcinogenic hydrocarbons possessed one thing in common—four benzene rings arranged in the following fashion:

In other words, they were all related to 1,2-benzanthracene or benz-(a)-anthracene.

In this molecule, the following numbering system is preferred:

1,2-benzanthracene
benz-(a)-anthracene

Methylcholanthrene has been reported to be one of the most active of the carcinogenic hydrocarbons tested. When injected subcutaneously into selected strains of mice, in concentrations of 0.00025 grams per mouse, methylcholanthrene produced cancer in every one of eighty mice tested, within an average of 9.7 weeks. See Figure 3-11. Apparently, there seems to be an irreversible binding of the carcinogen to the proteins of the skin.

Since certain steroids can be converted into methylcholanthrene in a chemical apparatus, this transformation could *possibly* occur in animal and human tissue. The bodies of animals and humans have an ample supply of steroids. However, the exact cause of cancer is not known at present, and it is mere speculation to assume that abnormal steroid transformations in the body cause cancer.

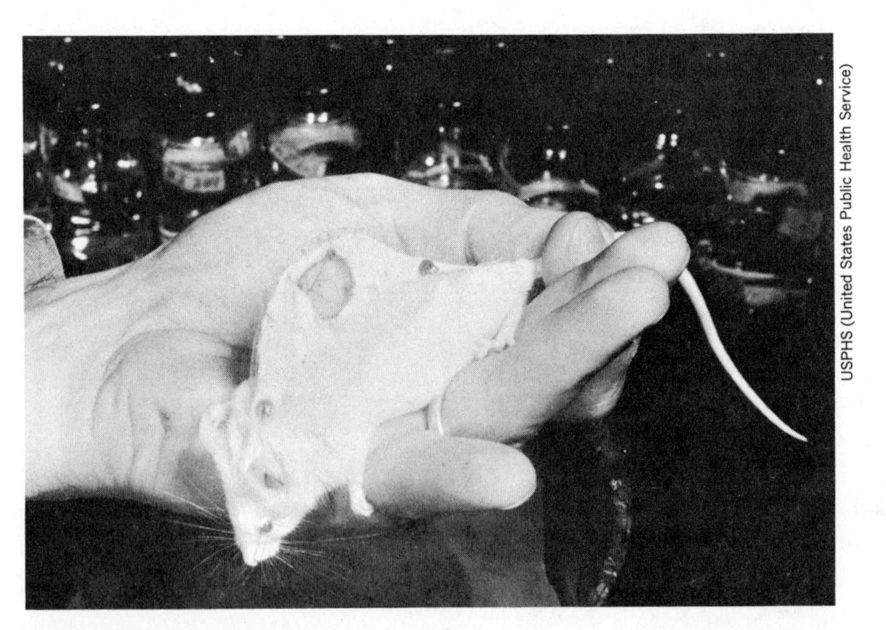

USPHS (United States Public Health Service)

Figure 3-11 Mouse with cancer.

Not all 1,2-benzanthracenes (benz-(a)-anthracenes) are carcinogenic. The following compounds are *noncarcinogenic:*

1. benz-(a)-anthracene
2. 1-methylbenzanthracene
3. 10-methylbenzanthracene
4. 11-methylbenzanthracene
5. 5,12-dimethylbenzanthracene
6. 9,11-dimethylbenzanthracene
7. 8,9,11-trimethylbenzanthracene

The following compounds apparently have no activity:

1. 2-methylbenzanthracene
2. 3-methylbenzanthracene
3. 8,11-dimethylbenzanthracene

The following compounds have activity:

Monomethyl derivatives of benz-(a)-anthracenes

1. 5-methylbenzanthracene
2. 6-methylbenzanthracene
3. 7-methylbenzanthracene
4. 8-methylbenzanthracene
5. 12-methylbenzanthracene

Dimethyl derivatives of benz-(a)-anthracenes

1. 7,8-dimethylbenzanthracene
2. 7,12-dimethylbenzanthracene
3. 8,12-dimethylbenzanthracene
4. 6,12-dimethylbenzanthracene

All of the activity was tested by subcutaneous injection. As can be seen, the relationship between activity and structure is not as clear as it could be. Extensive work (both experimental and theoretical) in this field is still going on.

Other substances not related to benzanthracenes are known to produce cancer. Most significant among these are the azo dyes. These compounds all contain nitrogen and some, in addition, contain oxygen. Some carcinogenic azo dyes are

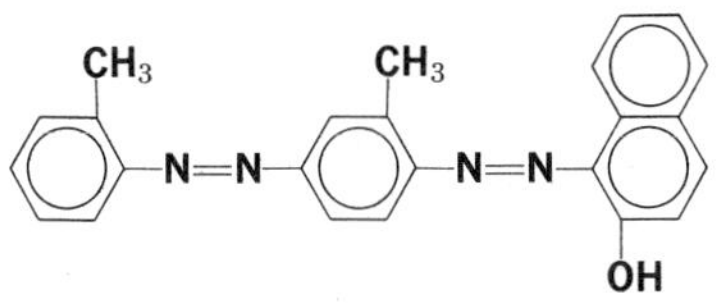

CH_3 CH_3 N=N N=N OH

scarlet red

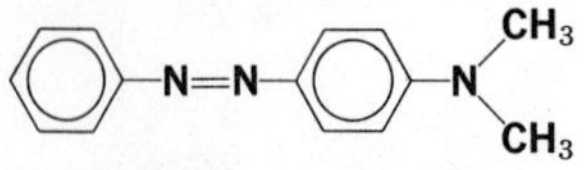

p-dimethylaminoazobenzene
(*yellow*)

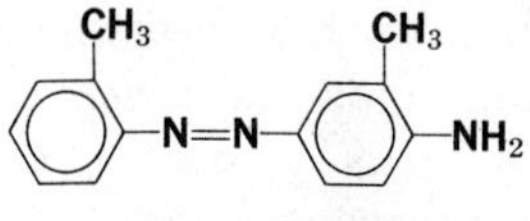

o-aminoazotoluene
(*common name*)

These substances produce cancer of the liver when fed to mice and rats. Apparently, these azo dyes become bound to the liver proteins.

Another substance that produces cancer is 2-acetylaminofluorene.

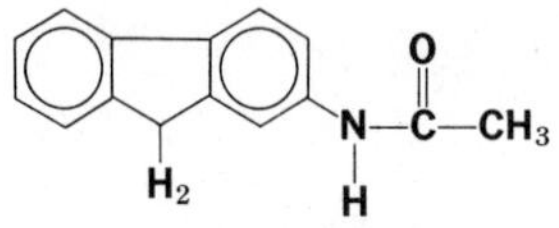

2-acetylaminofluorene

Whether there is any relationship between the carcinogenic hydrocarbons and these other compounds is not known.

Some Halogenated Aromatics

Para-dichlorobenzene (also known as paradichlor, dichlor, etc.) finds use as a cheap effective insecticide. It is used mostly against moths and larvae, roaches, and other small insects.

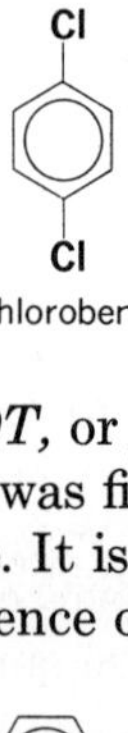

p-dichlorobenzene

DDT, or *p,p′dichlorodiphenyltrichloroethane,* although first prepared in 1874, was first used extensively during World War II as a remarkable insecticide. It is prepared from chloral (see Chapter 6) and chlorobenzene in the presence of a condensing agent.

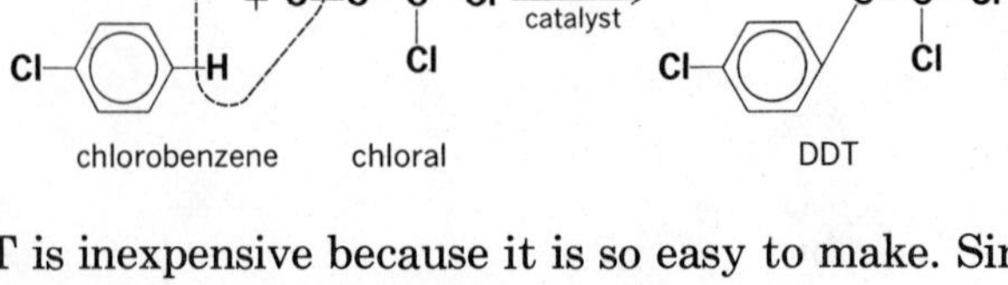

$\xrightarrow[\text{catalyst}]{-H_2O}$

chlorobenzene chloral DDT

DDT is inexpensive because it is so easy to make. Since DDT is such a stable molecule, its residual effects are great.

Chlorobenzene is produced in large amounts in this country by the chlorination of benzene in the presence of a catalyst. It is a reactive and valuable intermediate.

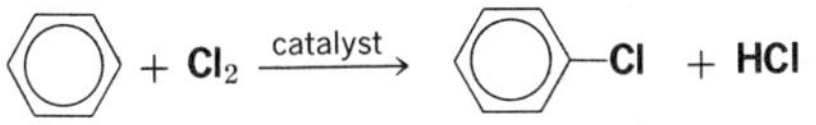

$$C_6H_6 + Cl_2 \xrightarrow{\text{catalyst}} C_6H_5Cl + HCl$$

chlorobenzene

Some Nitrated Aromatics

TNT or *2,4,6-trinitrotoluene,* is formed in the stepwise nitration of toluene.

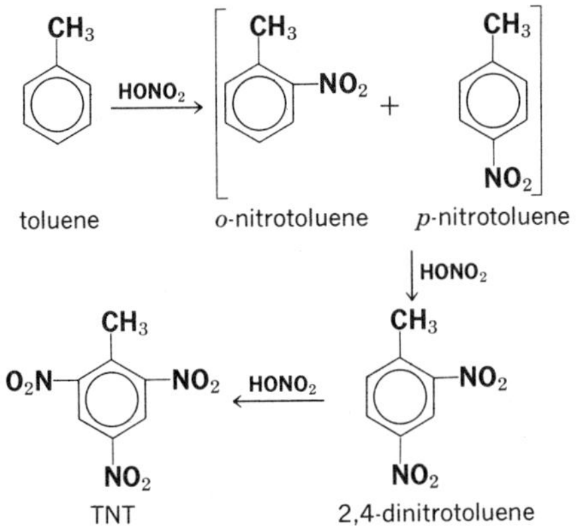

toluene $\xrightarrow{HONO_2}$ [*o*-nitrotoluene + *p*-nitrotoluene]

p-nitrotoluene $\xrightarrow{HONO_2}$ 2,4-dinitrotoluene $\xrightarrow{HONO_2}$ TNT

TNT is an excellent explosive and is widely used in making shells and bombs.

Heterocycles

We have defined heterocycles as ring compounds that have at least one atom other than carbon in the ring. Many of these are commonly encountered and possess interesting properties. Some heterocycles are aromatic in nature and some are aliphatic.

Some nitrogen-containing heterocycles from coal tar are

pyridine (C_5H_5N) (ring positions: N 1, 2 α, 3 β, 4 γ, 5, 6)

2-methylpyridine (C_6H_7N) (*α-picoline*)

3-methylpyridine (C_6H_7N) (*β-picoline*)

4-methylpyridine (C_6H_7N) (*γ-picoline*)

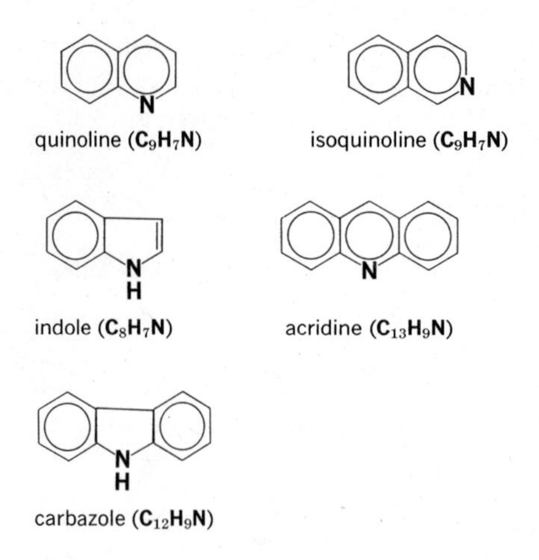

quinoline (C_9H_7N) isoquinoline (C_9H_7N)

indole (C_8H_7N) acridine ($C_{13}H_9N$)

carbazole ($C_{12}H_9N$)

Other nitrogen-containing heterocycles of importance in medicine are

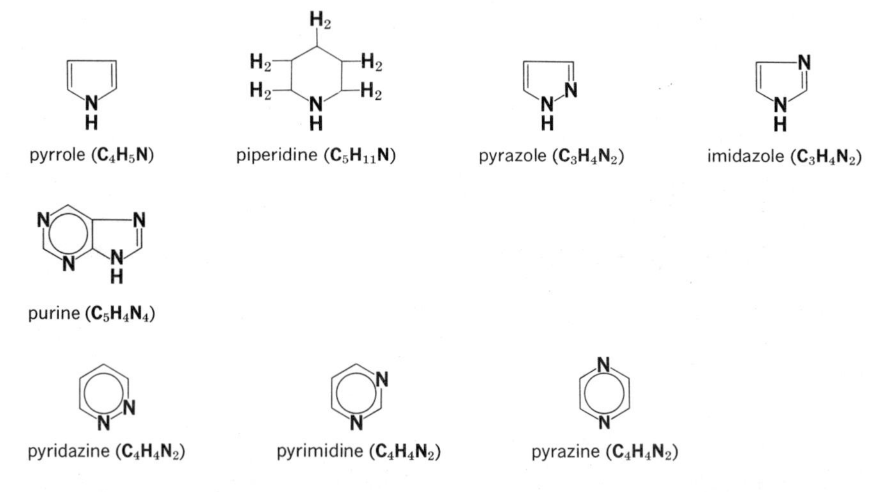

pyrrole (C_4H_5N) piperidine ($C_5H_{11}N$) pyrazole ($C_3H_4N_2$) imidazole ($C_3H_4N_2$)

purine ($C_5H_4N_4$)

pyridazine ($C_4H_4N_2$) pyrimidine ($C_4H_4N_2$) pyrazine ($C_4H_4N_2$)

Some oxygen-containing heterocycles of interest are

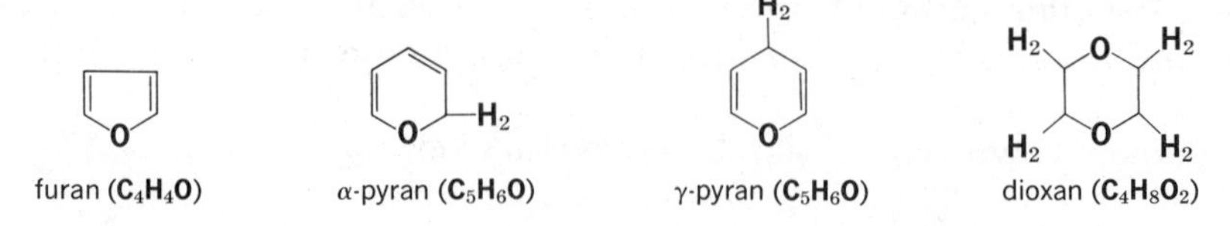

furan (C_4H_4O) α-pyran (C_5H_6O) γ-pyran (C_5H_6O) dioxan ($C_4H_8O_2$)

A sulfur-containing heterocycle of importance is

S

thiophene (C_4H_4S)

Many of the heterocycles contain two or more heterocyclic atoms in the ring. Some interesting examples are

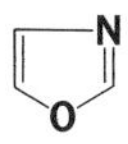

oxazole (C_3H_3NO)  thiazole (C_3H_3NS) 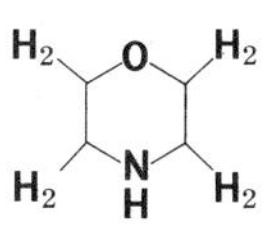 morpholine (C_4H_9NO) 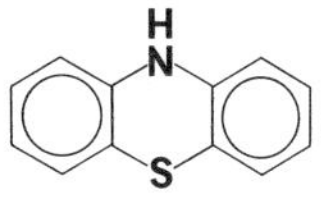 phenothiazine ($C_{12}H_9NS$)

The above heterocycles may be called "parent" compounds, because many compounds are formed from them. If methyl, hydrogen, phenyl, chlorine, and other groups or atoms were attached to the ring, we would recognize important compounds. We have indicated the ring systems and names so that the student may recognize and refer to them later in the course or in some other phase of advanced work.

The heterocycles are very important in medicine and biochemistry. Many substances such as hemin (coloring part of hemoglobin), chlorophyll, vitamins, sulfa drugs, dyes, and antibiotics contain these heterocyclic rings.

REVIEW QUESTIONS

1. Discuss the relative activities of saturated and unsaturated hydrocarbons.
2. What are the prefixes used to denote one to ten carbon atoms?
3. Write the structures for methyl, ethyl, *n*-propyl, iso-propyl, *n*-butyl, *sec*-butyl, isobutyl, and *tert*-butyl radicals.
4. What symbols do we use to differentiate between aliphatic and aromatic radicals?
5. Write the structures for the following compounds: 2-methylheptane, 3-methyloctane, 2,4-dimethylpentane, 2,4,6-trimethylnonane.
6. Draw all possible structural isomers for $C_4H_6Cl_2$, C_5H_{12}, and $C_5H_{11}Br$.
7. Discuss some of the methods of producing saturated hydrocarbons and write an equation illustrating each method.
8. Name the following isomers of the C_7H_{14} olefins.

```
(a) C=C—C—C—C—C—C          (b) C=C—C—C—C—C
                                        |
                                        C

(c) C=C—C—C—C—C            (d) C=C—C—C—C—C
                |                   |
                C                   C

                C
                |
(e) C=C—C—C—C              (f) C=C—C—C—C
            |                       |   |
            C                       C   C

(g) C=C—C—C—C—C            (h) C=C—C—C—C
        |                           |  |
        C                           C  C
```

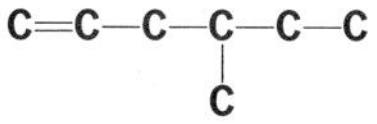

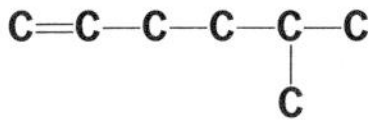

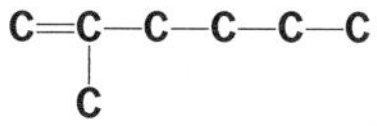

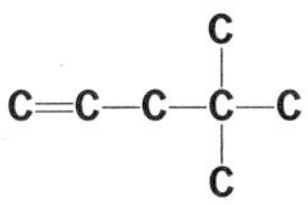

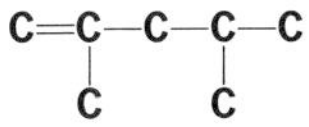

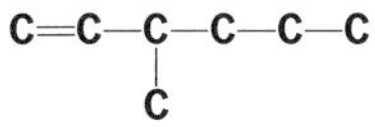

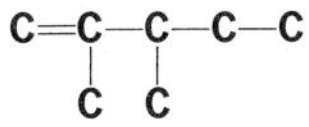

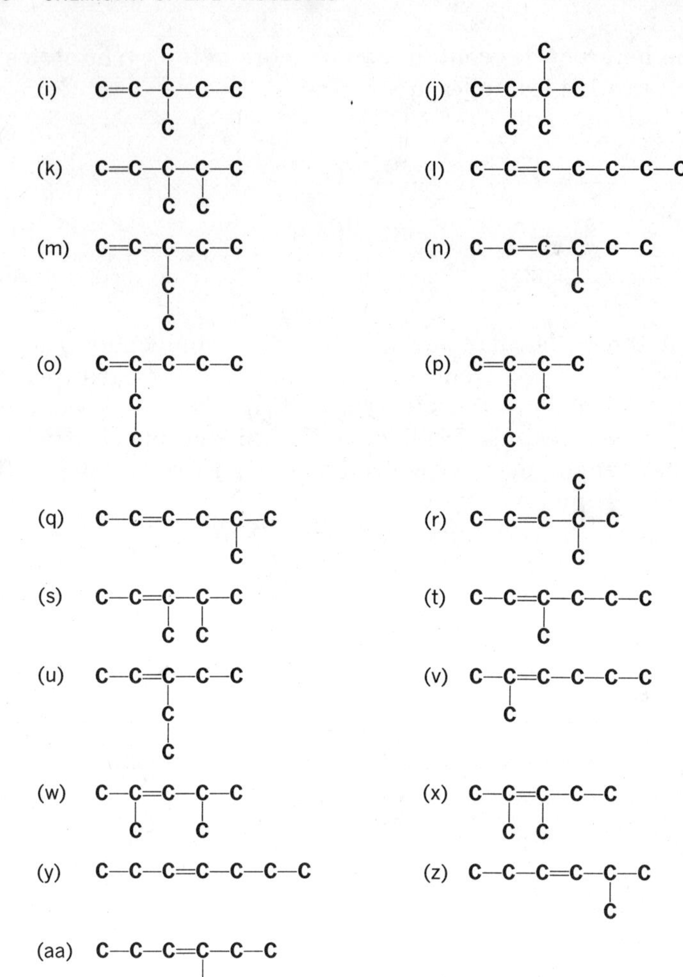

9. Define the terms "reduction" and "hydrogenation."
10. What is known about the reactivity of the paraffins with the halogens chlorine, bromine, and iodine?
11. Write structures for methyl chloride, methylene chloride, chloroform, and carbon tetrachloride. How may these be produced?
12. What is natural gas? Discuss its composition and utility.
13. What is petroleum? Discuss its composition.
14. What are gasoline, kerosene, mineral oil, Vaseline, paraffin wax, and ligroin? Define the term "octane number."
15. Define the cracking process.
16. Contrast the structures of paraffins and olefins.
17. Write the structures for 2-methyl-2-butene, 3-methyl-2-hexene, 3,5-dimethyl-2-hexene, 3,4,5-trimethyl-2-hexene.
18. What are some methods of producing olefins? Write representative equations.

19. What is meant by dehydrogenation of an alcohol? dehydrohalogenation of an alkyl halide?
20. Write an equation for the production of an olefin with zinc as the dehalogenating agent.
21. Write representative equations for the addition of Br_2, HBr, and H_2SO_4, followed by water, to ethylene, propylene, and 2-butene.
22. Write equations illustrating the reduction of ethylene, propylene, and 2-butene.
23. Write equations for the reaction of $KMnO_4$ in basic solution with ethylene, propylene, and 2-pentene.
24. Of what use is ethylene oxide?
25. Discuss the effect of ethylene and propylene as anesthetics.
26. How is ethylene oxide prepared?
27. What are some of the uses of olefins in general?
28. What is the structure of trichloroethylene?
29. Write the structures of the three types of diolefins.
30. Write the structures for 1,5-hexadiene, 1-3-hexadiene, isoprene, and chloroprene.
31. Discuss the structure of natural rubber. Discuss the units used to make several types of synthetic rubber.
32. Write structures for styrene and 1,3-butadiene. Write structures for several acetylenes and name them.
33. Write structures for 4-methyl-1-pentyne, 4-methyl-2-pentyne, 4,4-dimethyl-1-hexyne.
34. What are the reactions for producing acetylene? Write representative equations and name all compounds. Write equations illustrating the reaction between acetylene and bromine, and between acetylene and $KMnO_4$, in basic solution.
35. Write an equation illustrating the hydrogenation of acetylene. What are some of the uses of acetylene and its homologs?
36. Write the structures for cyclopropane, cyclobutane, cyclopentane, and cyclohexane. Of what use is cyclopropane in medicine?
37. What is the structure for gammexane, and how is it used?
38. Discuss the structure for benzene from the electronic point of view and from the stability point of view. What is the concept of resonance? How does benzene react toward hydrogen, bromine, hydrogen bromide, and sulfuric acid?
39. What is meant by a substitution reaction? How does it differ from an addition reaction? Write several substitution reactions for benzene.
40. Draw the structure for toluene, the three xylenes, diphenyl, naphthalene, anthracene, and phenanthrene.
41. What is coal tar? Discuss its composition.
42. How is benzene obtained commercially? What is its position in the economics of the chemical industry?
43. Write the structures for indene, fluorene, acenaphthene, pyrene, and chrysene.
44. What structure is common to many carcinogenic hydrocarbons? Write structures for several carcinogenic hydrocarbons. What is a very potent one?
45. Write the structures for para-dichlorobenzene and DDT, for chlorobenzene and TNT.
46. Draw structures for pyridine, any picoline, quinoline, isoquinoline, indole, acridine, carbazole, pyrrole, pyrimidine, furan, thiophene, and morpholine.
47. Starting with the organic compound on the left, how would you prepare the or-

ganic compound on the right? The compound on the left is your *only* source of organic chemicals. You may use any inorganic chemical you want whenever necessary.

n-propyl chloride	isopropyl chloride
acetylene	*sec*-butyl chloride
acetylene	3,4-dibromohexane
acetylene	1,2-dibromo-3-methylpentane
chlorocyclopentane	1,2-dibromocyclopentane

48. From methyl chloride and benzene, how would you make toluene?
49. From *p*-chlorotoluene, how would you make toluene?
50. What would be the first product in the nitration of *p*-xylene?

4

alcohols

Alcohols are important compounds in organic chemistry because they are easily obtained and are conveniently reactive. Thus, many other groups of compounds can be made from them.

Alcohols are characterized by the functional group —OH, commonly called the *hydroxyl* group or the *hydroxy* group. In aliphatic alcohols, the

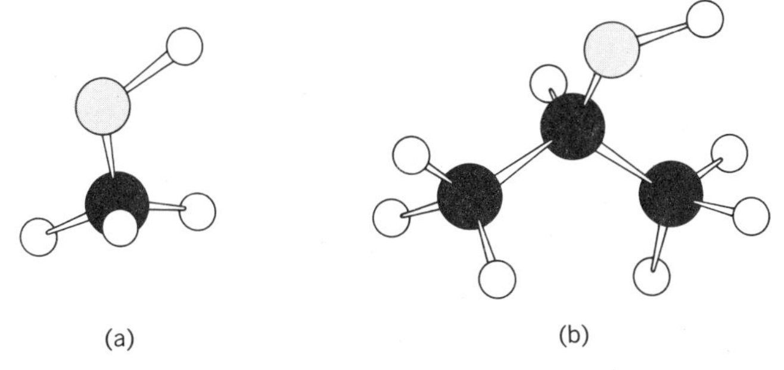

Figure 4-1 (a) Methyl alcohol; (b) isopropyl alcohol.

hydroxyl group is attached to an alkyl group (e.g., ROH). When the hydroxyl group is attached to an aryl group (e.g., ArOH), the compounds are known not as aromatic alcohols, but rather as phenols, because their properties are significantly different from those of the alcohols.

Alcohols in general are divided into three classes. If the hydroxyl group is attached to a carbon atom that is not bound to any other carbon atom (e.g., CH_3OH) or to a carbon atom that is bound to only one other carbon atom (e.g., RCH_2OH), we call the compound a *primary* alcohol. For example,

```
    H             H  H             H  H  H
    |             |  |             |  |  |
  H-C-H         H-C--C-OH        H-C--C--C-OH
    |             |  |             |  |  |
    OH            H  H             H  H  H
```

methanol (*methyl alcohol*) ethanol (*ethyl alcohol*) 1-propanol (*n-propyl alcohol*)

```
                                        H
                                        |
    H  H  H  H                  H  H----C--H  H
    |  |  |  |                  |       |     |
  H-C--C--C--C-OH             H-C-------C-----C-OH
    |  |  |  |                  |       |     |
    H  H  H  H                  H       H     H
```

1-butanol (*n-butyl alcohol*) 2-methyl-1-propanol (*isobutyl alcohol*)

In *secondary* alcohols, the hydroxyl group is attached to a carbon atom that is bound to two other carbon atoms. For example,

```
    H  H  H             H  H  H  H
    |  |  |             |  |  |  |
  H-C--C--C-H         H-C--C--C--C-H
    |  |  |             |  |  |  |
    H  OH H             H  H  OH H
```

2-propanol (*isopropyl alcohol*) 2-butanol (*sec-butyl alcohol*)

```
    H  H  H  H  H             H  H  H  H  H  H
    |  |  |  |  |             |  |  |  |  |  |
  H-C--C--C--C--C-H         H-C--C--C--C--C--C-H
    |  |  |  |  |             |  |  |  |  |  |
    H  H  OH H  H             H  OH H  H  H  H
```

3-pentanol 2-hexanol

```
    H        H        H  H  H
    |        |        |  |  |
  H-C--------C--------C--C--C-H
    |        |        |  |  |
    H   H----C--H     OH H  H
             |
             H
```

2-methyl-3-pentanol

If the hydroxyl group is attached to a carbon atom that is bound to three other carbons, we call the compound a *tertiary* alcohol. For example,

$$R{-}\overset{\overset{\displaystyle R'}{|}}{\underset{\underset{\displaystyle OH}{|}}{C}}{-}R''$$

$$CH_3{-}\overset{\overset{\displaystyle CH_3}{|}}{\underset{\underset{\displaystyle OH}{|}}{C}}{-}CH_3$$

2-methyl-2-propanol
(*tert-butyl alcohol*)

$$CH_3{-}\overset{\overset{\displaystyle OH}{|}}{\underset{\underset{\displaystyle CH_3}{|}}{C}}{-}CH_2CH_2CH_3$$

2-methyl-2-pentanol

$$CH_3CH_2{-}\overset{\overset{\displaystyle CH_3}{|}}{\underset{\underset{\displaystyle OH}{|}}{C}}{-}CH_2CH_3$$

3-methyl-3-pentanol

$$CH_3CH_2{-}\overset{\overset{\displaystyle CH_2CH_3}{|}}{\underset{\underset{\displaystyle OH}{|}}{C}}{-}CH_2CH_3$$

3-ethyl-3-pentanol

Nomenclature

Because they are so common, alcohols are named by several different methods. In the *IUPAC method,* the longest carbon chain *containing the hydroxyl group* is counted; the ending -ol is used, dropping the -e of the alkane name. The carbons are numbered so that the hydroxyl group is given the lowest number, and any other group on the chain is given a name and number. For example,

$$H{-}\overset{\overset{\displaystyle H}{|}}{\underset{\underset{\displaystyle OH}{|}}{C}}{-}H$$

methanol

In this case, the location of the —OH group is not questionable, and the number can be omitted.

$$H{-}\overset{\overset{\displaystyle H}{|}}{\underset{\underset{\displaystyle H}{|}}{C}}{-}\overset{\overset{\displaystyle H}{|}}{\underset{\underset{\displaystyle OH}{|}}{C}}{-}H$$

ethanol

Here again, there is no question about the location of the —OH group, and the number is omitted.

$$H{-}\overset{\overset{\displaystyle H}{|}}{\underset{\underset{\displaystyle H}{|}}{C}}{-}\overset{\overset{\displaystyle H}{|}}{\underset{\underset{\displaystyle H}{|}}{C}}{-}\overset{\overset{\displaystyle H}{|}}{\underset{\underset{\displaystyle OH}{|}}{C}}{-}H$$

1-propanol

Note that 3-propanol would be incorrect, because the alcohol group must be given the lowest number.

```
    H  H  H
    |  |  |
 H—C—C—C—H
    |  |  |
    H  OH H
```
2-propanol

```
    H  H  H  H
    |  |  |  |
 H—C—C—C—C—H
    |  |  |  |
    H  H  H  OH
```
1-butanol

```
    H  H  H  H
    |  |  |  |
 H—C—C—C—C—H
    |  |  |  |
    H  H  OH H
```
2-butanol

```
    H  H  H  H  H
    |  |  |  |  |
 H—C—C—C—C—C—H
    |  |  |  |  |
    H  H  OH H  H
```
3-pentanol

```
    H       H       H
    |       |       |
 H—C———————C———————C—H
    |       |       |
    H    H—C—H     OH
            |
            H
```
2-methyl-1-propanol

```
    H       OH      H
    |       |       |
 H—C———————C———————C—H
    |       |       |
    H    H—C—H      H
            |
            H
```
2-methyl-2-propanol

```
                     H
                     |
    H  H  H       H—C—H     H
    |  |  |          |       |
 H—C—C—C————————————C———————C—H
    |  |  |          |       |
    H  OH H       H—C—H     H
                     |
                     H
```
4,4-dimethyl-2-pentanol

We use di- to designate two —OH groups in a molecule, tri- to designate three —OH groups, etc. For example,

```
H2C—CH2          H2C—CH—CH2
 |    |            |   |   |
 OH   OH           OH  OH  OH
```
ethanediol   propanetriol

In these two examples, we need not number the alcohol groups, because there is no question about their location, since *two hydroxyl groups cannot be on the same carbon atom.* In the following cases, however, we indicate the numbers to avoid ambiguity.

```
H2CCH2CHCH2CH3          H2C—CH—CHCH3
 |     |                  |   |   |
 OH    OH                 OH  OH  OH
```
1,3-pentanediol   1,2,3-butanetriol

Another method uses the name of the alkyl group or radical to which the hydroxyl is attached, and the ending alcohol. For example,

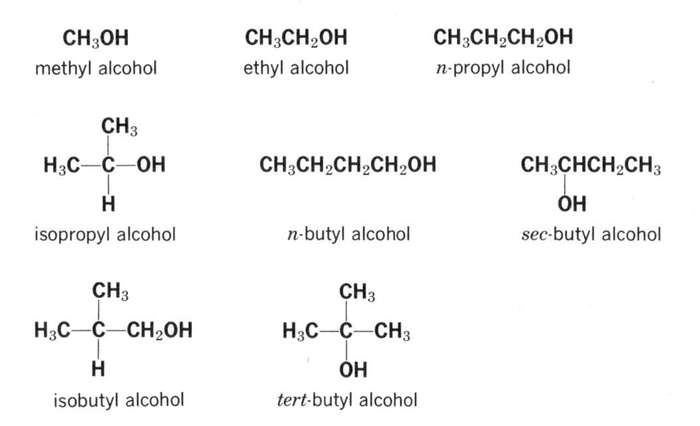

The limitations of this method are that it is convenient for the simple alcohols but fails with complicated alcohols because of the difficulty in naming the radicals.

Another system uses the *common name.* These names are simple and sometimes indicate the origin of the substance. For example,

CH_3OH	CH_3CH_2OH	$CH_2(OH)CH_2(OH)$
wood alcohol	grain alcohol	glycol

$CH_2(OH)CH(OH)CH_2(OH)$

glycerin
(*glycerol*)

Preparation

Water may be added to an olefin (in the presence of sulfuric acid) to produce an alcohol. (See Chapter 3.) Essentially, the —OH group goes to one carbon atom of the double bond, and the —H goes to the other carbon atom.

$$\underset{\text{ethylene}}{H_2C{=}CH_2} + H{-}OH \xrightarrow{H_2SO_4} \underset{\text{ethyl alcohol}}{H{-}CH_2{-}CH_2{-}OH}$$

About half of the ethyl alcohol in the United States is produced by this method, because ethylene is a cheap substance obtained in the cracking of petroleum.

If there is a question which group goes to which carbon atom, the —OH generally goes to the carbon atom bonded to *the fewer hydrogens* (Markownikoff's rule).

$$H-\overset{\overset{H}{|}}{\underset{\underset{H}{|}}{C}}-\overset{\overset{H}{|}}{C}=\overset{\overset{H}{|}}{C}-H \xrightarrow[H-OH]{H_2SO_4} H-\overset{\overset{H}{|}}{\underset{\underset{H}{|}}{C}}-\overset{\overset{H}{|}}{\underset{\underset{OH}{|}}{C}}-\overset{\overset{H}{|}}{\underset{\underset{H}{|}}{C}}-H$$

propylene isopropyl alcohol

Alcohols may also be produced by the reduction of aldehydes and ketones (essentially the reverse of oxidation of alcohols) in the presence of a catalyst. The addition of hydrogen to an aldehyde gives a primary alcohol. The addition of hydrogen to a ketone gives a secondary alcohol. One hydrogen atom goes to the oxygen, and the other hydrogen goes to the carbon atom bonded to the oxygen. For example,

$$R-\overset{\overset{H}{|}}{C}=O + H_2 \xrightarrow{\text{catalyst}} R-\overset{\overset{H}{|}}{\underset{\underset{H}{|}}{C}}-OH$$

aldehyde hydrogen primary alcohol

$$CH_3-\overset{\overset{H}{|}}{C}=O + H_2 \xrightarrow{\text{catalyst}} CH_3-\overset{\overset{H}{|}}{\underset{\underset{H}{|}}{C}}-OH$$

acetaldehyde hydrogen ethyl alcohol

$$R-\overset{\overset{O}{\|}}{C}-R + H_2 \xrightarrow{\text{catalyst}} R-\overset{\overset{H}{|}}{\underset{\underset{OH}{|}}{C}}-R$$

ketone hydrogen secondary alcohol

$$CH_3-\overset{\overset{O}{\|}}{C}-CH_3 + H_2 \xrightarrow{\text{catalyst}} CH_3-\overset{\overset{H}{|}}{\underset{\underset{OH}{|}}{C}}-CH_3$$

acetone hydrogen isopropyl alcohol

Physical Properties

Primary, secondary, and tertiary alcohols vary considerably in many chemical and physical properties. Aliphatic alcohols and phenols also vary in their chemical and physical properties. Table 4-1 lists some aliphatic alcohols with their physical properties.

Some long-chain primary alcohols are important constituents of *waxes*. For example,

$n\text{-}C_{12}H_{25}OH$	$n\text{-}C_{14}H_{29}OH$
1-dodecanol	1-tetradecanol
(*lauryl alcohol*)	(*myristyl alcohol*)
m.p. 26°C	m.p. 39–40°C

$n\text{-}C_{16}H_{33}OH$	$n\text{-}C_{18}H_{37}OH$
1-hexadecanol	1-octadecanol
(cetyl alcohol)	*(stearyl alcohol)*
m.p. 50°C	m.p. 58.5°C

Because they resemble water in structure, the smaller alcohols are very soluble in it. As the alkyl group increases in size, however, its organic nature becomes more prominent, and the solubility decreases considerably.

Some unsaturated alcohols are

$CH_2{=}CH{-}CH_2OH$

2-propen-1-ol
(allyl alcohol)

$CH_3{-}C{\equiv}C{-}CH_2OH$

2-butyn-1-ol

$CH_2{=}CH{-}CH{=}CH{-}CH_2{-}CH(OH){-}CH_3$

4,6-heptadien-2-ol

Remember, the alcohol group gets preference for the lower number, for the groups studied so far. Also,

OH

cyclobutanol
(cyclobutyl alcohol)

OH

cyclohexanol
(cyclohexyl alcohol)

Table 4-1 Some physical properties of some aliphatic alcohols

NAME	FORMULA	MELTING POINT (°C)	BOILING POINT (°C)	TYPE
methanol	CH_3OH	−97.8	64.96	primary
ethanol	CH_3CH_2OH	−117.3	78.5	primary
1-propanol	$CH_3CH_2CH_2OH$	−127	97.1	primary
2-propanol	$(CH_3)_2CHOH$	−89.5	82.4	secondary
1-butanol	$CH_3(CH_2)_2CH_2OH$	−89.8	117.5	primary
2-methyl-1-propanol	$(CH_3)_2CHCH_2OH$	−108	108.1	primary
2-butanol	$CH_3CHOHCH_2CH_3$	−114.7	99.5	secondary
2-methyl-2-propanol	$(CH_3)_3COH$	+25.5	82.2	tertiary
1-pentanol	$CH_3(CH_2)_3CH_2OH$	−79	137.3	primary
3-methyl-1-butanol	$(CH_3)_2CHCH_2CH_2OH$	−117	131–132	primary
1-hexanol	$CH_3(CH_2)_4CH_2OH$	−47	158	primary
1-heptanol	$CH_3(CH_2)_5CH_2OH$	−35	177	primary
1-octanol	$CH_3(CH_2)_6CH_2OH$	−16.7	194–195	primary
1-nonanol	$CH_3(CH_2)_7CH_2OH$	−5	212	primary
1-decanol	$CH_3(CH_2)_8CH_2OH$	+7	229	primary

Table 4-2 Some properties of phenols

NAME	FORMULA	MELTING POINT (°C)
phenol	OH	43
2-methylphenol (*o*-cresol)	OH, CH_3	30
3-methylphenol (*m*-cresol)	OH, CH_3	11.1
4-methylphenol (*p*-cresol)	H_3C, OH	34.8
thymol	CH_3, OH, HC, H_3C, CH_3	51
saligenin	OH, CH_2OH	86
catechol	OH, OH	105
resorcinol	OH, OH	111
hydroquinone	OH, OH	170
4-*n*-hexylresorcinol	$CH_2(CH_2)_4CH_3$, OH, OH	68–71
pyrogallol	OH, OH, OH	132.8

(Continued)

Table 4-2 (Continued)

NAME	FORMULA	MELTING POINT (°C)
phloroglucinol	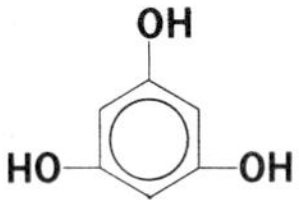 OH, HO, OH	217–219
α-naphthol	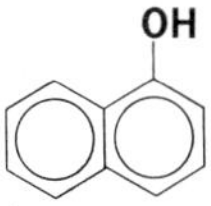 OH	93.35
β-naphthol	 OH	122
picric acid	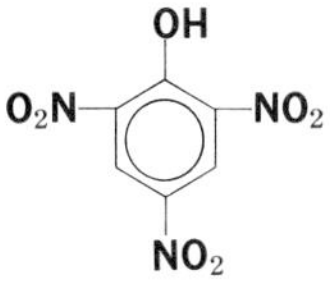 OH, O_2N, NO_2, NO_2	122–123

Phenols are usually solids and are often acidic in character. Some examples are

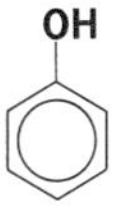

OH

phenol

Actually, this structure should be called *phen*yl alcoh*ol*, but the name has been contracted to phenol as indicated. Phenol is sometimes called carbolic acid.

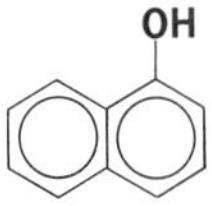

OH

α-naphthol

This structure should be called *α-naphth*yl alcoh*ol*, but the name has been contracted to α-naphthol as indicated.

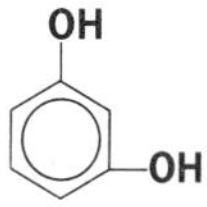

OH
OH

resorcinol

This structure is resorcinol, or *m*-dihydroxybenzene, or 1,3-dihydroxybenzene.

Table 4-2 gives the physical properties of some phenols.

Reactions of Alcohols

OXIDATION

Some alcohols are easily oxidized. Before we can discuss this topic further, we must define what we mean by oxidation and reduction.

When an alcohol is oxidized, essentially two hydrogen atoms are removed. It is very important *which* hydrogens are removed. One hydrogen is *from the* —OH *group,* and the other must be a *hydrogen attached to the carbon that is bonded to* —OH *group.* Oxidation of an alcohol yields a new type of organic compound. *The oxidation of a primary alcohol gives an aldehyde.* For example,

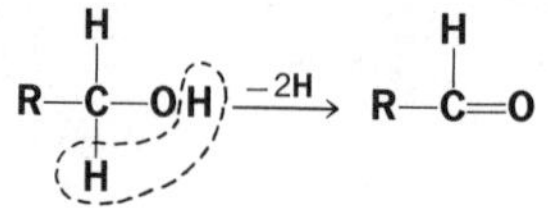

$$R-CH(H)-OH \xrightarrow{-2H} R-CH{=}O$$

a primary alcohol → an aldehyde

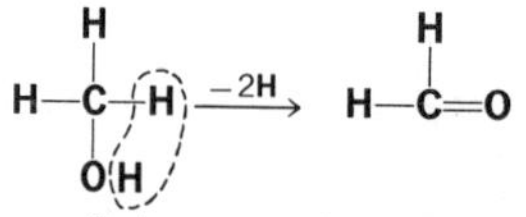

$$H-CH(H)-OH \xrightarrow{-2H} H-CH{=}O$$

methyl alcohol → formaldehyde

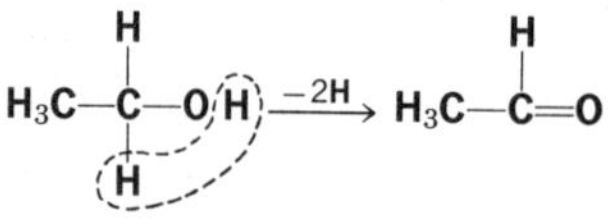

$$H_3C-CH(H)-OH \xrightarrow{-2H} H_3C-CH{=}O$$

ethyl alcohol → acetaldehyde

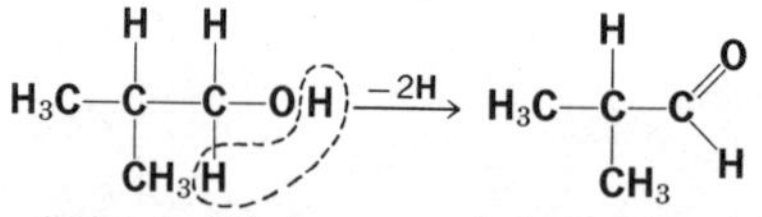

$$H_3C-CH(CH_3)-CH(H)-OH \xrightarrow{-2H} H_3C-CH(CH_3)-CH{=}O$$

isobutyl alcohol → isobutyraldehyde

The naming of aldehydes will be discussed later.

The oxidation of a secondary alcohol gives a ketone. For example,

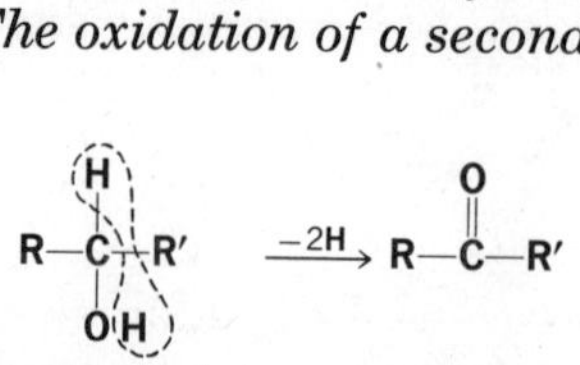

$$R-CH(OH)-R' \xrightarrow{-2H} R-C({=}O)-R'$$

secondary alcohol → a ketone

$$(CH_3)_2CH{-}OH \xrightarrow{-2H} H_3C{-}C(CH_3){=}O$$

isopropyl alcohol — dimethyl ketone (*acetone*)

$$H_3C{-}CH_2{-}CH(OH){-}CH_3 \xrightarrow{-2H} H_3C{-}CH_2{-}C(=O){-}CH_3$$

secondary butyl alcohol, *sec*-butyl alcohol — methyl ethyl ketone

$$H_3C{-}CH_2{-}CH(OH){-}CH_2{-}CH_3 \xrightarrow{-2H} H_3C{-}CH_2{-}C(=O){-}CH_2{-}CH_3$$

3-pentanol — diethyl ketone

The naming of ketones will be discussed later.

The reader can easily see that tertiary alcohols *cannot be oxidized,* because the carbon atom containing the hydroxyl group does not have any hydrogens attached to it.

$$R{-}C(R')(R''){-}OH$$

Tertiary alcohols are thus stable toward oxidizing agents.

Phenols may be regarded as tertiary alcohols, and they cannot be oxidized without causing some profound change in the aromatic ring to which the hydroxyl group is attached. The oxidation of phenols and subsequent dearomatization of the ring does happen, however, but the details need not concern us here.

METHODS OF OXIDATION

Potassium permanganate $KMnO_4$ and potassium dichromate $K_2Cr_2O_7$ are good examples of oxidizing agents.

When, for example, an alcohol is oxidized by potassium permanganate in acid solution, the alcohol is oxidized (it loses two hydrogens), and the manganese is reduced (it changes from a $+7$ to a $+2$ oxidation state). In neutral or basic solution, the manganese is reduced from a $+7$ to a $+4$ oxidation state. For example,

$$\underset{\text{ethyl alcohol}}{5CH_3CH_2OH} + \underset{\text{potassium permanganate}}{\overset{+7}{2KMnO_4}} + \underset{\text{sulfuric acid}}{3H_2SO_4} \longrightarrow \underset{\text{acetaldehyde}}{5CH_3\overset{H}{\overset{|}{C}}{=}O} + \underset{\text{manganese sulfate}}{\overset{+2}{2MnSO_4}} + 8H_2O + \underset{\text{potassium sulfate}}{K_2SO_4}$$

$$\underset{\text{ethyl alcohol}}{3CH_3CH_2OH} + \underset{\text{potassium permanganate}}{\overset{+7}{2KMnO_4}} \longrightarrow \underset{\text{manganese dioxide}}{\overset{+4}{2MnO_2}} + \underset{\text{acetaldehyde}}{3CH_3\overset{H}{C}{=}O} + 2H_2O + 2KOH$$

When potassium dichromate is used to oxidize an alcohol to an aldehyde or ketone, the alcohol is oxidized (it loses two hydrogen atoms), and the chromium is reduced from a +6 to a +3 oxidation state in acid or neutral solution. For example,

$$\underset{n\text{-propyl alcohol}}{3CH_3CH_2CH_2OH} + \overset{+6}{K_2Cr_2O_7} + 4H_2SO_4 \longrightarrow \underset{\text{propionaldehyde}}{3CH_3CH_2\overset{O}{\overset{//}{C}}{-}H} + K_2SO_4 + \overset{+3}{Cr_2(SO_4)_3} + 7H_2O$$

$$\underset{\text{isopropyl alcohol}}{3CH_3\underset{OH}{\underset{|}{C}}HCH_3} + \overset{+6}{K_2Cr_2O_7} + 4H_2SO_4 \longrightarrow \underset{\text{acetone}}{3H_3C{-}\overset{O}{\overset{\|}{C}}{-}CH_3} + K_2SO_4 + \overset{+3}{Cr_2(SO_4)_3} + 7H_2O$$

An alcohol can be converted into an aldehyde or ketone by a dehydrogenation (removal of hydrogen) process, using a catalyst. Copper metal or copper alloys are efficient in accomplishing this reaction. Because a catalyst is unchanged in a chemical reaction, the two hydrogen atoms come off as hydrogen gas. If the vapors of methyl alcohol are passed over hot copper metal, hydrogen gas is evolved, and the odor of formaldehyde is noted.

$$\underset{\text{methyl alcohol}}{CH_3OH} \xrightarrow[\text{heat}]{\text{Cu (catalyst)}} \underset{\text{formaldehyde}}{H{-}\overset{O}{\overset{//}{C}}{-}H} + H_2$$

Acetone is conveniently prepared from isopropyl alcohol in a similar manner. The vapors of isopropyl alcohol are passed over a copper catalyst at 300°C, and acetone and hydrogen are formed.

$$\underset{\text{isopropyl alcohol}}{H_3C{-}\overset{CH_3}{\overset{|}{\underset{H}{\underset{|}{C}}}}{-}OH} \xrightarrow[\text{heat}]{\text{Cu}} \underset{\text{acetone}}{H_3C{-}\overset{O}{\overset{\|}{C}}{-}CH_3} + H_2$$

In the human body, we do not have any strong oxidizing agents such as potassium permanganate or dichromate, nor do we have any hot copper metal. However, we do have organic catalysts called *enzymes*. For an alcohol molecule to be oxidized in the human body, it must give or donate two hydrogen atoms to something able to accept the atoms. Enzymes cause these reactions to occur. The alcohol acts as the donor molecule, and some reducible molecule acts as the acceptor molecule. The two compounds, then, act as an oxidation-reduction system.

DEHYDRATION

The ease of dehydration of alcohols varies with the type of alcohol. Tertiary alcohols are easiest to dehydrate, and primary alcohols are the hardest to dehydrate. Because dehydration is essentially the splitting off of a molecule of water, olefins (unsaturated compounds) are formed in the reaction. Dehydration can sometimes be accomplished by heating, but more generally it is accomplished by a dehydrating agent, such as phosphorus pentoxide P_2O_5 or sulfuric acid H_2SO_4.

When an alcohol is dehydrated, the —OH *group* and the *hydrogen atom attached to the carbon atom immediately adjacent to the carbon containing the* —OH *group* are removed.

$$CH_3CH_2OH \longrightarrow H_2C{=}CH_2 + H_2O$$

ethyl alcohol → ethylene

$$H_3C\text{—}CH(H)\text{—}CH_2(OH) \longrightarrow H_3C\text{—}CH{=}CH_2 + H_2O$$

n-propyl alcohol → propylene

$$H_3C\text{—}C(OH)H\text{—}CH_2\text{—}H \longrightarrow H_3C\text{—}CH{=}CH_2 + H_2O$$

isopropyl alcohol → propylene

$$H\text{—}CH_2\text{—}C(CH_3)(OH)\text{—}CH_2\text{—}H \longrightarrow H_3C\text{—}C(CH_3){=}CH_2 + H_2O$$

tert-butyl alcohol → isobutylene

Alcohols may also be converted into esters and ethers. We shall discuss these topics later.

Alcohols can be converted into alkyl halides in various ways by replacing the —OH group with a halogen (e.g., Cl, Br, or I), by using, for example, concentrated halogen acids (e.g., HCl, HBr, and HI):

$$R\text{—}CH_2\text{—}OH + HX \longrightarrow R\text{—}CH_2X + H_2O$$

alcohol → alkyl halide

$$CH_3CH_2OH + HBr \longrightarrow CH_3CH_2Br + H_2O$$

ethyl alcohol → bromoethane

$$H_3C-\underset{OH}{\overset{CH_3}{C}}-CH_3 + HI \longrightarrow H_3C-\underset{CH_3}{\overset{CH_3}{C}}-I + H_2O$$

t-butyl alcohol → 2 methyl-2-iodopropane

The phosphorus halides may also be used, for example, PCl_5, PCl_3, PBr_3, or PI_3:

$$3CH_3CH_2CH_2OH + PBr_3 \longrightarrow 3CH_3CH_2CH_2Br + P(OH)_3$$

n-propyl alcohol → 1-bromopropane

$$3H_3C-\underset{OH}{\overset{H}{C}}-CH_2CH_3 + PI_3 \longrightarrow 3H_3C-\underset{I}{\overset{H}{C}}-CH_2CH_3 + P(OH)_3$$

sec-butyl alcohol → 2-iodobutane

Special reagents such as thionyl chloride $SOCl_2$ may be used. For example,

$$ROH + SOCl_2 \longrightarrow RCl + SO_2 + HCl$$

$$H_3C-\underset{OH}{\overset{CH_3}{C}}-CH_2CH_3 + SOCl_2 \longrightarrow H_3C-\underset{Cl}{\overset{CH_3}{C}}-CH_2CH_3 + SO_2 + HCl$$

2-methyl-2-butanol → 2-chloro-2-methyl-butane

$$CH_3CH_2CH_2OH + SOCl_2 \longrightarrow CH_3CH_2CH_2Cl + SO_2 + HCl$$

1-propanol → 1-chloropropane

In *all* these preparation methods, a tertiary alcohol will react the fastest of the three types of alcohols, and a secondary alcohol will react faster than a primary alcohol. Phenols do not undergo these reactions.

The hydrogen of the —OH group in alcohols is somewhat acidic. This phenomenon is more pronounced in phenols than in aliphatic alcohols. Often the hydrogen atom can be replaced by sodium or potassium. In the reaction of sodium metal with an alcohol, hydrogen is evolved, and the sodium salt of the alcohol is formed.

$$2ROH + 2Na^0 \longrightarrow 2RONa + H_2$$

The sodium salt is named from the alcohol with the ending -oxide replacing the -anol ending. For example, we get CH_3ONa, sodium methoxide; CH_3CH_2ONa, sodium ethoxide; $CH_3CH_2CH_2ONa$, sodium *n*-propoxide; and $(CH_3)_2CHONa$, sodium isopropoxide.

The hydrogen of the —OH in phenols is so acidic that it can even form a salt with a strong base; that is,

$$C_6H_5OH + NaOH \longrightarrow C_6H_5ONa + H_2O$$

phenol sodium phenoxide

Thus, the sodium salts of phenols are more stable in water than the aliphatic (alkyl) alcohol salts. The sodium salt of aliphatic alcohols decomposes in water to give sodium hydroxide and the alcohol (reverse of the preceding reaction).

$$RONa + H_2O \longrightarrow ROH + NaOH$$

$$CH_3ONa + H_2O \longrightarrow CH_3OH + NaOH$$

sodium methoxide methyl alcohol

Important Aliphatic Alcohols

Methyl alcohol (wood alcohol) can be produced by the destructive distillation of wood (wood heated in the absence of air). Approximately 100 pounds of dried wood yield almost 2 pounds of methyl alcohol, along with other products. Today, most methyl alcohol is made by the reaction of hydrogen and carbon monoxide.

$$2H_2 + CO \xrightarrow[3{,}000\text{ psi}]{\Delta} CH_3OH$$

The reaction is favored by high temperature, 400°C; high pressures, 3,000 pounds per square inch (psi); and a catalyst of chromium and zinc oxides.

Methyl alcohol is widely used industrially as a solvent and as a readily available alcohol in chemical synthesis. It is sometimes employed as a denaturant in ethyl alcohol. It is a poisonous substance and renders the ethyl alcohol deadly. The poisoning due to methyl alcohol results from its oxidation in the body to formic acid HCOOH, which causes severe acidosis. In addition, the intermediate oxidation product of methyl alcohol is formaldehyde, which apparently has a specific toxicity for the retinal cells. Many cases of blindness are reported due to intake of methyl alcohol. The poisonous effects of methyl alcohol are also manifest on inhalation of or continued exposure to the vapors of the alcohol.

Since ancient times *ethyl alcohol* has been prepared by the fermentation of sugar and other carbohydrate material (such as corn [bourbon], potatoes [vodka], rice [saki], and sugar cane [rum]) by yeast. A considerable quantity of ethyl alcohol is also made by the hydration of ethylene. Much can be said concerning ethyl alcohol, but it should be realized that it is probably of greater social than therapeutic use.

Ethyl alcohol (or as it is commonly called, simply alcohol) injures cells by precipitating and desiccating protoplasm; it is irritating to mucous membranes and subcutaneous tissue. The optimal bactericidal (germ-killing) concentration is 70% by weight. This concentration is apparently very critical; the bactericidal efficacy of concentrations above and below this figure cannot be guaranteed. Alcohol kills germs by dehydrating or precipitating them.

The greatest use for alcohol today is as a beverage. Alcoholic beverages may be divided into two classes: distilled and undistilled. Distilled beverages have a much higher concentration of alcohol than undistilled beverages. Some undistilled beverages are wines (with alcohol content varying between 7–18% by volume)(all percentages will be by volume), beer (3–5%), and ciders (3–6%). Some distilled beverages are whiskey (40–50%), brandy (40–55%), rum (45–55%), and gin (40%). In the United States, 100 "proof" refers to 50% ethyl alcohol by volume. By this terminology, 95% alcohol is 190 proof, and absolute alcohol (100%) is 200 proof. The "proof" number is essentially double the percentage by volume. The term "bonded" means that the beverage is not less than 100 proof.

When ethyl alcohol is imbibed, it is rapidly absorbed by both the stomach and intestines. The stomach usually absorbs about 20% of the

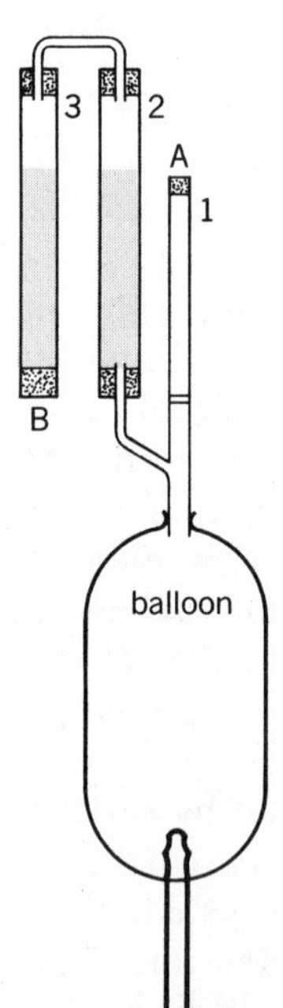

Figure 4-2 Simplified diagram of the intoximeter. Subject blows air into the balloon. Immediate test: A is opened to admit some sample into tube 1. This tube contains a standard amount of $KMnO_4$. Time required for its complete reduction, shown by color loss, is an indication of alcohol content. Later test: B is opened to admit remainder of sample into tubes 2 and 3. Magnesium perchlorate in tube 2 absorbs all the alcohol, which is tested quantitatively with acid potassium dichromate. Ascarite in tube 3 absorbs all the CO_2, indicating sample volume. (Reprinted from S. Nussenbaum, *Organic Chemistry,* Boston: Allyn and Bacon, 1963, p. 309.)

alcohol, and the intestinal tract absorbs the remainder. The blood stream then carries the alcohol to the liver, where the body oxidizes it to carbon dioxide, and energy is liberated. However, if the alcohol concentration is very great, the amount in the blood stream is large enough to damage the body by dangerous or lethal depression of respiration. Alcohol is not a stimulant, as supposed by the laity, but a central nervous system depressant. The coordination of the various parts of the body becomes poor, and normal inhibition and restraint are lost. A new inner person may become evident—one completely different in nature and character from the person not under the influence of alcohol. Table 4-3 gives a scale of the toxic symptoms.

Ethyl alcohol is an excellent solvent for medicine, flavoring extracts, and perfumes. In fact, any medicine labeled "tincture of ___" means an alcoholic solution of the indicated compound. Alcohol is routinely used on bed-ridden patients to prevent bed sores. The topical application of alcohol hardens and cleans the skin and helps to prevent sweating.

Isopropyl alcohol is becoming increasingly important as a rubbing alcohol. It is apparently not absorbed through the skin. Although it has a narcotic action on the central nervous system, isopropyl alcohol is less toxic than methyl alcohol.

Glycol, or ethylene glycol, is a viscous sweet-tasting liquid. In general, increasing the number of —OH groups in a molecule increases its sweetness. The simple sugars, which have five —OH groups, are good examples of very sweet alcohols.

Glycol is poisonous if swallowed. It acts as a depressant on the central nervous system and has a severe effect upon the kidneys. Approximately 100 ml is the fatal dose, and death is apparently caused by respiratory failure. Glycol is used as an antifreeze in automobile radiators and is sold under various trade names. A solution of 60% glycol and 40% water freezes at $-56°F$), making it an efficient antifreeze.

Glycerol (*glycerin*) is a very viscous sweet-tasting liquid. It is an ingredient of all *fats* and *oils* in living organisms and is consequently of great importance. Glycerin may be classified as a demulcent (i.e., it protects the skin). This trihydroxy alcohol is extensively used as a vehicle for many drugs applied to the skin; it is found in many hand lotions. Glycerin is somewhat hygroscopic (i.e., it absorbs water slowly); therefore, in high concentrations, it is somewhat dehydrating and irritating to exposed tissue. Concentrated solutions of glycerin, for this reason, are slowly bactericidal. Glycerin's irritant action accounts for its efficacy in promoting evacuation for the bowel when used rectally as suppositories. Glycerin is not poisonous in small doses, and, when taken orally, it is readily employed as a sweetening agent or vehicle in place of syrups. Large quantities are used in some tobacco products as a humectant. Certain toiletries, such as shampoos, liquid soaps,

Table 4-3 A scale of toxic symptoms

PERCENT ALCOHOL IN BLOOD	SUBJECTIVE STATE AND OBSERVABLE CHANGES IN BEHAVIOR UNDER CONDITIONS OF HEAVY SOCIAL DRINKING
0.010	Clearing of the head. Freer breathing through nasal passages. Mild tingling of mucous membranes of the mouth and throat.
0.020	Slight fullness and mild throbbing at the back of the head. Touch of dizziness. Sense of warmth and general physical well-being. Small bodily aches and fatigue relieved. Not fretful about the weather nor worried concerning personal appearance. Quite willing to talk with associates. Feeling tone of pleasantness.
0.030	Mild euphoria, "everything is all right," "very glad I came," "we will always be friends," "sure I will loan you some money," "it isn't time to go home yet!" No sense of worry. Feeling of playing a very superior game. Time passes quickly.
0.040	Lots of energy for the things he wants to do. Talks much and rather loudly. Hands tremble slightly, reaching and other movements a bit clumsy; laughs loudly at minor jokes; unembarrassed by mishaps, "you don't think I'm drunk, do you, why I haven't taken anything yet." Makes glib or flippant remarks. Memories appear rich and vivid.
0.050	Sitting on top of the world, "a free human being," normal inhibitions practically cut off, takes personal and social liberties of all sorts as impulse prompts. Is long-winded and enlarges on his past exploits. "Can lick anybody in the country," but has observable difficulty in lighting a match. Marked blunting of self-criticism.
0.070	Feelings of remoteness. Odd sensations on rubbing the hands together, or on touching the face. Rapid strong pulse and breathing. Amused at his own clumsiness or rather at what he takes to be the perversity of things about him. Asks others to do things for him. Upsets chair on rising.
0.100	Staggers very perceptibly. Talks to himself. Has difficulty in finding and putting on his overcoat. Fumbles long with the keys in unlocking and starting his car. Feels drowsy, sings loudly, complains that others don't keep on their side of the road.
0.200	Needs help to walk or undress. Easily angered. Shouts, groans, and weeps by turns. Is nauseated and has poor control of urination. Cannot recall with whom he spent the evening.
0.300	In a stuporous condition, very heavy breathing, sleeping and vomiting by turns. No comprehension of language. Strikes wildly at the person who tries to aid him.
0.400	Deep anesthesia, may be fatal.

For every 0.01% alcohol in the blood, 5 to 10 cc of alcohol are ingested.

(From L. S. Goodman and A. Gilman, *The Pharmacological Basis of Therapeutics,* New York: Macmillan, 1941, p. 117.)

and shaving creams, contain glycerin to insure smoothness. Approximately 30% of the glycerin manufactured is used in the preparation of nitroglycerin, an explosive. The alcohol is also used to make plastics, resins, and varnishes.

Half of the glycerin made in this country is produced by the saponification of fat (see Chapter 11); half is also made synthetically.

Sugars are a special classification of alcohols and will be discussed later.

Rose oil is an expensive and exceedingly fragrant mixture of unsaturated aliphatic alcohols. Two of the more important of these are geraniol and citronellol.

Geraniol is also found in the essence of the geranium plant.

$$H_3C{-}\underset{\displaystyle CH_3}{\underset{|}{C}}{=}CHCH_2CH_2\underset{\displaystyle CH_3}{\underset{|}{C}}{=}CHCH_2OH$$

geraniol ($C_{10}H_{17}OH$)

Citronellol is also found in the oil of citronella.

$$H_3C{-}\underset{\displaystyle CH_3}{\underset{|}{C}}{=}CHCH_2CH_2\underset{\displaystyle CH_3}{\underset{|}{C}}HCH_2CH_2OH$$

citronellol ($C_{10}H_{19}OH$)

The essence of the Lily of the Valley flower is *farnesol.*

$$H_3C{-}\underset{\displaystyle CH_3}{\underset{|}{C}}{=}CHCH_2CH_2\underset{\displaystyle CH_3}{\underset{|}{C}}{=}CHCH_2CH_2\underset{\displaystyle CH_3}{\underset{|}{C}}{=}CHCH_2OH$$

farnesol ($C_{15}H_{25}OH$)

Phytyl alcohol, or phytol, is an important naturally occurring alcohol. It can be isolated from chlorophyll and other sources.

$$H_3C{-}\underset{\displaystyle CH_3}{\underset{|}{C}}HCH_2CH_2CH_2\underset{\displaystyle CH_3}{\underset{|}{C}}HCH_2CH_2CH_2\underset{\displaystyle CH_3}{\underset{|}{C}}HCH_2CH_2CH_2\underset{\displaystyle CH_3}{\underset{|}{C}}{=}CHCH_2OH$$

phytyl alcohol ($C_{20}H_{39}OH$)

Inositol is a naturally occurring substance containing six hydroxyl groups attached to a cyclohexane ring. It will be discussed in Chapter 21.

Menthol occurs in peppermint oil, and its properties have been known for thousands of years.

—OH

menthol ($C_{10}H_{19}OH$)

When menthol is rubbed on the skin, it causes an unusual cooling, refreshing sensation. Because it is a stimulant to inflamed mucous surfaces, specifically in the nose and throat, menthol is used in nose and throat sprays, in inhalers, in cough drops, and in cigarettes.

Terpin hydrate finds some use as an expectorant.

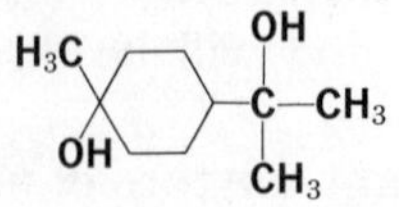

terpin hydrate ($C_{10}H_{18}(OH)_2$)

Elixer of terpin hydrate is an alcoholic solution of terpin hydrate.

Vitamins A and D are also alcohols, and we will discuss them in Chapter 21.

We will discuss cholesterol and other important steroidal alcohols occurring in the body in Chapter 11.

Important Aromatic Alcohols

Phenol (carbolic acid) is one of the oldest of the antiseptics known and was introduced by Lister in 1867. Although seldom used clinically today, because it is quite toxic to tissues, phenol is widely used as the standard of comparison for other possible antiseptic agents. The *phenol coefficient* is the ratio of the bactericidal activity of the chemical in question compared to phenol under certain standard conditions. Phenol is sometimes used to cauterize small wounds and animal bites. Since it is so cheap, it is also used to disinfect excrement. Phenol is prepared synthetically by the action of water on chlorobenzene under certain special conditions. Chlorobenzene is made from chlorine and benzene in the presence of a catalyst.

The substituted phenols are used mostly as antiseptics. The three cresols (*o*-, *m*-, and *p*-methylphenols) have phenol coefficients against *Eberthella typhosa* of about 2.5. A solution of the mixed cresols and soap is sold under the name Lysol.

Resorcinol is both bactericidal and fungicidal, but it is not as active as phenol. It is commonly used as a 5% solution in the treatment of ringworms, eczema, psoriasis, and other skin disorders. Resorcinols with alkyl groups substituted in the 4 position have greatly increased phenol coefficients.

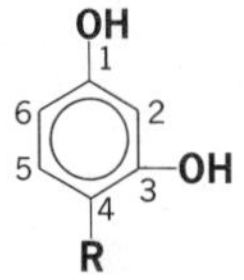

The R group has been varied from methyl to *n*-nonyl, and it was discovered that the most active compound contained the *n*-hexyl group. 4-*n*-Hexylresorcinol has a phenol coefficient of about 50. It was used at first as a urinary antiseptic but has been replaced by the sulfa drugs and antibiotics. 4-*n*-Hexylresorcinol is found in some cough drops, but its greatest use is as an anthelmintic (i.e., an agent effective against a certain group of parasitic worms called helminths: roundworm, hookworm, tapeworm, etc.), and, as such, it is often the drug of choice.

Hexachlorophene, which is a bis-phenol (contains two phenol groups), is a potent bacteriostatic agent found in many proprietary soaps and deodorants.

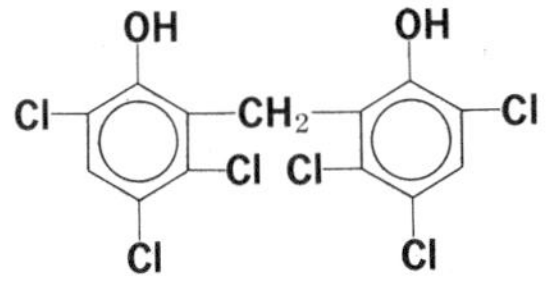

hexachlorophene

It works slowly, but when it has accumulated on the skin due to repeated usage, it greatly reduces the concentration of microorganisms.

Pyrogallol is a powerful reducing agent used as a photographic developer. It has some value in the treatment of some skin disorders, but its decided toxicity precludes its wide usage.

Thymol occurs in certain essential oils and is related to the naturally occurring terpenes. Thymol is used mostly as an effective agent against certain fungus growths and also possesses some bactericidal and anthelmintic properties.

Because *picric acid,* or 2,4,6-trinitrophenol, is capable of precipitating proteins, it is an efficient germicide. Picric acid finds some use in the treatment of minor burns, because it precipitates the proteins on the wounds and acts like a dam. It thus prevents the loss of valuable body fluids and also keeps the air and microorganisms away from the burn, thereby decreasing the pain and possible infection. Butesin picrate is an ointment that combines the antiseptic and precipitating properties of picric acid with the anesthetic properties of butesin.

Urushiol is an alkylated catechol and may be one of the active principles of poison ivy.

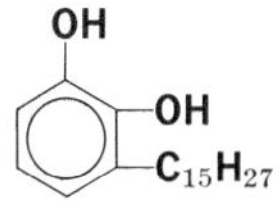

urushiol

REVIEW QUESTIONS

1. Write structures for a primary, a secondary, and a tertiary alcohol.
2. How many quaternary alcohols are known?
3. Write structures for 3-pentanol, methyl, ethyl, *n*-propyl, isopropyl, *sec*-butyl, *n*-butyl, *iso*butyl, and *tert*-butyl alcohols.

4. Write structures for glycol, glycerol, phenol, and resorcinol.
5. Write structures for thymol, hydroquinone, 4-*n*-hexylresorcinol, hexachlorophene, and picric acid.
6. What are several ways of defining oxidation and reduction?
7. Write balanced equations for the reaction of $KMnO_4$ in sulfuric acid solution with ethyl alcohol, *n*-propyl alcohol, isopropyl alcohol, and *sec*-butyl alcohol.
8. Write balanced equations for the reaction of $KMnO_4$ in basic solution with ethyl alcohol, *n*-propyl alcohol, isopropyl alcohol, and *sec*-butyl alcohol.
9. Write balanced equations for the reaction of $K_2Cr_2O_7$ in sulfuric acid solution with ethyl alcohol, *n*-propyl alcohol, isopropyl alcohol, and *sec*-butyl alcohol.
10. What is the difference between dehydration and dehydrogenation? Write dehydration reactions for ethyl alcohol, isopropyl alcohol, and *sec*-butyl alcohol.
11. Write balanced equations for the preparation of methyl iodide, ethyl chloride, isopropyl bromide, and *tert*-butyl chloride.
12. Write reactions illustrating the hydration of ethylene, propylene, and 2-butene.
13. How is methyl alcohol produced commercially? Of what use is it?
14. In what two ways is ethyl alcohol produced commercially?
15. What are the percentages of alcohol in wine, beer, whiskey, brandy, rum, and gin? Define the terms proof and bonded. Discuss the digestion, absorption, nutritive character, and physiological effect of ethyl alcohol on the body.
16. What is meant by the term "tincture of ____"?
17. Discuss the use of isopropyl alcohol, glycol, and glycerol.
18. Name the following compounds:

```
            CH3 H  H                       H  H  H
            |   |  |                       |  |  |
(a) H3C—C———C——C—CH3             (b) H—C——C——C—OH
            |   |  |                       |  |  |
            OH  H  OH                      H  |  H
                                           (benzene ring)

                                              OH
                                              |
(c) (cyclobutane ring)—OH         (d)  (benzene ring)
                                              |
                                          CH2CH2CH3
```

5

ethers

Ethers can be considered alcohol derivatives. The ether linkage is an oxygen atom between two carbon atoms (C—O—C). Ethers can have two alkyl groups (R—O—R), an alkyl and an aryl (R—O—Ar), or two aryls (Ar—O—Ar), one on either side of the oxygen.

Nomenclature

To name ethers by the common methods, we give the radicals attached to the oxygen their common names and use the ending ether. If both groups are the same, we do not necessarily have to use the prefix di-, although it is used sometimes. Table 5-1 lists some common ethers.

Another *useful* method of naming ethers is to name a simple or relatively simple radical with the oxygen, calling it alkoxy, and then to indicate its position on some hydrocarbon position. For example,

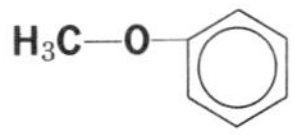

$H_3C—O—C_6H_5$

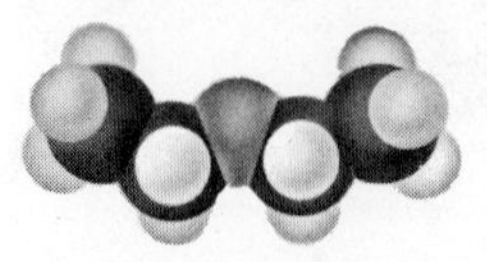

Figure 5-1 Diethyl ether.

may be called methoxybenzene. (The CH_3O— is the methoxy part.)

$$OCH_2CH_2CH_3$$ (on naphthalene ring, position 1)

may be called 1-*n*-propoxynaphthalene. The 1- indicates where the ether linkage is on the naphthalene ring, and the —O—$CH_2CH_2CH_3$ is the *n*-propoxy group.

CH_3CH_2O—(benzene ring)
ethoxy part
ethoxybenzene

(benzene ring)—O—(benzene ring)—CH_3
phenoxy part
p-phenoxytoluene

$$\left(CH_3CH_2CH_2CH_2CH_2CH_2\underset{\large OCH_3}{\underset{|}{C}}HCH_3\right)$$

2-methoxyoctane

This method is most useful when one of the R groups does not have a common name.

Preparation

DEHYDRATION OF ALCOHOL

Ethers can be produced by the removal of one molecule of water from two molecules of alcohol. Sulfuric acid is commonly used as the dehydrating agent.

$$\underset{\text{alcohol}}{RO\text{—}H} + \underset{\text{alcohol}}{H\text{—}O\text{—}R} \xrightarrow{H_2SO_4} \underset{\text{ether}}{R\text{—}O\text{—}R} + \underset{\text{water}}{H_2O}$$

$$\underset{\text{methyl alcohol}}{CH_3OH} + \underset{\text{methyl alcohol}}{HOCH_3} \xrightarrow{H_2SO_4} \underset{\text{methyl ether}}{CH_3\text{—}O\text{—}CH_3} + \underset{\text{water}}{H_2O}$$

$$\underset{\text{ethyl alcohol}}{CH_3CH_2OH} + \underset{\text{ethyl alcohol}}{HOCH_2CH_3} \xrightarrow{H_2SO_4} \underset{\text{ethyl ether}}{CH_3CH_2\text{—}O\text{—}CH_2CH_3} + \underset{\text{water}}{H_2O}$$

The above method is convenient if two identical groups on each side of the ether oxygen are desired.

Table 5-1 Ethers

NAME	FORMULA
methyl ether	$\begin{array}{ccccccccc} & & H & & & & H & & \\ H & - & C & - & O & - & C & - & H \\ & & H & & & & H & & \end{array}$
ethyl ether	$\begin{array}{ccccccccccccc} & & H & & H & & & & H & & H & & \\ H & - & C & - & C & - & O & - & C & - & C & - & H \\ & & H & & H & & & & H & & H & & \end{array}$
methyl ethyl ether	$\begin{array}{ccccccccccc} & & H & & & & H & & H & & \\ H & - & C & - & O & - & C & - & C & - & H \\ & & H & & & & H & & H & & \end{array}$
isobutyl *tert*-butyl ether	$\begin{array}{ccccccccccccccc} & & H & & H_3C & & H & & & & CH_3 & & H & & \\ H & - & C & - & C & - & C & - & O & - & C & - & C & - & H \\ & & H & & H & & H & & & & CH_3 & & H & & \end{array}$
vinyl ether	$\begin{array}{ccccccccc} H & & H & & & & H & & H \\ C & = & C & - & O & - & C & = & C \\ H & & & & & & & & H \end{array}$
isopropyl phenyl ether	$C_6H_5-OCHCH_3$ (with CH_3 on the CH)
β-chloroethyl ether	$\begin{array}{ccccccccccccc} & & H & & H & & & & H & & H & & \\ & & \beta & & \alpha & & & & \alpha & & \beta & & \\ Cl & - & C & - & C & - & O & - & C & - & C & - & Cl \\ & & H & & H & & & & H & & H & & \end{array}$
methyl phenyl ether	$C_6H_5-OCH_3$
phenyl ether	$C_6H_5-O-C_6H_5$
methyl *β*-naphthyl ether	$C_{10}H_7-OCH_3$
phenyl *α*-naphthyl ether	$C_{10}H_7-O-C_6H_5$

Actually, the sulfuric acid reacts with the first molecule of alcohol to form an alkyl sulfuric acid.

$$\underset{\text{alcohol}}{ROH} + \underset{\text{sulfuric acid}}{HOSO_2OH} \longrightarrow \underset{\text{alkyl sulfuric acid}}{ROSO_2OH} + \underset{\text{water}}{H_2O}$$

$$\underset{\text{ethyl alcohol}}{CH_3CH_2OH} + \underset{\text{sulfuric acid}}{HOSO_2OH} \longrightarrow \underset{\text{ethyl sulfuric acid}}{CH_3CH_2OSO_2OH} + \underset{\text{water}}{H_2O}$$

The alkyl sulfuric acid is the same type of product formed in the reaction of sulfuric acid and an olefin.

$$\underset{\text{olefin}}{R{-}CH{=}CH_2} + \underset{\text{sulfuric acid}}{HOSO_2OH} \longrightarrow \underset{\text{alkyl sulfuric acid}}{R{-}\underset{|\atop OSO_2OH}{CH}{-}CH_3}$$

or

$$\underset{\text{ethylene}}{CH_2{=}CH_2} + \underset{\text{sulfuric acid}}{HOSO_2OH} \longrightarrow \underset{\text{ethyl sulfuric acid}}{CH_3CH_2OSO_2OH}$$

The alkyl sulfuric acid can now react with another molecule of alcohol to form the ether and regenerate the sulfuric acid.

$$\underset{\text{alkyl sulfuric acid}}{ROSO_2OH} + \underset{\text{alcohol}}{HOR} \longrightarrow \underset{\text{ether}}{ROR} + \underset{\text{sulfuric acid}}{H_2SO_4}$$

$$\underset{\text{ethyl sulfuric acid}}{CH_3CH_2OSO_2OH} + \underset{\text{ethyl alcohol}}{HOCH_2CH_3} \longrightarrow \underset{\text{ethyl ether}}{CH_3CH_2OCH_2CH_3} + \underset{\text{sulfuric acid}}{H_2SO_4}$$

The sulfuric acid is now free to react with another alcohol molecule to form the alkyl sulfuric acid, which can react with an additional molecule of alcohol to form an ether, and so on. Temperature control is important in this reaction. At certain temperatures, the alkyl sulfuric acid can split off sulfuric acid and thus form the olefin, thereby wasting that molecule of alcohol. For example,

$$\underset{\text{ethyl sulfuric acid}}{CH_3CH_2OSO_2OH} \xrightarrow{180°C} \underset{\text{ethylene}}{CH_2{=}CH_2} + \underset{\text{sulfuric acid}}{H_2SO_4}$$

or, in general,

$$R{-}CH_2{-}\underset{|\atop OSO_2OH}{CH}{-}CH_3 \xrightarrow[\text{temp.}]{\text{high}} R{-}CH{=}CH{-}CH_3 + H_2SO_4$$

In preparing ethyl ether, it is practical to maintain a temperature of 140°C so that dehydration does not prevail, the formation of ether proceeds smoothly and continuously, and the ether distills out of the reaction mixture as it is formed.

ALKYL HALIDE WITH SODIUM SALT

A more general method of preparing ethers of all types is to react an alkyl halide with the sodium salt of an alcohol. In this reaction, an ether is produced, and sodium halide is eliminated. The general reaction is

$$\underset{\text{sodium salt of an alcohol}}{R{-}O{-}Na} + \underset{\text{alkyl halide}}{R'X} \longrightarrow \underset{\text{ether}}{R{-}O{-}R'} + \underset{\text{sodium halide}}{NaX}$$

Some specific examples are

$$\underset{\text{sodium salt of methyl alcohol}}{CH_3ONa} + \underset{\text{ethyl bromide}}{CH_3CH_2Br} \longrightarrow \underset{\text{methyl ethyl ether}}{CH_3OCH_2CH_3} + \underset{\text{sodium bromide}}{NaBr}$$

$$\underset{\text{sodium salt of ethyl alcohol}}{CH_3CH_2ONa} + \underset{\text{ethyl iodide}}{CH_3CH_2I} \longrightarrow \underset{\text{ethyl ether}}{CH_3CH_2OCH_2CH_3} + \underset{\text{sodium iodide}}{NaI}$$

$$\underset{\text{sodium salt of isopropyl alcohol}}{CH_3\underset{\substack{|\\ CH_3}}{C}HONa} + \underset{n\text{-propyl bromide}}{CH_3CH_2CH_2Br} \longrightarrow \underset{\text{isopropyl } n\text{-propyl ether}}{CH_3\underset{\substack{|\\ CH_3}}{C}HOCH_2CH_2CH_3} + \underset{\text{sodium bromide}}{NaBr}$$

$$\underset{\text{sodium salt of } n\text{-butyl alcohol}}{CH_3CH_2CH_2CH_2ONa} + \underset{\text{isopropyl iodide}}{(CH_3)_2CHI} \longrightarrow \underset{\text{isopropyl } n\text{-butyl ether}}{CH_3CH_2CH_2CH_2{-}O{-}CH(CH_3)_2} + \underset{\text{sodium iodide}}{NaI}$$

This method is best for making many different ethers, especially those with different R— groups.

Properties

Ethers are inert to oxidizing agents, to reducing agents, and generally to acids and bases. Under certain conditions, ethers may be cleaved (broken down).

From the boiling points listed in Table 5-2, it is evident that the lower members of the ether series are very volatile. This is a property to consider seriously, because ethers are also very flammable. The combination of flammability and low boiling point makes ethyl ether, for example, a very dangerous chemical to use. Great care must be taken to avoid sparks near its vapors. Most of the ethers have some anesthetic properties.

Important Ethers

Ethyl ether is the only saturated ether in common usage as an anesthetic, since the others are somewhat toxic and possess varying degrees of narcotic activity. *Ethyl ether,* or, as it is commonly called, "ether," is made by the action of concentrated sulfuric acid on ethyl alcohol. The temperature of the reaction must be carefully controlled and kept at 130–140°C,

Table 5-2 Some ethers and boiling points

FORMULA	NAME	BOILING POINT (°C)
CH_3OCH_3	methyl ether	−24.9
$CH_3OCH_2CH_3$	methyl ethyl ether	8
$CH_3CH_2OCH_2CH_3$	ethyl ether	34.6
$CH_3CH_2CH_2OCH_2CH_2CH_3$	*n*-propyl ether	91
$CH_3CH(CH_3)OCH(CH_3)CH_3$	isopropyl ether	69
$CH_3CH_2CH_2CH_2OCH_2CH_2CH_2CH_3$	*n*-butyl ether	142
$CH_2{=}CHOCH{=}CH_2$	vinyl ether	39
$C_6H_5{-}O{-}C_6H_5$	phenyl ether	305
$H_3CO{-}C_6H_5$	methyl phenyl ether	154

because at higher temperatures, the yield of ether is decreased and olefin (ethylene) is produced. At temperatures of 180–200°C, ethylene is obtained almost exclusively.

Ether is hygroscopic (i.e., it picks up water from the air), and ordinary ether contains 1–2% water. Ordinary ether, which also contains small amounts of ethyl alcohol, may be converted into absolute ether (100% pure ether) by several methods. Precautions must always be taken to prevent the atmospheric moisture from coming into contact with the ether. To prepare dry ether conveniently, first boil ordinary ether with concentrated sulfuric acid to remove most of the alcohol and water. Then distill the ether from the sulfuric acid, in a water-free system, and introduce sodium metal into the distilled ether. The sodium metal completely removes the last traces of water. When the ether is distilled from the sodium metal, it is 100% pure, dry ether. The dried liquid must be carefully sealed to exclude all moisture.

One disadvantage is that ether tends to form peroxides. The peroxide is formed by the reaction of ether with oxygen from the atmosphere. When ether is evaporated or distilled, the solid peroxide is left; the solid may explode if heated, rubbed, or otherwise disturbed. Consequently, it is important that the ether used not contain peroxides. Ether is shipped in iron containers, in glass containers with iron wire inside the liquid, or in copper containers. Iron and copper prevent the formation of peroxides. To determine if an ether solution contains peroxides, shake the ether with a water solution of sodium iodide NaI. If peroxides are present, iodine will be liberated and will color the ether solution purple. Once a sealed can of ether has been opened and exposed to oxygen of the air, it should not be used for anesthetic purposes, because peroxides may have formed.

Ether fumes are heavy and sink to the floor. If used in the laboratory, ether fumes can travel along a desk top for 10–20 feet, which emphasizes the importance of not having open flames in the vicinity of the exposed ether. Certain ether-air mixtures are explosive, which again demonstrates the caution necessary in handling this substance.

The low boiling point of ether indicates a very volatile substance. Ordinary room temperature may be about 25°C, and ether boils at 35°C. Body temperature is approximately 37°C. Thus, if liquid ether were dropped on the face, for example, the liquid would vaporize and form gaseous ether, which could be conveniently inhaled. Because it vaporizes very quickly, when liquid ether is dropped on the skin, it abstracts heat and has a cooling effect. To avoid any cooling effects and to provide a more even anesthetic, ether may be dropped on a mask, not directly on the skin. The vapors are evenly distributed by the mask, and one has a better control of the anesthetic. Of course, ether may be administered with other gases by a machine. In tropical regions, where the temperature may be above 35°C, the use of ether presents quite a problem, because at that temperature, ether is not a liquid and cannot be conveniently dropped.

Ether is a relatively slow inhalation anesthetic, sometimes taking 10–15 minutes to bring a patient to the surgical stage. For this reason, a quicker acting anesthetic is often given as an inductive agent to start the anesthetic; then ether is given. Ether has been a very widely used anesthetic because of its wide margin of safety. A concentration of 4% by volume of ether in inhaled air maintains surgical anesthesia, whereas a concentration of 10% ether in inhaled air causes respiratory failure. This provides the anesthetist with a great degree of latitude in the administration of the chemical. Because of its very low death rate (failures due to anesthetic death average one in every 20,000 cases), ether is often used in operations on children, unless contraindicated. Naturally, the choice of any anesthetic is subject to many variables, and so the actual chemical used depends upon the hospital, its locale, its personnel, etc.

Because many types of organic compounds are very soluble in ether, it is used to separate organic material from inorganic material. Lipids are very soluble in ether, whereas carbohydrates and proteins usually are not. Thus, we have an elegant method of separating oils and fats from certain naturally occurring materials. Because it is also relatively inert, ether is used as a solvent in many organic reactions, in the Grignard reaction, for example, which we discussed in Chapter 3.

The vinyl group in organic chemistry is $CH_2{=}CH{-}$. *Vinyl ether* is prepared in the following manner. Ethylene chlorohydrin is converted into β-chloroethyl ether by the action of sulfuric acid.

$$\underset{\text{ethylene chlorohydrin}}{Cl{-}CH_2CH_2{-}OH} + \underset{\text{ethylene chlorohydrin}}{HO{-}CH_2CH_2{-}Cl} \xrightarrow{H_2SO_4} \underset{\beta\text{-chloroethyl ether}}{Cl{-}CH_2CH_2{-}O{-}CH_2CH_2{-}Cl} + H_2O$$

Then, in a typical dehydrohalogenation process, two molecules of hydrogen chloride are eliminated from the β-chloroethyl ether to form vinyl ether.

$$\underset{\beta\text{-chloroethyl ether}}{Cl{-}CH_2CH_2{-}O{-}CH_2CH_2{-}Cl} \xrightarrow[\text{alcohol}]{NaOH} \underset{\text{vinyl ether}}{CH_2{=}CH{-}O{-}CH{=}CH_2} + \underset{\text{hydrogen chloride}}{2HCl}$$

Vinyl ether boils at 31°C and closely resembles ethyl ether in many of its physical properties. Vinyl ether, commonly called Vinethene by the anesthetist, is both flammable and explosive. Therefore, great care must be taken when handling it. Because of its double bonds, vinyl ether has a pronounced tendency to decompose; for this reason, it is marketed in dark bottles and should be kept in a cool place away from the air. An opened bottle should never be used if a day has passed since the opening of the bottle. Generally, the manufacturer puts small amounts of certain solids (oxidation inhibitors) in vinyl ether to prevent oxidation and decomposition of the product.

Vinyl ether is a rapidly acting inhalation anesthetic. It has enjoyed great popularity as an inductive agent. Induction occurs quickly, 1–2 minutes, and recovery is pleasant and similarly rapid. For short operations, vinyl ether may be used to great advantage, because it produces muscular relaxation comparable to that obtained with ethyl ether. Because of its tendency to produce salivation, the possibility of liver damage, and the probability of anoxia, vinyl ether is not recommended for operations that last more than one hour.

Eugenol occurs in cloves and can be conveniently obtained by passing steam into cloves. During this process (steam distillation), the volatile eugenol comes over with the steam and is easily separated.

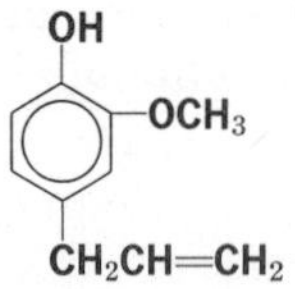

OH

$-OCH_3$

$CH_2CH{=}CH_2$

eugenol

Eugenol can be converted into vanillin, which has a big industrial market. Actually, eugenol is a mild local anesthetic and is used by the dentist to lessen pain in tooth cavities.

Guaiacol can be obtained by the distillation of beechwood, or it can be prepared synthetically.

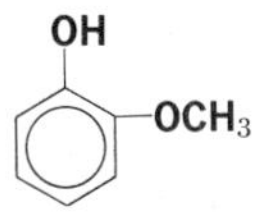

OH
$-OCH_3$
guaiacol

Although guaiacol has some use in the therapy of chronic lung abscesses, its greatest use is as an expectorant to lessen the effects of bronchitis and bronchiectasis.

Eucalyptol is a peculiar "inner type" ether related to the terpenes and is found in eucalyptus oil.

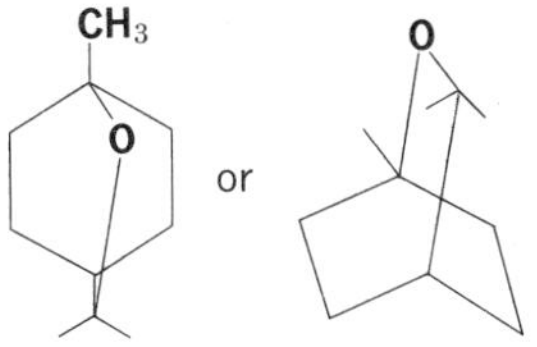

CH_3 O or O

eucalyptol

This colorless and pungent liquid has some use as an expectorant.

Safrole is a diether type compound that may also be considered an acetal. Inspection of its formula will show its close relationship to eugenol. Safrole occurs in the oil of sassafras. Safrole can be conveniently converted into isosafrole by boiling the liquid with sodium hydroxide. Isosafrole can be oxidized to piperonal, which possesses an odor resembling heliotrope and is used in the perfume industry.

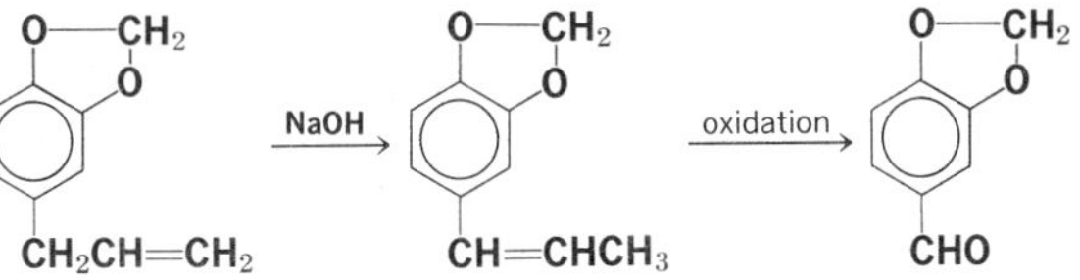

O—CH_2 O (NaOH →) O—CH_2 O (oxidation →) O—CH_2 O

$CH_2CH{=}CH_2$ safrole | $CH{=}CHCH_3$ isosafrole | CHO piperonal

REVIEW QUESTIONS

1. Draw structures for the following ethers: *n*-propyl ether, phenyl ethyl ether, α-naphthyl ether, benzyl phenyl ether, *n*-butyl *n*-hexyl ether.
2. Discuss in detail the commercial production of ethyl ether. Why must the temperature be accurately controlled? What are two important general ways of making ethers?
3. Discuss in detail the physical and chemical properties of ethyl ether.
4. What is done commercially to prevent the formation of peroxides in ethyl ether? How is it possible to detect the presence of these peroxides in ethyl ether?

5. Criticize the following statements: Ether fumes are light and rise to the ceiling. Ether is combustible but will not explode when mixed with air. A can of ether used for anesthetic purposes may be opened and closed many times and used repeatedly.
6. Is there any advantage to ethyl ether as an anesthetic?
7. How is vinyl ether produced commercially? Discuss its chemical and physical properties.
8. Of what use are eugenol and eucalyptol?
9. Name the following compounds:

(a) $CH_3OCH_2(CH_2)_3CH_3$ (b) $CH_3(CH_2)_6CH_2—O—CH_2(CH_2)_6CH_3$

(c) 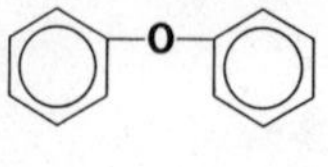 —O— (d) 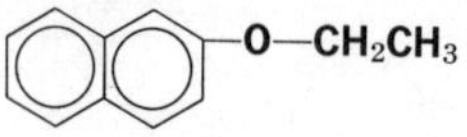 —O—CH_2CH_3

(e) 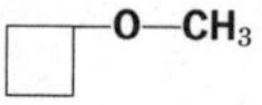 —O—CH_3

6

aldehydes and ketones

Aldehydes and ketones are classes of homologous compounds, both characterized by the *carbonyl group* (C=O). Although they are both very reactive, aldehydes are much more reactive than ketones. In fact, some aldehydes will react with the oxygen in the air, with water, and with themselves. Ketones are stable under these conditions. Many compounds in the body and in the pharmacological field are either aldehydes or ketones, and, consequently, we cannot overemphasize their importance.

Nomenclature

The aldehyde group is

```
  H
  |
—C=O     or     —CHO
```

The general formula for an aliphatic or alicyclic aldehyde is RCHO; the general formula for an aromatic aldehyde is ArCHO. When the R is hydrogen, we have HCHO, an exceptionally reactive compound.

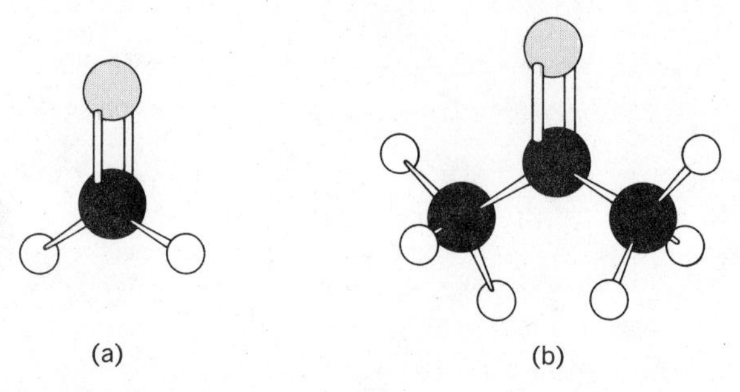

Figure 6-1 (a) Formaldehyde; (b) acetone.

To name aldehydes by the IUPAC system, we pick the longest chain of carbon atoms containing the aldehyde group, use the hydrocarbon name, drop the -e of the alkane name, and add the ending -al. We locate groups on the chain by the number of the carbon atom to which they are attached. The aldehyde group is carbon 1, and its number is commonly omitted. The common name system of naming aldehydes takes advantage of the fact that aldehydes, when oxidized, are converted into compounds called acids (see Chapter 7). Aldehydes are given the common name of the acid with the suffix -aldehyde. This system is inadequate when an aldehyde is oxidized to yield an acid without a common name. As is usual in the naming of organic compounds, we often have a common name, which has no significance whatsoever, except that it is convenient and short.

Ketones are characterized by the functional group

$$-\overset{|}{\underset{|}{C}}-\overset{\overset{O}{\|}}{C}-\overset{|}{\underset{|}{C}}-$$

Ketones may contain two alkyl groups,

$$RCOR,\ R\overset{\overset{O}{\|}}{C}R$$

one alkyl and one aryl group,

$$RCOAr,\ R\overset{\overset{O}{\|}}{C}Ar$$

or two aryl groups,

$$ArCOAr,\ Ar\overset{\overset{O}{\|}}{C}Ar$$

attached to either side of the carbonyl group. When the two groups are the same, the ketone is symmetrical; when the two groups differ, the ketone is unsymmetrical.

To name ketones by the IUPAC system, we pick the longest chain of carbon atoms containing the carbonyl group, use the hydrocarbon name, drop the -e of the alkane name, and use the ending -one. We give the carbonyl group the lowest possible number, and we designate the groups attached to the chain by numbers.

The common method used for the simpler ketones is to name the two groups as radicals attached to either side of the carbonyl group and use the ending -ketone. This method is obviously inadequate when the R groups have no common name.

Preparation

Primary alcohols are oxidized to aldehydes when treated with potassium permanganate $KMnO_4$ in acid or basic solution, or potassium dichromate in acid solution. This method is very good if the aldehyde is volatile and will distill out of the reaction mixture. If the aldehyde is not volatile, it will be further oxidized in solution. For example,

$$CH_3CH_2CH_2CH_2OH \xrightarrow{KMnO_4} CH_3CH_2CH_2C(=O)\text{—}H$$

n-butyl alcohol → *n*-butyraldehyde

$$C_6H_5\text{—}CH_2OH \xrightarrow{K_2Cr_2O_7} C_6H_5\text{—}C(=O)\text{—}H$$

benzyl alcohol → benzaldehyde

Secondary alcohols are oxidized to ketones when treated with oxidizing agents. For example,

$$CH_3CH(OH)CH_3 \xrightarrow{K_2Cr_2O_7} CH_3C(=O)\text{—}CH_3$$

2-propanol → propanone (*dimethyl ketone*)

$$CH_3CH_2CH(OH)CH_2CH_3 \xrightarrow{K_2Cr_2O_7} CH_3CH_2C(=O)\text{—}CH_2CH_3$$

3-pentanol → 3-pentanone (*diethyl ketone*)

Physical Properties

Table 6-1 lists the formulas, names, and boiling points of some aliphatic aldehydes.

Table 6-1 Aliphatic aldehydes

FORMULA	IUPAC NAME	COMMON NAME	BOILING POINT (°C)
HCHO	methanal	formaldehyde	−21
CH_3CHO	ethanal	acetaldehyde	20.8
CH_3CH_2CHO	propanal	propionaldehyde	48.8
$CH_3CH_2CH_2CHO$	butanal	*n*-butyraldehyde	75.7
$CH_3CH(CH_3)CHO$	2-methylpropanal	isobutyraldehyde	61
$CH_3CH_2CH_2CH_2CHO$	pentanal	*n*-valeraldehyde	102–103
$CH_3CH_2CH_2CH_2CH_2CH_2CHO$	heptanal	*n*-heptaldehyde	155

Other important aldehydes are

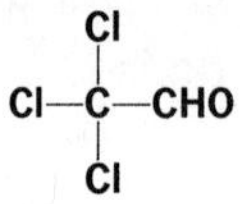

$$Cl_3C{-}CHO$$

chloral
(*trichloroacetaldehyde*)
b.p. 97.75°C

which contains chlorine;

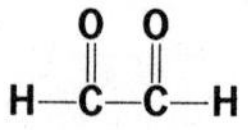

$$H{-}\overset{O}{\overset{\|}{C}}{-}\overset{O}{\overset{\|}{C}}{-}H$$

ethanedial
(*glyoxal*)
b.p. 50.4°C

which contains two aldehyde groups; and

$$CH_2{=}CHCHO$$

acrolein
(*acrylaldehyde or propenal*)
b.p. 52.5–53.5°C

which has a double bond in conjugation with the aldehyde group.

Some interesting aromatic aldehydes are

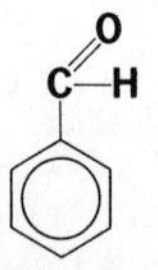

benzaldehyde
b.p. 178.1°C

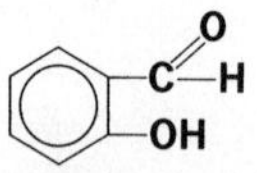

2-hydroxy-benzaldehyde
(*salicylaldehyde*)
b.p. 197°C

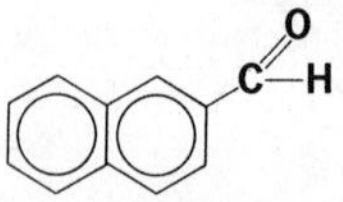

β-naphthaldehyde
b.p. 160°C

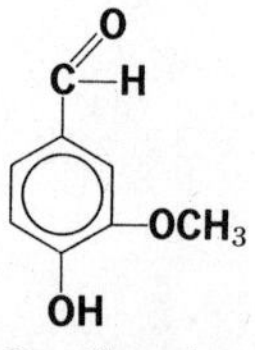

4-hydroxy-3-methoxy-benzaldehyde
(*vanillin*)
b.p. 285°C

Table 6-2 lists the formula, name, and boiling points of some aliphatic ketones.

We can omit the numbers in propanone and butanone, because there is no question about the location of the carbonyl group.

It is possible to have two carbonyl groups next to each other in one molecule, such as $CH_3COCOCH_3$, 2-3-butandione (the di-one meaning two ketone groups) (common name: diacetyl)(the numbers can be omitted in this case); two ketone groups may be separated by CH_2 groups as in $CH_3COCH_2COCH_3$, 2,4-pentanedione (common name: acetylacetone).

Some ketones that contain one or more aromatic groups are

C_6H_5–C(=O)–CH_3

methyl phenyl ketone
(*acetophenone*)
m.p. 19.6°C, b.p. 202.0°C

C_6H_5–C(=O)–CH_2CH_3

ethyl phenyl ketone
(*propiophenone*)
m.p. 21°C

C_6H_5–C(=O)–C_6H_5

diphenyl ketone
(*benzophenone*)
b.p. 305.9°C

C_6H_5–C(=O)–$C_{10}H_7$

phenyl β-naphthyl ketone
m.p. 82°C, b.p. 398°C

C_6H_5–C(=O)–C_4H_7

phenyl cyclobutyl ketone
b.p. 114°C at 7 mm Hg

Table 6-2 Aliphatic ketones

FORMULA	IUPAC NAME	COMMON NAME	BOILING POINT (°C)
CH_3COCH_3	propanone	dimethyl ketone (acetone)	56.2
$CH_3COCH_2CH_3$	butanone	methyl ethyl ketone	79.6
$CH_3CH_2COCH_2CH_3$	3-pentanone	diethyl ketone	102.7
$CH_3COCH_2CH_2CH_3$	2-pentanone	methyl *n*-propyl ketone	102
$CH_3COCH(CH_3)CH_3$	3-methyl-2-butanone	methyl isopropyl ketone	95
$CH_3CH_2COCH(CH_3)CH_3$	2-methyl-3-pentanone	ethyl isopropyl ketone	114.5–115
$CH_3CH(CH_3)COCH(CH_3)CH_3$	2,4-dimethyl-3-pentanone	diisopropyl ketone	124–125
$CH_3COCH_2CH(CH_3)CH_3$	4-methyl-2-pentanone	methyl isobutyl ketone	116.85

Reactions

THE OXIDATION OF ALDEHYDES

Aldehydes are exceedingly easy to oxidize and can be further oxidized to acids. Thus, we have a convenient method for differentiating between aldehydes and ketones, because ketones *cannot be oxidized* without tearing the entire molecule apart.

When an aldehyde is oxidized, essentially an oxygen atom is inserted between the hydrogen and the carbonyl carbon atom; that is,

$$\underset{\text{aldehyde}}{R-C(=O)-H} \xrightarrow[\text{oxidation}]{(O)} \underset{\text{acid}}{R-C(=O)-OH}$$

Ketones cannot be oxidized because the carbon-carbon bond is stable, and oxygen cannot be readily inserted into the molecule.

As a complete picture, a primary alcohol can be oxidized to an aldehyde, which in turn can be oxidized to an acid. The basis for naming acids will be given later. For example,

$$\underset{\text{methyl alcohol}}{CH_3OH} \xrightarrow{KMnO_4} \underset{\text{formaldehyde}}{H-C(=O)-H} \xrightarrow{KMnO_4} \underset{\text{formic acid}}{H-C(=O)-OH}$$

$$\underset{\text{ethyl alcohol}}{CH_3CH_2OH} \xrightarrow{K_2Cr_2O_7} \underset{\text{acetaldehyde}}{CH_3C(=O)H} \xrightarrow{K_2Cr_2O_7} \underset{\text{acetic acid}}{CH_3C(=O)OH}$$

$$\underset{n\text{-propyl alcohol}}{CH_3CH_2CH_2OH} \xrightarrow{K_2Cr_2O_7} \underset{\text{propionaldehyde}}{CH_3CH_2C(=O)-H} \xrightarrow{K_2Cr_2O_7} \underset{\text{propionic acid}}{CH_3CH_2C(=O)-OH}$$

Aldehydes can be oxidized simply by shaking them in the air (slow reaction), by using an oxidizing agent such as potassium dichromate in acid solution (rapid reaction) or potassium permanganate in acid or basic solution, or by certain special reagents.

REDUCTION OF THE CARBONYL GROUP

It is relatively easy to add hydrogen, in the presence of a proper catalyst (Pt), and reduce the carbonyl group to an alcohol group. Under these conditions, we reverse the oxidation process in that aldehydes are reduced to primary alcohols and ketones are reduced to secondary alcohols.

$$CH_3CHO + H_2 \xrightarrow{(Pt)} CH_3CH_2OH$$

acetaldehyde → ethanol (*a primary alcohol*)

$$CH_3CH_2CH_2CHO + H_2 \xrightarrow{(Pt)} CH_3CH_2CH_2CH_2OH$$

butyraldehyde → 1-butanol (*a primary alcohol*)

$$CH_3COCH_3 + H_2 \xrightarrow{(Pt)} CH_3CH(OH)CH_3$$

acetone → 2-propanol (*a secondary alcohol*)

$$CH_3CH_2COCH_3 + H_2 \xrightarrow{(Pt)} CH_3CH_2CH(OH)CH_3$$

methyl ethyl ketone → 2-butanol (*a secondary alcohol*)

ACETAL AND KETAL FORMATION

With a strong acid or a strong base as a catalyst, an aldehyde can add an alcohol molecule to form a moderately stable product called a hemiacetal. The general equation is

$$R{-}CHO + H{-}OR' \underset{OH^-}{\overset{H^+ \text{ or}}{\rightleftharpoons}} R{-}CH(OR'){-}OH$$

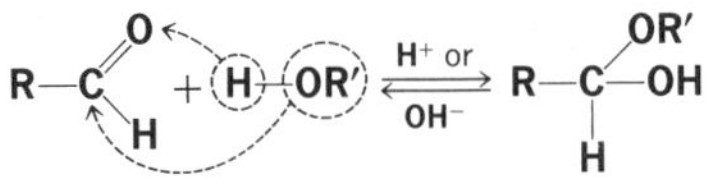

aldehyde, alcohol → hemiacetal

A specific example is

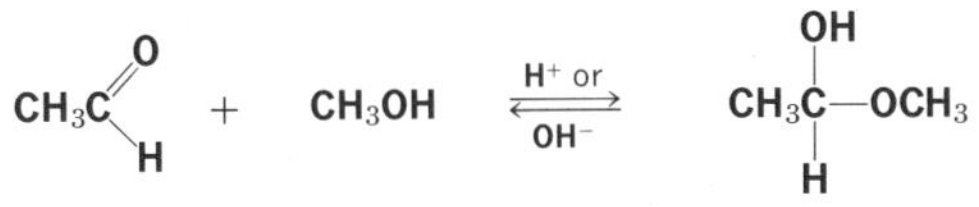

$$CH_3CHO + CH_3OH \underset{OH^-}{\overset{H^+ \text{ or}}{\rightleftharpoons}} CH_3CH(OH){-}OCH_3$$

acetaldehyde, methyl alcohol → hemiacetal of methyl alcohol and acetaldehyde

This reaction is reversible; that is, a hemiacetal will react with acid or base to give the aldehyde and alcohol.

If the original chemicals are very dry and a strong acid is used as a catalyst, a hemiacetal can react with a second alcohol molecule to form an acetal and water. The acetal is a stable compound. The general equation is

$$R{-}CH(OR')(OH) + H{-}OR' \xrightarrow{H^+} R{-}CH(OR'){-}OR' + H_2O$$

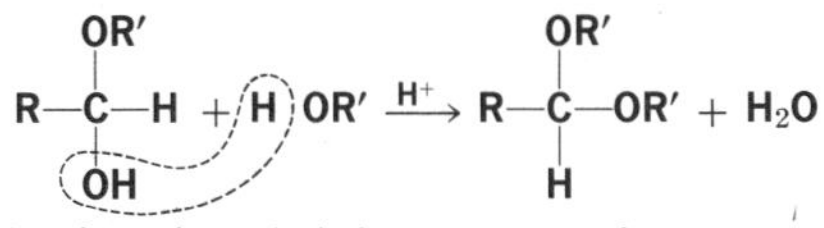

hemiacetal, alcohol → acetal

A specific example is

$$\underset{\substack{\text{hemiacetal of methyl}\\\text{alcohol and acetaldehyde}}}{CH_3\overset{\displaystyle OH}{\underset{\displaystyle H}{\overset{|}{\underset{|}{C}}}}{-}OCH_3} + \underset{\text{methyl alcohol}}{CH_3OH} \xrightarrow{H^+} \underset{\substack{\text{acetal}\\\text{of acetaldehyde}\\\text{and methyl alcohol}}}{CH_3\overset{\displaystyle OCH_3}{\underset{\displaystyle H}{\overset{|}{\underset{|}{C}}}}{-}OCH_3} + H_2O$$

Acetals are stable to alkaline reagents and oxidizing agents. They may be hydrolyzed by boiling under acidic conditions. Recall that free aldehydes are not stable to bases and oxidizing agents.

Under similar conditions, a ketone will react with an alcohol to form a compound like the hemiacetal but called a hemiketal. The general equation is

$$\underset{\text{ketone}}{R{-}\overset{\displaystyle O}{\overset{\|}{C}}{-}R} + \underset{\text{alcohol}}{R'OH} \underset{OH^-}{\overset{H^+ \text{ or}}{\rightleftharpoons}} \underset{\text{hemiketal}}{R{-}\overset{\displaystyle OR'}{\underset{\displaystyle R}{\overset{|}{\underset{|}{C}}}}{-}OH}$$

A specific example is

$$\underset{\text{acetophenone}}{C_6H_5{-}\overset{\displaystyle O}{\overset{\|}{C}}{-}CH_3} + \underset{\text{ethyl alcohol}}{CH_3CH_2OH} \underset{OH^-}{\overset{H^+ \text{ or}}{\rightleftharpoons}} \underset{\substack{\text{hemiketal of acetophenone}\\\text{and ethyl alcohol}}}{C_6H_5{-}\overset{\displaystyle OCH_2CH_3}{\underset{\displaystyle CH_3}{\overset{|}{\underset{|}{C}}}}{-}OH}$$

Similarly, if an excess of alcohol is used with acid as a catalyst, a ketal is formed, but the reaction is slower and more difficult than the reaction of an aldehyde and an alcohol under the same conditions. For example,

$$\underset{\substack{\text{hemiketal of}\\\text{acetophenone}\\\text{and ethyl alcohol}}}{C_6H_5{-}\overset{\displaystyle OCH_2CH_3}{\underset{\displaystyle CH_3}{\overset{|}{\underset{|}{C}}}}{-}OH} + \underset{\text{ethyl alcohol}}{CH_3CH_2OH} \xrightarrow{H^+} \underset{\substack{\text{ketal of acetophenone}\\\text{and ethyl alcohol}}}{C_6H_5{-}\overset{\displaystyle OCH_2CH_3}{\underset{\displaystyle CH_3}{\overset{|}{\underset{|}{C}}}}{-}OCH_2CH_3}$$

Ketals and acetals are of comparable stability.

Because sugars contain aldehyde and ketone groups and thus may form acetals and ketals, we will discuss this topic later.

Tests for Aldehydes

Glucose is a sugar and also an aldehyde, which occurs normally in the blood stream. Its presence in the blood and urine is easily detectable. The amount present furnishes an important clue to the patient's health.

FEHLING'S TEST

Fehling's solution is made in two parts: one part contains copper sulfate $CuSO_4$; the other part contains sodium hydroxide NaOH and Rochelle's salt (potassium acid tartrate) $KHC_4H_4O_6$. When the two parts are mixed, the tartrate forms a complex with the copper, which prevents the copper from precipitating as a hydroxide in the basic solution. This complex solution is a deep blue. For convenience only, in writing a simple equation, the copper in Fehling's test will be written as $Cu(OH)_2$. The $Cu(OH)_2$ is a blue precipitate (insoluble in water). Note that actually the $Cu(OH)_2$ has been rendered soluble by the tartrate ions.

An aldehyde will reduce blue cupric hydroxide $Cu(OH)_2$ to red-orange cuprous oxide Cu_2O, an insoluble substance. In this reaction, the aldehyde is oxidized simultaneously to an acid.

BENEDICT'S TEST

Benedict's solution is made by adding copper sulfate to an alkaline solution of sodium citrate. The citrate forms a complex with the copper, which prevents the copper from precipitating as a hydroxide in this basic solution. Benedict's solution is to be preferred over Fehling's solution for tests in hospitals. The sodium carbonate is not as strongly alkaline as the sodium hydroxide, and thus Benedict's solution is more sensitive than Fehling's solution. In addition, it is more convenient to use one solution instead of two.

A general equation for Fehling's test and Benedict's test is[1]

$$R{-}\overset{\displaystyle O}{\overset{\|}{C}}{-}H + 2Cu(OH)_2 \xrightarrow[\text{boiling water for 5 min}]{\text{immerse in}} R{-}\overset{\displaystyle O}{\overset{\|}{C}}{-}OH + Cu_2O\downarrow + 2H_2O$$

aldehyde; solution of cupric hydroxide in soluble complex form (*blue*); acid; cuprous oxide (*red-orange*); water

Because the solution is basic, the salt of the acid is actually formed.

$$CH_3\overset{\displaystyle O}{\overset{\|}{C}}{-}H + 2Cu(OH)_2 \xrightarrow[\text{or citrate}]{\text{tartrate}} CH_3\overset{\displaystyle O}{\overset{\|}{C}}{-}OH + Cu_2O\downarrow + 2H_2O$$

acetaldehyde; acetic acid

$$CH_3CH_2\overset{\displaystyle O}{\overset{\|}{C}}{-}H + 2Cu(OH)_2 \xrightarrow[\text{or citrate}]{\text{tartrate}} CH_3CH_2\overset{\displaystyle O}{\overset{\|}{C}}{-}OH + Cu_2O\downarrow + 2H_2O$$

propanal; propionic acid

If Benedict's test or Fehling's test for sugar in urine turned completely red-orange (all the copper was reduced), it would indicate the presence of a large quantity of available aldehyde or glucose. More commonly, how-

[1] ↓ indicates a precipitate and ↑ indicates a gas.

ever, all the copper is not reduced; the resulting solution still contains some unreacted blue cupric solution complex and some red-orange insoluble cuprous oxide. Under these conditions, the solution's color may appear to be anywhere between blue and orange.

Color charts ranging from blue through green, yellow, orange, and red are usually available in hospitals. The nurse can thus compare the color obtained in the test with a known color standard. This comparison technique enables her to estimate quickly the amount of aldehyde or free glucose present in the test sample, because the Cu_2O, and consequently the color intensity, is proportional to the available aldehyde or glucose.

In some hospitals, the Benedict's test is so standardized that a pellet containing the ingredients of Benedict's solution is used. The pellet contains copper sulfate, sodium carbonate, sodium citrate, and sodium hydroxide. To estimate the aldehyde in a sample, all the nurse need do is drop one pellet into a predetermined volume of test solution (i.e., water + urine) and match the color against a series of color standards. The excess sodium hydroxide reacts with the water to evolve heat, thus obviating the need for immersing the test solution in boiling water.

TOLLENS' TEST

This test also takes advantage of the ease of oxidation of aldehydes. An aldehyde will reduce a silver salt in ammonium hydroxide to free, metallic silver, which is evident by the formation of a shiny mirror. In this test, of course, the aldehyde is oxidized to an acid.

Tollens' reagent is an ammoniacal solution of a silver salt. Here again, a complex silver compound that prevents the silver from precipitating as the oxide in the basic solution is formed. Ag_2O is a mud-brown precipitate in equilibrium with AgOH.

$$\underset{\text{silver nitrate}}{AgNO_3} + \underset{\text{ammonium hydroxide}}{2NH_4OH} \longrightarrow \underset{\text{silver diammine nitrate}}{Ag(NH_3)_2NO_3} + \underset{\text{water}}{H_2O}$$

Again for convenience we write the silver as silver hydroxide AgOH, with the understanding that actually the silver is a complex with ammonium hydroxide. The following general equation illustrates Tollens' test:

$$\underset{\text{aldehyde}}{R{-}C(=O){-}H} + \underset{\text{colorless silver hydroxide in form of solution complex}}{2AgOH} \longrightarrow \underset{\text{acid}}{R{-}C(=O){-}OH} + \underset{\text{silver metal}}{2Ag^0\downarrow} + \underset{\text{water}}{H_2O}$$

A specific example is

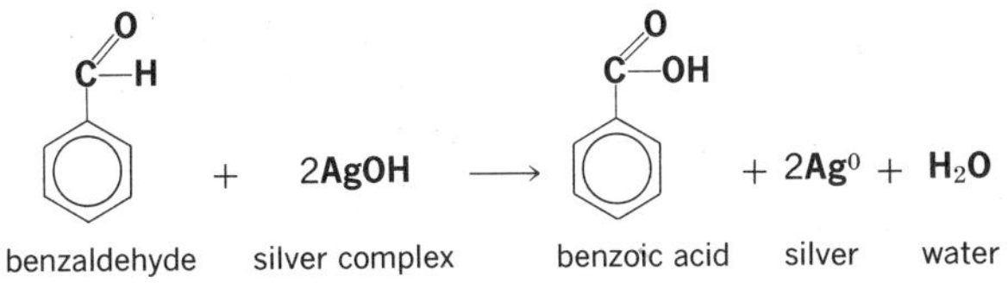

$$C_6H_5\text{—}C(=O)\text{—}H + 2AgOH \longrightarrow C_6H_5\text{—}C(=O)\text{—}OH + 2Ag^0 + H_2O$$

benzaldehyde | silver complex | benzoic acid | silver | water

Here again, because the solution is basic, the salt of the acid is formed. Tollens' reagent is used also in the silvering of mirrors and other objects that can be conveniently coated with metallic silver, such as thermos jugs.

SCHIFF'S TEST

Schiff's reagent is made by treating the dye fuchsin (magenta) with sulfur dioxide or sulfurous acid until the solution is colorless. In the presence of an aldehyde, the reagent turns a deep red or purple. This is a very sensitive test for aldehydes.

Benedict's, Tollens', and Schiff's tests are positive only for aldehydes; most *ketones do not give these tests.*

Tests for Ketones

IODOFORM TEST

The iodoform test indicates a certain structural unit in the molecule. The formula for iodoform is CHI_3. The structural unit indicated is CH_3CO— or anything that will oxidize to give CH_3CO—. Methyl ketones will, of course, give this test.

The groups that will give a positive test are

$$CH_3CO\text{—}R \qquad CH_3C(OH)(H)\text{—}R \qquad CH_3C(=O)\text{—}H \qquad CH_3CH_2OH$$

Actually, acetaldehyde gives a positive test because of the CH_3CO— grouping in it, but it is the only aldehyde to give a positive reaction. Ethyl alcohol gives a positive test because it can be oxidized to acetaldehyde. Because it is the only primary alcohol to give a positive reaction, the iodoform test is used to test for ethyl alcohol. All other compounds that give positive reactions are methyl ketones and those compounds which can be oxidized to produce methyl ketones (e.g., secondary alcohols).

The iodoform reagent is essentially iodine I_2 in sodium hydroxide. This is actually a solution of NaOI or sodium hypoiodite, but we can illustrate the reaction quite well with just iodine and sodium hydroxide.

The first step is an oxidation step. (If an alcohol is present, this step is necessary.)

$$CH_3\text{—}\underset{\underset{OH}{|}}{\overset{\overset{H}{|}}{C}}\text{—}R + I_2 \longrightarrow CH_3\text{—}\overset{\overset{O}{\|}}{C}\text{—}R + 2HI$$

The next reaction is iodination; that is, the iodine atoms replace the hydrogen atoms on the methyl group.

$$CH_3\overset{\overset{O}{\|}}{C}\text{—}R + 3I_2 \longrightarrow I\text{—}\underset{\underset{I}{|}}{\overset{\overset{I}{|}}{C}}\text{—}\overset{\overset{O}{\|}}{C}\text{—}R + 3HI$$

This is followed by breaking the bond between the CI_3— and the —COR by means of NaOH in the manner indicated.

$$I\text{—}\underset{\underset{I}{|}}{\overset{\overset{I}{|}}{C}}\text{—}\overset{\overset{O}{\|}}{C}\text{—}R \;\;(H\text{—}ONa) \longrightarrow \underset{\text{iodoform}}{CHI_3} + \underset{\text{sodium salt of an acid}}{R\text{—}\overset{O}{\overset{/\!/}{C}}\text{—}ONa}$$

We can combine these steps in one equation for an aldehyde or ketone. For example,

$$\underset{\text{acetaldehyde}}{CH_3\overset{O}{\overset{/\!/}{C}}\text{—}H} + 3I_2 + 4NaOH \longrightarrow \underset{\text{iodoform}}{CHI_3} + \underset{\text{sodium formate}}{H\overset{O}{\overset{/\!/}{C}}\text{—}ONa} + 3NaI + 3H_2O$$

$$\underset{\text{butanone}}{CH_3\overset{\overset{O}{\|}}{C}CH_2CH_3} + 3I_2 + 4NaOH \longrightarrow \underset{\text{iodoform}}{CHI_3} + \underset{\text{sodium propionate}}{CH_3CH_2\overset{O}{\overset{/\!/}{C}}\text{—}ONa} + 3NaI + 3H_2O$$

We use two equations for an alcohol. For example,

$$\underset{\text{2-pentanol}}{CH_3\underset{\underset{H}{|}}{\overset{\overset{OH}{|}}{C}}\text{—}CH_2CH_2CH_3} + I_2 \longrightarrow \underset{\text{2-pentanone}}{CH_3\overset{\overset{O}{\|}}{C}\text{—}CH_2CH_2CH_3} + 2HI$$

$$\underset{\text{2-pentanone}}{CH_3\overset{\overset{O}{\|}}{C}\text{—}CH_2CH_2CH_3} + 3I_2 + 4NaOH \longrightarrow \underset{\text{iodoform}}{CHI_3} + \underset{\text{sodium butyrate}}{CH_3(CH_2)_2\overset{O}{\overset{/\!/}{C}}\text{—}ONa} + 3NaI + 3H_2O$$

Iodoform is a yellow, slightly antiseptic powder with a characteristic odor. When in contact with tissue, free iodine is slowly liberated, which accounts for its mild antibacterial action. Previously, iodoform was often used in the dressing of wounds, but it is now used less frequently.

LEGAL TEST

This is a test for acetone. When added to an alkaline solution of acetone, a freshly prepared solution of sodium nitroprusside $Na(Fe(CN)_5NO)$ turns red. If urine is to be tested for acetone, complications may arise because creatinine, which can also be present, may also cause the solution to turn red. In testing for acetone in urine, therefore, it is best to acidify the solution with acetic acid after the test, which causes the red color created by the creatinine to disappear. The red color from the acetone would persist.

Important Aldehydes

Formaldehyde is made commercially by passing methanol vapors over a heated copper catalyst. The copper is a dehydrogenating agent, and by removing the two hydrogens it oxidizes the alcohol. The gaseous product is absorbed in water and sold as Formalin (37% formaldehyde by weight in water containing some methyl alcohol). The reagent keeps well in this condition. Formaldehyde possesses some bactericidal action and is the most potent of all the aldehydes in this respect.

In the proper concentrations, formaldehyde is an effective germicide against all forms of organisms: It can kill spore formers and non-spore formers, anaerobes, and viruses and fungi. Formaldehyde is too irritating to be used on body tissue; it is used to disinfect surgical instruments, gloves, human excreta, hair brushes, books, etc. Because formaldehyde also causes hardening of the skin, it is used to preserve anatomical specimens and as an embalming fluid.

Formaldehyde can add to itself to form a cyclic trimer (three molecules of formaldehyde), trioxane. The formula is

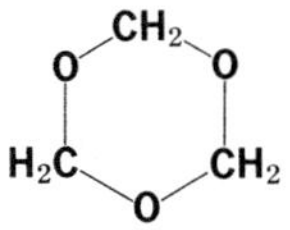

CH_2
O O
H_2C CH_2
O

A long-chain linear polymer of formaldehyde is called paraformaldehyde. All polymers of formaldehyde when heated can be converted into formaldehyde itself. This is a convenient method of storing and handling formaldehyde.

Formaldehyde, a particularly reactive aldehyde, is unique in that it condenses with ammonia to form a crystalline solid of formula $C_6H_{12}N_4$ (hexamethylenetetramine) of unusual structure.

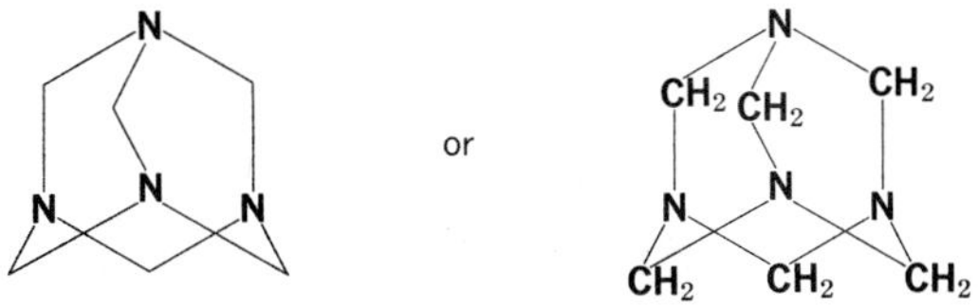

N
N N N

or

N
CH_2 CH_2 CH_2
N N N
CH_2 CH_2 CH_2

Hexamethylenetetramine (also known as Methenamine, hexamine, and urotropin) is a urinary antiseptic. It is active because in acid solution (urine) it slowly liberates formaldehyde. Methenamine is absorbed from the small intestines and rapidly excreted in the urine. An acidic substance should also be given so that the urine will be properly acidic. Methenamine, formerly one of the most effective of the urinary antiseptics, has been replaced today to a large extent by the sulfa drugs and penicillin.

Heating acetaldehyde with a trace of acid converts it into a reasonably stable trimer called paraldehyde.

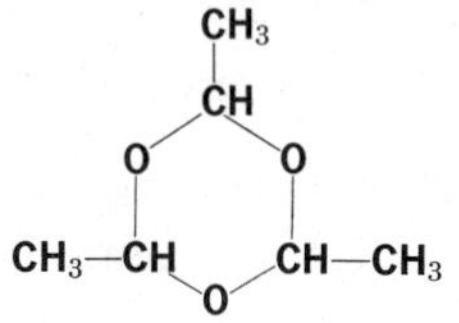

```
            CH3
            |
            CH
          /    \
         O      O
         |      |
  CH3—CH        CH—CH3
          \    /
            O
```

paraldehyde

Paraldehyde is an efficient hypnotic and affects the central nervous system. With proper dosage, sleep comes to a patient in approximately 10 minutes. The drug can be conveniently taken orally mixed with various syrups to mask the unpleasant taste and odor, but usually it is given intramuscularly. There are problems associated with the administration of paraldehyde. First, on standing in any bottle containing some air, paraldehyde slowly releases some free acetaldehyde, which slowly oxidizes to free acetic acid. Second, some nerve and skin disorders have been reported as a result of paraldehyde injections. Third, when a patient is completely uncooperative and thus might require immediate sedation and would resist all aid, this might require force to aid in the administration of the drug. Clearly, a very careful evaluation of all the factors is necessary before paraldehyde is given. The drug's odor usually will be evident on the breath of the patient for as long as 20 hours after its use. Paraldehyde should never be given in combination with morphine, because the pair produce a very toxic reaction.

Chloral is made by chlorinating ethyl alcohol. The first step is the oxidation of the alcohol to an aldehyde (acetaldehyde).

$$CH_3CH_2OH + Cl_2 \longrightarrow CH_3\overset{O}{\overset{\|}{C}}{-}H + 2HCl$$

The next step is the chlorination of the aldehyde.

$$CH_3\overset{O}{\overset{\|}{C}}{-}H + 3Cl_2 \longrightarrow Cl{-}\underset{Cl}{\underset{|}{\overset{Cl}{\overset{|}{C}}}}{-}\overset{O}{\overset{\|}{C}}{-}H + 3HCl$$

Chloral in water forms a stable hydrate, $CCl_3CH(OH)_2$, known as *chloral hydrate*. Chloral is a liquid and chloral hydrate is a solid. Chloral hydrate is one of the few compounds in organic chemistry that has two hydroxy groups on the same carbon. It is used mostly as a sedative and soporific; it has little analgesic activity. A proper dose of the drug causes sedation in approximately 10 minutes and usually causes sleep within the hour. Chloral hydrate is an effective drug, but it has been displaced to a large extent by the barbiturates.

Chloral is a starting material for the manufacture of DDT, the insecticide. When heated with chlorobenzene and fuming sulfuric acid, chloral reacts readily to form DDT.

$$CCl_3CHO + 2H{-}C_6H_4{-}Cl \xrightarrow{H_2SO_4} Cl{-}C_6H_4{-}CH(CCl_3){-}C_6H_4{-}Cl$$

p,p′-dichlorodiphenyltrichloroethane (DDT)

Some aldehydes containing the aromatic nucleus follow.

Benzaldehyde has a very pleasant odor and is the chief constituent of the essential oils of the peach, cherry, and other fruits. Benzaldehyde is widely used in the synthetic chemical industry and is found in many artificial flavors and perfumes.

Vanillin is the aromatic aldehyde that is the essence of vanilla flavor. It can also be synthesized cheaply and is found in artificial vanilla extracts and flavors.

Cinnamaldehyde is found in the oil of cassia and is the chief constituent of the oil of cinnamon.

$$C_6H_5{-}CH{=}CHC({=}O){-}H$$

cinnamaldehyde (C_9H_8O)

Important Ketones

Simple ketones do not have much use in medicine. Ketones are, however, widely used in the chemical industry because of their excellent solvent properties and synthetic possibilities. *Acetone,* for example, is an extraordinarily versatile solvent. Women may be familiar with it in the form of nail polish remover.

Under certain conditions, acetone is excreted in the urine as an abnormal metabolic product. This will be discussed under the metabolism of fats.

Diacetyl, found in butter in minute quantities, is the chemical that gives the butter its characteristic odor.

β-Ionone, found in nature, is responsible in part for the odor of violets.

It can be produced synthetically and is found in artificial violet perfumes. *α-Ionone* has the aroma of cedar in high concentrations and that of violets in low concentrations.

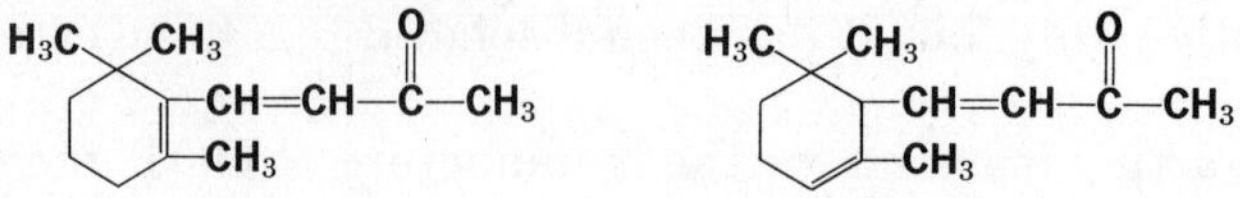

β-ionone

α-ionone

Jasmone is the ketone that gives jasmin its characteristic odor.

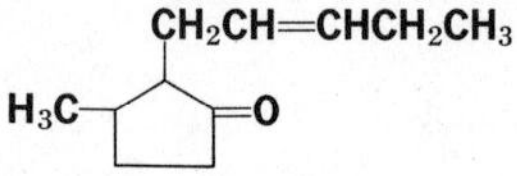

jasmone

Carvone is found in the oils of spearmint and causes the pleasant aroma.

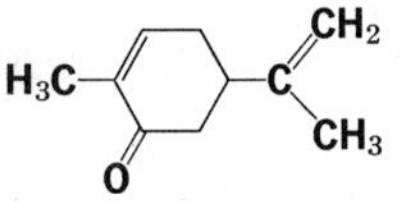

carvone

Camphor may be obtained from the camphor tree, *Cinnamomum camphora.*

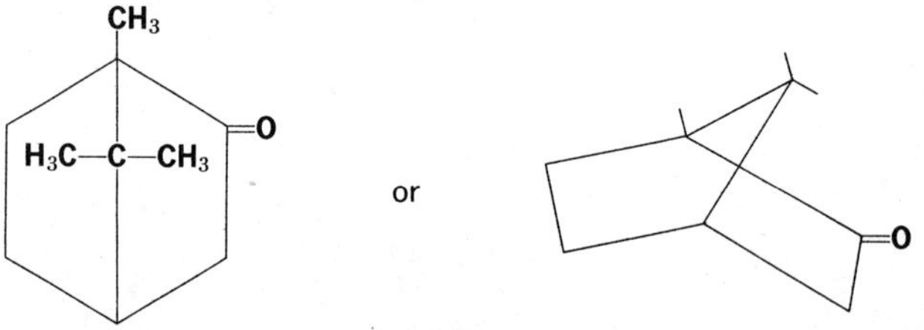

or

camphor

Camphor has weak antiseptic and analgesic properties and is found in some liniments. It has some use as an expectorant in the treatment of colds and is found in camphorated oils. It is also used to make celluloid, which is a mixture of camphor and nitrated cellulose.

Civetone is a very large cyclic ketone secreted, along with skatole and indole, by the civet cat, the African equivalent of the skunk.

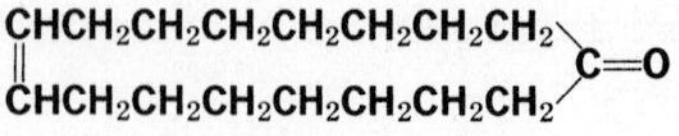

civetone

Although the pure molecule is extremely obnoxious and nauseating in odor, civetone becomes amazingly useful when present in minute amounts in perfumes, because it gives body and lasting quality to the perfume.

Muscone is the cyclic ketone secreted by the musk deer.

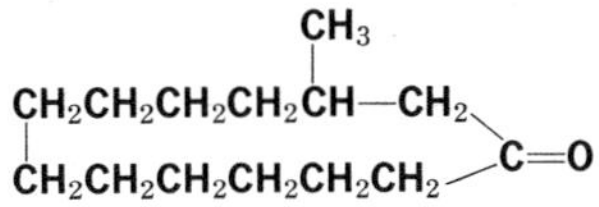

$$\begin{array}{l} CH_3 \\ | \\ CH_2CH_2CH_2CH_2CH{-}CH_2\diagdown \\ | \qquad\qquad\qquad\qquad\qquad\quad C{=}O \\ CH_2CH_2CH_2CH_2CH_2CH_2\diagup \end{array}$$

muscone

Muscone is also used in the manufacture of perfumes.

Many of the aromatic ketones have some hypnotic activity.

Acetophenone, otherwise known as hypnone, has been employed as a hypnotic but is too toxic for general use. Due to the development of more effective hypnotics, the aromatic ketones have more historical and academic interest than practical value.

Chloroacetophenone or phenacyl chloride (m.p. 56°C and b.p. 247°C) is a strong lachrymator.

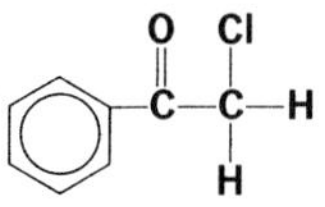

$$C_6H_5{-}\overset{\overset{\Large O}{\|}}{C}{-}\underset{\underset{\Large H}{|}}{\overset{\overset{\Large Cl}{|}}{C}}{-}H$$

α-chloroacetophenone
(*phenacyl chloride*)

In general, a compound of moderate or greater volatility with a halogen atom next to a carbonyl group

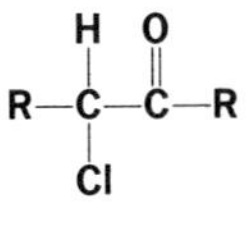

$$R{-}\underset{\underset{\Large Cl}{|}}{\overset{\overset{\Large H}{|}}{C}}{-}\overset{\overset{\Large O}{\|}}{C}{-}R$$

has a tendency to be a lachrymator. Lachrymators tend to hydrolyze in the presence of water (i.e., moisture on the eyeball or in the lungs) to liberate hydrochloric acid. The presence of concentrated hydrochloric acid on the surface of the eyeball would cause the tear glands to pour out their secretions in an effort to wash away this disturbing and irritating acid. Chloroacetophenone finds some use by police and other law-enforcing groups as a tear gas. It will produce lachrymation in concentrations as low as 0.0000003 g per liter of air and will cause death if a person breathes in a concentration as low as 0.00085 g per liter of air for 10 minutes.

All of the carbohydrates have either an aldehyde or a ketone group, or a potential aldehyde or ketone group, in them, and these will be discussed in greater detail in Chapter 10.

REVIEW QUESTIONS

1. Write structures for formaldehyde, acetaldehyde, propionaldehyde, pentanal, glyoxal, chloral, acrolein, benzaldehyde, salicylaldehyde, vanillin, acetone, butanone, benzyl methyl ketone, diphenyl ketone, acetophenone, and diacetyl.
2. Write schematic equations illustrating the oxidation of *n*-butyl alcohol, 2-methyl-1-pentanol, benzyl alcohol, isopropyl alcohol, 3-pentanol, and 2-hexanol. Name each organic compound.
3. Discuss the chemical components of Fehling's solution and Benedict's solution.
4. Write a balanced equation illustrating a positive reaction with Benedict's solution.
5. What is the chemical composition of Tollens' reagent? Write a balanced equation illustrating a positive Tollens' test.
6. What structural unit must be present to give a positive iodoform test? Write three equations illustrating a positive iodoform reaction.
7. How may acetone be detected in the urine?
8. Write representative structures for a hemiacetal, an acetal, and a ketal.
9. How is formaldehyde produced commercially? Discuss the uses of formaldehyde in industry and in medicine.
10. Identify Formalin, Methenamine, paraldehyde, hexamine, urotropin, trioxane, and hexamethylenetetramine.
11. Of what use are urotropin, Formalin, and paraldehyde?
12. How is chloral produced? What is its relationship to chloral hydrate?
13. Identify cinnamaldehyde, vanillin, diacetyl, β-ionone, jasmone, carvone, and camphor.
14. Of what use are civetone and muscone?
15. Define the term lachrymator and give one example.
16. How could you distinguish between the following by a simple chemical reaction?

(a) $CH_3\overset{O}{\overset{\|}{C}}-CH_3$ and $CH_3\overset{O}{\overset{\|}{C}}-H$ (b) $C_6H_5-CH_2OH$ and $C_6H_5-\overset{O}{\overset{\|}{C}}-CH_3$

(c) $CH_3CH_2CH_3$ and $CH_3CH_2\overset{O}{\overset{\|}{C}}-H$ (d) $C_6H_5-\underset{CH_3}{\overset{H}{C}}-OH$ and $C_6H_5-CH_2OH$

17. A compound with empirical formula $C_5H_{10}O$ gives negative Tollens' and Benedict's tests. It gives a positive iodoform test. Suggest a structural formula for the compound, which is consistent with this data. Explain your reasoning.

7

carboxylic acids

Organic acids are characterized by the carboxyl group

$$-\overset{\displaystyle O}{\overset{\|}{C}}-OH$$

and are called carboxylic acids. Aliphatic and alicyclic carboxylic acids have the general formula

$$R-\overset{\displaystyle O}{\overset{\|}{C}}-OH$$

or RCOOH; aromatic carboxylic acids have the general formula

$$Ar\overset{\displaystyle O}{\overset{\|}{C}}-OH$$

or ArCOOH.

These acids are important because they are found in all fats, oils, and waxes. Many straight-chain acids are found in fats; hence, they are called fatty acids.

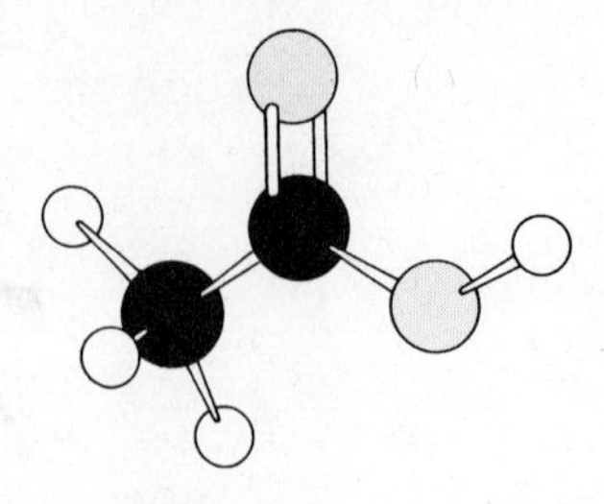

Figure 7-1 Acetic acid.

Nomenclature

To name organic acids by the IUPAC system, we count the longest carbon chain containing the carboxyl group, use the hydrocarbon name, and substitute the ending -oic. Give the carboxyl group the lowest number (usually 1), and assign appropriate numbers to the substituents along the chain. Acids encountered in fats, oils, and waxes are frequently referred to by their common names. In the common name, we can use a Greek letter instead of a number for the substituent. For example,

$$\underset{\underset{\beta}{3}}{CH_3}—\underset{\underset{\alpha}{2}}{\overset{\overset{Cl}{|}}{CH}}—\underset{1}{\overset{\overset{O}{\|}}{C}}—O—H$$

2-chloropropanoic acid (IUPAC)
α-chloropropionic acid (common)

$$\underset{\underset{\epsilon}{6}}{CH_3}—\underset{\underset{\delta}{5}}{CH_2}—\underset{\underset{\gamma}{4}}{\overset{\overset{Cl}{|}}{CH}}—\underset{\underset{\beta}{3}}{CH_2}—\underset{\underset{\alpha}{2}}{CH_2}—\underset{1}{\overset{\overset{O}{\|}}{C}}—O—H$$

4-chlorohexanoic acid (IUPAC)
γ-chlorocaproic acid (common)

Note: The alpha carbon is always the carbon next to the functional group. Remember to use numbers with IUPAC names and Greek letters with common names.

Not all organic acids are saturated; they may be unsaturated or aromatic, or they may contain substituents. Table 7-1 lists some common acids.

Table 7-1 Common acids

FORMULA	COMMON NAME	IUPAC NAME
$CH_2{=}CHCOOH$	acrylic acid	propenoic acid
$CH_3CH{=}CHCOOH$ (trans)	crotonic acid	2-butenoic acid
$CH_3CH{=}CHCOOH$ (cis)	isocrotonic acid	2-butenoic acid
$CH_3(CH_2)_7CH{=}CH(CH_2)_7COOH$	oleic acid	9-octadecenoic acid
$CH_3(CH_2)_4CH{=}CHCH_2CH{=}CH(CH_2)_7COOH$	linoleic acid	9,12-octadecadienoic acid

(Continued)

Table 7-1 (Continued)

FORMULA	COMMON NAME	IUPAC NAME
$CH_3CH_2CH{=}CHCH_2CH{=}CHCH_2CH{=}CH(CH_2)_7COOH$	α-linolenic acid	9,12,15-octadeca-trienoic acid
$CH_3(CH_2)_5CH(OH)CH_2CH{=}CH(CH_2)_7COOH$	ricinoleic acid	12-hydroxy-9-octadecenoic acid
$CH_3CH(OH)COOH$	lactic acid (α-hydroxy-propionic)	2-hydroxy propanoic acid
$HOCHCOOH$ / CH_2COOH	malic acid (α-hydroxy succinic)	2-hydroxy-1,4-butanedioic acid
$COOH$ / $CHOH$ / $CHOH$ / $COOH$	tartaric acid	2,3-dihydroxy-1,4-butanedioic acid
$HO{-}C(CH_2COOH)_2{-}COOH$	citric acid	2-hydroxy-1,2,3-propanetricarboxylic acid
Some other acids are		
$(CH_2)_{12}COOH$	chaulmoogric acid	
COOH	benzoic acid	
COOH, COOH	phthalic acid	
COOH, OH	salicylic acid	2-hydroxybenzoic acid
COOH, H_2N	*p*-aminobenzoic acid (PAB)	4-aminobenzoic acid
$HO{-}C({=}O){-}OH$ (H_2CO_3)	carbonic acid	
CHCOOH, OH	mandelic acid	

Alicyclics have their own system of nomenclature. The carbon containing the carboxylic acid group is carbon 1. As may be expected, the number 1 is not given, but it is assumed. For example,

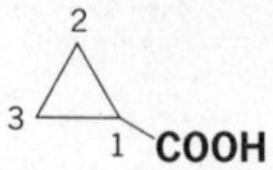

2
3
1 COOH

cyclopropane carboxylic acid
(the 1 is not necessary)

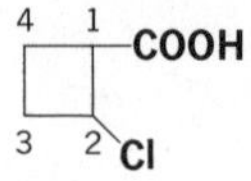

4 1 —COOH
3 2 Cl

2-chlorocyclobutane carboxylic acid

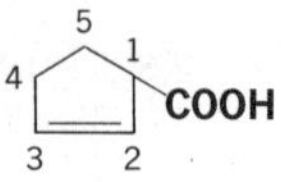

5
4 1
COOH
3 2

2-cyclopentene carboxylic acid

Preparation

Carboxylic acids may be prepared by the oxidation of primary alcohols or aldehydes with a strong oxidizing agent such as potassium permanganate or sodium dichromate.

When potassium permanganate is used in acid solution, manganese ion Mn^{++}, which is essentially colorless in solution, is formed. When potassium permanganate is used in basic solution, a brown solid, manganese dioxide MnO_2, is formed.

Potassium dichromate is commonly used in an acid solution, and the chromium (III) ion, which is green in solution, is formed.

$$CH_3CH_2CH_2CH_2CH_2CH_2OH \xrightarrow[\text{potassium permanganate}]{KMnO_4} CH_3(CH_2)_4C(=O)-OH$$

1-hexanol — hexanoic acid

$$CH_3C(=O)-H \xrightarrow[\text{potassium permanganate}]{KMnO_4} CH_3C(=O)-OH$$

acetaldehyde — acetic acid

Aromatic acids may be prepared by the oxidation of an alkyl side chain using a strong oxidizing agent.

The carbon next to the ring becomes the carboxylic acid. Every other carbon becomes carbon dioxide CO_2; that is,

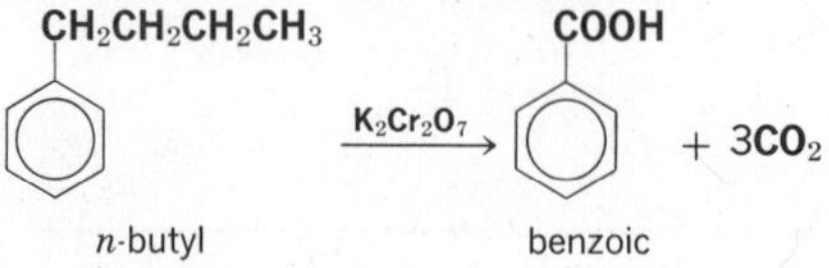

$$C_6H_5CH_2CH_2CH_2CH_3 \xrightarrow{K_2Cr_2O_7} C_6H_5COOH + 3CO_2$$

n-butyl benzene — benzoic acid

$$C_6H_5CH_2CH_3 \xrightarrow{K_2Cr_2O_7} C_6H_5COOH + CO_2$$

ethyl benzene — benzoic acid

For each carbon side chain, a carboxylic acid is produced.

$$CH_3C_6H_4CH_2CH_3 \xrightarrow{K_2Cr_2O_7} C_6H_4(COOH)_2 + CO_2$$

1-methyl-3-ethyl benzene — isophthalic acid

Other methods are possible, but these need not concern us now.

Physical Properties

Table 7-2 lists some common carboxylic acids and their boiling points.

The lower members of the fatty acid series, that is, formic, acetic, propionic, and butyric acids, are completely soluble in water. Valeric through pelargonic acids are partially soluble in water; the higher members of the series are very insoluble in water.

The fatty acids from formic through capric are volatile when steam distilled; that is, when steam is passed through a mixture of these acids, they will distill over with the steam even though the temperature is well

Table 7-2 Saturated carboxylic acids

FORMULA	COMMON NAME	IUPAC NAME	BOILING POINT (°C)
$HCOOH$	formic acid	methanoic acid	100.7
CH_3COOH	acetic	ethanoic	118.5
CH_3CH_2COOH	propionic	propanoic	141.1
$CH_3CH_2CH_2COOH$	butyric	butanoic	163.5
$CH_3CH(CH_3)COOH$	isobutyric	2-methylpropanoic	154.3
$CH_3CH_2CH_2CH_2COOH$	valeric	pentanoic	186–187
$CH_3(CH_2)_4COOH$	caproic	hexanoic	205
$CH_3(CH_2)_5COOH$	heptylic	heptanoic	223
$CH_3(CH_2)_6COOH$	caprylic	octanoic	238
$CH_3(CH_2)_7COOH$	pelargonic	nonanoic	253–255
$CH_3(CH_2)_8COOH$	capric	decanoic	270
$CH_3(CH_2)_{10}COOH$	lauric	dodecanoic	—
$CH_3(CH_2)_{12}COOH$	myristic	tetradecanoic	—
$CH_3(CH_2)_{14}COOH$	palmitic	hexadecanoic	—
$CH_3(CH_2)_{16}COOH$	stearic	octadecanoic	358–83

below their boiling points. This property has been useful in the analyses of butter and natural fats and oils for their fatty acid content.

Formic, acetic, and propionic acids have sharp, biting odors. Butyric through heptylic acids have offensive odors, and acids above heptylic have essentially no odors.

Note that the majority of the fatty acids found in nature contain an even number (14,16,18) of carbons. This will be further explained in Chapter 11.

Diacids

Diacids are compounds that have two acid groups. They can be represented by the general formula

$$(CH_2)_n \begin{cases} COOH \\ COOH \end{cases}$$

where n is any whole number, 0, 1, 2, 3, 4, etc. Table 7-3 lists the diacids.

You can remember these names by the mnemonic "Oh my! Such good apple pie, sweet and sour." (Oh for oxalic, my for malonic, etc. Some students memorize the expression omsgapsas.)

Chemical Properties

The term *acid* refers to a molecule that will give hydrogen ions or protons (H^+) when placed in water. Ionization is the process of an acid forming the hydrogen ion in water. The organic acids are usually considerably weaker than the common inorganic acids, such as hydrochloric acid HCl, nitric acid HNO_3, and sulfuric acid H_2SO_4.

Remember that the H^+ is actually present in the water solution as the hydronium ion H_3O^+. We represent the acidic particle formed in the ionization of an acid as H^+ *for convenience only;* although we write H^+, we really have H_3O^+ in the water solution.

The common, inorganic mineral acids are strong acids, because they give *many hydrogen ions.* In fact, HCl, HNO_3, and H_2SO_4 in dilute solutions ionize so completely that the equations proceed completely in the right-hand direction.

$$HCl \longrightarrow \underset{\text{hydrogen ion}}{H^+} + \underset{\text{chloride ion}}{Cl^-}$$

$$HNO_3 \longrightarrow \underset{\text{hydrogen ion}}{H^+} + \underset{\text{nitrate ion}}{NO_3^-}$$

$$H_2SO_4 \longrightarrow \underset{\text{hydrogen ion}}{H^+} + \underset{\text{bisulfate ion (acid sulfate ion)}}{HSO_4^-}$$

Table 7-3 Diacids

NAME	FORMULA
oxalic acid	COOH–COOH
malonic acid	$CH_2(COOH)_2$
succinic acid	CH_2COOH–CH_2COOH
glutaric acid	CH_2COOH–CH_2–CH_2COOH
adipic acid	CH_2CH_2COOH–CH_2CH_2COOH
pimelic acid	CH_2CH_2COOH–CH_2–CH_2CH_2COOH
suberic acid	$CH_2CH_2CH_2COOH$–$CH_2CH_2CH_2COOH$
azelaic acid	$CH_2CH_2CH_2COOH$–CH_2–$CH_2CH_2CH_2COOH$
sebacic acid	$CH_2CH_2CH_2CH_2COOH$–$CH_2CH_2CH_2CH_2COOH$

The bisulfate ion gives some H^+, but an equilibrium occurs.

$$HSO_4^- \rightleftharpoons \underset{\text{hydrogen ion}}{H^+} + \underset{\text{sulfate ion}}{SO_4^{--}}$$

You can consider the bisulfate ion a moderately strong acid, because it gives an appreciable amount of H^+, but note that the reaction does not go completely in the right-hand direction.

H_3PO_4 is a moderately strong acid: It ionizes in water to produce a large amount of H^+. However, the reaction does not go completely in the right-hand direction.

$$H_3PO_4 \rightleftharpoons \underset{\text{hydrogen ion}}{H^+} + \underset{\text{dihydrogen phosphate ion}}{H_2PO_4^-}$$

The dihydrogen phosphate ion is a weak acid: It furnishes few H^+ in solution.

$$H_2PO_4^- \rightleftharpoons \underset{\text{hydrogen ion}}{H^+} + \underset{\text{monohydrogen phosphate ion}}{HPO_4^{--}}$$

The monohydrogen phosphate ion is a very weak acid: It produces very few H^+ in water solution.

$$\underset{\text{monohydrogen phosphate ion}}{HPO_4^{--}} \rightleftharpoons \underset{\text{hydrogen ion}}{H^+} + \underset{\text{phosphate ion}}{PO_4^{3-}}$$

Although hydrochloric and nitric acids have only one replaceable hydrogen, sulfuric acid has two replaceable hydrogens, and each one can be replaced successively. Phosphoric acid has three replaceable hydrogens, which can be replaced one at a time.

Organic acids have only one replaceable hydrogen atom per carboxyl group. In other words, the H of the —COOH group is the only acidic hydrogen and the only one that forms hydrogen ions in solution.

The ion formed by the loss of the H^+ from the carboxyl group, that is, the ion $—COO^-$, is called the carboxylate ion. To name the ion by the IUPAC system, we replace the -ic ending of the acid name with the ending -ate.

Since organic acids are weak acids, the following reactions proceed only a very small amount to the right.

$$\underset{\text{acetic acid}}{CH_3COOH} \rightleftharpoons \underset{\text{hydrogen ion}}{H^+} + \underset{\text{acetate ion}}{CH_3COO^-}$$

$$\underset{\text{oleic acid}}{CH_3(CH_2)_7CH{=}CH(CH_2)_7COOH} \rightleftharpoons \underset{\text{hydrogen ion}}{H^+} + \underset{\text{oleate ion}}{CH_3(CH_2)_7CH{=}CH(CH_2)_7COO^-}$$

$$\underset{\text{lactic acid}}{CH_3CH(OH)COOH} \rightleftharpoons \underset{\text{lactate ion}}{CH_3CH(OH)COO^-} + \underset{\text{hydrogen ion}}{H^+}$$

Organic acids that have more than one carboxyl group can ionize each hydrogen successively.

The ion formed when one carboxyl group has ionized, that is,

$$\begin{array}{c} COO^- \\ | \\ (CH_2)_n \\ | \\ COOH \end{array}$$

is named as the hydrogen carboxylate or acid carboxylate ion to show the presence of the un-ionized carboxyl group. The ion formed when both hydrogens are removed is the carboxylate ion; that is,

$$\begin{array}{l} COOH \\ | \\ COOH \end{array} \rightleftharpoons H^+ + \begin{array}{l} COOH \\ | \\ COO^- \end{array}$$

oxalic acid — hydrogen ion — hydrogen oxalate ion (*acid oxalate ion*)

$$\begin{array}{l} COOH \\ | \\ COO^- \end{array} \rightleftharpoons H^+ + \begin{array}{l} COO^- \\ | \\ COO^- \end{array}$$

hydrogen ion — oxalate ion

$$H_2CO_3 \rightleftharpoons H^+ + HCO_3^-$$

carbonic acid — hydrogen ion — bicarbonate ion (*hydrogen carbonate ion*)

$$HCO_3^- \rightleftharpoons H^+ + CO_3^{--}$$

bicarbonate ion — hydrogen ion — carbonate ion

Although the organic acids are weakly acidic compared to inorganic acids, they are acidic enough to react with basic compounds to form salts. For example,

$$HCl + NaOH \longrightarrow NaCl + H_2O$$

hydrochloric acid — sodium hydroxide — sodium chloride — water

acid — *base* — *salt* — *water*

$$CH_3COOH + NaOH \longrightarrow H_2O + CH_3COONa$$

acetic acid — sodium hydroxide — water — sodium acetate

acid — *base* — *water* — *salt*

The student will recognize these equations as being general for acid + base $\longrightarrow$ salt + water.

If there are two carboxyl groups present, the positive ion of the base can replace one or both hydrogens. For example,

$$\begin{array}{l} COOH \\ | \\ CH_2 \\ | \\ COOH \end{array} + NaOH \longrightarrow \begin{array}{l} COONa \\ | \\ CH_2 \\ | \\ COOH \end{array} + H_2O$$

malonic acid — sodium hydroxide — sodium hydrogen malonate (*sodium acid malonate*) — water

$$\begin{array}{l} COONa \\ | \\ CH_2 \\ | \\ COOH \end{array} + NaOH \longrightarrow \begin{array}{l} COONa \\ | \\ CH_2 \\ | \\ COONa \end{array} + H_2O$$

sodium acid malonate — sodium hydroxide — sodium malonate — water just as

H_3PO_4	+ $NaOH$	$\longrightarrow$ NaH_2PO_4	+ H_2O
phosphoric acid	sodium hydroxide	sodium dihydrogen phosphate	water

NaH_2PO_4	+ $NaOH$	$\longrightarrow$ Na_2HPO_4	+ H_2O
sodium dihydrogen phosphate	sodium hydroxide	disodium hydrogen phosphate	water

Na_2HPO_4	+ $NaOH$	$\longrightarrow$ Na_3PO_4	+ H_2O
disodium hydrogen phosphate	sodium hydroxide	sodium phosphate	water

Instead of using a strong base, such as NaOH, we could use a weak base, such as NH_4OH. For example,

CH_3COOH	+ NH_4OH	$\rightleftharpoons$ CH_3COONH_4	+ H_2O
acetic acid	ammonium hydroxide	ammonium acetate	water

Salts of weak acids and weak bases are not very stable in water and tend to hydrolyze to form the free acid and the free base.

Organic acids are usually strong enough to turn litmus paper red, but because many of them are not very soluble in water, there are other ways to test their acidity. A useful test is to shake the acid solution or a suspension of the acid in water with a solution of sodium bicarbonate. In the presence of an acidic substance, a gas is evolved from the bicarbonate solution. The gas given off is carbon dioxide CO_2. For example,

CH_3COOH	+ $NaHCO_3$	$\longrightarrow$ CH_3COONa	+ H_2CO_3
acetic acid	sodium bicarbonate	sodium acetate	carbonic acid

(The carbonic acid is unstable and immediately decomposes to give carbon dioxide and water.)

H_2CO_3	$\longrightarrow$ H_2O	+ $CO_2\uparrow$
carbonic acid	water	carbon dioxide

$2CH_3(CH_2)_{16}COOH$	+ Na_2CO_3	$\longrightarrow$ $2CH_3(CH_2)_{16}COONa$	+ H_2CO_3
stearic acid	sodium carbonate	sodium stearate	carbonic acid

H_2CO_3	$\longrightarrow$ H_2O	+ $CO_2\uparrow$
carbonic acid	water	carbon dioxide

In general, sodium and potassium salts of all acids are soluble in water. Sodium butyrate

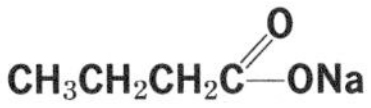

$$CH_3CH_2CH_2C(=O)—ONa$$

and potassium acetate

$$CH_3C(=O)—OK$$

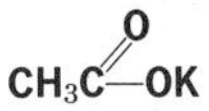

for example, are very soluble in water. When the number of carbon atoms increases, the solubility of the salts decreases. In some respects this is fortunate for us, because we can use the sodium salt of stearic acid as a soap [$CH_3(CH_2)_{16}COONa$], because it is only slightly soluble in water and therefore does not completely dissolve all at one time.

The salts of the heavy metals (calcium, barium, lead, silver, mercury, arsenic, etc.) are usually insoluble in water. Sodium stearate is slightly soluble in water, whereas calcium stearate $(CH_3(CH_2)_{16}COO)_2Ca$ is very insoluble. Sodium oxalate

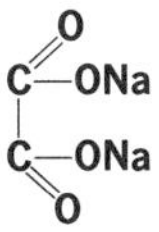

$$\begin{array}{l} O{=}C—ONa \\ \quad | \\ O{=}C—ONa \end{array}$$

is soluble in water, whereas calcium oxalate

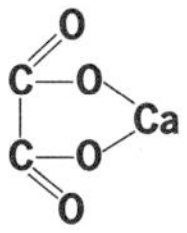

$$\begin{array}{l} O{=}C—O \\ \quad | \qquad\quad Ca \\ O{=}C—O \end{array}$$

is insoluble in water.

Hard water usually contains calcium ions, which react with a soap to form an insoluble scum (calcium salt of long-chain fatty acid). The precipitate formed remains in the water as a film; thus, more soap will be needed in very hard water than in soft water. (See Chapter 11.)

Important Acids and Their Uses

Formic acid is prepared industrially by heating carbon monoxide and sodium hydroxide at 150°C and at a pressure of 100 pounds per square inch.

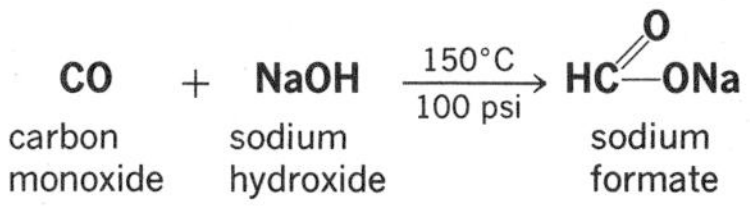

$$\underset{\text{carbon monoxide}}{CO} + \underset{\text{sodium hydroxide}}{NaOH} \xrightarrow[100\ psi]{150°C} \underset{\text{sodium formate}}{HC(=O)—ONa}$$

The sodium formate is acidified to give formic acid.

$$2HC(=O)\text{—}ONa + H_2SO_4 \longrightarrow 2HC(=O)\text{—}OH + Na_2SO_4$$

sodium formate, sulfuric acid, formic acid, sodium sulfate

Sodium formate, when heated strongly, loses hydrogen and forms sodium oxalate.

$$HC(=O)\text{—}ONa \xrightarrow{\Delta} \begin{matrix} COONa \\ | \\ COONa \end{matrix} + H_2$$

sodium formate, sodium oxalate, hydrogen

Formic acid is the strongest of the fatty acids and has a very irritating effect when injected beneath the skin. The stings of many insects, such as ants and bees, contain varying amounts of formic acid.

Acetic acid is produced when certain wines, beers, and hard ciders sour. Essentially, the ethyl alcohol (primary alcohol) is oxidized to acetic acid under the influence of certain bacteria. Industrially, acetic acid is made by the oxidation of pure ethyl alcohol. The 100% pure product is known as glacial acetic acid, because it freezes to an icy solid at 16.6°C. Commercial vinegar contains not less than 4% acetic acid by law. The actual percentage may vary slightly upward. In such low concentrations, acetic acid is readily digestible. The salts of acetic acid, that is, sodium acetate and potassium acetate, have some use as diuretics, because they are alkaline and tend to counteract an acidosis condition. Acetic acid is the most commonly used organic acid and is produced in large amounts in this country.

Propionic acid and its derivatives do not seem to occur in nature. However, synthetic propionic acid, in the form of its sodium salt, has some use in delaying the growth of certain fungi. The calcium salt is used to retard spoilage in bread.

Butyric acid is the smallest fatty acid found in fat. Its odor is very offensive, and it is responsible for the aroma of rancid butter.

Stearic acid finds some use in the salt form. Zinc stearate is used in powders because of its mild astringent and antiseptic actions.

Acrylic acid $CH_2{=}CHCOOH$ and *methacrylic acid* $CH_2{=}C(CH_3)COOH$ are used extensively to make resins and plastics.

10-Undecylenic acid $CH_2{=}CH(CH_2)_8COOH$ is found in some powders and ointments as either the zinc or copper salt and, as such, is somewhat effective in the treatment of athlete's foot.

Chaulmoogric acid has been used as a glyceride in the treatment of leprosy.

α-Halogenated organic acids are usually much stronger than the unsubstituted organic acids. *Trichloroacetic acid* is a very strong acid and has been used in the removal of warts.

Succinic acid, or *butanedioic acid,* is used medicinally in the form of its sodium or magnesium salts.

$$\begin{array}{l} C(=O)-ONa \\ | \\ CH_2 \\ | \\ CH_2 \\ | \\ COONa \end{array} \qquad \begin{array}{l} CH_2-COO \\ | \qquad\qquad\quad \backslash Mg \\ CH_2-COO \end{array}$$

sodium succinate magnesium succinate

These salts are basic in character and are effective in the treatment of diabetic acidosis. The salts are sometimes used to relieve the symptoms of rheumatic fever.

Benzoic acid has been employed as a food preservative, and when used in very dilute solutions (0.1%), it is capable of preventing bacterial growth. If taken in small amounts in the food, the acid (after being absorbed into the blood stream) reacts with glycine (an amino acid) and is excreted as hippuric acid in the urine. For this reason, benzoic acid may be used to test hepatic function. Approximately 5 grams of benzoic acid is given orally. The patient with a normally functioning liver will excrete between 3.0 and 3.5 grams of hippuric acid during the following four hours. Significant deviation from the above indicates abnormality. Benzoic acid is also used in various ointments for treatment of athlete's foot and ringworm.

Mandelic acid is used as an efficient urinary antiseptic. It is germicidal for many bacteria in an acidic medium. The drug is excreted by the kidney, rendering the urinary system slightly acidic, and thereby destroying many organisms.

Salicylic acid is so irritating that it is employed only externally. Its derivatives are used more frequently because they modify the irritating action. Although the derivatives of salicylic acid usually modify its action so that it can be taken internally, when used externally they are not as powerful as the parent acid. Salicylic acid has a strong kerotolytic effect (i.e., it is capable of destroying horny growths) and is employed in the treatment of warts, corns, and other types of skin irritations. We are familiar with ester derivatives of salicylic acid, such as acetylsalicylic acid (aspirin), phenyl salicylate (salol), and methyl salicylate (oil of wintergreen).

$C_6H_4(OH)COOH$ — salicylic acid

$C_6H_4(O-CO-CH_3)COOH$ — acetylsalicylic acid

$C_6H_4(OH)CO-O-C_6H_5$ — phenyl salicylate

$C_6H_4(OH)COOCH_3$ — methyl salicylate

The salicylates are mildly bacteriostatic. The analgesic properties of aspirin —a substance used perhaps too frequently in self-diagnosis by the laity— are also familiar. The antipyretic (fever-reducing properties) effects of the salicylates are well known, since the drugs effectively lower the body temperature by influencing the central nervous system. Aspirin is found in many cold remedies and is the most frequently used analgesic and antipyretic in this country.

Glycolic acid $HOCH_2COOH$ is the simplest hydroxy acid. It is present in tomatoes and grapes and is the chief acidic constituent in the juice obtained from sugar cane.

Lactic acid is present in sour milk. The acid is also produced in the body in the metabolism of carbohydrates. The salts of lactic acid are used to restore the metal ion to the body without producing acidosis. For example, calcium lactate $(CH_3CH(OH)COO)_2Ca$, administered orally, is used to restore low calcium blood to normal. Ferrous lactate $(CH_2CH(OH)COO)_2Fe$, administered orally, is used as an iron tonic. Silver lactate $CH_3CH(OH)COOAg$, applied to tissue surfaces, has effective antiseptic and astringent properties.

β-Hydroxybutyric acid $CH_3CH(OH)CH_2COOH$, in cases of diabetes, can occur in urine as one of the so-called acetone bodies. (See Chapter 18.)

Gluconic acid has uses similar to lactic acid. Calcium gluconate $(C_5H_{11}O_5COO)_2Ca \cdot 2H_2O$, which crystallizes with two molecules of water, is used frequently to supply calcium to the blood and thus to rectify a calcium deficiency. It can be administered orally or intravenously. Ferrous gluconate $(C_5H_{11}O_5CO)_2Fe \cdot H_2O$, which crystallizes with one molecule of water, is employed as an iron tonic in treatment of anemia. The drug is taken orally. The structure of gluconic acid will be discussed in greater detail in Chapter 10.

Malic acid is found in grapes, pears, and apples.

Citric acid is found in the familiar citrus fruits and accounts for their tart taste. The acid is very widely distributed in nature. Artificial lemon juice flavoring contains citric acid. Many citric acid salts are used as antacids, diuretics, and laxatives. For example, magnesium citrate has been widely used as a saline laxative.

Tartaric acid occurs in many fruits but mostly in grapes. The salts of tartaric acid are of interest. Potassium acid tartrate (cream of tartar) is effective as a laxative. It is also used in many baking powders.

```
    COOK
     |
  H—C—OH
     |
  H—C—OH
     |
    COOH
```
cream of tartar

Potassium sodium tartrate (Rochelle's salt) is an efficient cathartic.

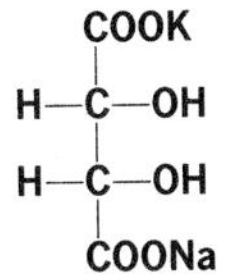

```
     COOK
     |
H—C—OH
     |
H—C—OH
     |
     COONa
```

Rochelle's salt

Potassium antimonyl tartrate (tartar emetic) has some use as an emetic. The drug is also of some value in treating parasite infections. The $[SbO]^+$ ion (antimonyl) has a net charge of +1.

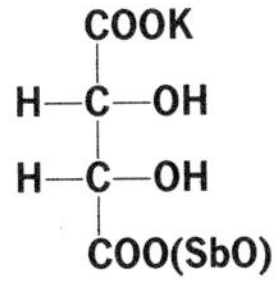

```
     COOK
     |
H—C—OH
     |
H—C—OH
     |
     COO(SbO)
```

tartar emetic

2,4-*Dichlorophenoxyacetic acid* (2,4-D) has come into prominence since 1944, when its weed-killing properties were discovered.

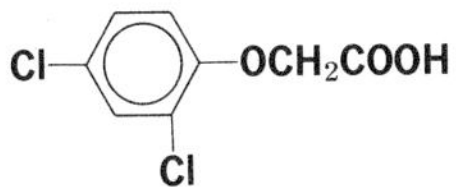

Cl—C$_6$H$_3$—OCH$_2$COOH (with Cl on the ring)

2,4-dichlorophenoxyacetic acid

It is used in great amounts in this country and is apparently nontoxic to animals.

Calcium levulinate $(CH_3COCH_2CH_2COO)_2Ca \cdot 2H_2O$, which crystallizes with two molecules of water, is used as a source of calcium to restore low calcium blood to normal.

Pyruvic acid $CH_3COCOOH$ will be discussed in Chapter 17.

Recently, particular attention has been directed to long branched-chain fatty acids because of their elaboration by the tubercle bacillus. *Phthioic acid* $C_{25}H_{51}COOH$, whose exact structure is still not known, is one of the most active of these acids.

There are a relatively large number of compounds called *amino acids,* some of which are the building blocks of proteins. We will discuss these acids in detail in Chapter 12.

Acid halides

Acid halides or acyl halides are compounds produced from acids by the replacement of the —OH of the carboxyl group by a halogen atom (chlorine, bromine, or iodine).

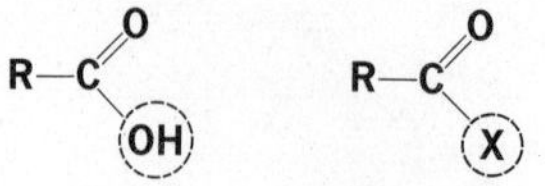

$$R-C(=O)-OH \quad \text{acid} \qquad R-C(=O)-X \quad \text{acid halide} \qquad (X = Cl, Br, I)$$

The

$$R-C(=O)-$$

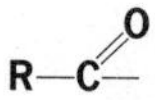

group is commonly called the acyl or acoyl group. The

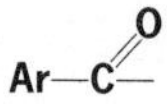

$$Ar-C(=O)-$$

group is the aroyl group. They are conveniently written RCOX or ArCOX.

Nomenclature

To name these compounds, we use the common name of the acid and replace the -ic ending with the ending -yl or -oyl. This is followed by the name of the halogen. The acid chlorides are much more common than the acid bromides or the acid iodides. Some examples are

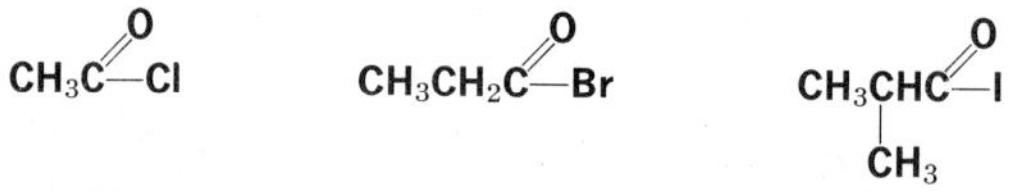

$$CH_3C(=O)-Cl \quad \text{acetyl chloride} \qquad CH_3CH_2C(=O)-Br \quad \text{propionyl bromide} \qquad CH_3CH(CH_3)C(=O)-I \quad \text{isobutyryl iodide}$$

$$C_6H_5-C(=O)-Cl \quad \text{benzoyl chloride} \qquad C_{10}H_7-COBr \quad \alpha\text{-naphthoyl bromide}$$

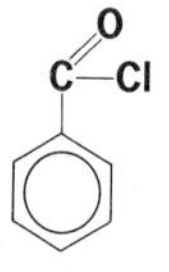

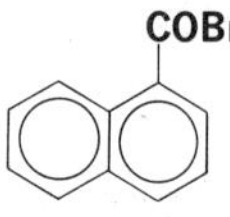

Preparation

Many convenient methods of preparing the chlorides are known. One method is to react the acid with thionyl chloride $SOCl_2$.

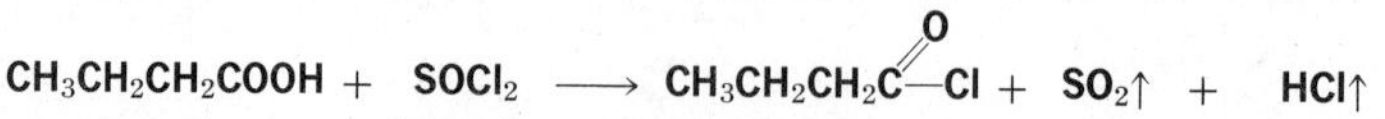

$$\underset{\text{butyric acid}}{CH_3CH_2CH_2COOH} + \underset{\text{thionyl chloride}}{SOCl_2} \longrightarrow \underset{\text{butyryl chloride}}{CH_3CH_2CH_2C(=O)-Cl} + \underset{\text{sulfur dioxide}}{SO_2\uparrow} + \underset{\text{hydrogen chloride}}{HCl\uparrow}$$

$$\underset{\text{isobutyric acid}}{CH_3-CH(CH_3)-C(=O)-OH} + \underset{\text{thionyl chloride}}{SOCl_2} \longrightarrow \underset{\text{isobutyryl chloride}}{CH_3-CH(CH_3)-C(=O)-Cl} + \underset{\text{sulfur dioxide}}{SO_2\uparrow} + \underset{\text{hydrogen chloride}}{HCl\uparrow}$$

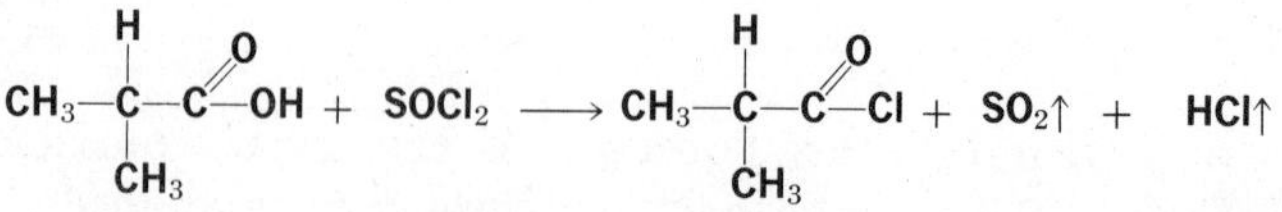

Another method is to react the acid with phosphorus pentachloride PCl_5.

$$CH_3C(=O)-OH + PCl_5 \longrightarrow CH_3C(=O)-Cl + POCl_3 + HCl$$

acetic acid + phosphorus pentachloride ⟶ acetyl chloride + phosphorus oxychloride + hydrogen chloride

$$C_6H_5COOH + PCl_5 \longrightarrow C_6H_5C(=O)-Cl + POCl_3 + HCl$$

benzoic acid + phosphorus pentachloride ⟶ benzoyl chloride + phosphorus oxychloride + hydrogen chloride

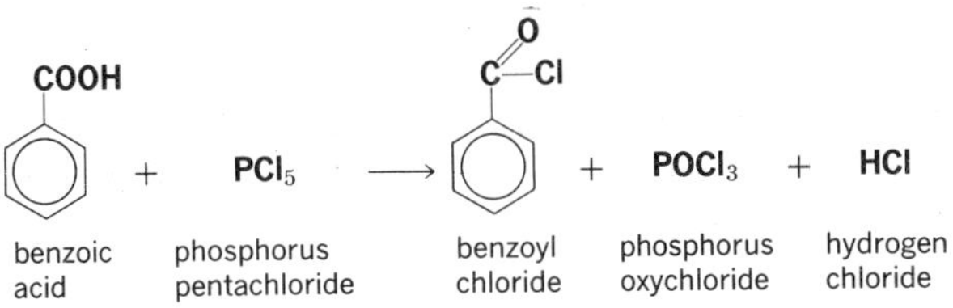

Reactions

HYDROLYSIS

Acid halides are very reactive compounds and are very susceptible to hydrolysis by water. In fact, they will fume in moist air to liberate hydrogen chloride and to form the organic acid. The reaction is known as hydrolysis (the reaction of a substance with water.) Aliphatic acid chlorides are more reactive than aromatic acid chlorides.

$$R-C(=O)-Cl + H_2O \longrightarrow RC(=O)-OH + HCl$$

acid chloride + water ⟶ acid + hydrogen chloride

$$CH_3CH_2C(=O)-Cl + H_2O \longrightarrow CH_3CH_2C(=O)-OH + HCl$$

propionyl chloride + water ⟶ propionic acid + hydrogen chloride

$$C_6H_5C(=O)-Cl + H_2O \longrightarrow C_6H_5C(=O)-OH + HCl$$

benzoyl chloride + water ⟶ benzoic acid + hydrogen chloride

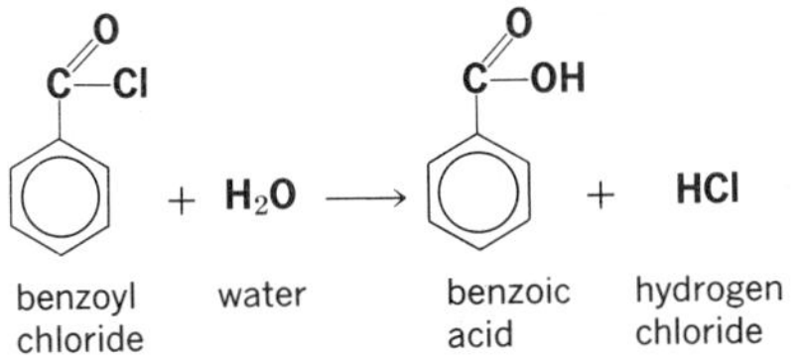

ALCOHOLYSIS

Acid chlorides react with alcohols to form hydrogen chloride and an ester. (We will discuss esters in Chapter 8.)

$$R-C(=O)-Cl + H-OR' \longrightarrow RC(=O)-OR' + HCl$$

acid chloride + alcohol ⟶ ester + hydrogen chloride

AMMONOLYSIS

Ammonolysis is the reaction of an acid chloride with ammonia. In this reaction, an amide is formed. We will discuss amides later in this chapter.

$$\underset{\text{acid chloride}}{R\text{—}\overset{O}{\overset{\|}{C}}\text{—}Cl} + \underset{\text{ammonia}}{2H\text{—}NH_2} \longrightarrow \underset{\text{amide}}{R\text{—}\overset{O}{\overset{\|}{C}}\text{—}NH_2} + \underset{\text{ammonium chloride}}{NH_4Cl}$$

Acid chlorides tend to react with any compound that has an active hydrogen to form hydrogen chloride. The two remaining parts link together. We can summarize these reactions as follows:

$$R\text{—}\overset{O}{\overset{\|}{C}}\text{—}Cl + H\text{—}OH \longrightarrow R\text{—}\overset{O}{\overset{\|}{C}}\text{—}OH + HCl$$

$$R\text{—}\overset{O}{\overset{\|}{C}}\text{—}Cl + H\text{—}OR' \longrightarrow R\text{—}\overset{O}{\overset{\|}{C}}\text{—}OR' + HCl$$

$$R\overset{O}{\overset{\|}{C}}\text{—}Cl + H\text{—}NH_2 \longrightarrow R\text{—}\overset{O}{\overset{\|}{C}}\text{—}NH_2 + HCl$$

Of course, the HCl reacts with the ammonia to form ammonium chloride (NH_4Cl).

Uses

Acid halides are used for synthetic purposes in organic chemistry but have no use in medicine as drugs. The compounds are actually dangerous, and care must be used in handling them. Whenever they are in contact with the body, acid halides will liberate concentrated hydrochloric acid by the hydrolysis reaction. Hydrochloric acid is so strong that it is very irritating to the skin and the eyes. Compounds that liberate hydrochloric acid on contact with water are known as lachrymators (tear producers) because of the greatly increased flow of tears when the eyes are exposed. If inhaled, hydrochloric acid will fume in the lungs and will produce violent coughing; it may be fatal.

Phosgene $COCl_2$ or

$$Cl\text{—}\overset{O}{\overset{\|}{C}}\text{—}Cl$$

is sometimes called carbonyl chloride, because it is the dichloride of carbonic acid. It is a particularly reactive and poisonous halide. Phosgene was used by the Germans in 1915 and was responsible for 80% of the gas fatalities in World War I. Its poisonous nature is due to its reaction with the water in the lungs to form concentrated hydrochloric acid. Exposure to air containing 0.0005 g of phosgene per liter is fatal within 10 minutes.

Acid anhydrides

The term "anhydride" in chemistry means a substance produced by the removal of water. Acid anhydrides, however, are usually *not* produced by the removal of water. Acid anhydrides are easily prepared by reacting an acid chloride with a salt of the acid. In this manner, salt is split out and the acid anhydride is formed. The general reaction is

$$\underset{\text{acid chloride}}{R{-}\overset{O}{\overset{\|}{C}}{-}Cl} + \underset{\text{sodium salt of an acid}}{Na{-}O{-}\overset{O}{\overset{\|}{C}}{-}R} \longrightarrow \underset{\text{salt}}{NaCl} + \underset{\text{acid anhydride}}{R{-}\overset{O}{\overset{\|}{C}}{-}O{-}\overset{O}{\overset{\|}{C}}{-}R}$$

Both simple and mixed anhydrides may be prepared by this reaction. A simple anhydride is one in which both R groups are alike. A mixed anhydride contains two different R groups.

$$\underset{\text{simple anhydride}}{R{-}\overset{O}{\overset{\|}{C}}{-}O{-}\overset{O}{\overset{\|}{C}}{-}R} \qquad \underset{\text{mixed anhydride}}{R{-}\overset{O}{\overset{\|}{C}}{-}O{-}\overset{O}{\overset{\|}{C}}{-}R'}$$

Some examples are

$$\underset{\text{benzoyl chloride}}{C_6H_5{-}\underset{O}{\underset{\|}{C}}{-}Cl} + \underset{\text{sodium benzoate}}{C_6H_5{-}\overset{O}{\overset{\|}{C}}{-}ONa} \longrightarrow \underset{\substack{\text{benzoic anhydride} \\ \textit{(a simple acid anhydride)}}}{C_6H_5{-}\underset{O}{\underset{\|}{C}}{-}O{-}\underset{O}{\underset{\|}{C}}{-}C_6H_5} + \underset{\text{salt}}{NaCl}$$

$$\underset{\text{propionyl chloride}}{CH_3CH_2\underset{O}{\underset{\|}{C}}{-}Cl} + \underset{\text{sodium propionate}}{CH_3CH_2\underset{O}{\underset{\|}{C}}{-}ONa} \longrightarrow \underset{\substack{\text{propionic anhydride} \\ \textit{(a simple acid anhydride)}}}{CH_3CH_2\overset{O}{\overset{\|}{C}}{-}O{-}\overset{O}{\overset{\|}{C}}{-}CH_2CH_3} + \underset{\text{salt}}{NaCl}$$

$$\underset{\text{acetyl chloride}}{CH_3{-}\overset{O}{\overset{\|}{C}}{-}Cl} + \underset{\text{sodium propionate}}{CH_3CH_2\overset{O}{\overset{\|}{C}}{-}ONa} \longrightarrow \underset{\substack{\text{a mixed anhydride of acetic} \\ \text{acid and propionic acid}}}{CH_3{-}\overset{O}{\overset{\|}{C}}{-}O{-}\overset{O}{\overset{\|}{C}}{-}CH_2CH_3} + \underset{\text{salt}}{NaCl}$$

Cyclic anhydrides

If a *diacid* is heated, water *may* be eliminated and an anhydride formed. These resulting anhydrides would be cyclic (ring) anhydrides. This reaction does not proceed to any practical extent unless a *five- or a six-membered ring is formed.*

Some examples are

$$\begin{array}{l} CH_2-\overset{\overset{O}{\|}}{C}-OH \\ | \\ CH_2-\underset{\underset{O}{\|}}{C}-OH \end{array} \xrightarrow{\Delta} \begin{array}{l} CH_2-\overset{\overset{O}{\|}}{C} \\ | \qquad\quad\; O \\ CH_2-\underset{\underset{O}{\|}}{C} \end{array} + H_2O$$

succinic acid — succinic anyhdride

$$C_6H_4(COOH)_2 \xrightarrow{\Delta} C_6H_4(CO)_2O + H_2O$$

phthalic acid — phthalic anhydride

$$CH_2(CH_2COOH)_2 \xrightarrow{\Delta} \begin{array}{l} CH_2-\overset{\overset{O}{\|}}{C} \\ CH_2 \qquad\quad O \\ CH_2-\underset{\underset{O}{\|}}{C} \end{array} + H_2O$$

glutaric acid — glutaric anhydride

Note: The heating of diacids such as oxalic acid, malonic acid, and sebacic acid does not yield acid anhydrides, because there is no opportunity to form a five- or a six-membered ring.

Reactions

HYDROLYSIS

Anhydrides are not so sensitive to water as the acid halides, but they are still quite reactive. An anhydride can be hydrolyzed by cold water in an hour or by boiling water in a few minutes.

In the hydrolysis reaction, we obtain two molecules of the organic acid.

$$C_6H_5-\overset{\overset{O}{\|}}{C}-O-\overset{\overset{O}{\|}}{C}-C_6H_5 + H_2O \longrightarrow 2\,C_6H_5-\overset{\overset{O}{\|}}{C}-OH$$

benzoic anhydride — water — benzoic acid

$$\begin{array}{l} CH_3-\overset{\overset{O}{\|}}{C} \\ \qquad\quad\; O \\ CH_3-\underset{\underset{O}{\|}}{C} \end{array} + H_2O \longrightarrow 2CH_3COOH$$

acetic anhydride — water — acetic acid

ALCOHOLYSIS

An anhydride reacts with an alcohol to give an ester and one molecule of the organic acid.

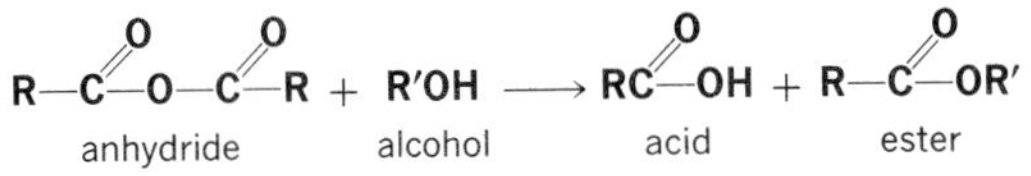

$$R{-}\overset{O}{\overset{\|}{C}}{-}O{-}\overset{O}{\overset{\|}{C}}{-}R + R'OH \longrightarrow R\overset{O}{\overset{\|}{C}}{-}OH + R{-}\overset{O}{\overset{\|}{C}}{-}OR'$$

anhydride — alcohol — acid — ester

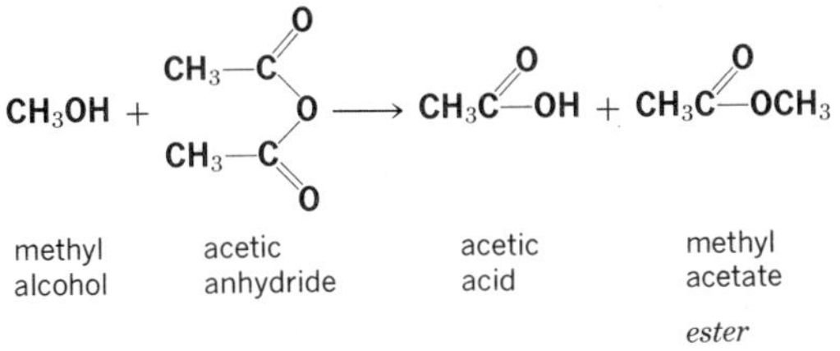

$$CH_3OH + (CH_3CO)_2O \longrightarrow CH_3\overset{O}{\overset{\|}{C}}{-}OH + CH_3\overset{O}{\overset{\|}{C}}{-}OCH_3$$

methyl alcohol — acetic anhydride — acetic acid — methyl acetate *ester*

We will discuss this reaction in Chapter 8.

AMMONOLYSIS

An anhydride reacts with ammonia to give an amide and the ammonium salt of the organic acid.

$$(RCO)_2O + 2NH_3 \longrightarrow R{-}\overset{O}{\overset{\|}{C}}{-}NH_2 + R\overset{O}{\overset{\|}{C}}{-}ONH_4$$

anhydride — ammonia — amide — ammonium salt of the organic acid

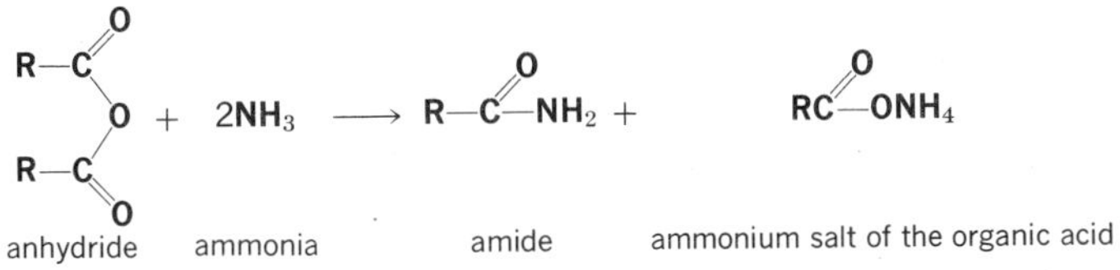

Anhydrides tend to react with any compound that has an active hydrogen and so will form the free acid; the remaining parts of each will link together. For example,

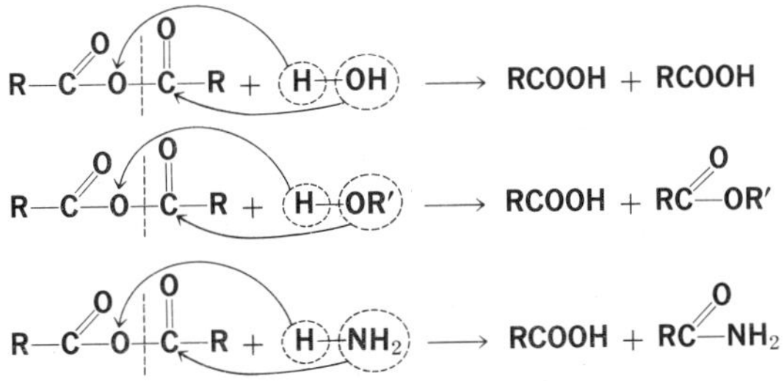

$$R{-}\overset{O}{\overset{\|}{C}}{-}O{-}\overset{O}{\overset{\|}{C}}{-}R + H{-}OH \longrightarrow RCOOH + RCOOH$$

$$R{-}\overset{O}{\overset{\|}{C}}{-}O{-}\overset{O}{\overset{\|}{C}}{-}R + H{-}OR' \longrightarrow RCOOH + R\overset{O}{\overset{\|}{C}}{-}OR'$$

$$R{-}\overset{O}{\overset{\|}{C}}{-}O{-}\overset{O}{\overset{\|}{C}}{-}R + H{-}NH_2 \longrightarrow RCOOH + R\overset{O}{\overset{\|}{C}}{-}NH_2$$

Of course, the organic acid reacts with the ammonia to form the ammonium salt ($RCOONH_4$).

Uses

Anhydrides are used extensively in organic synthetic research but have no use in medicine as drugs. Acetic anhydride is very cheap and very reactive. It is used in large amounts to make cellulose acetate and many other substances.

Amides

Amides are carboxylic acid derivatives characterized by the functional group

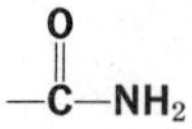

$$-\overset{\overset{\displaystyle O}{\|}}{C}-NH_2$$

Nomenclature

To name amides, we use the common name of the acid and replace the -ic ending of the acid with the ending -amide. If the acid has an -oic ending, we drop the -oic ending and add -amide. For example,

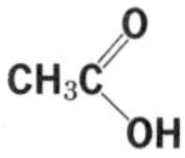

$CH_3C(=O)OH$
acetic acid

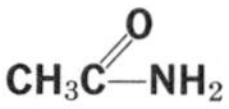

$CH_3C(=O)-NH_2$
acetamide

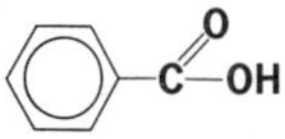

$C_6H_5-C(=O)-OH$
benzoic acid

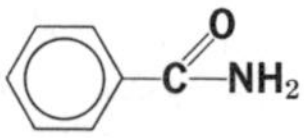

$C_6H_5-C(=O)-NH_2$
benzamide

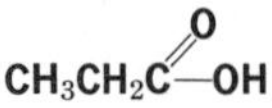

$CH_3CH_2C(=O)-OH$
propionic acid

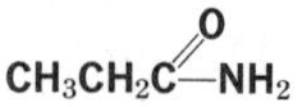

$CH_3CH_2C(=O)-NH_2$
propionamide

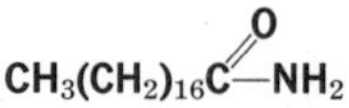

$CH_3(CH_2)_{16}C(=O)-NH_2$
stearamide

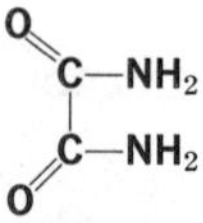

$O=C(-NH_2)-C(-NH_2)=O$
oxalamide
(*oxamide*)

Preparation

As was mentioned earlier in the chapter, amides are prepared by the ammonolysis of acid halides

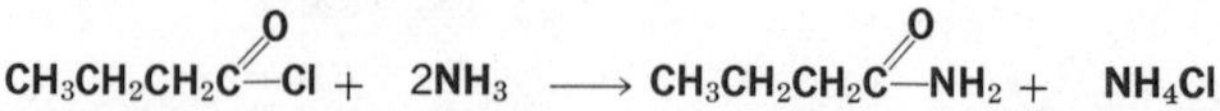

$$\underset{\text{butyryl chloride}}{CH_3CH_2CH_2C(=O)-Cl} + \underset{\text{ammonia}}{2NH_3} \longrightarrow \underset{\text{butyramide}}{CH_3CH_2CH_2C(=O)-NH_2} + \underset{\text{ammonium chloride}}{NH_4Cl}$$

$$C_6H_5CH_2COCl + 2NH_3 \longrightarrow C_6H_5CH_2CONH_2 + NH_4Cl$$

phenylacetyl chloride | ammonia | phenylacetamide | ammonium chloride

or by the ammonolysis of anhydrides

$$CH_3-\overset{O}{\overset{\|}{C}}-O-\overset{O}{\overset{\|}{C}}-CH_3 + 2NH_3 \longrightarrow CH_3-\overset{O}{\overset{\|}{C}}-NH_2 + CH_3\overset{O}{\overset{\|}{C}}-ONH_4$$

acetic anhydride | ammonia | acetamide | ammonium acetate

$$C_6H_4(CO)_2O + NH_3 \longrightarrow C_6H_4(CONH_2)(COOH)$$ as the ammonium salt

phthalic anhydride | ammonia | the half amide of phthalic acid (*phthalamic acid*)

Amides may also be prepared by the reaction of esters with ammonia. (See Chapter 8.)

A fourth method of preparation is the removal of a molecule of water from the ammonium salt of an organic acid.

$$CH_3CH_2\overset{O}{\overset{\|}{C}}-ONH_4 \xrightarrow{\text{heat}} CH_3CH_2\overset{O}{\overset{\|}{C}}-NH_2 + H_2O$$

ammonium propionate | propionamide | water

$$(CH_2)_2(CONH_4)_2 \xrightarrow{\Delta} (CH_2)_2(CONH_2)_2 + 2H_2O$$

ammonium succinate | succinamide | water

Properties

Substituted amides, particularly monosubstituted amides, are among the most important compounds in our body. Proteins may be regarded as complex structures containing many monosubstituted amides. Substituted amides may have alkyl or aryl groups attached to the nitrogen in place of one or both of the hydrogens. To name the substituted amides, we first use a capital N followed by the common name of the group attached to the nitrogen. Then the amide name follows. (The capital N is used to indicate that the group is on the amide nitrogen.) For example,

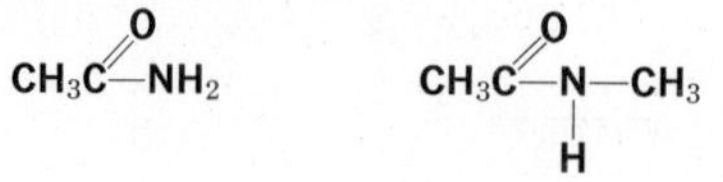

$$CH_3C(=O)-NH_2$$
acetamide

$$CH_3C(=O)-N(H)-CH_3$$
N-methylacetamide

$$CH_3CH_2C(=O)-N(H)-CH_2CH_3$$
N-ethylpropionamide

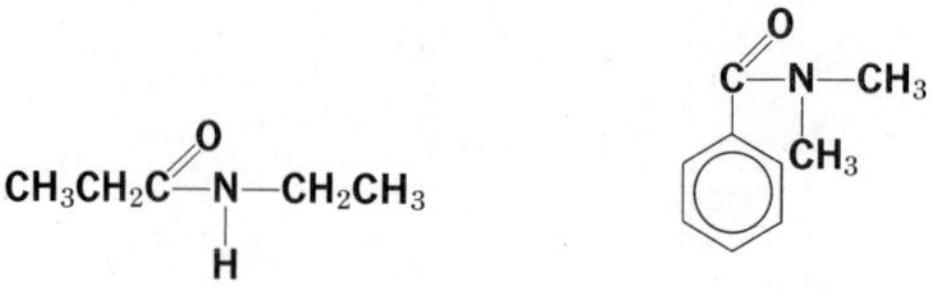

$$C_6H_5-C(=O)-N(CH_3)-CH_3$$
N,N-dimethylbenzamide

Fortunately for us, amides hydrolyze very slowly to acids and ammonia. This accounts for the stability of the proteins in our body. Certain enzymes, however, can accomplish the hydrolysis reaction in a relatively short interval of time. That time interval, then, is the time for the digestion of proteins. The hydrolysis reaction of an amide is of fundamental importance. The general reaction is

$$R-C(=O)-NH(R') + H_2O \xrightarrow{\text{catalyst}} R-C(=O)-OH + R'NH_2$$

amide (*the digestive process for proteins*) · water · acid · amine

Some simple examples are

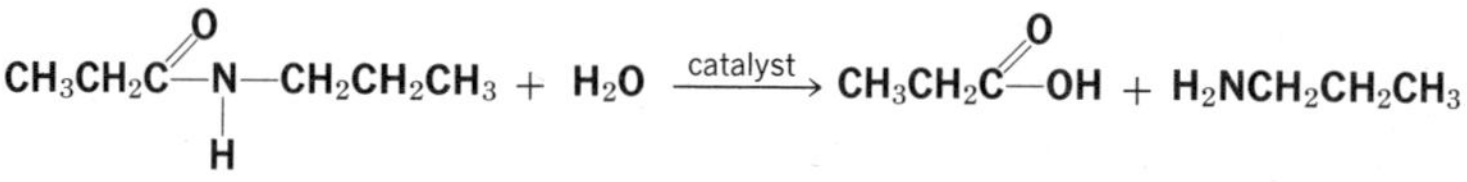

$$CH_3CH_2C(=O)-N(H)-CH_2CH_2CH_3 + H_2O \xrightarrow{\text{catalyst}} CH_3CH_2C(=O)-OH + H_2NCH_2CH_2CH_3$$

N-n-propylpropionamide · water · propionic acid · n-propylamine

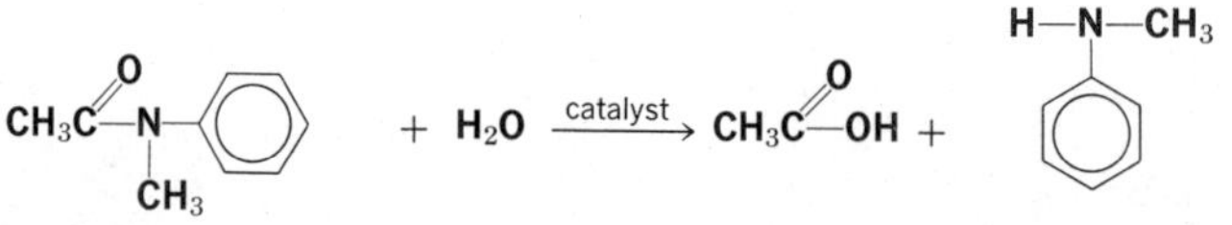

$$CH_3C(=O)-N(CH_3)-C_6H_5 + H_2O \xrightarrow{\text{catalyst}} CH_3C(=O)-OH + C_6H_5-N(H)-CH_3$$

N-phenyl-N-methylacetamide · water · acetic acid · phenylmethylamine N-methylaniline

We will discuss amides in greater detail in Chapter 12.

Lactams

Lactams are inner amides and, consequently, are ring compounds.

If a carboxylic acid has an amine group (i.e., a substituted ammonia group) on the γ or δ (third or fourth) carbon, the amine group can react with the acid to form an amide and water. The —OH comes from the acid; the H comes from the amine group.

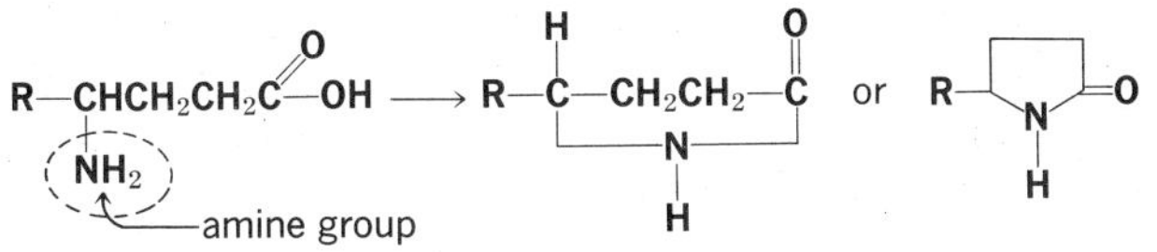

R—CHCH$_2$CH$_2$C(=O)—OH ⟶ R—CH—CH$_2$CH$_2$—C(=O) (ring closed through N—H) or R—(ring)—N(H)—C=O

NH_2 ← amine group

a lactam

Lactams prefer to exist in five- or six-membered rings, but exceptions are known (e.g., penicillin contains a four-membered ring lactam).

The diamide of carbonic acid is a very important substance. It is called urea, or carbamide:

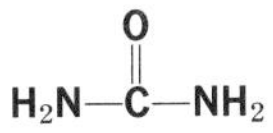

$$H_2N—C(=O)—NH_2$$

Urea is a normal and metabolic product of the animal body. Chemically, it is a particularly reactive substance and is used in making plastics and numerous medicinals. The barbiturates, for example, are made from urea.

Imides

An imide is an amide in which an NH group is bonded to two carbonyl groups.

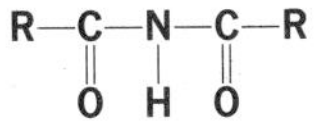

R—C(=O)—N(H)—C(=O)—R

imide group

Imides usually occur in five- and six-membered rings.

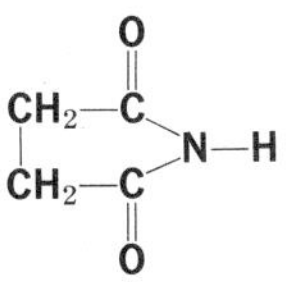

succinimide

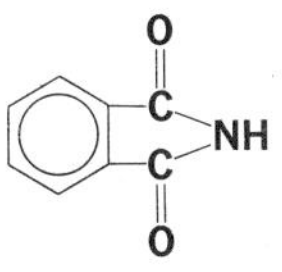

phthalimide

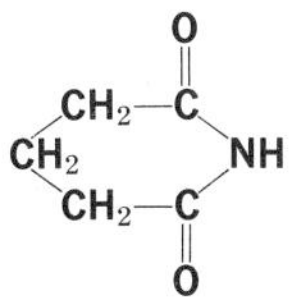

glutarimide

If the hydrogen on the nitrogen is substituted by any group, a capital N is used to indicate that the group is indeed attached to the nitrogen.

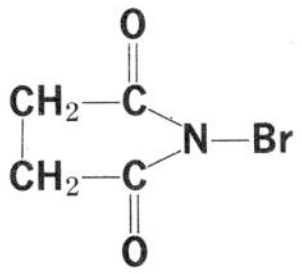

N-bromosuccinimide

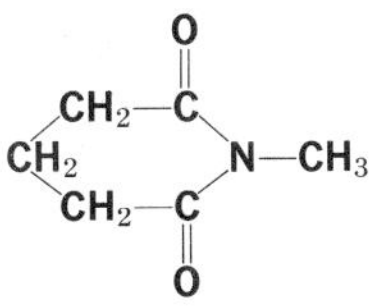

N-methylglutarimide

Nitriles

Nitriles are derivatives of carboxylic acid and do not contain a carbonyl group. The functional group of the nitrile is —C≡N. Note that the nitriles are not salts, such as KCN (potassium cyanide), but contain a carbon covalently bonded to the nitrile group (R—CN).

Nomenclature

Nitriles may be readily converted into carboxylic acids by hydrolysis. The name of the nitrile starts with the name of the acid that would be obtained by hydrolysis and then uses the suffix -nitrile.

$CH_3—C(=O)—OH$ acetic acid	$CH_3—C≡N$ acetonitrile
$CH_2=CH—C(=O)—OH$ acrylic acid	$CH_2=CH—C≡N$ acrylonitrile
$CH_3CH_2CH_2—C(=O)OH$ butanoic acid (*butyric acid*)	$CH_3CH_2CH_2CN$ butanonitrile (*butyronitrile*)

The nitrile group is hydrated in acid or basic solution to give an intermediate that becomes the amide.

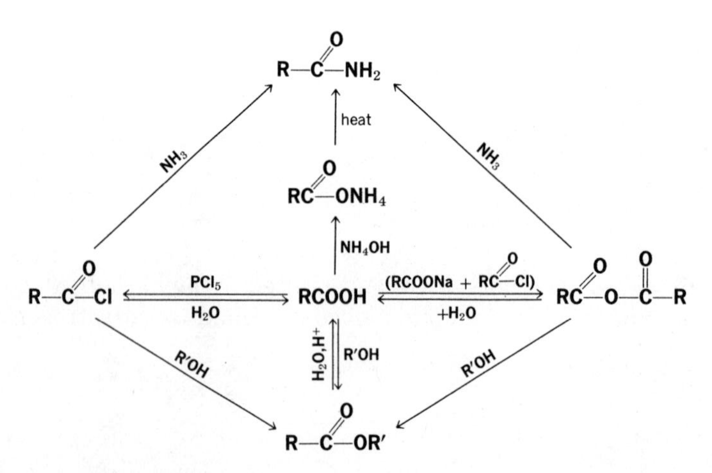

Figure 7-2 Carboxylic acids and their derivatives.

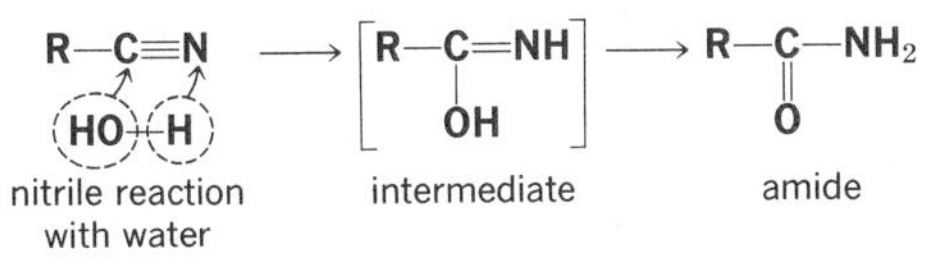

$$\underset{\text{nitrile reaction with water}}{R{-}C{\equiv}N \atop HO{-}H} \longrightarrow \underset{\text{intermediate}}{\left[R{-}\underset{\large OH}{\underset{|}{C}}{=}NH \right]} \longrightarrow \underset{\text{amide}}{R{-}\underset{\large O}{\underset{\|}{C}}{-}NH_2}$$

On continued hydrolysis an amide may be readily converted into a carboxylic acid. Nitriles find use in chemistry as versatile solvents and as interesting reactive intermediates for chemical syntheses. Nitriles as such are usually not useful as medicines.

Figure 7-2 summarizes the reactions of carboxylic acids and their derivatives.

REVIEW QUESTIONS

1. Write structures for several fatty acids. Name these acids in two ways: common names and IUPAC names.
2. Write structures for acetic, isobutyric, lauric, palmitic, stearic, pentanoic, ethanoic, octadecanoic, acrylic, crotonic, oleic, lactic, chaulmoogric, succinic, tartaric, carbonic, phthalic, salicyclic, mandelic, and *p*-aminobenzoic acids.
3. Draw structures for sodium tartrate, calcium oxalate, sodium bicarbonate, and potassium benzoate.
4. What is the essential difference between a strong acid and a weak acid?
5. Name some acids that are completely ionized in dilute solutions.
6. Write structures for some weak acids.
7. How can you detect the presence of an acid?
8. What organic acid is prepared commercially in very large quantities?
9. How is acetic acid produced?
10. How can you detect butyric acid?
11. Of what use are acrylic acid, benzoic acid, mandelic acid, salicylic acid, and citric acid?
12. Of what use are the salicylates?
13. Of what use are ferrous lactate and ferrous gluconate?
14. Identify cream of tartar, Rochelle's salt, tartar emetic, 2,4-D, and phthioic acid.
15. Write structures for acetyl bromide, benzoyl chloride, phosgene, acetic anhydride, acetamide, benzamide, N-ethylacetamide, and urea.
16. Name the following compounds:

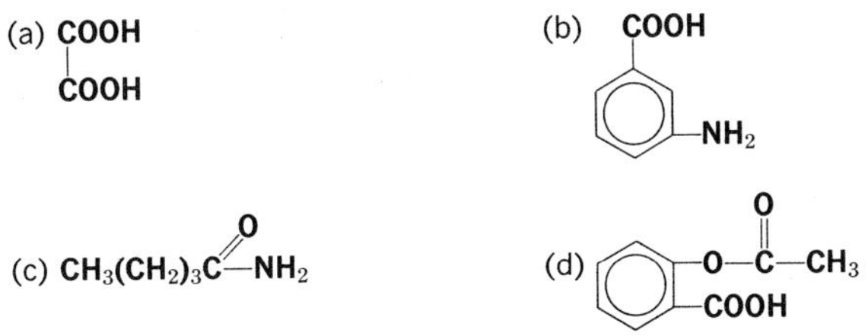

(a) $\underset{\large COOH}{\overset{\large COOH}{|}}$

(b) benzene ring with COOH and NH_2 substituents (COOH at top, NH_2 at meta position)

(c) $CH_3(CH_2)_3\overset{O}{\overset{\|}{C}}{-}NH_2$

(d) benzene ring with $-O-\overset{O}{\overset{\|}{C}}-CH_3$ and $-COOH$ substituents (ortho)

(e) 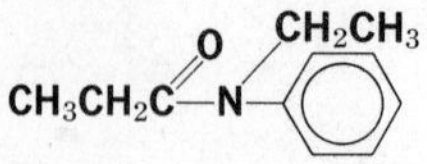 $CH_3CH_2C(=O)$—N(CH_2CH_3)—C_6H_5

(f) 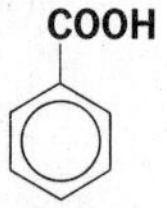 COOH on a benzene ring (C_6H_5COOH)

(g) 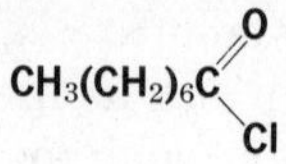 $CH_3(CH_2)_6C(=O)Cl$

(h) 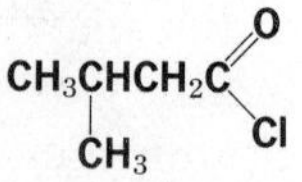 $CH_3CH(CH_3)CH_2C(=O)Cl$

(i) 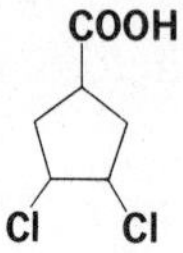 COOH on a cyclopentane ring, with Cl on each of two adjacent ring carbons

(j) 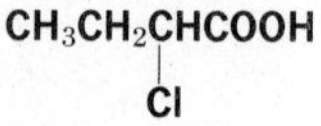 $CH_3CH_2CH(Cl)COOH$

(k) 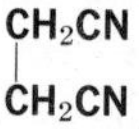 CH_2CN—CH_2CN

(l) 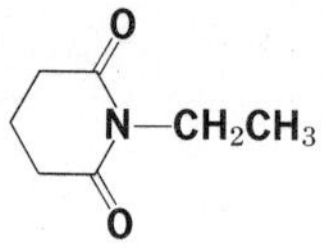 ring with two C=O groups on either side of N—CH_2CH_3

(m) 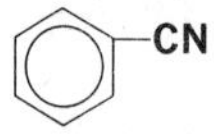 CN on a benzene ring (C_6H_5CN)

17. Complete the following equations:

(a) benzoyl chloride + NH_3
(b) acetyl chloride + sodium acetate
(c) succinic acid + heat
(d) propionic anhydride + NH_3
(e) butyryl chloride + H_2O
(f) phthalic anhydride + H_2O
(g) acetic anhydride + H_2O
(h) sodium formate + heat
(i) propionitrile + NaOH + H_2O

8

esters

Esters are carboxylic acid derivatives noted for their pleasant, fruity aroma. The functional group of the ester is

$$RC(=O)—OR$$

Nomenclature

To name esters, we use the alcohol name with the ending -yl. We then add the acid name with the -ic ending replaced by the ending -ate. For example, the ester of acetic acid and methyl alcohol would be called methyl acetate (methyl for the alcohol, acetate for the acid).

$$\underset{\substack{\text{acetic acid} \\ \textit{acid}}}{CH_3C(=O)—OH} + \underset{\substack{\text{methyl alcohol} \\ \textit{alcohol}}}{CH_3OH} \xrightleftharpoons{\text{strong acid}} \underset{\substack{\text{methyl acetate} \\ \textit{ester}}}{CH_3C(=O)—OCH_3} + \underset{\text{water}}{H_2O}$$

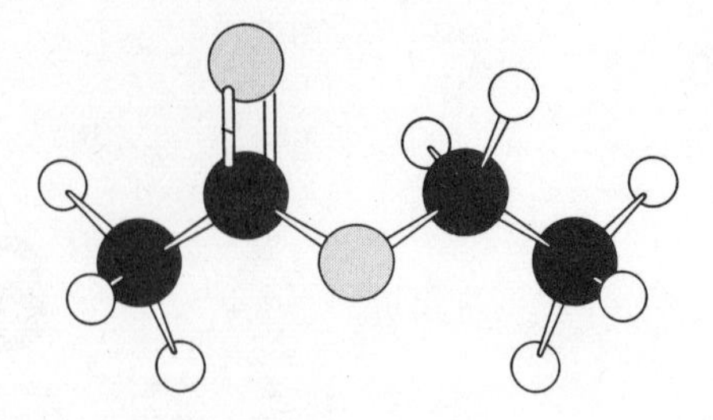

Figure 8-1 Ethyl acetate.

The common names of the alcohol and acid are often used. Some examples are

$$\underset{\text{formic acid}}{H{-}\overset{\overset{\displaystyle O}{\|}}{C}{-}OH} + \underset{\text{ethyl alcohol}}{CH_3{-}CH_2{-}OH} \xrightleftharpoons{H_2SO_4} \underset{\text{ethyl formate}}{H{-}\overset{\overset{\displaystyle O}{\|}}{C}{-}OCH_2CH_3} + H_2O$$

$$\underset{\text{caproic acid}}{CH_3CH_2CH_2CH_2CH_2\overset{\overset{\displaystyle O}{\|}}{C}{-}OH} + \underset{\text{isobutyl alcohol}}{CH_3\underset{\underset{\displaystyle CH_3}{|}}{C}HCH_2OH} \xrightleftharpoons{H_2SO_4} \underset{\text{isobutyl caproate}}{CH_3(CH_2)_4{-}\overset{\overset{\displaystyle O}{\|}}{C}{-}O{-}CH_2CH(CH_3)_2}$$

Some aromatic esters are

$$\underset{\text{methyl benzoate}}{C_6H_5{-}\overset{\overset{\displaystyle O}{\|}}{C}{-}O{-}CH_3} \qquad \underset{\text{methyl mandelate}}{C_6H_5{-}\overset{\overset{\displaystyle OH}{|}}{C}H{-}\overset{\overset{\displaystyle O}{\|}}{C}{-}OCH_3} \qquad \underset{\text{methyl }\beta\text{-naphthoate}}{C_{10}H_7{-}\overset{\overset{\displaystyle O}{\|}}{C}{-}O{-}CH_3}$$

Esters of long-chain alcohols and long-chain acids may be formed. These special esters are called waxes. For example,

$$\underset{\text{cetyl palmitate}}{CH_3(CH_2)_{14}{-}\overset{\overset{\displaystyle O}{\|}}{C}{-}O{-}C_{16}H_{33}} \qquad \underset{\text{lauryl laurate}}{CH_3(CH_2)_{10}{-}\overset{\overset{\displaystyle O}{\|}}{C}{-}O{-}C_{12}H_{25}}$$

$$\underset{\text{cetyl stearate}}{CH_3(CH_2)_{16}{-}\overset{\overset{\displaystyle O}{\|}}{C}{-}O{-}C_{16}H_{33}}$$

Preparation

DIRECT ESTERIFICATION

Esterification is the formation of an ester from an acid and an alcohol. Generally, when a carboxylic acid and an alcohol are mixed, no reaction occurs because the acid is weak. However, if a small amount of a strong mineral acid is added, the reagents react to form an ester and water. Sulfuric acid is commonly used because it is both a strong acid and a dehydrating agent. In this manner, sulfuric acid tends to absorb the water formed; thus, the reaction goes to completion.

$$\underset{\text{acid}}{R\overset{O}{\overset{\|}{C}}{-}OH} + \underset{\text{alcohol}}{HO{-}R'} \xrightleftharpoons{H_2SO_4} \underset{\text{ester}}{R{-}\overset{O}{\overset{\|}{C}}{-}O{-}R'} + \underset{\text{water}}{H_2O}$$

Experiments using labeled oxygen, O^{18}, have proved that the acid usually loses the OH and alcohol loses the H to form the water.

If more than one acid group is present in the molecule, each acid group may react with an alcohol molecule to form the corresponding ester. Thus, a diacid forms a diester with an excess of alcohol, a triacid forms a triester, etc.

$$\underset{\text{oxalic acid}}{(COOH)_2} + \underset{\text{methyl alcohol}}{2CH_3OH} \xrightleftharpoons{H_2SO_4} \underset{\text{methyl oxalate}}{(COOCH_3)_2} + 2H_2O$$

$$\underset{\text{phthalic acid}}{C_6H_4(COOH)_2} + \underset{n\text{-butyl alcohol}}{2CH_3CH_2CH_2CH_2OH} \xrightleftharpoons{H_2SO_4} \underset{n\text{-butyl phthalate}}{C_6H_4(C(=O){-}O{-}CH_2CH_2CH_2CH_3)_2} + 2H_2O$$

$$\underset{\text{tartaric acid}}{HOOC{-}CH(OH){-}CH(OH){-}COOH} + \underset{n\text{-propyl alcohol}}{2CH_3CH_2CH_2OH} \xrightleftharpoons{H_2SO_4} \underset{n\text{-propyl tartarate}}{CH_3CH_2CH_2OOC{-}CH(OH){-}CH(OH){-}COOCH_2CH_2CH_3} + 2H_2O$$

If more than one alcohol group is present, each can react to form an ester. Glycol may react with two acid groups. Glycerol reacts with three moles of acid to form the triester.

$$\underset{\text{glycol}}{CH_2OH{-}CH_2OH} + \underset{\text{acetic acid}}{2CH_3COOH} \xrightleftharpoons{H_2SO_4} \underset{\text{glycol diacetate}}{CH_2{-}O{-}\overset{O}{\overset{\|}{C}}{-}CH_3 \;|\; CH_2{-}O{-}\overset{O}{\overset{\|}{C}}{-}CH_3} + 2H_2O$$

$$\underset{\text{glycerol}}{CH_2OH{-}CHOH{-}CH_2OH} + \underset{\text{stearic acid}}{3CH_3(CH_2)_{16}COOH} \xrightleftharpoons{H_2SO_4} \underset{\text{glyceryl stearate}}{CH_2OOC(CH_2)_{16}CH_3{-}CHOOC(CH_2)_{16}CH_3{-}CH_2OOC(CH_2)_{16}CH_3} + 3H_2O$$

$$\begin{array}{l} CH_2OH \\ | \\ CHOH \\ | \\ CH_2OH \end{array} + 3CH_3COOH \overset{H_2SO_4}{\rightleftharpoons} \begin{array}{l} CH_2OOCCH_3 \\ | \\ CHOOCCH_3 \\ | \\ CH_2OOCCH_3 \end{array} + 3H_2O$$

glycerol — acetic acid — glyceryl acetate

The esters of glycerol are among the most important compounds in the body, since *fats* and *oils* are esters of glycerol and long-chain fatty acids.

If a compound has both an acid group and an alcohol group, they can each react with an alcohol or acid, respectively, to form an ester. Salicylic acid, for example, is such a compound.

$$C_6H_4(COOH)(OH) + CH_3OH \overset{H_2SO_4}{\rightleftharpoons} C_6H_4(COOCH_3)(OH)$$

salicylic acid — methyl alcohol — methyl salicylate (*oil of wintergreen*)

$$C_6H_4(COOH)(OH) + CH_3COOH \overset{H_2SO_4}{\rightleftharpoons} C_6H_4(COOH)(O{-}\underset{\displaystyle \overset{\|}{O}}{C}{-}CH_3)$$

salicylic acid — acetic acid — *o*-carboxyphenyl acetate (*acetylsalicylic acid*) (*aspirin*)

ALCOHOL WITH ACID HALIDE

Esters may also be prepared by the reaction of alcohols with acid chlorides. Hydrogen chloride is formed as the inorganic product instead of water. The general reaction is

$$R{-}OH + R'\overset{O}{\overset{/\!\!/}{C}}{-}Cl \longrightarrow R'\overset{O}{\overset{/\!\!/}{C}}{-}OR + HCl$$

alcohol — acid chloride — ester

Some specific examples are

$$CH_3CH_2OH + CH_3COCl \longrightarrow CH_3{-}COOCH_2CH_3 + HCl$$

ethanol — acetyl chloride — ethyl acetate

$$CH_3CH_2CH_2CH_2OH + C_6H_5{-}\underset{\displaystyle \overset{\|}{O}}{C}{-}Cl \longrightarrow C_6H_5{-}\underset{\displaystyle \overset{\|}{O}}{C}{-}OCH_2CH_2CH_2CH_3 + HCl$$

n-butyl alcohol — benzoyl chloride — *n*-butyl benzoate

No catalyst is needed for the reaction of an acid chloride with an alcohol. However, it is customary to add some type of basic substance (pyridine) to remove the HCl so that it will not reverse the reaction.

ALCOHOL WITH ACID ANHYDRIDE

An acid anhydride will react with alcohol to form the ester and the acid. One mole of anhydride and one mole of alcohol will react to form one mole of ester and one mole of acid. The general reaction is

$$\underset{\text{acid anhydride}}{RC(=O)-O-C(=O)R} + \underset{\text{alcohol}}{R'-OH} \longrightarrow \underset{\text{ester}}{RC(=O)-OR'} + \underset{\text{acid}}{RC(=O)-OH}$$

Some specific examples are

$$\underset{\text{butyric anhydride}}{[CH_3(CH_2)_2-C(=O)]_2O} + \underset{\text{methyl alcohol}}{CH_3OH} \longrightarrow \underset{\text{methyl butyrate}}{CH_3(CH_2)_2\overset{O}{\overset{\|}{C}}OCH_3} + \underset{\text{butyric acid}}{CH_3(CH_2)_2COOH}$$

$$\underset{\text{phthalic anhydride}}{C_6H_4(CO)_2O} + \underset{\text{isopropyl alcohol}}{CH_3CHOHCH_3} \longrightarrow \underset{\text{isopropyl acid phthalate}}{C_6H_4(COOH)-C(=O)-O-CH(CH_3)_2}$$

(*isopropyl hydrogen phthalate*)

$$\underset{\text{acetic anhydride}}{(CH_3-C(=O))_2O} + \underset{\text{ethyl alcohol}}{CH_3CH_2OH} \longrightarrow \underset{\text{ethyl acetate}}{CH_3-C(=O)-OCH_2CH_3} + \underset{\text{acetic acid}}{CH_3COOH}$$

If sulfuric acid and an excess of alcohol are used, the free carboxylic acid formed will also be esterified. Thus, two moles of alcohol will react with one mole of anhydride to yield two moles of ester.

$$\underset{\text{anhydride}}{R\overset{O}{\overset{\|}{C}}-O-\overset{O}{\overset{\|}{C}}-R} + \underset{\text{alcohol}}{2R'-OH} \xrightarrow{H_2SO_4} \underset{\text{ester}}{2R-\overset{O}{\overset{\|}{C}}-OR'} + H_2O$$

$$\underset{\text{propionic anhydride}}{(CH_3CH_2-C(=O))_2O} + \underset{\text{methyl alcohol}}{2CH_3OH} \xrightarrow{H_2SO_4} \underset{\text{methyl propionate}}{2CH_3CH_2\overset{O}{\overset{\|}{C}}-OCH_3} + H_2O$$

$$\begin{matrix} CH_2-C(=O) \\ | \quad\quad \diagdown O \\ CH_2-C(=O) \end{matrix} + 2CH_3CH_2CH_2OH \xrightarrow{H_2SO_4} \begin{matrix} CH_2COOCH_2CH_2CH_3 \\ | \\ CH_2COOCH_2CH_2CH_3 \end{matrix} + H_2O$$

succinic anhydride — *n*-propyl alcohol — *n*-propyl succinate

Reactions

ACID HYDROLYSIS

Esters may be hydrolyzed to the carboxylic acid and the alcohol by heating with a water solution of a strong mineral acid. This reaction is the reverse of esterification. The general reaction is

$$\underset{\text{ester}}{R-\overset{O}{\overset{\|}{C}}-O-R'} + \underset{\text{water}}{H_2O} \overset{HCl}{\rightleftharpoons} \underset{\text{acid}}{R\overset{O}{\overset{\|}{C}}-OH} + \underset{\text{alcohol}}{R'-OH}$$

Some specific examples are

$$\underset{\text{phenyl benzoate}}{C_6H_5-\underset{\overset{\|}{O}}{C}-O-C_6H_5} + H_2O \overset{HCl}{\rightleftharpoons} \underset{\text{benzoic acid}}{C_6H_5-COOH} + \underset{\text{phenol}}{C_6H_5-OH}$$

$$\underset{\text{ethyl acetate}}{CH_3\overset{O}{\overset{\|}{C}}-OCH_2CH_3} + H_2O \overset{HCl}{\rightleftharpoons} \underset{\text{ethyl alcohol}}{CH_3CH_2OH} + \underset{\text{acetic acid}}{CH_3COOH}$$

SAPONIFICATION

When an ester is heated with a strong base, such as sodium hydroxide, the sodium salt of the acid is formed along with the alcohol. If the acid part of the molecule is a long-chain fatty acid (usually 16–18 carbons), the sodium salt is commonly referred to as a soap. The word saponification is derived from the Latin words *sapo,* meaning soap, and *facere,* to make; thus, saponification means *soap making.* Industrially, soaps are prepared by saponifying fats and oils. Naturally, one mole of base is needed for each ester group.

$$\underset{\text{ester}}{R\overset{O}{\overset{\|}{C}}-OR'} + \underset{\text{base}}{NaOH} \longrightarrow \underset{\text{salt of acid}}{R\overset{O}{\overset{\|}{C}}-ONa} + \underset{\text{alcohol}}{R'-OH}$$

Some specific examples are

$$\underset{\text{ethyl formate}}{H-\overset{O}{\overset{\|}{C}}-OCH_2CH_3} + \underset{\text{strong base}}{NaOH} \longrightarrow \underset{\text{sodium formate}}{H-\overset{O}{\overset{\|}{C}}-O-Na} + \underset{\text{ethanol}}{CH_3CH_2OH}$$

$$\begin{array}{l} CH_2-O-\overset{\displaystyle O}{\overset{\|}{C}}-(CH_2)_{16}CH_3 \\ | \\ CH-O-\overset{\displaystyle O}{\overset{\|}{C}}-(CH_2)_{16}CH_3 \\ | \\ CH_2-O-\overset{\displaystyle O}{\overset{\|}{C}}-(CH_2)_{16}CH_3 \end{array} + 3NaOH \longrightarrow 3CH_3(CH_2)_{16}COONa + \begin{array}{l} CH_2OH \\ | \\ CHOH \\ | \\ CH_2OH \end{array}$$

glyceryl stearate — sodium stearate — glycerol

AMMONOLYSIS

Esters react with ammonia, as do some of the other carboxylic acid derivatives, to form an amide and an alcohol. The general reaction is

$$R-\overset{\displaystyle O}{\overset{\|}{C}}-OR' + NH_3 \longrightarrow R\overset{\displaystyle O}{\overset{\|}{C}}-NH_2 + R'OH$$

Some specific examples are

$$CH_3-\overset{\displaystyle O}{\overset{\|}{C}}-OCH_2CH_3 + NH_3 \longrightarrow CH_3-\overset{\displaystyle O}{\overset{\|}{C}}-NH_2 + CH_3CH_2OH$$

ethyl acetate — ammonia — acetamide — ethyl alcohol

$$\begin{array}{l} O \\ \| \\ C-OCH_3 \\ | \\ C-OCH_3 \\ \| \\ O \end{array} + 2NH_3 \longrightarrow \begin{array}{l} O \\ \| \\ C-NH_2 \\ | \\ C-NH_2 \\ \| \\ O \end{array} + 2CH_3OH$$

methyl oxalate — ammonia — oxamide (*oxalamide*) — methyl alcohol

Uses

ESTERS OF INORGANIC ACIDS

Glyceryl nitrate, or nitroglycerin, is an explosive, yellow liquid, which can be prepared by adding glycerol to a cooled mixture of nitric and sulfuric acids.

$$\begin{array}{l} CH_2OH \\ | \\ CHOH \\ | \\ CH_2OH \end{array} + 3HNO_3 \xrightarrow{+H_2SO_4} \begin{array}{l} CH_2ONO_2 \\ | \\ CHONO_2 \\ | \\ CH_2ONO_2 \end{array} + 3H_2O$$

glycerol — nitroglycerin

It can be administered to a patient either in tablet form or as an alcoholic solution (Spirit of Glyceryl Trinitrate). In each case, the material is placed under the tongue. Medically, nitroglycerin is used to dilate the smaller blood vessels and to relax the smooth muscles, so that it reduces the blood pressure and relieves heart pain in diseases associated with aortic malfunction.

Dynamite is a mixture of kieselguhr and nitroglycerin. Alfred Nobel discovered that the product obtained when the dangerous liquid nitroglycerin is mixed with kieselguhr is much more stable and more convenient to handle than the original reagents.

Ethyl nitrite CH_3CH_2ONO is a gas used to dilate peripheral blood vessels. It is the ester of ethyl alcohol and nitrous acid. It is known as Sweet Spirit of Nitre and is administered as an alcohol solution.

Amyl nitrite $C_5H_{11}ONO$ is a yellow liquid with a pungent odor. It is administered as an antispasmodic in angina pectoris and is a dilator of the smaller blood vessels.

ESTERS OF ORGANIC ACIDS

The esters of organic acids, even those acids such as butyric and valeric with disagreeable odors, are very pleasant smelling. The aromas of many flowers and fruits are due to esters naturally present in them. Artificial flavors and essences are combinations of synthetic esters blended to be almost identical to the natural product. Table 8-1 summarizes some of these esters and their aromas.

Note that not all pleasantly aromatic compounds are esters; some are other types of organic or inorganic compounds.

Lactones

Lactones are inner esters and, consequently, are always found as ring structures. If a molecule contains both an acid group and an alcohol group, it may form an ester with itself; that is, the alcohol group may react with the acid group, lose water, and form the ester.

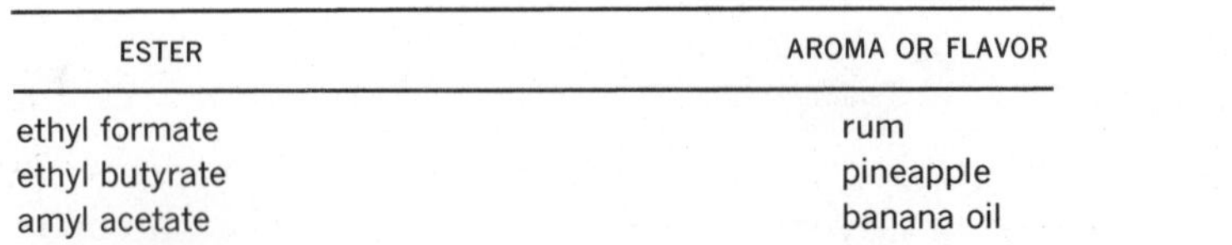

$$\underbrace{R{-}\underset{H}{\overset{OH}{C}}}_{\text{alcohol part}}{-}CH_2CH_2{-}\underbrace{\overset{OH}{C}{=}O}_{\text{acid part}} \longrightarrow \underbrace{R\underset{H}{C}{-}CH_2CH_2{-}C{=}O}_{\text{lactone}}\ (\text{ring closed through } O)$$

or (ring structure with R, O, and =O)

Table 8-1 Esters

ESTER	AROMA OR FLAVOR
ethyl formate	rum
ethyl butyrate	pineapple
amyl acetate	banana oil
isoamyl acetate	pear oil
octyl acetate	orange
methyl anthranilate	grape

The most stable lactones are the five- and six-membered ring lactones, and they are the easiest to prepare.

Ascorbic acid is a naturally occurring lactone found in fresh fruits. It is vitamin C and will be discussed in Chapter 21 (Vitamins).

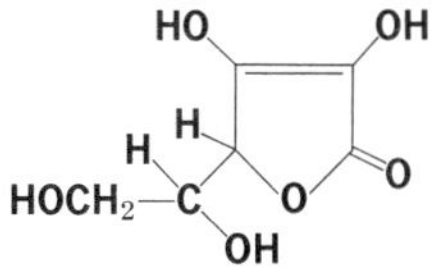

ascorbic acid

Nepetalactone is a complex compound found in oil of catnip. When a member of the cat family is exposed to nepetalactone, he or she can be aroused immediately from a state of lethargy to one of intense excitement by the odor of the lactone and will follow the odor to its source. It has been reported that when they (the cats) acquire the material with the odor, they become ludicrously playful and their main interest seems to be to get the odoriferous material transferred to their fur. They show no desire to eat the material, nor is there any evidence of sexual stimulation.

The structure of nepetalactone is

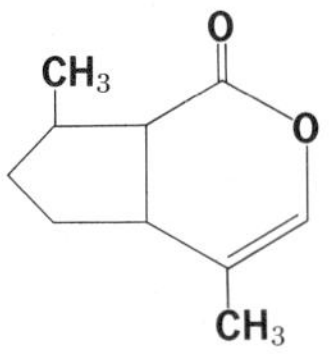

nepetalactone

REVIEW QUESTIONS

1. What is esterification? Write four equations illustrating esterification and name all the compounds involved.
2. Give the three methods of preparing esters. Use equations to illustrate each method.
3. Write three equations illustrating the saponification of esters.
4. Write balanced equations for the following reactions:

   (a) acetic anhydride + pentyl alcohol $\xrightarrow{H_2SO_4}$

   (b) ethyl benzoate + **NaOH** $\longrightarrow$

   (c) isopropyl alcohol + butanoyl chloride $\longrightarrow$

   (d) glyceryl stearate + **NaOH** $\longrightarrow$

   (e) benzoyl chloride + phenol $\longrightarrow$

   (f) benzyl acetate + ammonia $\longrightarrow$

   (g) succinic acid + ethyl alcohol $\xrightarrow{H_2SO_4}$

   Name all the organic compounds.

5. Draw structural formulas for the following compounds: *n*-butyl propionate, *n*-butyl phthalate, methyl oxalate, phenyl benzoate, isobutyl citrate, acetylsalicylic acid, and oil of wintergreen.
6. What is a lactone? Draw the structure of a lactone.
7. What compound is responsible for the effect of catnip?
8. What is dynamite? What is nitroglycerin?
9. What are the commercial and medicinal uses of nitroglycerin?
10. How are esters used commercially?

9

amines and alkaloids

The amines may be classified as the organic bases and are all derived from ammonia NH_3. There are three types of amines: primary, secondary, and tertiary.

A primary amine is one in which one hydrogen of ammonia has been replaced by an organic group, that is,

NH_3	$R—NH_2$	$Ar—NH_2$
ammonia	primary aliphatic amine	primary aromatic amine

A secondary amine is one in which two hydrogens of ammonia have been replaced by organic groups, that is,

$R(R')N—H$	$R(Ar)N—H$	Ar_2NH
aliphatic secondary amine	mixed aliphatic aromatic secondary amine	aromatic secondary amine

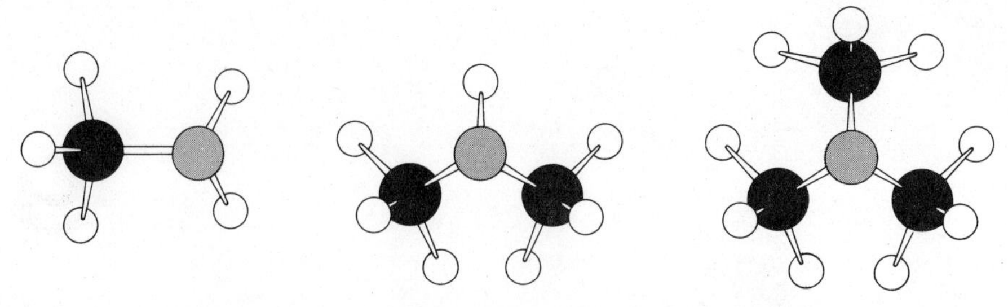

Figure 9-1 (a) Methylamine, (b) dimethylamine, and (c) trimethylamine.

From the formulas drawn, it is evident that the organic groups may be like (symmetrical amine) or unlike (unsymmetrical amine).

Tertiary amines are ammonia derivatives in which all the hydrogens have been replaced by organic groups. The general formula of a tertiary amine is

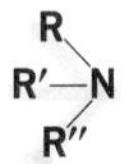

the R groups may be the same or different—aliphatic or aromatic

Nomenclature

To name primary amines, we first identify the organic radical and then use the ending -amine. Table 9-1 lists some common primary amines.

Table 9-1

CH_3NH_2	methylamine	$CH_3CH_2CH_2CH_2NH_2$	*n*-butylamine
$CH_3CH_2NH_2$	ethylamine	$CH_3CH_2CH(NH_2)CH_3$	*sec*-butylamine
$CH_3CH_2CH_2NH_2$	*n*-propylamine	$CH_3CH(CH_3)CH_2NH_2$	isobutylamine
$CH_3CH(NH_2)CH_3$	isopropylamine	$(CH_3)_3CNH_2$	*tert*-butylamine
$C_6H_5NH_2$	phenylamine (aniline)	$C_{10}H_7NH_2$	α-naphthylamine

When the radical has no common name, we call the $—NH_2$ group the amino group and designate by a number its position on the longest chain of carbon atoms containing the NH_2 group. For example,

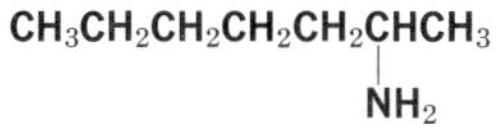

$$CH_3CH_2CH_2CH_2CH_2\underset{\displaystyle NH_2}{\underset{|}{C}}HCH_3$$

2-aminoheptane
(*Tuamine*)

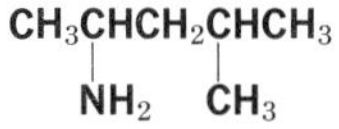

$$CH_3\underset{\displaystyle NH_2}{\underset{|}{C}}HCH_2\underset{\displaystyle CH_3}{\underset{|}{C}}HCH_3$$

2-amino-4-methylpentane

To name secondary amines, we identify the two groups attached to the nitrogen by their common names and use the ending -amine. For example,

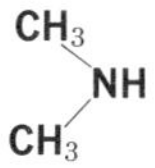

$(CH_3)_2NH$ — dimethylamine

$C_6H_5—NH—CH_3$ — N-methylaniline

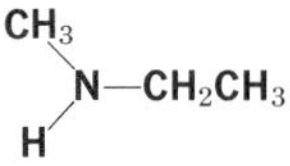

$CH_3—NH—CH_2CH_3$ — methylethylamine

$C_6H_5—NH—C_6H_5$ — diphenylamine

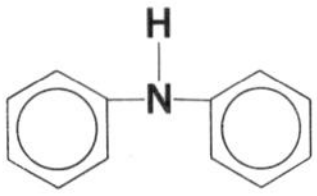

When the radicals have no common names, other methods, which need not concern us here, are used.

To name tertiary amines, we designate the three radicals and use the ending -amine. For example,

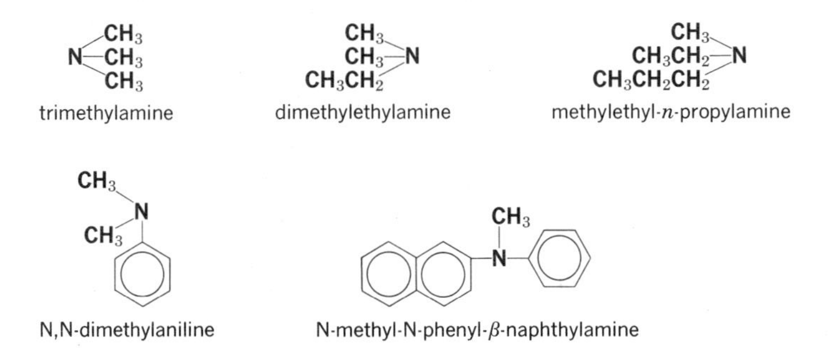

trimethylamine; dimethylethylamine; methylethyl-*n*-propylamine

N,N-dimethylaniline; N-methyl-N-phenyl-β-naphthylamine

A compound can contain more than one amino group in the molecule. Some examples are

$NH_2CH_2CH_2NH_2$

1,2-diaminoethane
(*ethylenediamine*)

$$\underset{\displaystyle NH_2}{\underset{|}{C}}H_2CH_2CH_2\underset{\displaystyle NH_2}{\underset{|}{C}}H_2$$

1,4-diaminobutane
(*tetramethylenediamine, putrescine*)

$$\underset{\displaystyle NH_2}{\underset{|}{C}}H_2CH_2CH_2CH_2\underset{\displaystyle NH_2}{\underset{|}{C}}H_2$$

1,5-diaminopentane
(*pentamethylenediamine, cadaverine*)

$$\underset{\displaystyle NH_2}{\underset{|}{C}}H_2CH_2CH_2CH_2CH_2\underset{\displaystyle NH_2}{\underset{|}{C}}H_2$$

1,6-diaminohexane
(*hexamethylenediamine*)

Some compounds have other functional groups present in the molecule in addition to the amino group. For example,

$HOCH_2CH_2NH_2$

ethanolamine
(*β-hydroxyethylamine*)

The amino acids are important compounds that we shall discuss in detail in Chapter 12.

As indicated by the various names, many common or trivial names are used more frequently than the technical or scientific names.

Physical Properties

Their pronounced fishlike odor makes the lower molecular weight amines easily recognizable. The characteristic odor of fish is attributed to the presence of these amines in the fish fluids.

The primary amines with few carbon atoms, such as methylamine and ethylamine, are gases like ammonia and have a very pungent odor. An increase in carbon content raises the boiling point. The primary amines from *n*-propyl through *n*-decylamine are liquids. *n*-Lauryl amine and higher primary amines are solids with diminished odor.

Dimethylamine is the only gaseous secondary amine; it has a penetrating odor. Secondary amines such as diethylamine and methylethylamine are liquids with somewhat diminished odor; secondary amines such as di-*n*-butylamine are solids with much diminished odor.

The only gaseous tertiary amine is trimethylamine, again a very odoriferous substance. Triethylamine, tri-*n*-propylamine, and tri-*n*-butylamine are pungent liquids, and tri-*n*-pentylamine is a solid with diminished odor.

Chemical Properties

THE BASICITY OF AMINES

Ammonia NH_3 has a pair of unshared electrons, which can accept a proton such as H^+ to form the ammonium ion.

$$\mathrm{H{:}\ddot{N}{:}H} + H^+ \longrightarrow \left[\begin{array}{c}\mathrm{H}\\ \mathrm{H{:}\ddot{N}{:}H}\\ \mathrm{H}\end{array}\right]^+$$

Any compound that can accept a proton is a base; therefore, ammonia is a base.

When ammonia gas is passed into water, it reacts with the water to a very small extent to form ammonium hydroxide, $NH_4^+OH^-$.

$$\underset{\text{ammonia}}{\ddot{N}H_3} + \underset{\text{water}}{H_2O} \rightleftharpoons \underset{\text{ammonium ion}}{NH_4^+} + \underset{\text{hydroxyl ions}}{OH^-}$$

Amines, which are substituted ammonia compounds and have a pair of unshared electrons, behave in an identical manner when placed in water: They are also weak bases.

$$\underset{\text{methylamine}}{CH_3\ddot{N}H_2} + \underset{\text{water}}{H_2O} \rightleftharpoons \underset{\text{methylammonium ion}}{CH_3NH_3^+} + \underset{\text{hydroxyl ion}}{OH^-}$$

$$\underset{\text{methylethylamine}}{CH_3{-}\ddot{N}(CH_2CH_3){-}H} + \underset{\text{water}}{H_2O} \rightleftharpoons \underset{\text{methylethylammonium ion}}{CH_3{-}NH_2^+(CH_2CH_3)} + \underset{\text{hydroxyl ion}}{OH^-}$$

$$\underset{\text{trimethylamine}}{CH_3{-}N{:}(CH_3)_2} + \underset{\text{water}}{H_2O} \rightleftharpoons \underset{\text{trimethyl-ammonium ion}}{H_3C{-}NH^+(CH_3)_2} + \underset{\text{hydroxyl ion}}{OH^-}$$

The simple aliphatic amines are about 10 times more basic than ammonia, and diethylamine is about 100 times more basic than ammonia. If the amino group is attached to an aromatic ring, the basicity is decreased enormously. Aniline is 100,000 times less basic than ammonia; since ammonia is a weak base, aniline is indeed an extremely weak base. Two or three aromatic rings attached to the nitrogen essentially remove all traces of basicity.

Reactions

One of the characteristics of bases is that they react with acids to form salts. For example,

$$NH_3 + HCl \longrightarrow NH_4^+Cl^-$$

ammonia; hydrochloric acid; ammonium chloride *ionic salt*

or

$$NH_4OH + HCl \longrightarrow NH_4^+Cl^- + H_2O$$

ammonium hydroxide; hydrochloric acid; ammonium chloride; water

Similar equations may be written for the amines.

$$CH_3NH_2 + HCl \longrightarrow CH_3NH_3^+Cl^-$$

methylamine; hydrochloric acid; methylammonium chloride

$$(CH_3)_2NH + HBr \longrightarrow CH_3{-}NH_2^+Br^-(CH_3)$$

dimethylamine; hydrobromic acid; dimethylammonium bromide

$$(CH_3)_3N + HI \longrightarrow (CH_3)_3NH^+I^-$$

trimethylamine; hydriodic acid; trimethylammonium iodide

When tertiary amines are heated with alkyl halides, an interesting group of compounds known as *quaternary ammonium salts* are formed. In quaternary amines, the derived ammonium ion contains four organic groups: All the hydrogens of the ammonium ion NH_4^+ have been replaced by organic groups (NR_4^+).

$$(CH_3)_3N + CH_3Br \longrightarrow (CH_3)_4N^+Br^-$$

trimethylamine; methyl bromide; tetramethylammonium bromide

$$C_6H_5{-}CH_2{-}N(CH_3)_2 + CH_3I \longrightarrow \left[C_6H_5{-}CH_2{-}\overset{\oplus}{N}(CH_3)_3\right] I^{\ominus}$$

benzyldimethylamine; methyl iodide; benzyltrimethylammonium iodide

The benzyl radical is

$$C_6H_5-CH_2-$$

The treatment of organic quaternary ammonium salts with a strong base forms the organic quaternary ammonium hydroxide.

$$\underset{\text{tetramethylammonium chloride}}{(CH_3)_4N^+Cl^-} + \underset{\text{sodium hydroxide}}{Na^+OH^-} \rightleftharpoons \underset{\text{tetramethyl-ammonium hydroxide}}{(CH_3)_4N^+OH^-} + \underset{\text{sodium chloride}}{Na^+Cl^-}$$

Organic quaternary ammonium hydroxides are completely ionized and are very strong bases, *comparable to sodium hydroxide and potassium hydroxide*. From the previous equation it is evident that all the reactants and products are ionic. Thus, an equilibrium reaction, governed mainly by the solubilities of the products, occurs, and all the ions exist simultaneously in solution. To make a *pure* quaternary ammonium hydroxide, we can conveniently use silver hydroxide instead of sodium hydroxide, since the resulting silver halide is insoluble and the reaction goes in the right-hand direction.

$$\underset{\text{tetramethylammonium iodide}}{(CH_3)_4N^+I^-} + \underset{\text{silver hydroxide}}{Ag^+OH^-} \longrightarrow \underset{\text{silver iodide}}{AgI\downarrow} + \underset{\text{tetramethylammonium hydroxide}}{(CH_3)_4N^+OH^-}$$

When the reaction is run in the indicated manner, the silver iodide can be filtered off, leaving pure organic quaternary ammonium hydroxide.

Many amines can be formed by the decomposition of proteins, which are composed of α-amino acids. In the decarboxylation process (i.e., removal of carbon dioxide), amines are formed.

$$\underset{\alpha\text{-amino acid}}{R-\overset{H}{\underset{NH_2}{C}}-COOH} \longrightarrow \underset{\text{amine}}{R-CH_2NH_2} + \underset{\text{carbon dioxide}}{CO_2}$$

This is sometimes known as a putrefaction process and is responsible in part for the odor of decaying flesh (see Chapter 16.)

Amines of Interest

So many compounds used in medicine contain nitrogen as amine derivatives that a complete discussion of these would fill numerous volumes. We can, at best, mention only a few of the more interesting ones.

2-Aminoheptane (Tuamine) is available as the sulfate or carbonate and is effective in the treatment of nasal congestion. As the carbonate, it is used in an inhaler, and as a sulfate, it is used in nose drops. Many quaternary compounds are useful as germicides. An example is *Zephiran chloride,* which is benzyldimethylalkylammonium chloride (the size of the alkyl group may vary).

$$C_6H_5\text{—}CH_2\text{—}N^+(CH_3)_2(R)\,Cl^- \qquad R = \text{8–18 carbon atoms}$$

Zephiran chloride

Zephiran is a member of a group of compounds called invert soaps. Invert soaps are detergents in which the group possessing detergent properties is the positive (+) ion [in ordinary soap, the part characteristic of the soap is the negative (−) ion]. Like the detergents, Zephiran can be used satisfactorily in hard water (see Chapter 11). Because it is a detergent and a cleansing agent, Zephiran removes surface film and penetrates to tissue surfaces. It is excellent for sterilizing equipment and external tissues.

Aniline, the most important amine made industrially, is prepared by the reduction of nitrobenzene. It is a weak base and toxic to the body. Aniline derivatives are used extensively in medicine, because they modify the properties of aniline and produce very interesting pharmaceutical compounds.

Acetanilide (antifebrin) is an antipyretic and an analgesic that is found in many headache powders.

$$C_6H_5\text{—}N(H)\text{—}C(=O)\text{—}CH_3$$

acetanilide

Acetanilide may also be called N-phenylacetamide. Although less toxic than aniline, acetanilide is still somewhat toxic and must be used with caution; for this reason, it ranks second to the salicylates in use.

Acetophenetidine (phenacetine) exhibits properties similar to acetanilide.

$$CH_3\text{—}CH_2\text{—}O\text{—}C_6H_4\text{—}N(H)\text{—}C(=O)\text{—}CH_3$$

acetophenetidine

Although useful as an antipyretic and an analgesic, acetophenetidine is also somewhat toxic, and care must be exercised in its usage.

The *ethanolamines* possess both an alcohol group and an amino group, and chemically each group retains its characteristic activity. The ethanolamines are interesting because of their relation to certain naturally occurring compounds in the body. For example, cephalin, a naturally occurring component of lipids, contains ethanolamine.

$H-O-CH_2CH_2NH_2$

β-hydroxyethylamine
(*ethanolamine*)

Diethanolamine is $(HOCH_2CH_2)_2NH$, and *triethanolamine* is $(HOCH_2CH_2)_3N$. The ethanolamines, especially triethanolamine, possess detergent properties and are used as vehicles for certain skin preparations.

Alkaloids

Alkaloids (alkali-like) are basic nitrogen-containing compounds with pronounced physiological activity and are usually found in plants. We arbitrarily exclude compounds such as amino acids and simple amines (e.g., methylamine and triethylamine) from this classification. Most alkaloids are complex structures, many of which have the nitrogen in a ring system (heterocycles).

Plants containing alkaloids are prevalent; any one plant may contain many different alkaloids, which are usually closely related chemically. Alkaloids that are simple in chemical structure may be found in a variety of botanically unrelated plants, but the more complicated alkaloids are usually limited to a definite variety or species of plant and may characterize that particular species.

Because alkaloids are basic, they occur naturally in the form of their salts and in combination with many common plant acids such as acetic, malic, tartaric, oxalic, and citric. We shall arbitrarily classify the alkaloids depending on the particular ring structure. Some of the naturally occurring alkaloids have been synthesized and others have not. There have been extensive attempts by chemists to synthesize structures similar to those occurring in nature. In this way, new drugs that may be superior to those found in nature are created and often possess the good effects and minimize the side effects. In our following discussion, we shall mention many synthetic drugs of value.

Alkaloids Derived from β-Phenylethylamine

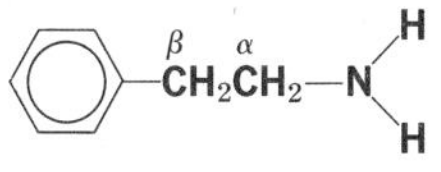

$C_6H_5-\overset{\beta}{C}H_2\overset{\alpha}{C}H_2-NH_2$

β-phenylethylamine

Ephedrine occurs naturally in the *Ephedra* genus, which is a gymnosperm related to pines and firs, accompanied by other similar alkaloids.

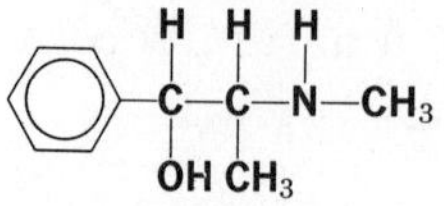

$$C_6H_5-CH(OH)-CH(CH_3)-NH-CH_3$$

ephedrine

It is a highly active compound and is effective in increasing the blood pressure. Because it contracts the capillaries in mucous membranes, ephedrine is useful in treating asthma, hay fever, and allied phenomena. Ephedrine can be given orally and is more stable and longer acting than Adrenaline. Ephedrine can also be administered intramuscularly or intravenously.

Tyramine is produced when the amino acid tyrosine is decarboxylated (i.e., when it loses CO_2).

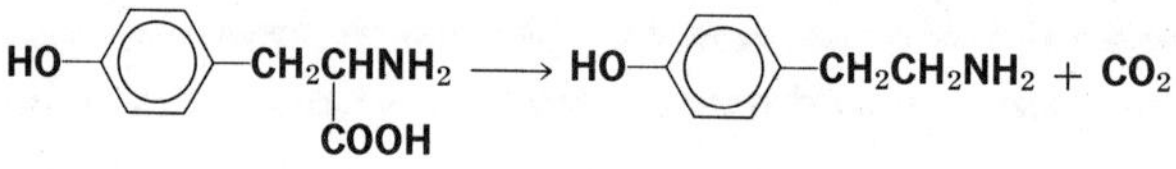

$$HO-C_6H_4-CH_2CH(COOH)NH_2 \longrightarrow HO-C_6H_4-CH_2CH_2NH_2 + CO_2$$

tyrosine — tyramine

The decarboxylation can occur by heating the amino acid or by bacterial action. The physiological action is similar to ephedrine. Tyramine exerts a strong contracting effect on the uterus, and thus it is often called *uteramine.* The drug is usually administered by hypodermic in the form of its hydrochloride.

Synephrin, a synthetic product, is used in the form of its tartrate. It is reported to be less toxic but also less active than Adrenaline.

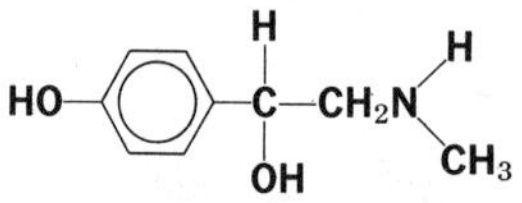

$$HO-C_6H_4-CH(OH)-CH_2N(H)CH_3$$

Synephrin

Hordenine and *mescaline* are alkaloids found in the species *anhalonium* of the cactus.

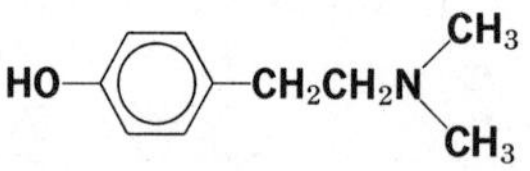

$$HO-C_6H_4-CH_2CH_2N(CH_3)_2 \qquad (CH_3O)_3C_6H_2-CH_2CH_2NH_2$$

hordenine 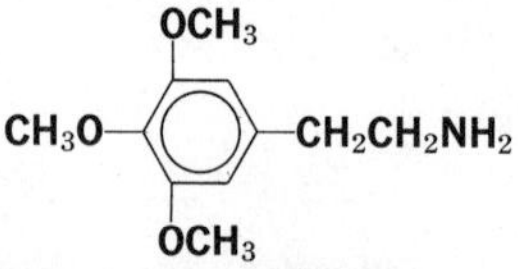 — mescaline

Hordenine is only weakly effective in increasing the blood pressure and has been employed as a myocardial stimulant, and in small doses as intestinal relaxant and in large doses as intestinal stimulant.

Interest in mescaline centers on the fact that it causes unusual psychic effects and visual hallucinations. The usual oral dose (5 mg/kg) in the average normal subject causes anxiety, sympathomimetic effects, hyperreflexia of the limbs, static tremors, and vivid hallucinations that are usually visual and consist in brightly colored lights, geometric designs, animals, and occasionally people; color and space perception are often concomitantly impaired, but otherwise the sensorium is normal and insight is retained. When the psychic alterations are mild, the EEG is usually normal; but, in more severe intoxication, there may be disturbances in the EEG. An extreme anxiety state may develop in some schizophrenic patients given mescaline. The hallucinations in others may have a decided sexual content. The effects of a single does of mescaline persist for about 12 hours. In some respects, the psychic changes are similar to those caused by very minute doses of LSD. Peyote does not cause addiction; there is no valid evidence that abstinence symptoms occur when the drug is no longer available.[1]

Norepinephrine (arterenol) is found in small amounts with adrenaline.

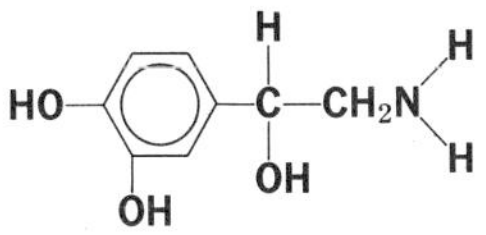

norepinephrine

It is a highly active substance, having the most potent pressor activity reported.

Epinephrine (Adrenalin, Suprarenin) is produced by the medulla of the adrenal glands. We will discuss this hormone further in Chapter 22.

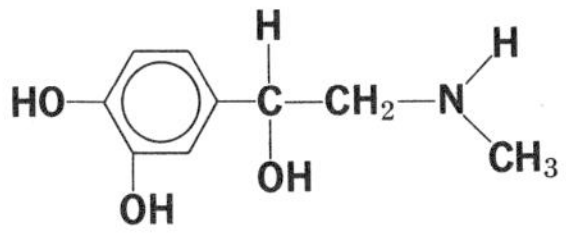

epinephrine

Benzedrine (amphetamine) is a synthetic product capable of shrinking the nasal mucosa.

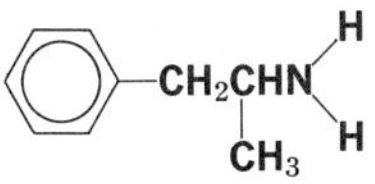

Benzedrine

Because of the volatility of the free base and its carbonate, Benzedrine can be used effectively in inhalers. It is useful in relieving nasal and bronchial congestion such as occurs with asthma, hay fever, and common cold. Benzedrine, similar in action to ephedrine, is more effective in stimulating the cortex. Benzedrine is not recommended to overcome sleepiness, because too

[1] From L. S. Goodman and A. Gilman, eds., *The Pharmacological Basis of Therapeutics,* 3rd ed. New York: Macmillan, 1965. p. 205.

many complications may arise and habituation is possible. The sulfate is not volatile and can be used in solutions and in powder form or tablets.

Aludrine (Isuprel) is a synthetic product that is very effective in constricting surface capillaries.

HO–C$_6$H$_3$(OH)–CHCH$_2$–N–CH(CH$_3$)$_2$ (with OH on the CH, H on the N)

aludrine

Because of its strong effect in dilating the bronchi, aludrine is effective in the relief of bronchospasms.

Benzedrex, although not strictly a β-phenylethylamine, is a reduced derivative.

C$_6$H$_{11}$–CH$_2$CH(CH$_3$)N(H)–CH$_3$

Benzedrex

In Benzedrex, the cyclohexyl group replaces the phenyl group. Benzedrex is used in inhalers to relieve congestion in nasal mucosa. It is not as effective as benzedrine and is reported to be non-habit forming.

Alkaloids with a Pyrrole Nucleus

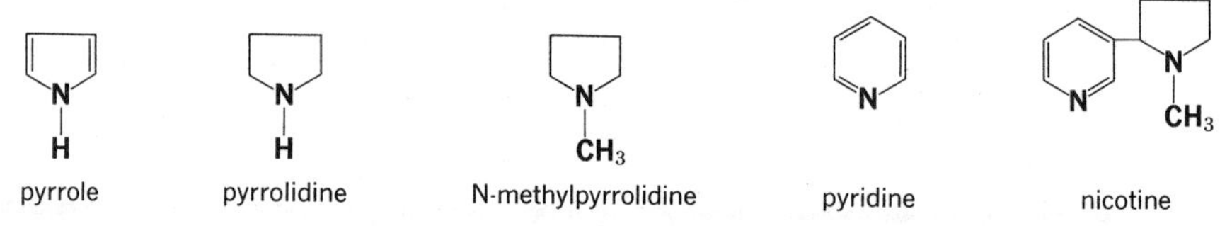

Nicotine was first obtained from leaves of tobacco, *Nicotiana tabacum,* native to America but now grown in other places in the world. Because nicotine contains the reduced pyrrole ring and the pyrrolidine ring, it can be classified under either category.

The action of nicotine on the body is complex. The liquid stimulates the central nervous system, and blood pressure and heart beat are irregular. The effect of nicotine in the gastrointestinal tract is an emptying one: vomiting and diarrhea may occur. Nicotine stimulates, then inhibits, gland secretions (salivary and bronchial secretions). The salivation caused by smoking results from the irritant smoke, rather than from the nicotine.

Nicotine is actually a violent poison, and the fatal dose is about 60 mg. If a nonsmoker absorbs 4 mg, then symptoms of nausea, vomiting, diarrhea, weakness, and prostration may arise. Smokers develop a tolerance to nicotine and may absorb about 8 mg and be unaffected. The nicotine absorbed by smoking two cigarettes is approximately 0.4 mg. Cigarette tobacco contains 0.7–3.0% nicotine. The smoke from one cigarette may contain 6 mg of nicotine; the smoke from one cigar may contain over 200 mg. Thus, not all the nicotine in the smoke is absorbed. The absorption varies according to moisture, heat, rapidity of smoking, amount of smoking, inhalation, etc. Most of the inhaled nicotine is exhaled.

It has been shown that hunger contractions of the stomach in humans can be abolished by smoking, and that the inhibition caused by smoking one cigarette lasts from 15 to 60 minutes.

There has been considerable discussion and investigation concerning the effect of smoking on humans. Generally, moderate smokers have a normal life expectancy and a state of health comparable to nonsmokers. Excessive smokers present a different problem.

Alkaloids with the Pyridine Ring

HEMLOCK ALKALOIDS

Hemlock (*Conium maculatum*) contains a series of related alkaloids, and the fruits and seeds are very rich in these bases. Many of these compounds contain the pyridine ring in the hydrogenated form. A fully reduced pyridine ring is called the piperidine ring.

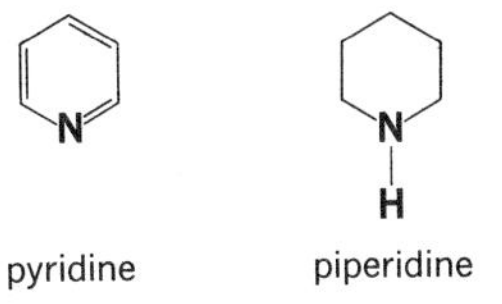

pyridine piperidine

Coniine is a poisonous substance that causes paralysis of the motor nerve endings, stimulation, and finally depression of the central nervous system. Death results from respiratory failure. The reader may remember that Socrates died by drinking the oil of Hemlock.

$-CH_2CH_2CH_3$ (N–H)

coniine

ARECA ALKALOIDS

The betel nut, the seed of *Areca catechu,* contains some alkaloids structurally related to pyridine and piperidine.

$-C(=O)-OCH_3$ (N–CH_3) $\qquad$ $-C(=O)-OH$ (N–H)

arecoline guvacine

The betel nut is chewed by the natives of the East Indies. *Arecoline* stimulates those smooth muscles and gland cells inervated by postganglionic cholinergic nerve fibers. Under the influence of the drug, sweat, salivary, and gastric glands increase their secretions. Acrecoline is not often used for human treatment but has some status as a vermifuge for horses. The worms are expelled probably not because of the greatly increased stimulation of peristalsis (as is usually stated), but because of the nicotinic action of the drug on the worm itself.

ALKALOIDS OF PEPPER

Piperine is the most important alkaloid isolable from pepper (*Piper nigrum*). It is responsible for the distinctive taste of pepper.

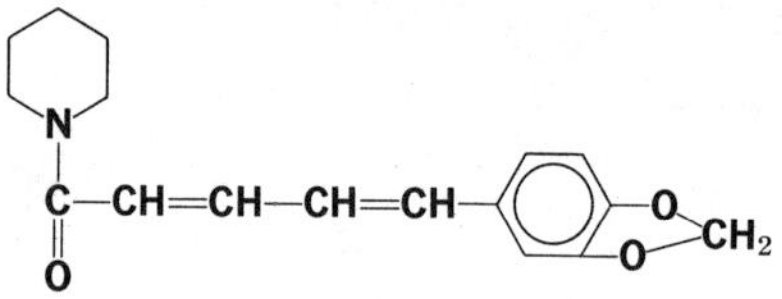

piperine

Alkaloids with Condensed Pyrrolidine and Piperidine Rings

ATROPINE GROUP

Many alkaloids, closely related chemically, occur in a series of different *Solanaceae,* especially in *Atropa belladonna* (deadly nightshade), *Hyoscyamus niger, Datura stramonium,* and *Scopola carniolica.*

Atropine contains many functional groups. Its ester characteristics are quite important.

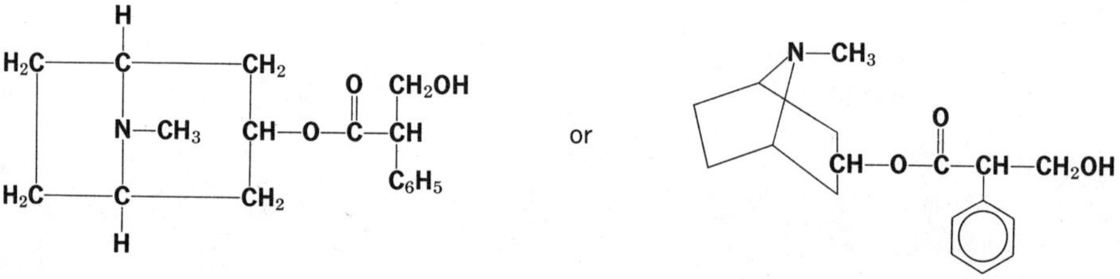

or

atropine

Close scrutiny shows that the left-hand portion of the molecule is a substituted pyrrolidine ring and that the right-hand portion is a substituted piperidine ring.

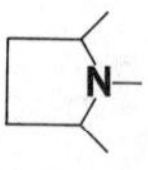

substituted pyrrolidine ring

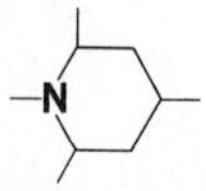

substituted piperidine ring

Atropine possesses mydriatic action (i.e., it dilates the pupil of the eye) and is very useful in eye surgery. If it is taken internally in relatively large doses, atropine acts as a poison and depresses the central nervous system; in small doses, it relieves abdominal pain due to severe muscular contractions. Because it dries up nose-throat secretions and facilitates a more even anesthetic, atropine is often used in combination with morphine as premedication for gas anesthesia.

Scopolamine is closely related to atropine. The structural formula shows that scopolamine has one more oxygen and two less hydrogens than atropine.

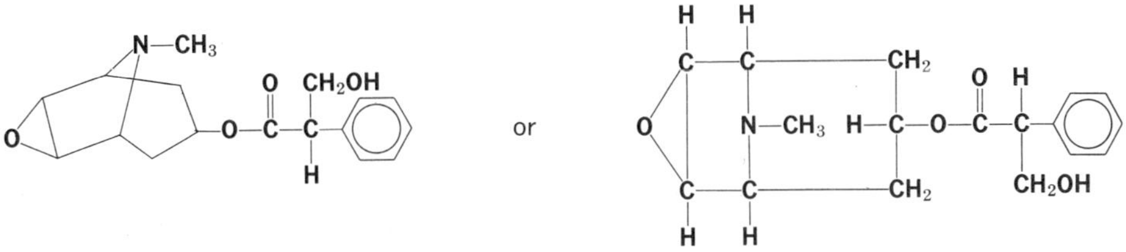

scopolamine

Scopolamine resembles atropine in its action. Atropine acts more strongly on the heart, intestinal, and bronchial muscles, whereas scopolamine is the stronger blocking agent for the iris and salivary, bronchial, and sweat glands. It is used to cause dreamless sleep in hard-to-manage patients.

COCAINE GROUP

Cocaine can be isolated from the leaves of *Erythroxylon coca.*

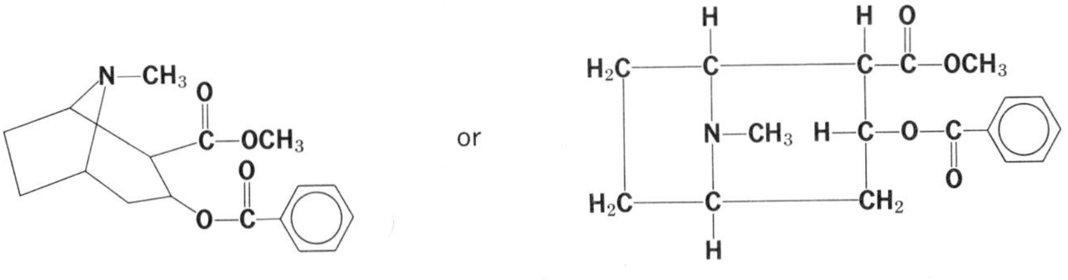

cocaine

Cocaine contains the substituted pyrrolidine and piperidine rings, similar to atropine. It is both a local anesthetic and a stimulant to the central nervous system. South American natives are known to chew the leaves of the *Erythroxylon coca* to lessen hunger (local anesthetic action of the gastric mucosa) and to increase endurance (central nervous system stimulant). Cocaine, once a great boon to anesthesia surgery, has some drawbacks. Cocaine is habit forming, produces considerable side effects, and, furthermore, is sensitive to heat and cannot be adequately sterilized because it hydrolyzes readily.

With these facts in mind, chemists have worked for many years to synthesize suitable substitutes for cocaine—substitutes with all the desirable properties and none of the bad features. The synthetic local anesthetics comprise a long list, and we shall mention only a few examples. Chemists have tried to duplicate the essential chemical features of cocaine: its ester group, its basic nitrogen group, and its carbon arrangement. It was first assumed that all effective substitutes would have to be esters, but many useful compounds were prepared that were not esters. It soon became evident that many different types of compounds can possess valuable anesthetic properties, even though the ester group is lacking.

One of the outstanding synthetic local anesthetics is *procaine*, which is an ester of *p*-aminobenzoic acid and *β*-diethylaminoethanol.

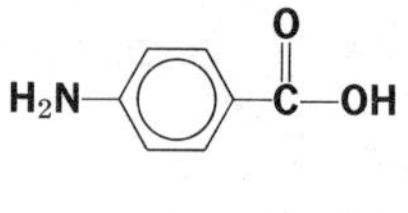

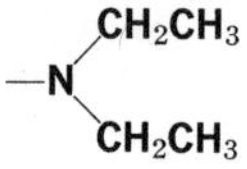

$H_2N-C_6H_4-C(=O)-OH$

p-aminobenzoic acid

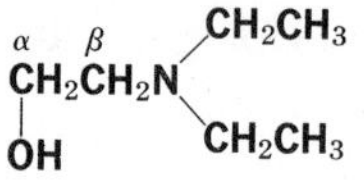

$\overset{\alpha}{C}H_2\overset{\beta}{C}H_2N(CH_2CH_3)_2$ with OH on the α carbon

β-diethylaminoethanol

$-N(CH_2CH_3)_2$

diethylamino group

$H_2N-C_6H_4-C(=O)-OCH_2CH_2N(CH_2CH_3)_2$

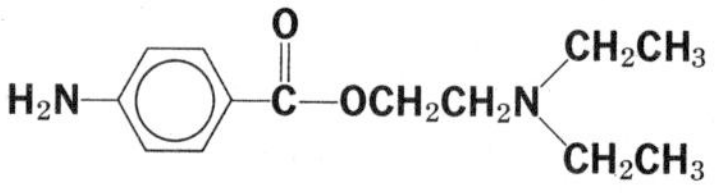

procaine

Procaine is usually administered in the form of its hydrochloride (Novocaine), although other salts are available. Procaine is quick-acting, powerful, and not very toxic. Its chief disadvantage is that anesthetic action is not well maintained, and, thus, the drug has limited use on intact mucous membranes.

Butacaine is used in the form of its sulfate. It is an ester of *p*-aminobenzoic acid and *γ*-di-*n*-butylaminopropanol.

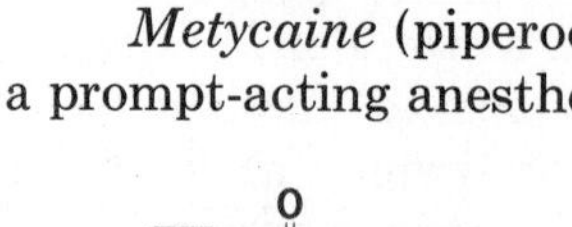

$\overset{\alpha}{C}H_2\overset{\beta}{C}H_2\overset{\gamma}{C}H_2N(CH_2CH_2CH_2CH_3)_2$ with OH on the α carbon

γ-di-*n*-butylaminopropanol

$\left(H_2N-C_6H_4-C(=O)-OCH_2CH_2CH_2-N(CH_2CH_2CH_2CH_3)_2\right)_2 \cdot H_2SO_4$

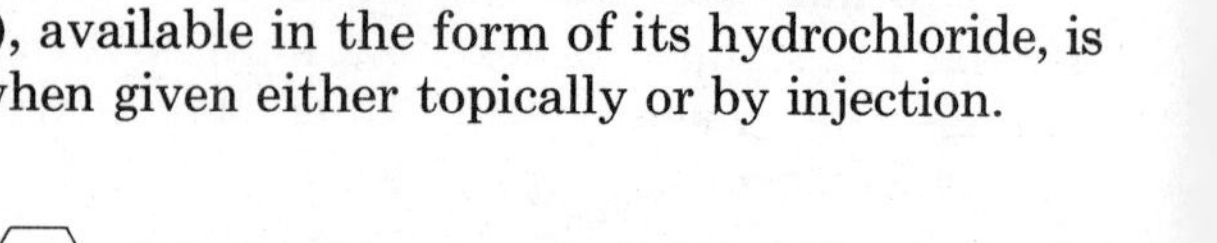

butacaine sulfate

Although butacaine sulfate is less toxic than cocaine, it is capable of penetrating mucous membranes and is also used in eye surgery.

Metycaine (piperocaine), available in the form of its hydrochloride, is a prompt-acting anesthetic when given either topically or by injection.

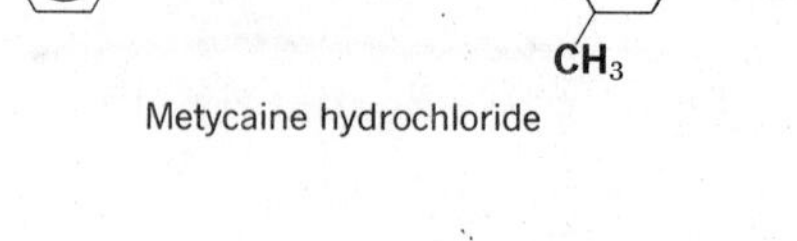

$C_6H_5-C(=O)-O-CH_2CH_2CH_2-N(C_5H_9CH_3) \cdot HCl$ (2-methylpiperidine ring, CH_3 on ring)

Metycaine hydrochloride

Surfacaine possesses many functional groups. It is an ester of a substituted benzoic acid, possessing the basic nitrogen, as well as the cyclohexyl, group.

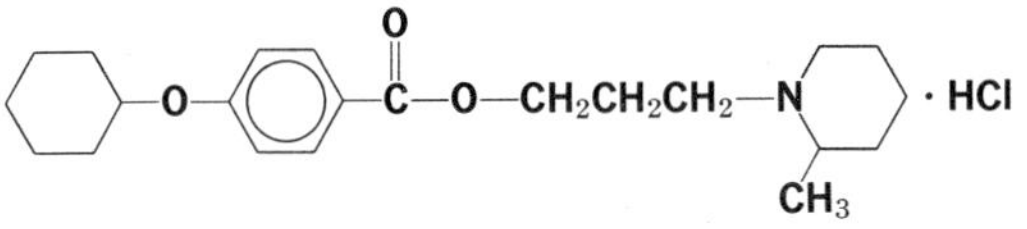

Surfacaine

It is a stable derivative and is reported to be particularly effective in treatment of abrasions of the skin, burns, and other damaged tissue. It is commonly available as the hydrochloride.

Alkaloids with a Quinoline Ring

CINCHONA ALKALOIDS

Many related alkaloids can be obtained from the stem, branches, and root bark of various trees of the species *Cinchona* and *Remijia*. Quinine is perhaps the most useful of these chemically related alkaloids.

Quinine is available in the form of many salts, each one with its characteristic solubility. The bisulfate is given orally; the more soluble dihydrochloride is used for intravenous injection. Quinine is remarkably successful in removing the acute symptoms of malaria, apparently killing the plasmodia organism very rapidly and relieving the fever and pain. Quinine is generally effective as an analgesic and antipyretic and is incorporated in many cold remedies.

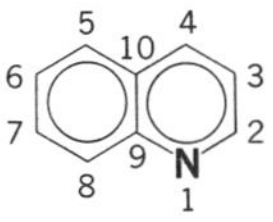

quinoline

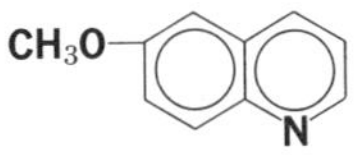

6-methoxyquinoline

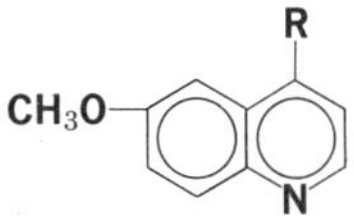

a 6-methoxyquinoline substituted in the 4-position

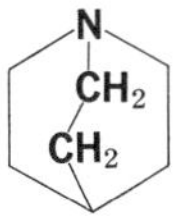

quinuclidine

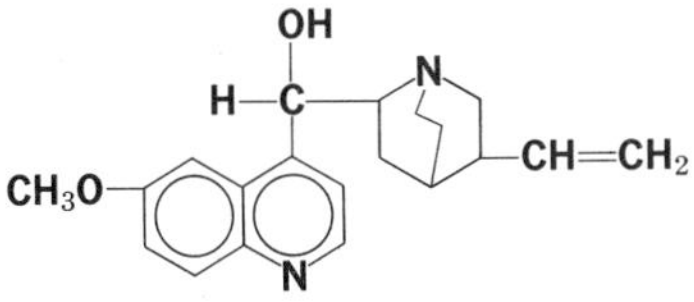

quinine

During World War II, the United States, cut off from its East Indian supply, produced suitable synthetic substitutes for quinine. The most outstanding substitutes are chloroquine, pentaquine, and paludrine.

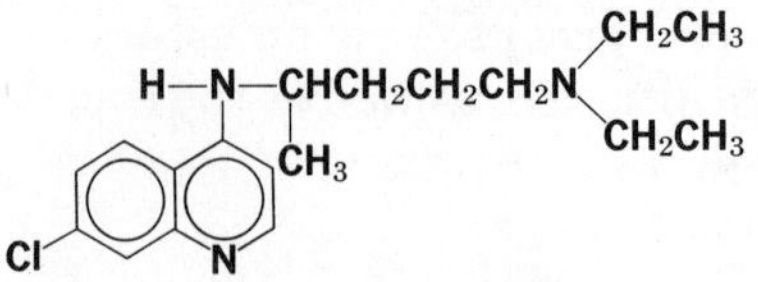

chloroquine

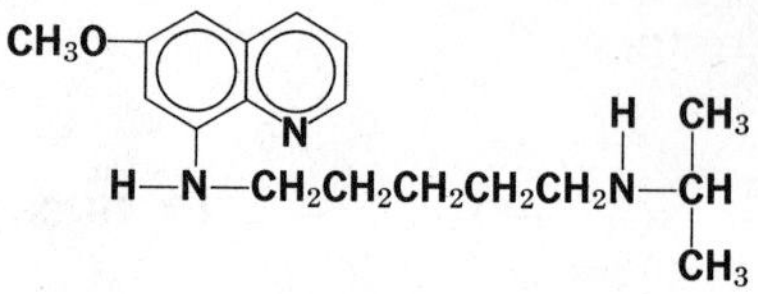

pentaquine

Both chloroquine and pentaquine are quinoline derivatives. Paludrine, however, is a derivative of biguanide.

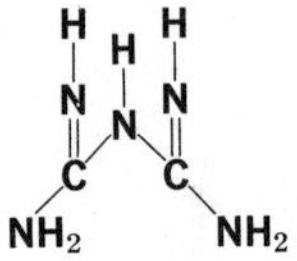

biguanide

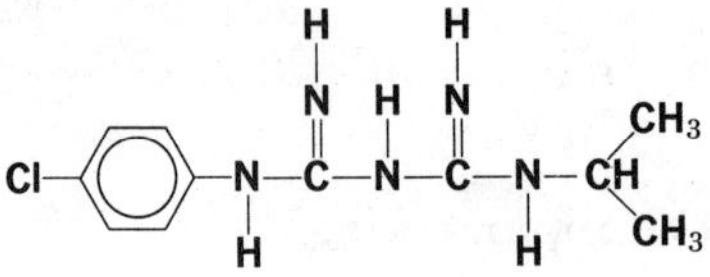

Paludrine

Chloroquine is a suppressive of the symptoms of malaria. Chloroquine is usually available as the diphosphate salt ($C_{18}H_{26}ClN_3 \cdot 2H_3PO_4$) for oral administration. *Pentaquine* is also a suppressive, and, when taken in conjunction with quinine, it is a cure for *Plasmodium vivax*. *Paludrine* is also a suppressive and is characterized by low toxicity. Paludrine is usually administered orally as the monohydrochloride salt.

Alkaloids with an Isoquinoline Ring

THE MORPHINE GROUP

The three main alkaloids that are isolable from opium are morphine (10% by weight of opium), codeine (1%), and thebaine (0.5%). Morphine is available as the hydrochloride and the sulfate. Codeine is the methyl ether formed at the aromatic position of morphine, and thebaine is the dimethyl ether of morphine.

From a structural viewpoint, morphine is an exceedingly complex molecule.

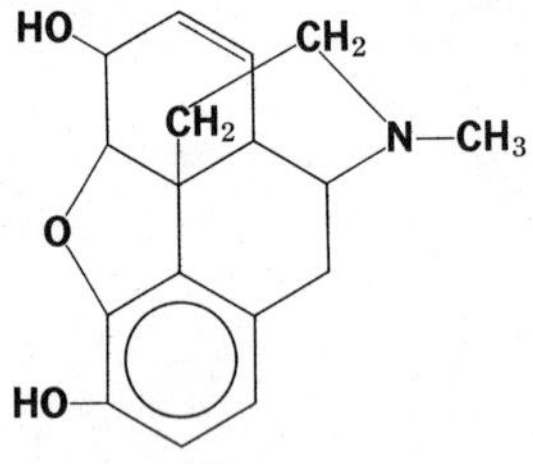

morphine

Morphine is so complex, so compact a molecule that it is a tribute to the chemical genius of nature. A great chemical achievement was the total synthesis of morphine in 1952.

Morphine and its chemical relatives are perhaps the best-known drugs used for the relief of pain. When opium is administered, the most discernible effects are due to morphine.

Morphine exerts in man a narcotic action manifested by analgesia, drowsiness, changes in mood, and mental clouding. A significant feature of the analgesia is that it occurs before and often without sleep. When small-to-moderate amounts of morphine (5 to 10 mg) are given to patients with pain, discomfort, worry, tension, or other complaints, euphoria is frequently experienced as a result of the relief obtained. In contrast, when morphine in the same dose is given to a presumably normal, pain-free individual, the experience is not always a pleasant one; sometimes dysphoria rather than euphoria results, consisting in mild anxiety or fear; frequently there is nausea and occasionally vomiting. Morphine also produces mental clouding characterized by drowsiness and inability to concentrate, difficulty in mentation, apathy, lessened physical activity, reduced visual acuity, and lethargy. Mental and physical performance is impaired; recently acquired and complex learned responses are first affected. The extremities feel heavy and the body warm, the face and especially the nose may itch, and the mouth is dry. Patients with pathological pain feel less distressed by their pain. Subjective feelings of hunger are variably affected, being suppressed in some subjects but unchanged in others. Drowsiness occurs commonly both in volunteers and in patients with clinical pain. If the external situation is favorable, sleep may ensue and dreams may be prominent. The psychological effects outlast the analgesic action by many hours. In some patients the vomiting induced by morphine is not associated with the usual unpleasant emotional reactions, and addicts often refer to it as a "good sick" because it is associated with the desired euphoria.[2]

Morphine is frequently given as preanesthetic medication to facilitate a better anesthetic.

Another important physiological action of morphine is its ability to contract smooth muscles. Its antidiarrhea action has been known for a long time. *Paregoric* (camphorated tincture of opium) is still used by some parents to treat their children.

One of the main disadvantages of morphine is its power to cause drug addiction. The drug and related compounds are under strict Federal Narcotic control.

Codeine, available as the sulfate and phosphate, possesses properties similar to but less effective than those of morphine. Although equivalent doses of codeine may be less effective than morphine, codeine is less likely to cause drug addiction.

[2] L. S. Goodman and A. Gilman, eds., *The Pharmacological Basis of Therapeutics,* 3rd ed. New York: Macmillan, 1965. p. 250.

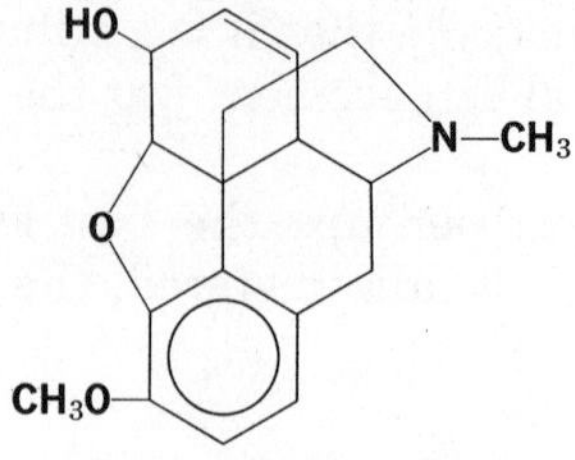

codeine

Codeine is used mainly to relieve a dry, irritating cough.

Thebaine is a powerful poison that causes convulsions. It is the most toxic of all the opium alkaloids and is not used in medicine.

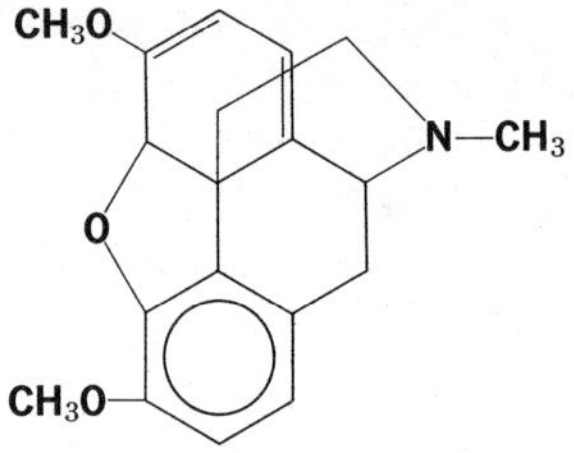

thebaine

Heroin, Dionin, and Dilaudid are synthetic alkaloids related to morphine. *Heroin* is diacetyl morphine (the two —OH groups are converted into acetate esters). It is the most analgesic of the morphine-type alkaloids and also has greatly increased narcotic activity. Because drug addiction is so likely to occur, the use of this drug in medicine has been essentially discontinued.

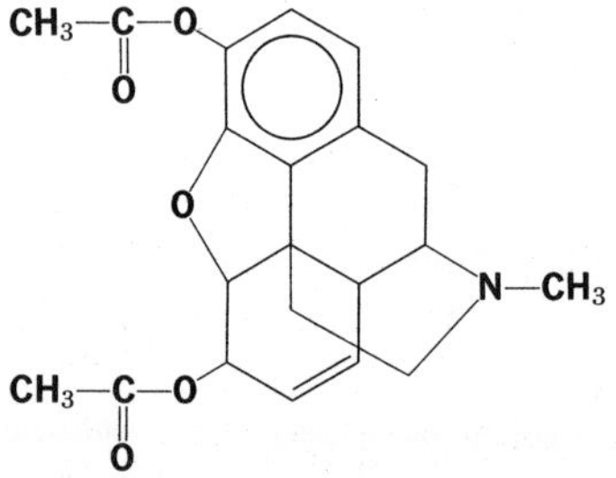

heroin

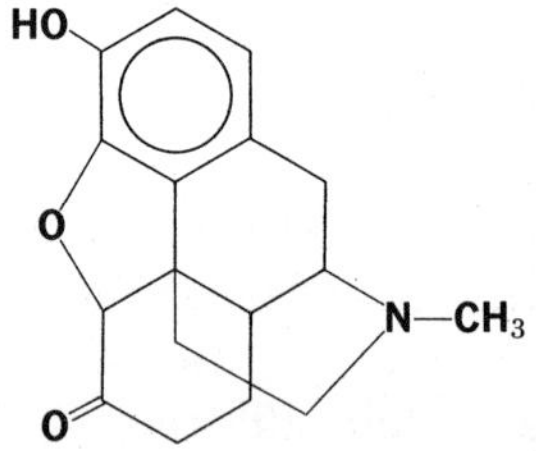

Dilaudid

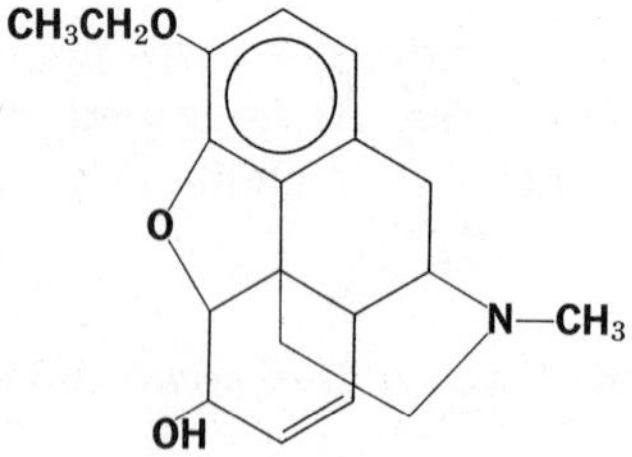

Dionin

Darvon (Propoxyphene Hydrochloride), in combination with aspirin, is currently enjoying wide popularity as a pain reliever.

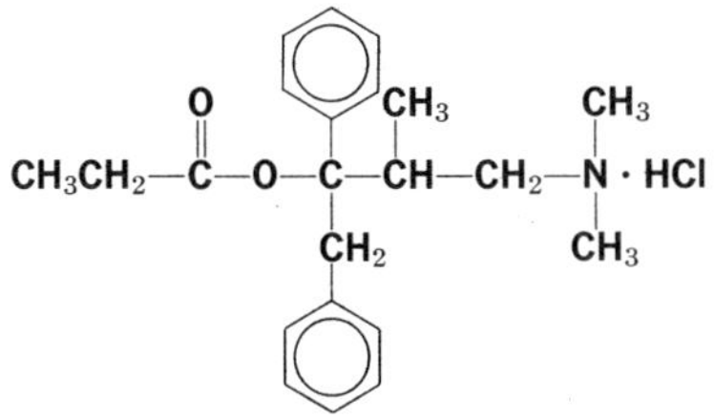

Darvon

Darvon apparently causes no addiction, and since it seems to be as good as the codeine-aspirin complex, it is used extensively.

Ergot Alkaloids

From the extracts of ergot, a fungus (*Claviceps purpurea*) growing on grain, particularly rye, many chemically related alkaloids can be isolated. The ergot alkaloids are also exceedingly complex. Their complexity is not only structural in nature, but also stereochemical.

These alkaloids are all oxytocic in nature and stimulate the motility of the uterus. Oxytocic agents usually effect all smooth muscles, but the ergot alkaloids are quite selective on the uterus muscle. The most important ones used clinically are ergotamine, ergotoxine, and ergonovine.

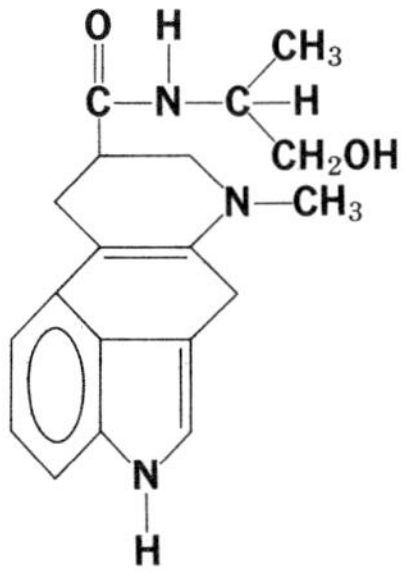

ergonovine

Ergotoxine ethanesulfonate is most important as a standard of reference for other similarly acting drugs. Ergonovine is available under the name Ergotrate.

$CH_3CH_2SO_2OH$

ethanesulfonic acid

Ipecac Alkaloids

Ipecac is a mixture of alkaloids obtained from the roots of *Cephaelis ipecacuanha* and *Cephaelis acuminata* by an extraction process. The most important isolable alkaloid from ipecac is *emitine,* which has, among other groups, two nitrogen heterocyclic rings.

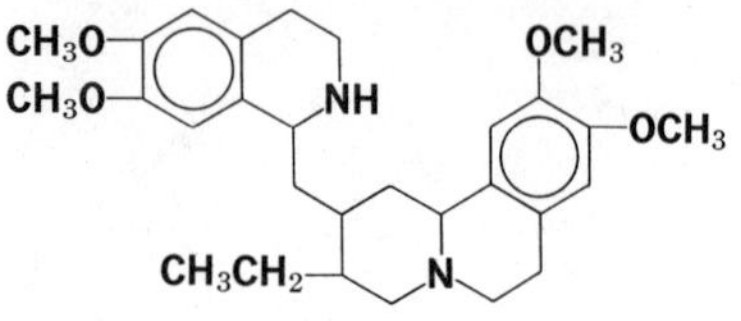

emetine

Emetine, used in the form of its hydrochloride, is an efficient amebicide and is administered intramuscularly. In the form of its bismuth iodide, emetine can be taken orally.

Other amebicides, although not in the ipecac group of alkaloids, are the iodinated oxyquinolines chiniofon (Yatren), Vioform, and Diodoquin.

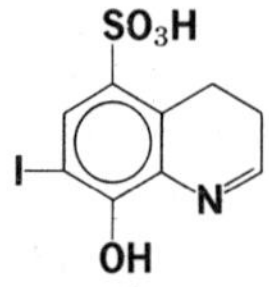

chiniofon (Yatren) 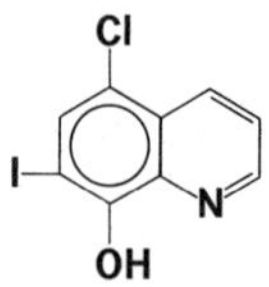 Vioform 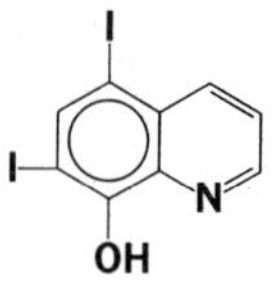 Diodoquin

In the treatment of amebiosis, drugs such as the antibiotics terramycin, aureomycin, and bacitracin, the sulfonamides, and the organometallic compounds, such as Carbarsone, thiocarbarsone, and Milibis, have also been of value.

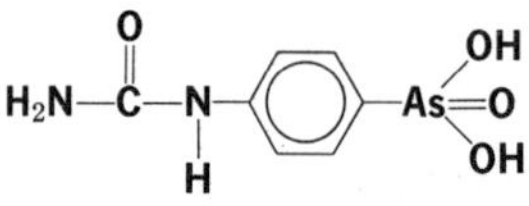

Carbarsone 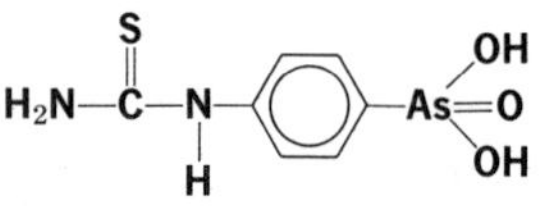 thiocarbarsone 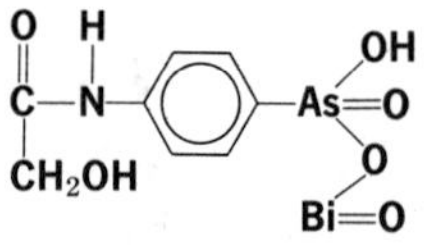 Milibis

Apparently, there is no prophylactic drug upon which one can depend in all cases.

Curare Alkaloids

Curare is dark-colored resinous mass used by the South American Indians in their poisoned arrows. Different types of curare come from different sources, mostly from the *Chondrodendron tomentosum* and from the *Strychnos* species. Tubocurarine chloride is of exceeding chemical complexity. It contains two isoquinoline rings and two additional benzene rings. The alkaloid has come into increased usage as an adjunct to a general anesthetic. It produces complete muscular relaxation but does not have any pain-removing properties. A patient injected with intocostrin may be momentarily paralyzed but may be very aware of pain. In operative technique, a curarized patient must be properly anesthetized before surgery starts; if not, the patient would feel great pain and would not be able to express himself.

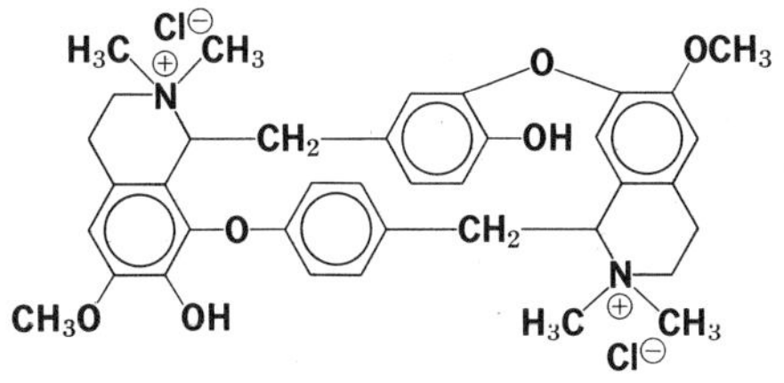

tubocurarine chloride

Strychnos Alkaloids

Strychnine is the principal alkaloid present in *nux vomica,* the seeds of a tree that grows in India, *Strychnos nux-vomica.* Strychnine has the following formula:

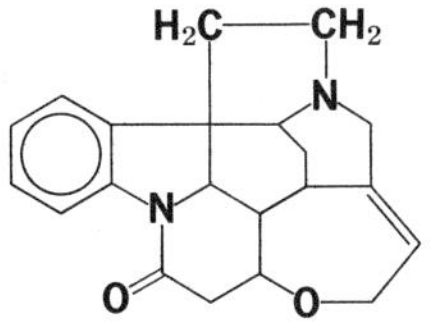

strychnine

As the formula shows, strychnine is very complex, and it is a tribute to chemists that its structure has been elucidated. Strychnine is a powerful stimulant to the central nervous system. The alkaloid is an extremely bitter substance and is poisonous in large doses.

Methadone (amidon) is available as the hydrochloride.

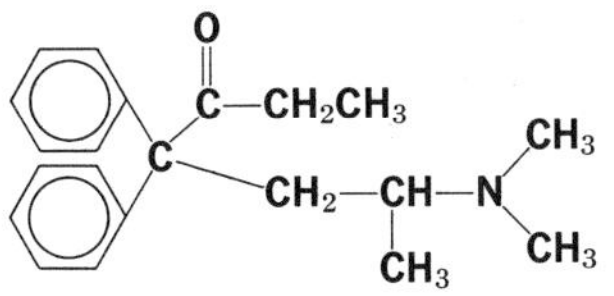

methadone

The levorotating stereoisomer possesses analgesic and morphinelike activity. Methadone is a better analgesic than morphine but is more toxic. It has been used to treat withdrawal symptoms in morphine addicts. Methadone itself has some addiction properties and is under narcotic control.

p-Aminosalicylic acid (PAS), which contains a carboxyl group, a phenolic group, and an amino group, is used in the treatment of tuberculosis.

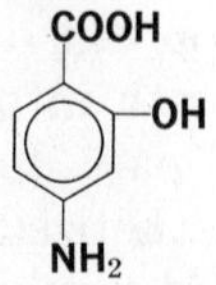

p-aminosalicylic acid

Demerol (meperidine), available as the hydrochloride, possesses both the antispasmodic action of atropine and the analgesic action of papaverine. It is a derivative of piperidine.

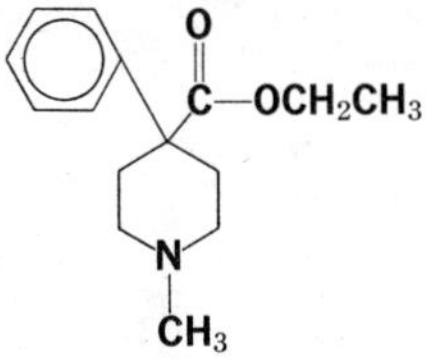

demerol

Demerol has been used to prevent withdrawal symptoms in morphine addicts, but it itself is habit forming.

Hydantoin is essentially a diketone derivative of imidazole. Several substituted hydantoins are of interest.

hydantoin 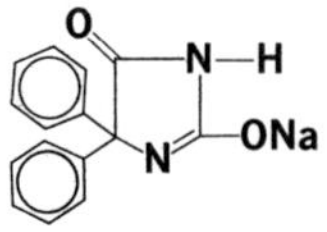   Dilantin sodium 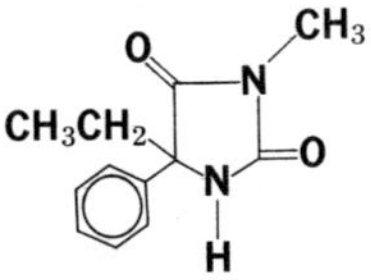   mesantoin

Dilantin sodium is an anticonvulsant and has been used effectively to treat epilepsy seizures. Mesantoin is also effective in the treatment of epilepsy, particularly in coping with grand mal seizures.

The Barbiturates

Barbituric acid is related to pyrimidine.

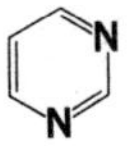

pyrimidine 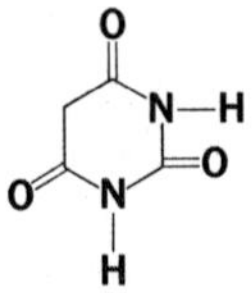   barbituric acid   or   barbituric acid

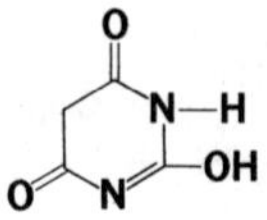

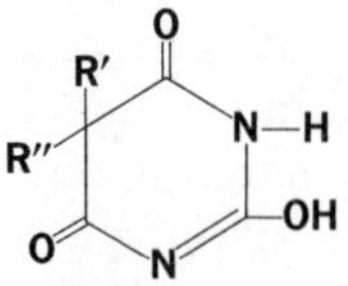

substituted barbituric acid 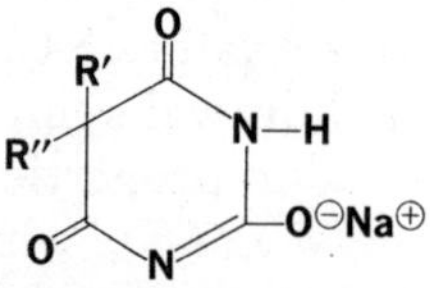   sodium salt of substituted barbituric acid

The barbiturates act by depressing the central nervous system. The barbiturates vary in properties, depending upon the structure of the substituting group. The various barbiturates may be classified as hypnotics, sedatives, anticonvulsants, and anesthetics.

It is convenient to divide barbiturates into certain groups depending upon the onset of action of the drug and the duration of its effects. We arbitrarily classify them as follows: short-acting, moderate-acting, and long-acting barbiturates. (Table 9-2 gives some typical examples.) As can be seen from Table 9-2, the common ending is -al with a few exceptions.

Probably the most important use for the barbiturates is to induce sleep. When taken orally, the quick-acting barbiturates cause sleep in from 10 to 15 minutes. With proper dosage, almost all the barbiturates cause sleep within 1 hour. The effects of the long-acting barbiturates may last from 6 to 12 hours.

Table 9-2

Short-acting barbiturates	
$CH_3CH_2CH_2CH(CH_3)$–, $CH_2{=}CHCH_2$–; ring with C=O, N, C–$O^{\ominus}Na^{\oplus}$, N–H Seconal	$CH_3CH_2CH_2CH(CH_3)$–, CH_3CH_2–; ring with C=O, N, C–$O^{\ominus}Na^{\oplus}$, N–H pentobarbital sodium (*Nembutal*)
Barbiturates of moderate duration	
$CH_3CH(CH_3)CH_2CH_2$–, CH_3CH_2–; ring with C=O, N–H, C=O, N–H, C=O amobarbital (*Amytal*)	$CH_3CH_2CH{=}C(CH_3)$–, CH_3CH_2–; ring with C=O, N, C–$O^{\ominus}Na^{\oplus}$, N–H vinbarbital
CH_3CH_2–, CH_3CH_2–; ring with C=O, N–H, C=O, N–H, C=O barbital	C_6H_5–, CH_3CH_2–; ring with C=O, N–H, C=O, N–H, C=O phenobarbital

Some thiobarbiturates of interest are (the prefix thio- usually denotes a sulfur atom):

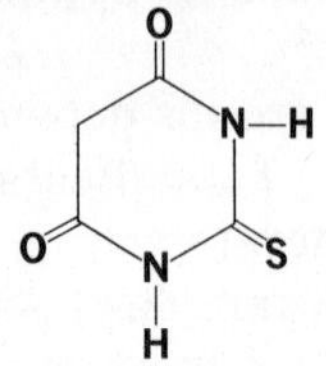

thiobarbituric acid   or   thiobarbituric acid

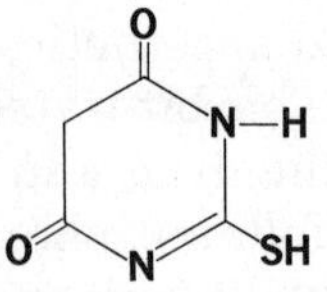

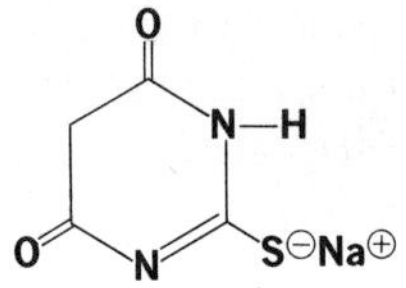

sodium salt of thiobarbituric acid

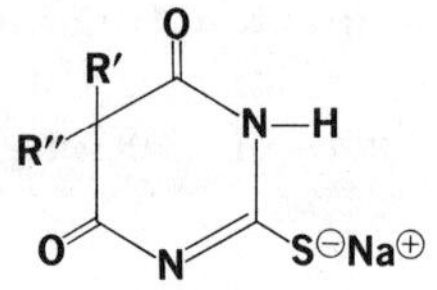

sodium salt of a substituted thiobarbituric acid

Sodium pentothal, the most important member of this series, is the most frequently used intravenous anesthetic. It acts rapidly (i.e., it takes effect in less than 1 minute), and recovery is fairly rapid. There are no explosion hazards or fire dangers. When used by itself, the greatest relaxation in the patient is not obtained; when used in conjunction with another anesthetic, the desired surgical plane may be reached. Sodium pentothal is recommended for operations of short duration.

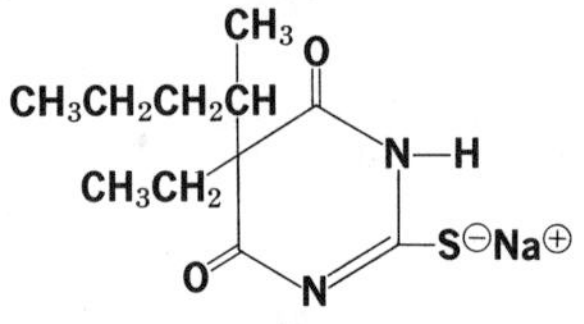

Pentothal sodium
(*thiopental sodium*)

REVIEW QUESTIONS

1. Write the structures of a primary aliphatic and a primary aromatic amine.
2. Write the structures for *n*-heptylamine, aniline, 2-aminoheptane, and 2-aminonaphthalene.
3. Distinguish between a secondary aliphatic amine, a secondary aromatic amine, and a mixed aliphatic and aromatic amine by drawing their structures.
4. Draw structures for diisopropylamine, di-α-naphthylamine, *n*-propyl-*n*-butylamine, and N-ethylaniline.
5. Write the general structure for any tertiary amine. Draw structures for triphenylamine, triethylamine, N-methyl-N-ethylaniline, and ethyl-*n*-propyl-*n*-butylamine.

6. Draw the structure for any compound that contains two amino groups. Name the compound.
7. What are the structures of putrescine and cadaverine?
8. Draw structures for 1,10-diaminodecane, 2,4-diaminopentane, and ethanolamine.
9. What is the association between the more volatile amines and the odor of a fish?
10. Draw structures for tri-*n*-propylammonium hydroxide, methylethylammonium hydroxide, phenylammonium hydroxide, triethylammonium chloride, di-*n*-propylammonium bromide, benzylammonium iodide, and tetraethylammonium chloride.
11. Contrast the basicity of the simple amines with that of sodium and potassium hydroxides. Contrast the basicity of the quaternary ammonium hydroxide with that of sodium and potassium hydroxides.
12. What is Tuamine?
13. What is Zephiran chloride? How does it function?
14. Draw structures for triethanolamine, acetanilide, and phenacetin. What are the uses of these compounds?
15. Define the term alkaloid.
16. List and draw the structures of several alkaloids derived from β-phenylethylamine.
17. What are the names and structures of several synthetic β-phenylethylamines?
18. Identify ephedrine, epinephrine, Benzedrex, and Benzedrine.
19. What alkaloid is present in tobacco? Draw its structure.
20. Draw the structures of several alkaloids that contain the pyridine ring; the piperidine ring.
21. Identify coniine, arecoline, piperine.
22. What ring systems are present in the atropine molecule? the cocaine molecule?
23. Draw the structures of several synthetic local anesthetics.
24. What ring systems are present in quinine? What synthetic compounds have been used as substitutes for quinine?
25. What is paregoric? What is heroin? What alkaloid is present in ergot? What alkaloid is present in ipecac?
26. Of what use are demerol and hydantoin?
27. Draw the structures of barbituric acid and thiobarbituric acid.
28. Draw structures for Seconal, Nembutal, phenobarbital, and sodium pentothal.
29. Complete the following equations. Name the organic compounds.

(a) $CH_3-N(H)-CH_2CH_3 + HCl \longrightarrow$

(b) 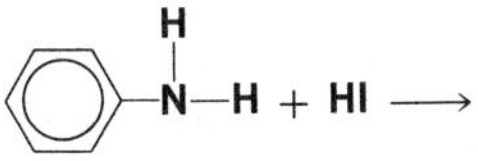 $C_6H_5-NH_2 + HI \longrightarrow$ (phenyl ring bonded to N bearing two H)

(c) $N(CH_3)_3 + CH_3I \xrightarrow{\Delta}$

(d) 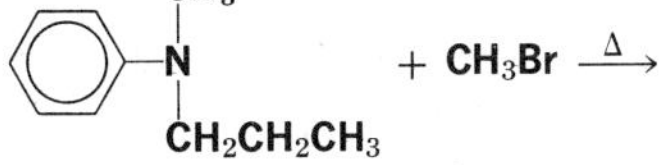 $C_6H_5-N(CH_3)(CH_2CH_2CH_3) + CH_3Br \xrightarrow{\Delta}$

(e) 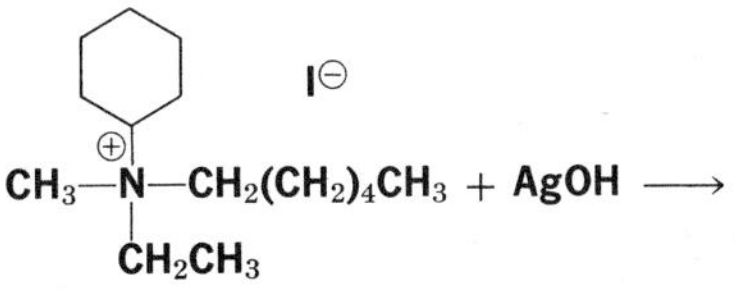 $CH_3-\overset{\oplus}{N}(C_6H_{11})(CH_2CH_3)-CH_2(CH_2)_4CH_3\ I^{\ominus} + AgOH \longrightarrow$ (cyclohexyl group on N)

(f) 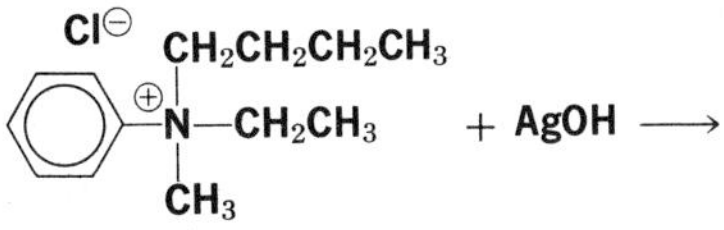 $C_6H_5-\overset{\oplus}{N}(CH_2CH_2CH_2CH_3)(CH_3)-CH_2CH_3\ Cl^{\ominus} + AgOH \longrightarrow$

10

carbohydrates

Optical isomerism

Radiation, such as light, seems to have some unusual properties, and to this day it remains somewhat of an enigma. Light exhibits properties consistent with the theory that it is propagated in a *continuous wave pattern,* and yet there is much evidence that light is composed of discrete bundles, or quanta of energy, called photons. When a single photon of light travels from the point A until it reaches point B, the line AB being in the plane of this page, the photon vibrates in a wave pattern (see Figure 10-1).

The wavelength (λ) is the distance between adjacent peaks of the wave pattern. Photons can have various wavelengths, and by these wavelength variations we can differentiate between the various types of photons and, therefore, between the various types of radiation. See Table 10-1.

Ordinary (white) light may be regarded as a mixture of photons vibrating in patterns of different wavelengths. By proper choice of the light source, or by use of suitable filters that prevent certain photons from

Table 10-1

TYPE OF RADIATION	WAVELENGTH IN ANGSTROM UNITS (A = 10^{-8} cm)
γ-rays	1×10^{-2}–1.0
X-rays	6×10^{-2}–1.0×10^{3}
ultraviolet rays	1.36×10^{2}–3.9×10^{3}
visible rays	3.9×10^{3}–7.7×10^{3}
violet	3900–4220
blue	4220–4920
green	4920–5350
yellow	5350–5860
orange	5860–6420
red	6420–7700
infrared rays	7.7×10^{3}–4×10^{6}
short radio waves	1×10^{6}–1×10^{11}
radio waves	1×10^{11}–3×10^{14}
broadcasting band	2×10^{12}–5.5×10^{12}

passing through, we may obtain photons that vibrate in patterns of only a *single wavelength.* Such photons constitute what is called *monochromatic light.*

If a beam of such photons (monochromatic light) is shown from a projector at a target, such as the page of this book, we see the circular projection. See Figure 10-2.

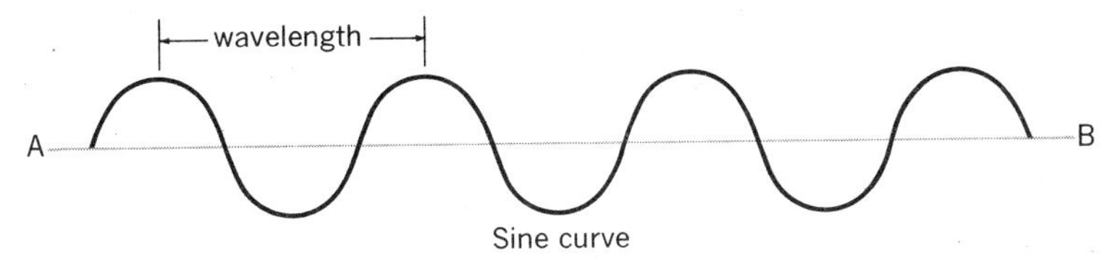

Figure 10-1 Wave pattern of a photon of light.

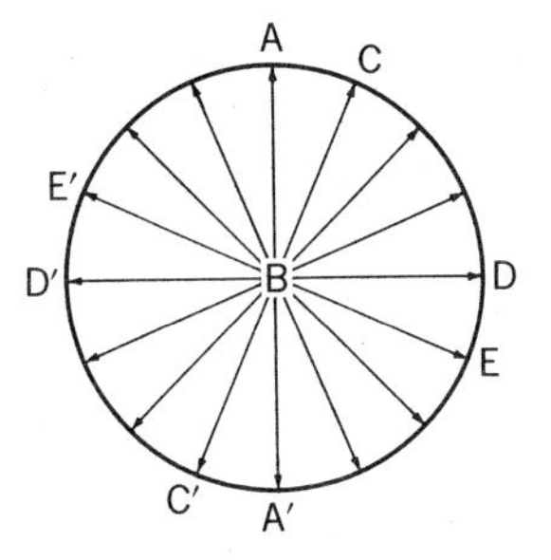

Figure 10-2 Target of beam of light indicating only a few of the infinite number of possible planes in which the light vibrates.

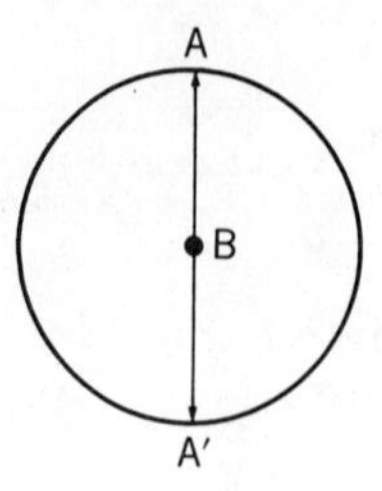

Figure 10-3 Plane polarized light showing vibration in only one plane.

The photons of the light in such a three-dimensional beam vibrate at random in every possible plane through point *B*. For example, *ABA′*, *CBC′*, *DBD′*, and *EBE′* indicate some of the planes of vibration of the light.

If we could modify monochromatic light so that the photons would vibrate in only one plane, we would call the light *plane polarized light.* For example, if monochromatic light were shown on this page and the light were plane polarized before it hit the page, instead of the vibrations as indicated in the previous drawing, we would have vibration in only one plane, that is, the vertical plane, for instance, *ABA′* (see Figure 10-3).

Certain crystals such as potassium nitrate KNO_3, potassium dichromate $K_2Cr_2O_7$, and urea H_2NCONH_2, are capable of polarizing light. Polaroid lenses contain crystals capable of polarizing light and are commonly used.

Optical activity

Experimentally, it has been observed that certain substances possess the power to rotate a plane of polarized light. To make measurements of this nature, we use a *polarimeter* (see Figure 10-4). We adjust the polar-

Figure 10-4 Polarimeter.

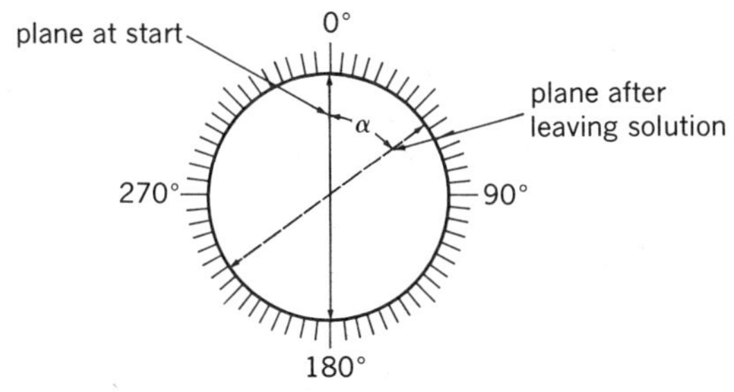

Figure 10-5 Rotation of a plane.

imeter so that the plane of polarized light is vertical at the start. If we shine this light through a distilled water solution, the light emerges vibrating in exactly the same plane as before (vertical). This means that water does not affect the plane of polarized light (optically inactive).

However, if we shine this polarized light through a solution of glucose (body sugar) in water, we find that the plane of polarized light emerging from the solution is vibrating in a different plane. The number of degrees of rotation of the plane can be conveniently read on a scale and is measured as α, the number of degrees of the change (see Figure 10-5).

If the plane is rotated to the right, we call the compound dextrorotatory, and if the plane is rotated to the left, we call the compound levorotatory (Figure 10-6).

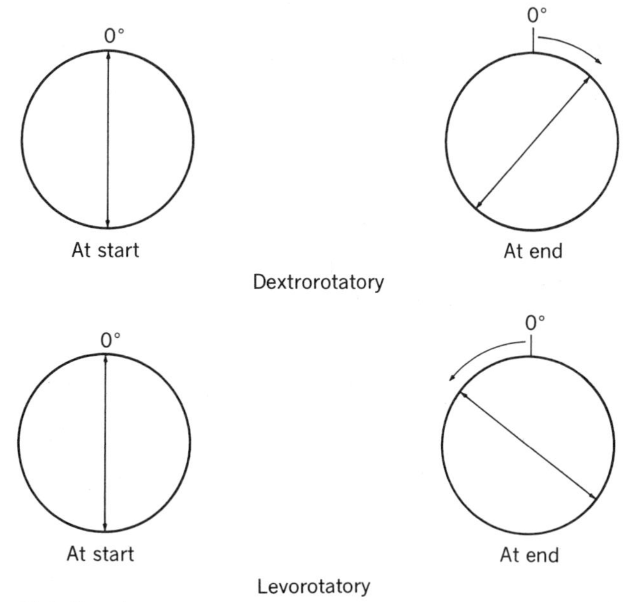

Figure 10-6 Rotation.

Many factors influence the rotation of the compound: (1) wavelength of plane polarized light used, (2) temperature, (3) solvent, (4) concentration, and (5) length of tube containing the solution. Rotations are commonly measured at 20°C using the yellow sodium D line, and the specific rotation (α) is represented as

$$[\alpha]_{\mathrm{D}}^{20^\circ} = \frac{\alpha}{lC}$$

where l = the lengths of the tube in decimeters, C = concentration, expressed in grams per cm³, and α = the observed rotation in degrees.

On some occasions, it may be necessary or convenient to measure the optical rotation at another temperature, that is, 25°C, and possibly to use another source of light, that is, the green mercury light of wavelength 5461 A. In this case, the specific rotation is expressed as

$$[\alpha]_{5461}^{25^\circ}$$

Often it may be convenient to determine the optical rotation on a pure liquid itself. This is called a *neat liquid.* The optical rotation of a substance is a very important property and just as characteristic as the boiling point, melting point, density, etc.

Compounds that can rotate a plane of polarized light are called *optically active.* Scrutiny of the structures of such compounds will reveal that all have mirror images that are not superimposable.

For example, the mirror image of your right hand is your left hand. The two may look alike, yet when one is placed upon the other we see that they are not identical. Compounds that exhibit optical activity have asymmetry in the molecule (see Figure 10-7). Symmetrical molecules are never optically active.

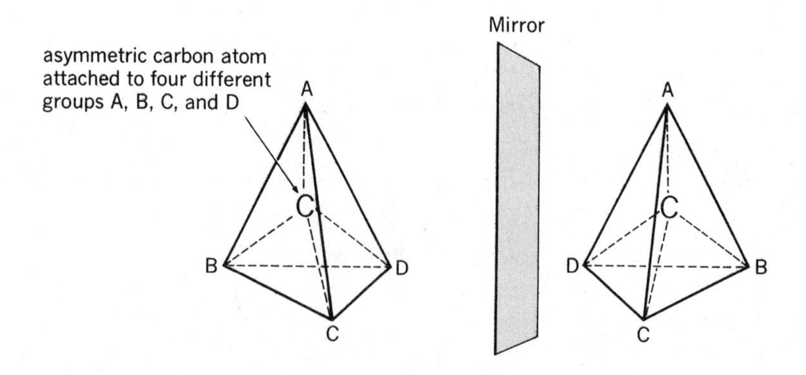

Figure 10-7 Asymmetric molecule.

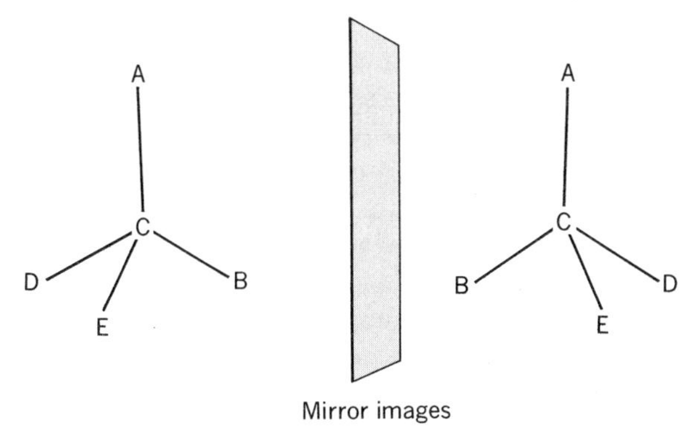

Figure 10-8 Mirror images.

The subject of optical activity is extensive and complex. Organic compounds that have four different organic groups or four different atoms attached to a carbon atom are asymmetrical and may exist in optically active forms.

We shall draw the structures indicating the tetrahedral structure of the carbon atom (see Chapter 2).

Instead of leaving the two drawings in Figure 10-7 as they are, let us remove the two molecules from the tetrahedra so that we can focus our attention on the molecules themselves (see Figure 10-8).

Since this is a three-dimensional drawing in perspective on a two-dimensional surface (projection on a plane), chemists usually compromise and draw the structures as shown in Figure 10-9.

If drawings were always done in perspective, they would vary considerably, depending on the angle at which the chemist viewed the molecule and on the artistic ability of the chemist. Most scientists draw optical isomers as shown in Figure 10-9 and realize that this is, perhaps, a poor but acceptable representation of a three-dimensional model.

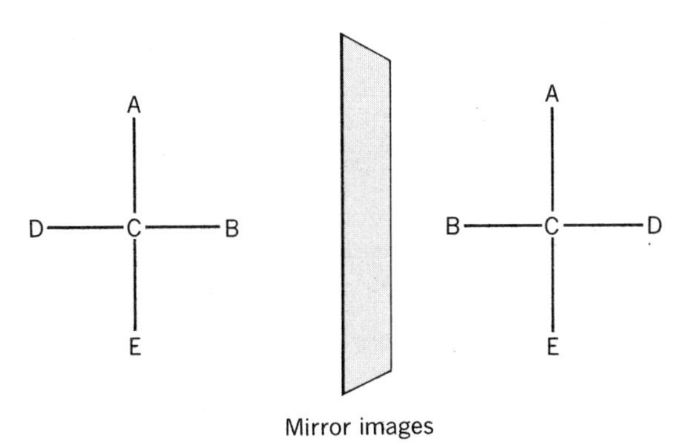

Figure 10-9 Mirror images.

Since the two are non-superimposable mirror images, one of them would be dextrorotatory and the other one would be levorotatory. Henceforth, in this text, non-superimposable mirror images will be called simply mirror images. A mixture of equal amounts of each would *not* be optically active. We call this a *racemic mixture,* because one form tries to rotate to the right and the other form tries to rotate to the left; the net result is that the plane of polarized light is not rotated at all.

Mirror images, often called *enantiomorphs* or *enantiomers,* are *identical in all chemical and physical properties except in their optical activity;* one will be dextrorotatory a certain number of degrees and the other will be levorotatory the same number of degrees.

However, one substance that is *already optically active can* differentiate between the optical isomers in a racemic mixture. For example, we associate a pleasant flavor-enhancing property to *levorotatory* monosodium glutamate (Accent), and yet the dextrorotatory isomer has no special effect (our taste buds can easily tell the difference between the two isomers).

Certain microorganisms can easily react with a racemic mixture and *react with only one of the two optical isomers.* This means that the enzymes of the microorganisms can distinguish between a mixture of dextrorotatory and levorotatory mirror images, pull out the one they need, and *leave the mirror image untouched.*

As indicated, enzymes are themselves optically active, are very selective in their reactions, and can readily differentiate between mirror images. A chemical that is not optically active cannot differentiate between mirror images and reacts the same with both isomers.

Many organic compounds associated with living organisms are usually not in a racemic state and are usually optically active; thus, they are very selective in their chemical reactions.

One of the simplest cases of optical activity is encountered in 2-octanol (see Figure 10-10).

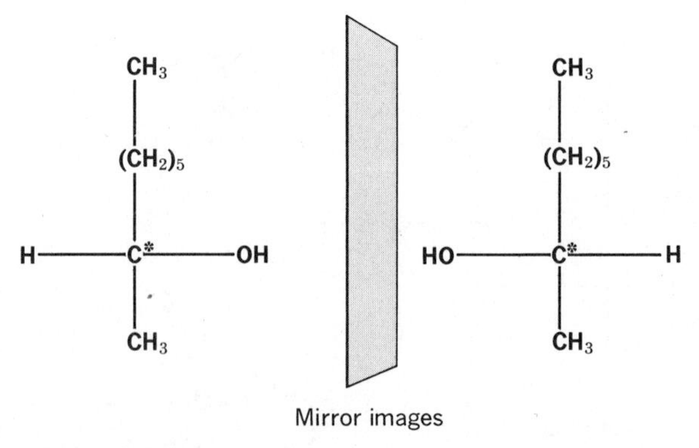

Figure 10-10 2-Octanol.

The asymmetric carbon atom (with asterisk) has four different groups attached to it. One structure will be dextrorotatory ($\alpha = +10.3°$) and the other structure levorotatory ($\alpha = -10.3°$). It is not possible to tell which is which by inspection of the formula. By use of a polarimeter, however, it is easy to determine whether a compound is optically active, the direction of the rotation, and the number of degrees of the rotation.

Many naturally occurring compounds have asymmetric carbon atoms; usually these compounds can be isolated in an optically active form. This means that the biological synthesis of molecules does not obey the laws of chance and that the enzymatic process is certainly biased in the direction of one of the isomers, to the exclusion of the other. It is not uncommon for compounds to have more than one asymmetric carbon atom in the *same* molecule. Let us examine the case of a molecule with two different asymmetric carbon atoms (3-phenyl-2-butanol):

$$CH_3-\overset{\times}{C}HOH-\overset{\times}{C}H(CH_3)-C_6H_5$$

CH_3
H—$\overset{\times}{C}$—OH
H—$\overset{\times}{C}$—C_6H_5
CH_3
$[\alpha]_D^{25} = -0.69°$
(*pure liquid*)
(A)

CH_3
HO—$\overset{\times}{C}$—H
C_6H_5—$\overset{\times}{C}$—H
CH_3
$[\alpha]_D^{25} = +0.69°$
(*pure liquid*)
(B)

mirror images

CH_3
HO—$\overset{\times}{C}$—H
H—$\overset{\times}{C}$—C_6H_5
CH_3
$[\alpha]_D^{25} = -30.9°$
(*pure liquid*)
(C)

CH_3
H—$\overset{\times}{C}$—OH
C_6H_5—$\overset{\times}{C}$—H
CH_3
$[\alpha]_D^{25} = +30.9°$
(*pure liquid*)
(D)

mirror images

In this case, we have 4 optical isomers. Formulas A and B are mirror images. They have, as usual, all properties alike except for the sign of rotation (A is levorotatory and B is dextrorotatory). Formulas C and D are mirror images and likewise have all properties alike except for the sign of rotation. A and B are enantiomorphs, as are C and D. However, any *one* of the A-B pair is *not* a mirror image of one of the C-D pair. Optical isomers that are *not* mirror images are called *diastereoisomers.* Diastereoisomers do *not* have identical properties.

If we had a racemic mixture (an optically inactive mixture of equal amounts of mirror images), we would find it essentially impossible to separate out one of the isomers in the presence of the other, because each one would have identical solubilities, tendencies to crystallize out, etc. If, however, each one could be converted into a diastereoisomer, then they could be separated.

For example, let us assume that we have two acids that are mirror images. We shall assign a (+) to the dextrorotatory one and a (−) to the levorotatory one. Let us react this racemic mixture with an optically active base (i.e., strychnine), which we have obtained from a plant. In this case, the optically active strychnine is levorotatory, and we shall assign a (−) to it and the symbol S. If an acid and a base react, a salt is formed; since we have started with two different acids, we will get two salts.

$$A(+) + S(-) \longrightarrow A(+)S(-)$$
$$A(-) + S(-) \longrightarrow A(-)S(-)$$

mirror images of the two acids — diastereoisomers (two different salts)

The two salts [A(+)S(−) and A(−)S(−)] are no longer mirror images; they are diastereoisomers. The two salts now have different properties and can be separated by crystallization. Once separated, the salt can be broken down into the free acid and the free base again, and we have achieved the separation or resolution of the mirror images:

$$A(+)S(-) \longrightarrow A(+) + S(-)$$

salt separated by crystallization — free acid, optically active (*dextrorotatory*) — free base

Let us examine the structure of tartaric acid; this will exhibit another interesting phenomenon of optical activity.

$$HOOC—\overset{\times}{C}HOH—\overset{\times}{C}HOH—COOH$$

As we see, tartaric acid also has two asymmetric carbon atoms, and, as before, we should be able to draw four different structures.

(A)	(B)	(C)	(D)
COOH	COOH	COOH	COOH
H—C—OH	HO—C—H	H—C—OH	HO—C—H
HO—C—H	H—C—OH	H—C—OH	HO—C—H
COOH	COOH	COOH	COOH

(A) and (B): mirror images; (C) and (D): identical

A and B are certainly mirror images, as the following data illustrate:

	DEXTROROTATORY TARTARIC ACID	LEVOROTATORY TARTARIC ACID
melting point (°C)	170	170
density (g/cm³)	1.76	1.76
solubility (g/100 g of water at 15°C)	139	139
boiling points of diethyl esters (°C at 11 mm pressure)	157	157
specific rotation (deg)	+12	−12

However, an inspection of C and D shows that they are identical (superimposable). This means that only one form exists; this form is optically *inactive* and is called the *meso* form. A meso form results whenever the molecule, containing two or more asymmetric carbon atoms, has a plane of symmetry.

```
        COOH
        |
    H—C—OH
        |
- - - - - - - - - - - - - plane of symmetry
        |
    H—C—OH
        |
        COOH
```

meso tartaric acid
m.p. 140°
(*optically inactive*)

The foregoing has been a brief discussion of a very complicated subject. We must be on the lookout for asymmetry in molecules associated with the life processes.

Carbohydrates

The three most important classes of compounds in biochemistry are carbohydrates, lipids, and proteins. Carbohydrates occur in plants as quick available energy (sugars), reserve energy (starches), and structural material (cellulose). They also occur in animals and humans as available energy (sugars) and reserve energy (glycogen). From a nutritional standpoint, carbohydrates are a very important source of heat and mechanical energy for the body.

Early investigators showed that carbohydrates contained carbon, hydrogen, and oxygen. Because many of them possessed the empirical formula $[C(H_2O)]_n$, they appeared to be hydrates of carbon. Although this formula is not universally true, the name hydrate of carbon (carbohydrate) still persists.

Most carbohydrates are compounds that contain either an aldehyde group, a ketone group, a modified aldehyde group, or a modified ketone group, and other carbon atoms with the alcoholic hydroxyl (—OH) group. We also recognize many sugar derivatives: the sugar alcohols with all alcohol groups (the aldehyde or the ketone group having been reduced) and the sugar acids (the aldehyde or the terminal alcohol group having been oxidized). Other derivatives need not concern us now.

Important modifications of the aldehyde and ketone groups are the hemiacetal and acetal groups and the hemiketal and ketal groups, which are generic terms that represent substances formed by the interaction of the carbonyl function with alcohols.

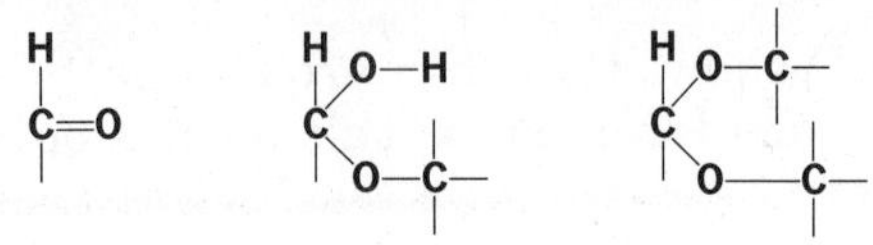

aldehyde hemiacetal acetal

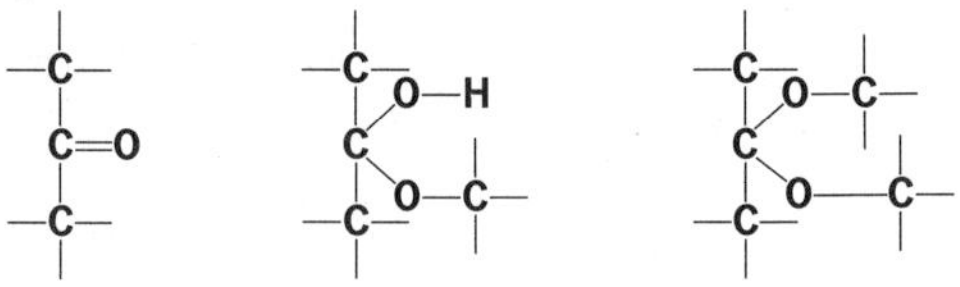

ketone hemiketal ketal

In carbohydrate reactions it will be helpful to recall that hemiacetals give rise to acetals by continued reaction with alcohols, usually under acidic conditions:

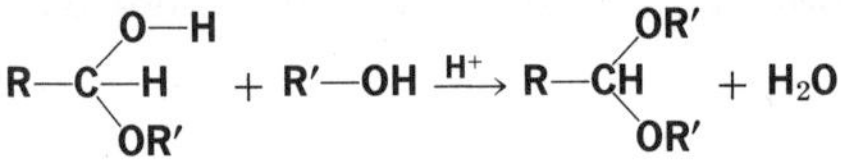

$$R{-}CH(OH)(OR') + R'{-}OH \xrightarrow{H^+} R{-}CH(OR')(OR') + H_2O$$

Most carbohydrates have an oxygen atom (of aldehyde, ketone, or alcohol class) on every carbon. A few carbohydrates lack one or more such oxygen atoms, and we call these the deoxy sugars. Such sugars are minus (de-) one or more oxygen atoms.

Classification

We can classify carbohydrates by the products obtained in hydrolysis (i.e., breakdown by reaction with water). If we cannot break a carbohydrate into smaller carbohydrate units by hydrolysis, we call the compound a *simple sugar* or *monosaccharide*. A *disaccharide* is a carbohydrate that can be broken into two monosaccharide units. A *trisaccharide* gives three monosaccharide units on hydrolysis. In general, we shall classify tetrasaccharides and higher saccharides as *polysaccharides,* because, on hydrolysis, they yield more than three monosaccharide constituents.

Monosaccharides can be classified by carbon content. We use a prefix denoting the number of carbon atoms in the simple sugar (tri = 3, tetr = 4, pent = 5, hex = 6, etc.) and add the ending -ose, characteristic of carbohydrates. We shall discuss trioses, tetroses, pentoses, and hexoses.

Monosaccharides can also be classified by whether they contain an aldehyde or a ketone group. We call the former aldoses and the latter ketoses. Another generic term for *any* sugar is *glycose.*

We might mention a few physical differences of interest. The mono- and disaccharides are crystalline, sweet-tasting substances, which form true solutions in water. Polysaccharides are amorphous, tasteless substances, which can be put into "solution" only in the colloidal form.

Optical Activity

An adequate discussion of carbohydrates must include some mention of optical activity, and, to be sure, the optical activity of the carbohydrates is as important a property as the melting point, the solubility, and the reducing ability. The maximum number of optical isomers of sugars depends on the number of asymmetric carbon atoms and may be calculated from the very simple formula

$$\text{maximum number of optical isomers} = 2^n$$

where n = the number of asymmetric carbon atoms.

An asymmetric carbon atom has four different groups or atoms attached to it. For example,

```
      R
      |
  H—*C—O—H
      |
      R'
```

*C = asymmetric carbon atom

Carbohydrates may be dextrorotatory (i.e., they may rotate a plane of polarized light to the right) or levorotatory (i.e., they may rotate a plane of polarized light to the left). We designate a dextrorotatory sugar by a *plus* sign written in parenthesis (+) and a levorotatory sugar by a *minus* sign written in parenthesis (−). However, since it depends on so many factors (such as wavelength of monochromatic light, the solvent, and the temperature), the sign of rotation should be used with some caution.

Monosaccharides

The simplest monosaccharide is glycerose, or glyceraldehyde. It is also the simplest monosaccharide containing an asymmetric carbon atom, and, for this reason, it is the standard of reference for all monosaccharides. Glycerose is a triose and may be written in a noncommital form as follows:

$$\begin{array}{l} CHO \\ | \\ CHOH \\ | \\ CH_2OH \end{array}$$

glycerose

If we examine the formula of glycerose, we see that the asymmetric carbon atom must be the middle carbon atom. The aldehyde group or the ketone group *is never asymmetric written* as

$$\begin{array}{c} H \\ | \\ C{=}O \\ | \end{array} \qquad \begin{array}{c} \quad O \\ | \quad \| \quad | \\ -C-C-C- \\ | \qquad\quad | \end{array}$$

aldehyde group ketone group

(Note: There are two bonds to the same oxygen.) We shall usually use the condensed forms

$$\begin{array}{c} CHO \\ | \end{array} \quad \text{and} \quad \begin{array}{c} | \\ CO \\ | \end{array}$$

aldehyde ketone

The last carbon atom of sugars is almost always

$$\begin{array}{c} | \\ H-C-OH \\ | \\ H \end{array}$$

and since it has two like hydrogens on the same carbon, that carbon *can never be asymmetric.* We shall write the condensed form

$$\begin{array}{c} | \\ CH_2OH \end{array}$$

Thus, the middle carbon atom must be asymmetric, and we can now write two different forms of glycerose (glyceraldehyde):

$$\begin{array}{c} CHO \\ | \\ H-C-OH \\ | \\ CH_2OH \end{array} \qquad \begin{array}{c} CHO \\ | \\ HO-C-H \\ | \\ CH_2OH \end{array}$$

D-glycerose L-glycerose

The D-form (unrelated to the term dextrorotatory) has the —OH group *on the right-hand side* of the asymmetric carbon atom when the aldehyde group is at the top. The D is always printed as a small capital letter. The L-form (unrelated to the term levorotatory) has the —OH group *on the left-hand side* of the asymmetric carbon atom as indicated. The L is always printed as a small capital letter.

From the formulas we see that D- and L-glycerose are mirror images of one another; that is, they are enantiomorphs. D-Glycerose is dextrorotatory, and L-glycerose is levorotatory. If we wish to designate this physical property in the name, we can write D(+)-glycerose and L(−)-glycerose. The rotation must actually be *measured* in solution; it cannot be determined by *looking at the formula.*

Since glycerose has one asymmetric carbon atom, the number of optical isomers is 2^1. We know that 2^1 is 2, and we have seen that there are indeed two different glyceroses. Glycerose is an example of a triose that is an aldose.

We emphasize the fact that the above formulas for the two isomers are *projection* formulas in two dimensions, but these should be thought of as projections of *perspective* formulas in three dimensions:

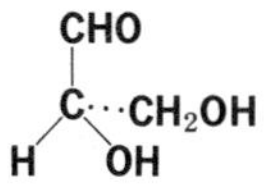

```
    CHO                    CHO
     |                      |
     C···CH2OH              C···CH2OH
    / \                    / \
   H   OH                HO   H
 D-glycerose            L-glycerose
```

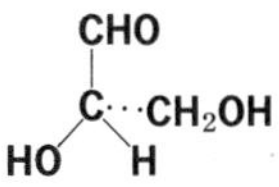

One may imagine the three lower bonds as comprising a tripod with the two solid lines (to H and OH) directed toward the reader and the dotted line away from the reader. Thus, the sequence from H to OH to CH_2OH is clockwise in one formula and counterclockwise in the other. In the two projection formulas that result by "flattening" the perspective formulas, one should keep in mind that the H and OH groups are "above" the plane of the paper and that the CH_2OH is "behind" it.

There is another triose, a ketose:

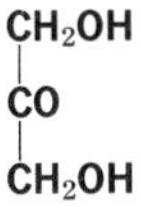

```
CH2OH
 |
CO
 |
CH2OH
```

1,3-dihydroxyacetone

There is no asymmetric carbon atom; hence, only one ketose is a triose ($2^0 = 1$). This means, finally, that three different trioses are possible: two aldoses and one ketose.

The Tetroses

If we examine the tetroses that are aldoses, we see that they possess two asymmetric carbon atoms.

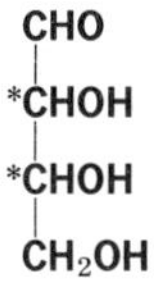

```
 CHO
  |
*CHOH
  |
*CHOH
  |
 CH2OH
```

tetrose that is an aldose
(*noncommital form*)

This means that 2^2 or 4 isomers are possible. With glycerose, we had no problem deciding structurally which isomer was D and which was L. Classifying the tetroses as D or L, however, calls for a decision. One must choose as the position of reference the asymmetric carbon either next to the carbonyl group or farthest from it. Actually, the second of these choices has been made. In the structures below, the OH on carbon 3 (the aldehyde carbon is carbon 1) extends to the right for both D sugars and to the left for both L sugars. This procedure will hold in naming the higher monosaccharides: The highest numbered asymmetric carbon atom is the one determining D or L in the name.

The four possible aldotetroses may be represented as the following two pairs:

```
    CHO             CHO                 CHO              CHO
    |               |                   |                |
 H—C—OH         HO—C—H              HO—C—H            H—C—OH
    |               |                   |                |
 H—C—OH         HO—C—H               H—C—OH          HO—C—H
    |               |                   |                |
    CH2OH           CH2OH               CH2OH            CH2OH
 \_____________________________/     \_____________________________/
         mirror images                       mirror images
        (racemic pair)                      (racemic pair)
D(−)-erythrose   L(+)-erythrose     D(−)-threose     L(+)-threose
```

The D- and L-erythrose are mirror images; that is, they have exactly the same degrees of rotation but in opposite directions. Equal amounts of the two would constitute a racemic mixture, (i.e., a mixture that would allow a plane of polarized light to pass through the solution unchanged but could be separated into dextrorotatory and levorotatory isomers). The same comments hold for D- and L-threose. However, D-erythrose and L-threose are not mirror images; they are diastereoisomers (i.e., stereoisomers that are not mirror images), and the degrees of rotation of each would probably differ. The student will readily recognize why the D-sugars are indeed designated as D- by looking at the position of the —OH on the second carbon up from the bottom; these —OH groups are on the right-hand side. D-Erythrose and D-threose are levorotatory, giving additional evidence that *no relationship* exists between the symbol D- and the term dextrorotatory.

How many tetroses are 2-ketoses? The structure below shows that only one carbon atom is asymmetric, hence, only two isomers.

```
 CH2OH
 |
 CO
 |
*CHOH
 |
 CH2OH
```

tetrose that is a ketose
(*noncommital form*)

```
     CH2OH              CH2OH
       |                  |
      C=O                C=O
       |                  |
  H—C—OH          HO—C—H
       |                  |
     CH2OH              CH2OH
```

mirror images
(*racemic mixture*)

D-glycero-tetrulose L-glycero-tetrulose

Pentoses

An examination of the noncommital formula of a pentose that is an aldose shows that three carbon atoms are asymmetric. Thus, 2^3 or 8 isomers are possible.

```
   CHO
    |
  *CHOH
    |
  *CHOH
    |
  *CHOH
    |
   CH2OH
```

pentose that is an aldose
(*noncommital formula*)

The eight isomers (four racemic pairs) are as follows:

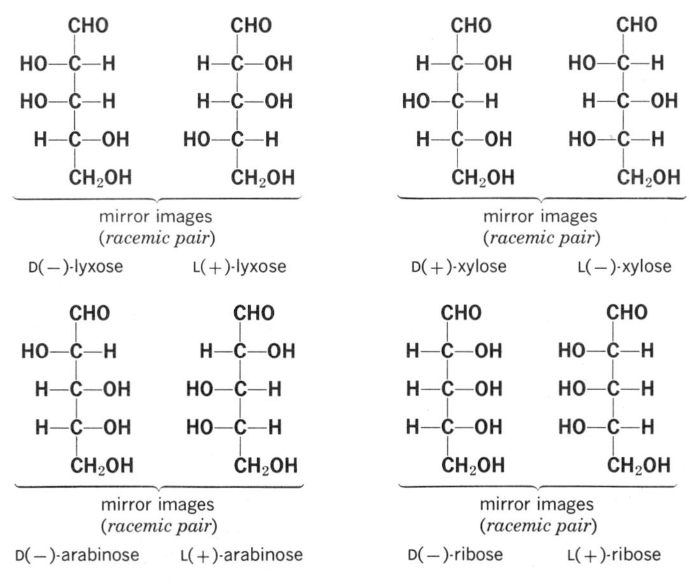

Of the D-pentoses lyxose, arabinose, and ribose are levorotatory, whereas D-xylose is dextrorotatory. Of the L-pentoses, lyxose, arabinose, and ribose are dextrorotatory, whereas L-xylose is levorotatory.

An important deoxy aldopentose is D-2-deoxyribose, the monosaccharide found in DNA.

CHO
|
CH_2
|
H—C—OH
|
H—C—OH
|
CH_2OH

D-2-deoxyribose

The pentoses that are 2-ketoses (pentuloses) have two asymmetric carbon atoms and consequently four possible stereoisomers (two racemic pairs).

CH_2OH
|
CO
|
*CHOH
|
*CHOH
|
CH_2OH

pentose that is a 2-ketose
(*noncommital formula*)

The four isomers are

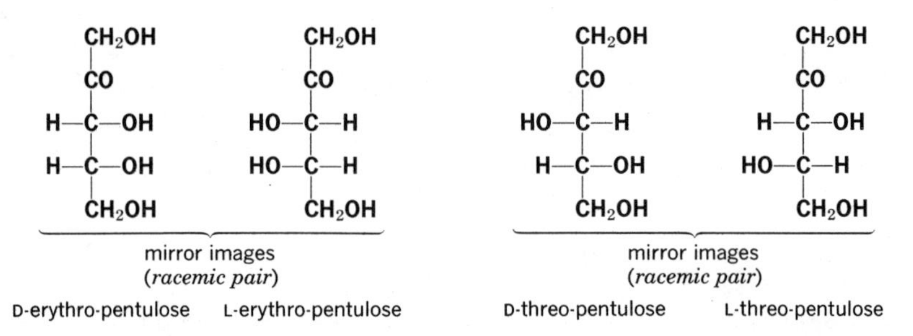

Only four of the eight pentoses that are aldoses occur in nature: D- and L-arabinose, D-xylose, and D-ribose. L-Arabinose is found in vegetable gums, such as gum arabic, mesquite gum, and cherry tree gum, and in pectins. D-Arabinose occurs in aloes but is best made by chemical degradation of dextrose. D-Xylose occurs in corn cobs, wheat bran, oat hulls, and cotton seed hulls. D-Ribose is an important monosaccharide occuring in many nucleic acids, for example, RNA.

Under certain abnormal conditions, the pentoses may occur in urine in a condition known as *pentosuria*. It is questionable if the pentoses have any nutritional value for humans. Herbivorous animals, however, can utilize pentoses for food. An important distinction between pentoses and hexoses is that common yeast will ferment hexoses but not pentoses.

Hexoses

The hexoses that are aldoses are the most important group of monosaccharides. Since four carbon atoms are asymmetric, 16 isomers or 8 pairs are possible.

$$\begin{array}{c} CHO \\ | \\ {}^{*}CHOH \\ | \\ {}^{*}CHOH \\ | \\ {}^{*}CHOH \\ | \\ {}^{*}CHOH \\ | \\ CH_2OH \end{array}$$

hexose that is an aldose
(*noncommital formula*)

The 16 isomers are

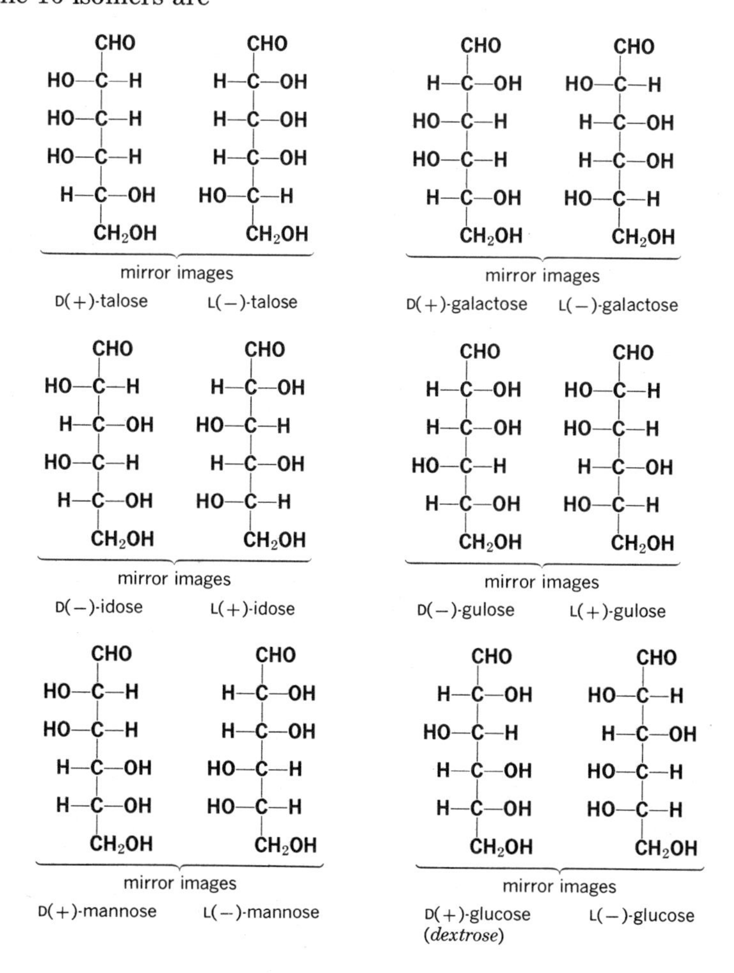

$$
\begin{array}{cccc}
\text{CHO} & \text{CHO} & \text{CHO} & \text{CHO} \\
\text{HO—C—H} & \text{H—C—OH} & \text{H—C—OH} & \text{HO—C—H} \\
\text{H—C—OH} & \text{HO—C—H} & \text{H—C—OH} & \text{HO—C—H} \\
\text{H—C—OH} & \text{HO—C—H} & \text{H—C—OH} & \text{HO—C—H} \\
\text{H—C—OH} & \text{HO—C—H} & \text{H—C—OH} & \text{HO—C—H} \\
CH_2OH & CH_2OH & CH_2OH & CH_2OH
\end{array}
$$

mirror images — D(+)-altrose, L(−)-altrose

mirror images — D(+)-allose, L(−)-allose

From the above formulas it can be seen that the D- and L-sugars conform to the definition previously given, and that no connection exists between a D-sugar and the term dextrorotatory, and an L-sugar and the term levorotatory.

From a noncommital formula we see that the hexoses that are ketoses (hexuloses) have 8 isomers (4 pairs).

$$
\begin{array}{c}
CH_2OH \\
CO \\
{}^*CHOH \\
{}^*CHOH \\
{}^*CHOH \\
CH_2OH
\end{array}
$$

hexose that is a 2-ketose
(*noncommital formula*)

The structures of the eight hexoses that are 2-ketoses are

$$
\begin{array}{cccc}
CH_2OH & CH_2OH & CH_2OH & CH_2OH \\
CO & CO & CO & CO \\
\text{HO—C—H} & \text{H—C—OH} & \text{H—C—OH} & \text{HO—C—H} \\
\text{H—C—OH} & \text{HO—C—H} & \text{HO—C—H} & \text{H—C—OH} \\
\text{H—C—OH} & \text{HO—C—H} & \text{H—C—OH} & \text{HO—C—H} \\
CH_2OH & CH_2OH & CH_2OH & CH_2OH
\end{array}
$$

mirror images — D(−)-fructose (*levulose*), L(+)-fructose

mirror images — D(+)-sorbose, L(−)-sorbose

$$
\begin{array}{cccc}
CH_2OH & CH_2OH & CH_2OH & CH_2OH \\
CO & CO & CO & CO \\
\text{HO—C—H} & \text{H—C—OH} & \text{H—C—OH} & \text{HO—C—H} \\
\text{HO—C—H} & \text{H—C—OH} & \text{H—C—OH} & \text{HO—C—H} \\
\text{H—C—OH} & \text{HO—C—H} & \text{H—C—OH} & \text{HO—C—H} \\
CH_2OH & CH_2OH & CH_2OH & CH_2OH
\end{array}
$$

mirror images — D-tagatose, L-tagatose

mirror images — D-psicose, L-psicose

Some of the heptoses are known to occur naturally. Some octoses, nonoses, and decoses have been prepared synthetically, but none have been found in nature.

Of the 16 possible aldohexoses, only D-glucose, D-mannose, and D- and L-galactose are found in nature. D-Glucose is the most important monosaccharide and certainly one of the most important compounds in the body. D-Glucose is also called dextrose, because it is dextrorotatory and was earlier named grape sugar (because it occurs in relatively high concentration in grapes). D-Glucose is very widely distributed in nature in fruits and plants and is the monosaccharide distributed in our circulatory system. Normal human blood has about 100 mg of glucose per 100 ml. If the glucose concentration increases to about 160 mg per 100 ml, the glucose begins to appear in the urine, and the Benedict's test on urine becomes positive.

Industrially, D-glucose is prepared by acidic or enzymic hydrolysis of starch. Of the many starches, corn starch is the most frequently used, and the uncrystallized product is called corn syrup. This product may contain maltose and dextrins because of incomplete hydrolysis. By appropriate purification steps, one can obtain pure glucose.

Since D-glucose requires no digestive changes and is absorbed as such in the membranes of the small intestines into the blood stream, it can be administered intravenously to those people who are unable to take food by mouth. When given intravenously, glucose may be given with physiological saline solution (NaCl) or with Ringer's solution (a mixture of calcium and potassium salts in addition to sodium chloride) to better simulate the natural conditions in the blood stream. Glucose may be used as a supplement to an infant's diet to ease the digestive process.

Glucosamine is an interesting derivative of glucose containing an $—NH_2$ group in place of one of the —OH groups.

```
      CHO
       |
   H—C—NH2
       |
  HO—C—H
       |
   H—C—OH
       |
   H—C—OH
       |
      CH2OH
```

glucosamine

Glucosamine is found in *mucin,* a glycoprotein found in saliva, which renders the saliva slippery and is consequently an aid to swallowing, and in *chitin,* the hard substance in shells of lobsters and bony structures of other crustaceans.

D-Mannose occurs in mannans, a group of polysaccharides. Vegetable ivory, the seed of the tagua palm that is used in button manufacture, gives a good yield of D-mannose on hydrolysis. A trisaccharide composed of two mannoses and one glucosamine is found in egg albumin, serum albumin, and serum globulin.

D-Galactose is important because of its occurrence in lactose (milk sugar), in which it is combined with glucose. Galactose is widely distributed in nature and is found in algae, lichens, pectins, and some wood gums. In the human, the synthesis of D-galactose, which is necessary for the production of lactose in milk, occurs in the mammary glands, by the conversion of D-glucose into D-galactose. D-Galactose has additional importance in that it is a constituent of glycolipids of brain and nerve tissue, in the form of galactosides. Agar-agar, a mucilage, contains a polysaccharide that yields D-galactose on hydrolysis. Agar-agar is used to prepare solid bacteriological culture media.

The most important ketose that is a hexose is D-fructose, which is also the only ketose commonly met. It is the sweetest of the common sugars. See Table 10-2.

Because diabetics must carefully regulate carbohydrate intake, and because diet-conscious individuals regulate caloric intake, there is a great demand today for sweeteners that are noncaloric and noncarbohydrate in nature. Two such structures are

$$\left[C_6H_{11}\text{—}\overset{H}{\underset{|}{N}}\text{—}\overset{O}{\underset{O}{\overset{\|}{\underset{\|}{S}}}}\text{—}O^- \right]_2 Ca^{++}$$

Sucaryl calcium
(cyclamate calcium)
(40 times sweeter than sucrose)

saccharin
(500 times sweeter than sucrose)

D-Fructose is also called levulose (since it is levorotatory) and was earlier named fruit sugar, because it occurs in many sweet fruits. Honey contains about equal amounts of dextrose and levulose, and the presence of levulose in large concentrations in honey accounts for its sweet taste. Fructose is widely distributed in nature in the form of sucrose (a disaccharide that also contains glucose). When sucrose is hydrolyzed, we get fructose

Table 10-2 The relative sweetness of common sugars

SUGAR	RELATIVE SWEETNESS[a]
fructose	173.3
sucrose	100.0
glucose	74.3
xylose	40.0
maltose	32.5
galactose	32.1
raffinose	22.6
lactose	16.0

[a] Sucrose is given a value of 100, and the values of the other sugars are relative to it.

and glucose; this mixture is sweeter than the original sucrose because of the fructose content. It is called invert sugar, because sucrose is dextrorotatory and an equal mixture of glucose and fructose is levorotatory. We see that the sign of rotation has been inverted. Invert sugar, prepared from sucrose, is the basis of most pancake syrups.

A natural polysaccharide, inulin, is constituted mostly of fructose residues and, hence, is a good source material for fructose by hydrolysis. Inulin is found in dahlia tubers and in Jerusalem artichoke roots. The production of fructose from sucrose would be complicated by the necessity of separating an equal mixture of glucose and fructose. In the body, fructose is easily convertible into glucose.

Mutarotation

Although we have drawn the structure of D-glucose in the straight-chain form for convenience, evidence indicates that the structure is more complicated. For example, D-glucose water solutions give no Schiff test that indicates that the glucose structure has no more than a trace of free aldehyde group.

If a solution of glucose in hot water is chilled, colorless crystals of a hydrated form of glucose, $C_6H_{12}O_6 \cdot H_2O$, separate. This is the usual crystalline variety of glucose sold commercially. It may be desiccated, however, to the anhydrous form, a compound melting at 146°C and showing a rotation of +112° in the polarimeter. If this anhydrous material is fused and then chilled rapidly, a new crystalline product appears with a melting point of 150°C and a rotation of +19°. The first form because it was first noticed, was called α-D-glucose, and the second form was called β-D-glucose. One has only to redissolve the β-form in water and recrystallize it to obtain again the α-form. Thus, the two forms are interconvertible, and neither one gives the Schiff test.

The existence of two D-glucoses requires explanation. Fortunately, there is a very simple one based on the fact (discussed in Chapter 6 on aldehydes and ketones) that an alcohol may be added to an aldehyde to form a hemiacetal:

$$\mathrm{R(H)C{=}O + CH_3OH \rightleftharpoons R(H)C(OH)(OCH_3)}$$

hemiacetal

The aldose molecule contains not only the aldehyde function, but also several alcoholic hydroxyl groups. Because the C—C tetrahedral angles are known to be 109°28′ and the C—C bonds are free to spin around, it is obvious that one or two of the hydroxyls in this twisting process should practically touch the aldehyde group. When this happens, a hemiacetal structure is predictable. Let us strip glucose of all H and O atoms except those on carbons 1 and 5. This leaves but one visible alcohol function and one aldehyde function. Coiling the carbons places these two groups close to each other, as in structure I. Two hemiacetal forms result, structures II and III, depending upon which bond of the double bond in C=O opens to receive the hydroxyl group.

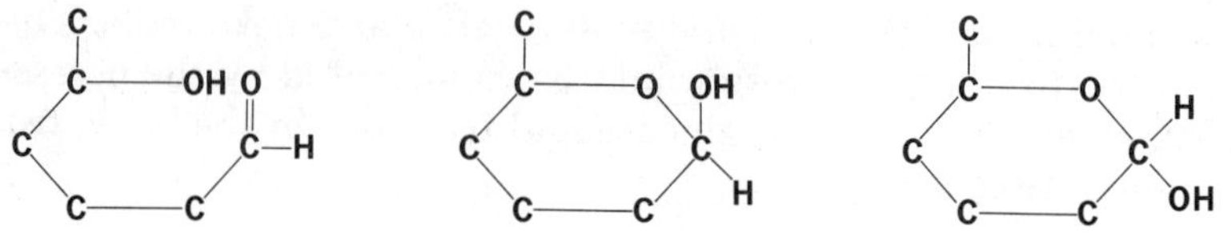

I II III

One of the two new forms is the α and the other is the β. In addition to the original four asymmetric carbons in the open-chain structure of glucose, there is an asymmetric carbon atom in the cyclic hemiacetal forms (carbon 1), making a total of five.

If we now restore the other atoms to structures I, II, and III and assign names to each, we call the isomer with the hemiacetal hydroxyl (at carbon 1) down, the α-form, and the one with this hydroxyl up the β-form. In the convention used here for drawing sugar structures, with the oxygen atom of the ring where shown, the CH_2OH group (carbon 6) points up in the D-form. The six-membered rings of the cyclic form of a glycose are designated as pyranose rings. The suffix -pyranose attached to the name of a glycose tells of this type of structure, as α-D-glucopyranose. Generally, this structural relationship of α to represent *down* and β to represent *up* holds for other aldoses, but it must be emphasized that α really designates the member of such pairs having the higher dextrorotatory power in the D-series, and β the member with the lower rotation. In the L-series the opposite holds. α-L-Arabinose is the compound with the higher levorotation, and β-L-arabinose is the one with the lower levorotation.

The α and β forms are not mirror images, but diastereoisomers (they have different melting points and different rotations). Remember that hemiacetal forms are susceptible to equilibrium reactions.

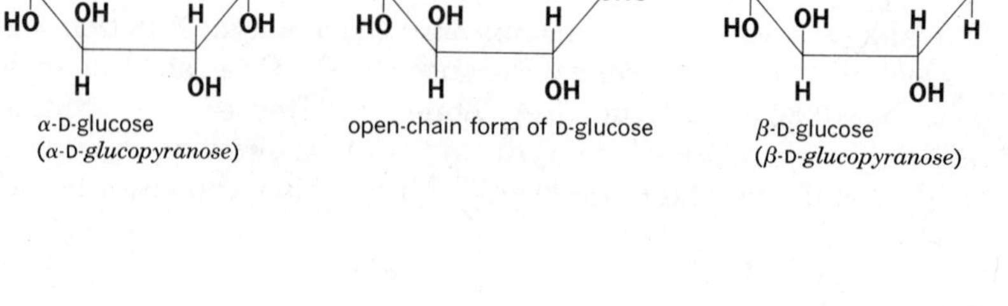

α-D-glucose (α-D-*glucopyranose*) ⇌ open-chain form of D-glucose ⇌ β-D-glucose (β-D-*glucopyranose*)

If crystals of pure α-D-glucose are placed in water, the rotation slowly decreases from +112° to +52°. If crystals of pure β-D-glucose are placed in water, the rotation increases from +19° to +52°. *Such a change in rotation with time is called mutarotation.* The +52° indicates an equilibrium mixture of the three forms of glucose shown above. Naturally, this is not a 50-50 mixture. All reducing sugars will mutarotate, and the equilibrium mixture of each reducing sugar is characteristic of that sugar. Thus, a glucose solution contains both α- and β-forms and a small amount of the open-chain form through which the α- and β-forms pass as each one forms the other.

Glycosides

If a methyl acetal were formed from the hemiacetal structure by reaction with methanol, the resulting structure would be quite stable and would not mutarotate in solution.

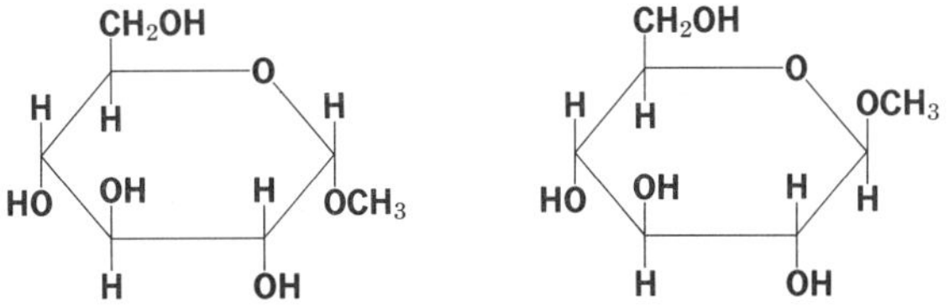

methyl α-D-glucoside methyl β-D-glucoside

(both forms are stable; neither form will mutarotate in solution)

The accepted nomenclature for the cyclic acetal-type combinations for sugars is the addition of the suffix -ide. Thus, we can have glucosides, mannosides, galactosides, etc.; to specifically designate the six-membered ring form they would be glucopyranosides, galactopyranosides, etc. A *glycoside* is a general name for an acetal sugar structure, because this does *not specify exactly* which sugar is involved. Glycosides occur widely in nature.

The sugar molecule may be attached to steroids as in the seeds of the foxglove (*Digitalis purpurea*), to a nitrogen heterocycle in the vitamin series (riboflavin), or to benzaldehyde (amygdalin), etc.

Sugar alcohols

Aldoses and ketoses can be reduced to form sugar alcohols, which contain an alcohol group on every carbon atom. The more important sugar alcohols are sorbitol (from glucose), mannitol (from mannose), and dulcitol (from galactose).

sorbitol	mannitol	dulcitol
CH_2OH	CH_2OH	CH_2OH
H—C—OH	HO—C—H	H—C—OH
HO—C—H	HO—C—H	HO—C—H
H—C—OH	H—C—OH	HO—C—H
H—C—OH	H—C—OH	H—C—OH
CH_2OH	CH_2OH	CH_2OH

Glycerol is another well-known sugar alcohol. In the laboratory, these alcohols can be synthesized by reducing the corresponding monosaccharide in the presence of hydrogen and a metal catalyst. In nature, the reduction of aldoses occurs in an analogous manner, catalyzed by enzymes. Glycerol, of course, is more readily obtained from oils and fats in soapmaking. Some sugar alcohols are found in nature.

The polyhydric alcohols are *sweet,* like the simple sugars, but do not behave as carbohydrates in fermentation processes; that is, they are not readily convertible into acids by microorganisms and so do not contribute to dental decay. Also, the sugar alcohols are not readily oxidized in the body and therefore do not contribute to the caloric intake of the body. For these reasons, the sugar alcohols have been used in artificial sweetening solutions.

Since the sugar alcohols have several —OH groups, they can form polyesters in a variety of ways and are useful in the preparation of polymers. Sorbitol is used to make vitamin C synthetically and is also important as a humectant (i.e., it keeps tobacco from drying out and becoming brittle).

Sugar acids

The sugar acids contain the carboxyl group. The acid group may be at either end of the sequence of carbon atoms or at both ends. Also, once the carboxyl group has been formed, dehydration may readily occur to yield five- and six-membered ring lactones.

In the normal oxidation of the aldehyde group into a carboxyl group, a group of acids known as the *aldonic acids* are formed.

	D-glucose		D-gluconic acid
group oxidized →	CHO		COOH
	H—C—OH		H—C—OH
	HO—C—H	$\xrightarrow{(ox)}$	HO—C—H
	H—C—OH		H—C—OH
	H—C—OH		H—C—OH
	CH_2OH		CH_2OH

D-Mannose would give D-mannonic acid, D-galactose would give D-galactonic acid, etc. A common and convenient way to administer calcium as a medicine is in the form of the salt, calcium gluconate.

In the body, the oxidation of an aldose can occur in such a way as to oxidize the end of the sugar molecule farthest away from the aldehyde group. The resulting acids are known as *alduronic acids*. D-Glucose would give D-glucuronic acid, D-galactose would give D-galacturonic acid, D-mannose would give D-mannuronic acid, etc.

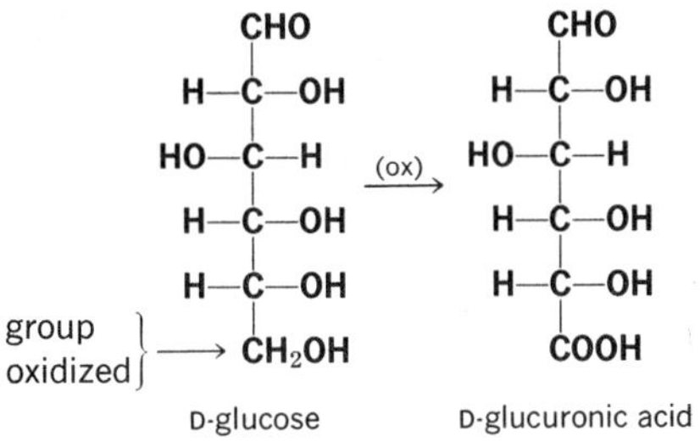

```
                  CHO                      CHO
                  |                        |
               H—C—OH                   H—C—OH
                  |                        |
              HO—C—H        (ox)      HO—C—H
                  |         ——→            |
               H—C—OH                   H—C—OH
                  |                        |
               H—C—OH                   H—C—OH
                  |                        |
group    }  ——→  CH2OH                    COOH
oxidized

             D-glucose              D-glucuronic acid
```

The alduronic acids are formed in the body and can combine with many chemical products formed in the intestines and elsewhere. Because some of the latter products may be quite toxic, their reaction with the alduronic acids may result in the formation of less toxic derived products, although this is not necessarily so. These derived products are commonly eliminated in the urine.

A sugar molecule can contain two acid groups, one at each end. Such di-acids containing 6 carbons are frequently called either the *saccharic acids* or the *mucic acids,* depending on the stereochemistry of carbons 3 and 4. Both gluconic acid and glucuronic acid can be oxidized to form saccharic acid.

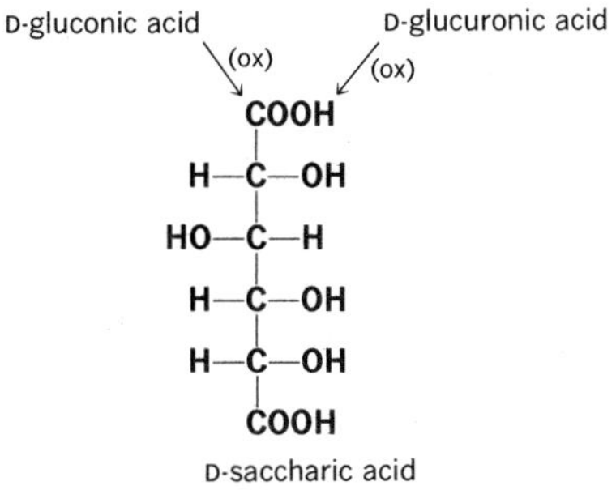

```
D-gluconic acid          D-glucuronic acid
          \ (ox)        / (ox)
           ↘           ↙
              COOH
               |
            H—C—OH
               |
           HO—C—H
               |
            H—C—OH
               |
            H—C—OH
               |
              COOH
        D-saccharic acid
```

D-Galactose can be oxidized to give mucic acid, D-mannose to give D-mannosaccharic acid, and L-talose to give L-talo-mucic acid.

	D-galactose	(ox)	mucic acid
group oxidized →	CHO		COOH
	H—C—OH		H—C—OH
	HO—C—H	→	HO—C—H
	HO—C—H		HO—C—H
	H—C—OH		H—C—OH
group oxidized →	CH_2OH		COOH

	D-mannose	(ox)	D-manno-saccharic acid
group oxidized →	CHO		COOH
	HO—C—H		HO—C—H
	HO—C—H	→	HO—C—H
	H—C—OH		H—C—OH
	H—C—OH		H—C—OH
group oxidized →	CH_2OH		COOH

	L-talose	(ox)	L-talo-mucic acid
group oxidized →	CHO		COOH
	H—C—OH		H—C—OH
	H—C—OH	→	H—C—OH
	H—C—OH		H—C—OH
	HO—C—H		HO—C—H
group oxidized →	CH_2OH		COOH

Reactions

THE MOLISCH COLOR TEST

The Molisch test is a general test for all carbohydrates. It is conducted by adding an alcoholic solution of α-naphthol (1-naphthol) to an aqueous solution or suspension of the carbohydrate to be tested.

OH

α-naphthol
(*1-naphthol*)

Then, concentrated sulfuric acid is added slowly and carefully down the side of the inclined test tube so that the acid, being relatively heavy, forms a layer on the bottom of the test tube. The formation of a violet color at the juncture of the layers indicates a positive test. The chemical reactions are complex and not clearly understood but seem to involve the reaction of the sulfuric acid in a dehydrating capacity with the carbohydrate to form a highly conjugated and unsaturated carbonyl function, which then condenses with the α-naphthol to form a colored condensation product.

THE ACTION OF CONCENTRATED SULFURIC ACID ON CARBOHYDRATES

When concentrated sulfuric acid is added to a carbohydrate (e.g., table sugar), the reaction is quite spectacular. The carbohydrate turns yellow, then brown, and soon black; the mixture begins to swell and smoke and steam; and then a black carbonaceous residue rises like an erupting volcano from the center of the reaction mixture. The chemical reaction is undoubtedly quite complicated, but the final product is a black carbonaceous mass resulting from the complete dehydration of the carbohydrate. The reaction is visually interesting but has no practical value.

THE ACTION OF BOILING HYDROCHLORIC ACID ON PENTOSES

This reaction results in the elimination of three molecules of water from the pentose. For this reaction 5*N* HCl or 12*N* H_2SO_4 may be used.

Pentose		$C_5H_{10}O_5$
($3\ H_2O = H_6O_3$)	$-$	$H_6\ O_3$
result		$C_5H_4\ O_2$

We see that, if we subtract three molecules of water from the pentose, we are left with $C_5H_4O_2$. This particular structure is furfural.

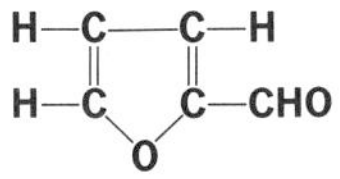

```
H—C———C—H
  ||   ||
H—C    C—CHO        or     [furan ring]—CHO
   \  /                         O
    O
```

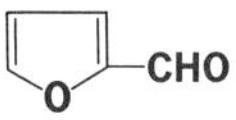

furfural

The furfural formed in this reaction mixture is volatile and immediately leaves the reaction mixture as a gas, which can later be condensed to a liquid, separated, and purified. In industry, it is customary to start with waste products, such as oat hulls and corn cobs, which contain pentoses in a polymeric form. Such polymeric pentoses are called pentosans. The pentosans are moistened, acidified with a little sulfuric acid, and heated under pressure to 160°C. This promotes hydrolysis to D-xylose and then dehydration to furfural. Furfural has many industrial uses, either as a starting chemical to make other chemicals, or as a solvent, or as a condensing agent. In many chemical reactions, furfural behaves like benzaldehyde.

THE ACTION OF BOILING HYDROCHLORIC ACID ON HEXOSES

The reaction resembles that of HCl on pentoses in that 3 molecules of water are readily eliminated.

$$\begin{array}{rcl} & \text{hexose} & C_6H_{12}O_6 \\ (3H_2O = H_6O_3) & - & H_6\ O_3 \\ \hline & \text{result} & C_6H_6\ O_3 \end{array}$$

The $C_6H_6O_3$ formed in this reaction is 5-hydroxymethylfurfural. The numbering system is designated below:

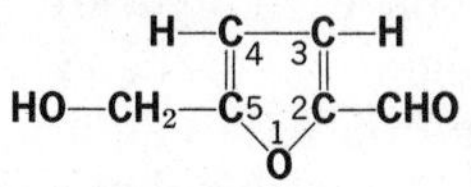

```
        H—C———C—H
          ||4  3||
HO—CH2—C5    2C—CHO
          \ 1 /
            O
```

5-hydroxymethylfurfural
($HO—CH_2—$ *is the hydroxymethyl group*)

The major difference here is that the 5-hydroxymethylfurfural is *not* volatile and reacts further with the boiling acidic solution. The net result is that two molecules of water are added to the $C_6H_6O_3$.

$$\begin{array}{rcl} & & C_6H_6\ O_3 \\ (2H_2O = H_4O_2) & + & H_4\ O_2 \\ \hline & & [C_6H_{10}O_5] \end{array}$$

Actually, we do not get $C_6H_{10}O_5$ as such; instead, we isolate two different products:

$$[C_6H_{10}O_5] = CH_2O_2 + C_5H_8O_3$$

The CH_2O_2 is formic acid, and the other product is $C_5H_8O_3$, levulinic acid, a γ-ketoacid.

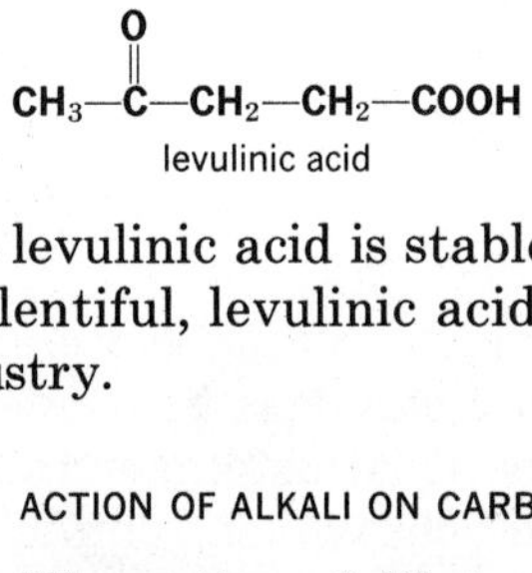

```
       O
       ||
CH3—C—CH2—CH2—COOH
```

levulinic acid

The levulinic acid is stable and can be readily isolated. Since hexoses are so plentiful, levulinic acid is a readily available product of the chemical industry.

ACTION OF ALKALI ON CARBOHYDRATES

The action of dilute alkali on monosaccharides is complex. You will recall that the hydrogen, α to a carbonyl group, is a reactive hydrogen. This reactivity is greatly enhanced in basic solution. The following illustrates, in a crude way, the enhanced reactivity of the α-hydrogen.

The D-glucose readily enolizes to form, in this case, an enediol, which is a key intermediate. (Note that in this formula, the first and second carbons are not asymmetric, and, consequently, when the hydrogen jumps back, it does not necessarily return to the same side from which it came).

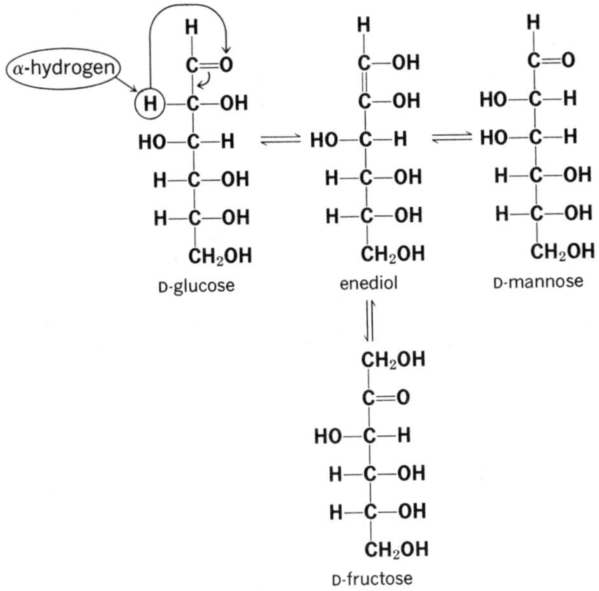

```
            H                      H                  H
            |                      |                  |
α-hydrogen  C=O                    C—OH               C=O
            |                      ||                 |
         (H)—C—OH                  C—OH           HO—C—H
            |                      |                  |
        HO—C—H       ⇌         HO—C—H     ⇌      HO—C—H
            |                      |                  |
         H—C—OH                 H—C—OH             H—C—OH
            |                      |                  |
         H—C—OH                 H—C—OH             H—C—OH
            |                      |                  |
           CH2OH                  CH2OH              CH2OH
         D-glucose               enediol           D-mannose
                                   ⇅
                                  CH2OH
                                   |
                                   C=O
                                   |
                               HO—C—H
                                   |
                                H—C—OH
                                   |
                                H—C—OH
                                   |
                                  CH2OH
                                D-fructose
```

Any one of three things can occur: First, the enediol can go back to form D-glucose; second, when the hydrogen jumps back, it can jump so that the second —OH is on the left-hand side to give D-mannose; third, the hydrogen on the second —OH can jump to carbon 1 to give a ketose, D-fructose.

It is interesting that whether you start with D-glucose, D-mannose, or D-fructose, you obtain the same mixture of the three monosaccharides. Ketoses and aldoses are interconvertible in basic solution.

On continued heating with a base, the reaction becomes even more complicated. D-fructose, for example, can form an additional enediol.

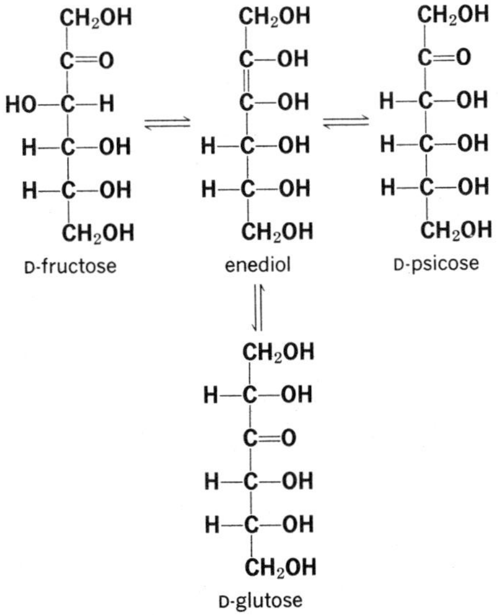

```
      CH2OH                CH2OH               CH2OH
       |                    |                   |
       C=O                  C—OH                C=O
       |                    ||                  |
   HO—C—H                   C—OH             H—C—OH
       |          ⇌         |         ⇌         |
    H—C—OH               H—C—OH              H—C—OH
       |                    |                   |
    H—C—OH               H—C—OH              H—C—OH
       |                    |                   |
      CH2OH                CH2OH               CH2OH
    D-fructose            enediol            D-psicose
                            ⇅
                           CH2OH
                            |
                         H—C—OH
                            |
                            C=O
                            |
                         H—C—OH
                            |
                         H—C—OH
                            |
                           CH2OH
                         D-glutose
```

D-glutose can exist in two forms: The α-form has the second —OH on the right-hand side, and the β-form has the second —OH on the left-hand side. D-glutose may react further with a strong base to form its own enediol:

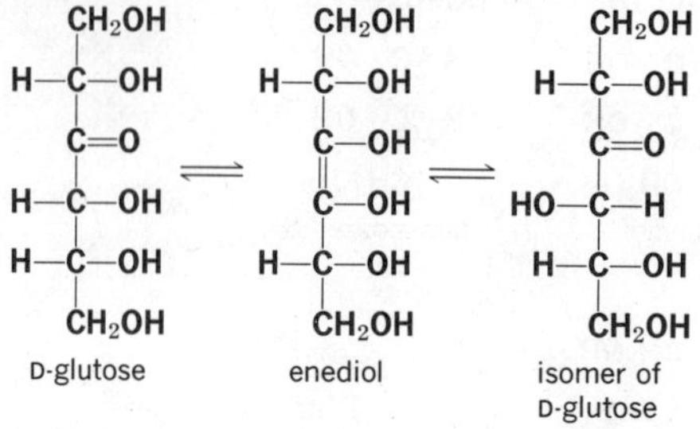

CH_2OH		CH_2OH		CH_2OH
H—C—OH		H—C—OH		H—C—OH
C=O	⇌	C—OH	⇌	C=O
H—C—OH		‖ C—OH		HO—C—H
H—C—OH		H—C—OH		H—C—OH
CH_2OH		CH_2OH		CH_2OH
D-glutose		enediol		isomer of D-glutose

Extensive action of alkali on monosaccharides causes the carbonyl group to wander up and down the chain of carbon atoms, creating all the possible isomers as it wanders. This wandering also creates carbohydrate isomers not found in nature. In addition, some oxidation and some splitting off of one, two, and three carbon fragments usually occur to complicate the reaction even more.

Theoretically, at any rate, all monosaccharides are convertible into all other monosaccharides under prolonged treatment with a strong base. It is not surprising, therefore, that under basic conditions and with proper enzymes the body can readily convert D-fructose into D-glucose, and D-galactose into D-glucose.

OXIDATION OF CARBOHYDRATES

Carbohydrates that give a positive Benedict's test are called reducing sugars. Benedict's test is run in a basic solution. Under these circumstances the sugar is oxidized to an acid, which remains in solution as the sodium salt. All monosaccharides give a positive Benedict's test. The aldoses are oxidized to sugar acids, and the ketoses are converted into enediols, which can either form aldoses (which are then oxidized to acids) or be cleaved by the base into two or more smaller fragments that are then oxidized to acids. Probably all these reactions occur in the oxidation of a substance like fructose. From the previous section concerning the action of alkali on monosaccharides, it is clear that the subject of oxidation products of monosaccharides in a basic solution is indeed very complex.

Disaccharides will give a positive test if they contain a free aldehyde or ketone group, or a potentially free aldehyde or ketone group (hemiacetal or hemiketal group). Carbohydrates with *only* modified carbonyl groups, such as acetal-type groups, are nonreducing sugars.

Benedict's reagent contains cupric sulfate, sodium carbonate, and sodium citrate. The active ingredient (oxidizing agent) is cupric sulfate.

The reaction occurs in a basic solution, and sodium carbonate is conveniently used because it is basic, readily available, and not so strong a base as sodium hydroxide. However, under basic conditions, cupric sulfate $CuSO_4$ is converted into cupric hydroxide $Cu(OH)_2$, which is a gelatinous blue precipitate that is difficult to work with. The sodium citrate converts the insoluble cupric hydroxide into a *soluble complex ion* so that the solution will remain clear blue, and the active ingredient will be readily available to react with the carbohydrate.

We can represent a positive Benedict's test by the equation given below. Note that we are using D-glucose as a reducing sugar. For simplicity we are drawing the oxidizing agent as cupric hydroxide and the oxidized glucose as a gluconic salt. Other oxidation products of glucose are possible. The cuprous oxide Cu_2O is an insoluble orange-red precipitate and is easily recognized.

$$\begin{array}{c} CHO \\ | \\ H-C-OH \\ | \\ HO-C-H \\ | \\ H-C-OH \\ | \\ H-C-OH \\ | \\ CH_2OH \end{array} + 2Cu(OH)_2 + OH^{\ominus} \longrightarrow Cu_2O\downarrow + \begin{array}{c} COO^{\ominus} \\ | \\ H-C-OH \\ | \\ HO-C-H \\ | \\ H-C-OH \\ | \\ H-C-OH \\ | \\ CH_2OH \end{array} + 3H_2O$$

D-glucose; cupric hydroxide (*as blue soluble citrate complex ion*); basic solution; insoluble cuprous oxide (*orange-red*); gluconic salt

As the reaction proceeds, more and more of the orange-red precipitate is formed. The orange-red color then mixes with the original blue, and the testing solution changes from blue to green to yellow-green to yellow and finally to orange-red. The extent of the color change, then, gives a good clue as to the amount of glucose in the sample being tested. The more the color has changed, the more glucose was in the solution to be tested. Benedict's test has many variations, and each variation tends to simplify the method of running the reaction. Usually, however, as the reaction is simplified, the sensitivity of the test is decreased.

Other reagents, such as Fehling's solutions, Barfoed's solution, Nylander's solution, and Tollens' reagent, can be used to test the reducing power of carbohydrates. These reagents work on the principle that the aldehyde group can be conveniently oxidized to an acid, and some other molecule or atom is reduced, producing a convenient change of color in the solution.

FERMENTATION OF CARBOHYDRATES

Fermentation is a decomposition process whereby a carbohydrate is changed into other compounds by the action of enzymes. The conversion of D-glucose into ethyl alcohol and carbon dioxide is one of the best-known fermentation processes. It is accomplished by a complicated series of reactions involving many intermediates and many different enzymes.

$$\underset{\text{D-glucose}}{C_6H_{12}O_6} \longrightarrow \underset{\text{ethyl alcohol}}{2C_2H_5OH} + \underset{\text{carbon dioxide}}{2CO_2}$$

Note that the equation is balanced. The reaction is anaerobic (i.e., it takes place in the absence of oxygen). This fermentation reaction does not occur in our bodies. In our bodies, the conversion of glucose into lactic acid is a similar anaerobic reaction and is called glycolysis.

An aerobic reaction takes place in the presence of oxygen. If oxygen is available, the alcohol might be oxidized further to acetic acid (vinegar), or it might produce more carbon dioxide. The complete aerobic oxidation of glucose would convert the glucose into carbon dioxide and water. In the fermentation of disaccharides and polysaccharides, the enzymes promote hydrolysis into monosaccharides before the fermentation can occur.

Note that many organisms can act on carbohydrates to produce products characteristic of the organism. *Streptococcus lactis,* the common milk-souring organism, produces lactic acid. *Propionibacterium* produces propionic acid from certain types of cheeses. *Aerobacter aerogenes,* acting under anaerobic conditions, converts D-glucose into many products, such as ethyl alcohol and carbon dioxide, and 2,3-butanediol. This dihydroxy compound is of interest since it can be converted into butadiene by dehydration. However, in the United States, the butadiene used to make synthetic rubber is not made this way; rather, it is made more cheaply from butane by catalytic dehydrogenation. *Escherichia coli* also produces products that include hydrogen, in addition to carbon dioxide and alcohols. Organisms of the genus *Clostridium* can convert D-glucose into acetone, *n*-butyl alcohol, other alcohols, carbon dioxide, and hydrogen.

In general, fermentation, an anaerobic process, results in the conversion of glucose to alcohols, ketones, and acids, which occur in the oxidative pathway between glucose and its complete oxidative end product, carbon dioxide.

Photosynthesis

Photosynthesis is a process whereby carbon dioxide and water are converted into carbohydrates by the action of sunlight and in the presence of certain catalysts. This is probably one of the most important chemical reactions occurring about us. By this process, the energy from the sun is stored in growing plants. We obtain our energy by eating these plants, and, after proper digestion of the carbohydrates and absorption, metabolic processes may then liberate the energy in a usable form. Whether we eat the carbohydrates, or some meat (i.e., the steer ate the carbohydrate), or some fat (possibly converted from carbohydrate into fat), we indirectly get our energy from the sun.

We can formulate an equation showing how glucose could be formed from carbon dioxide and water.

$$6CO_2 + 6H_2O + \text{energy} \xrightarrow[\text{chlorophyll}]{\text{sunlight}} C_6H_{12}O_6 + 6O_2$$

photosynthesis equation
(*energy-absorbing equation*)

We have put the term energy on the left-hand side of the equation to show that it is essential in the reaction. The energy is now stored in the carbohydrate (we have used glucose as the example of the carbohydrate). See Figure 10-11.

When glucose is burned, oxidized, or metabolized, the reverse reaction occurs. As glucose reacts with oxygen to form carbon dioxide and water, energy is released.

$$C_6H_{12}O_6 + 6O_2 \longrightarrow 6CO_2 + 6H_2O + \text{energy}$$

energy-releasing equation

This equation shows that energy is liberated, and this released energy is useful to us in our everyday needs. In the body, glucose is converted into carbon dioxide and water in a complicated series of steps. Energy released in this stepwise manner is more conveniently available.

In the photosynthesis equation, we see that oxygen is liberated. The "breathing" power of plants, then, is very important in replenishing the oxygen content of the atmosphere. The plant "breathes" in the carbon dioxide and "breathes" out oxygen. We breathe in oxygen, necessary in the energy-releasing equation, and breathe out carbon dioxide to complete the cycle.

A few pertinent facts concerning oxidation and reduction may be useful here. Usually, the most reduced organic substance (i.e., the substance

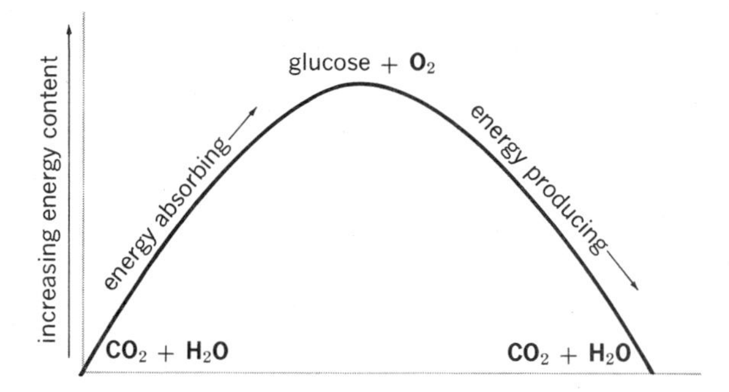

Figure 10-11 Photosynthesis.

with the greatest amount of hydrogen) has the most energy. As the organic substance is oxidized (i.e., as hydrogen is removed or oxygen is added), energy is released so that the resulting organic compound has less energy. When the hydrogen is gone and only oxygen is left, the least amount of energy remains in the organic compound. The following shows several compounds of one carbon, indicating the compound with the most energy, the compound with the least energy, and those in between.

$$\underset{\text{most energy; most reduced}}{CH_4} \xrightarrow{\text{add O}} CH_3OH \xrightarrow{-2H} CH_2O \xrightarrow{+O} CH_2O_2 \xrightarrow{-2H} \underset{\text{least energy; most oxidized}}{CO_2}$$

In photosynthesis, the sunlight helps to break the water into H_2 and O_2.

$$\text{sunlight} \longrightarrow 2H_2O \longrightarrow O_2 + (2H_2)$$

This is the oxygen liberated in photosynthesis by the plant. The hydrogen formed is then used to reduce the carbon dioxide, thus increasing its energy.

$$CO_2 + 2H_2 \longrightarrow [CH_2O] + H_2O$$

We know that glucose $C_6H_{12}O_6$ is a simple multiple of CH_2O.

$$6[CH_2O] \longrightarrow C_6H_{12}O_6$$

The catalyst as written for the photosynthesis equation is chlorophyll. Chlorophyll is a complex substance occurring in green plants. The heterocyclic ring systems in chlorophyll are combined in a unique fashion, but an interesting fact is the presence of magnesium in the center of the molecule. The chlorophyll may be considered the agent that carries the absorbed carbon dioxide in the plant, just as the very similar hemoglobin carries the absorbed oxygen in the human blood stream.

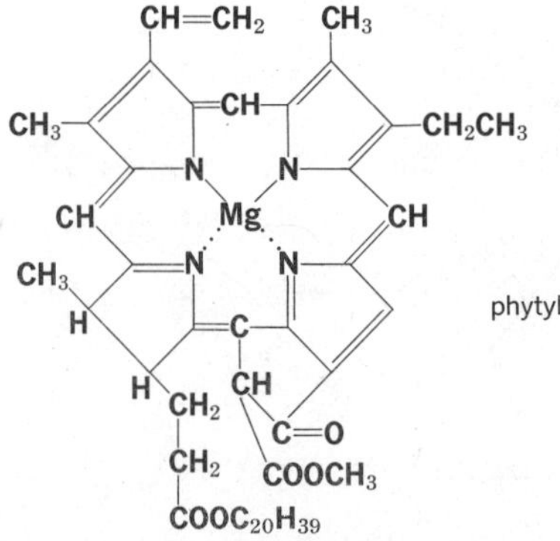

phytyl alcohol ($C_{20}H_{39}OH$)

chlorophyll

Disaccharides

A common disaccharide has the molecular formula $C_{12}H_{22}O_{11}$. Such a disaccharide is related to two monosaccharide molecules by the difference of a molecule of water.

$$\begin{array}{rl} & C_{12}H_{22}O_{11} \\ + & \underline{H_2O} \\ & C_{12}H_{24}O_{12} \text{ or } 2(C_6H_{12}O_6) \end{array}$$

It is of great importance to recognize how this water is involved. In the simplest cases known, at least *one* of the two monosaccharides participates as the cyclic acetal type structure, while the other sugar may still exist as the hemiacetal. The point is that the acetal structure is *stable and retains its proper shape and configuration.* However, if the disaccharide retains a hemiacetal function, then it is a reducing sugar (will reduce Benedict's solution), and will mutarotate (can exist in the α- and β-forms) in solution.

A well-known reducing disaccharide is *maltose.* Maltose may be hydrolyzed (i.e., it reacts with acidified water) to give two molecules of glucose. In addition, maltose may be hydrolyzed by maltase, a specific enzyme that breaks the α-glucosidic linkage of this disaccharide. This means that maltose is an α-glucoside (the two glucoses are linked together with the α linkage).

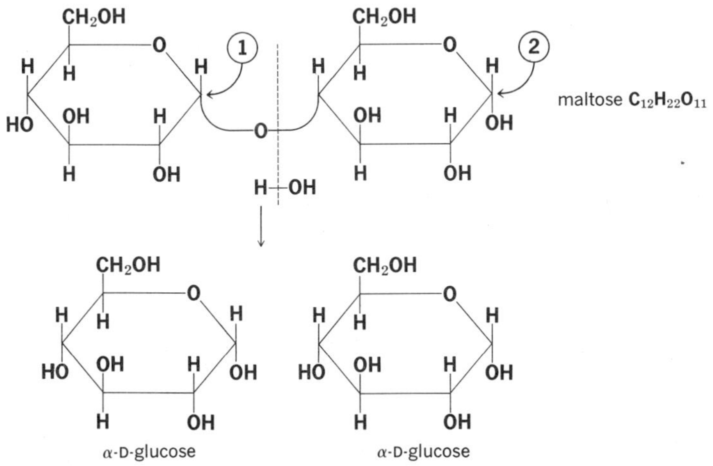

CH₂OH O H H HO OH H H OH (1) O H—OH CH₂OH O H H OH H OH H OH (2)

maltose $C_{12}H_{22}O_{11}$

↓

CH₂OH O H H H HO OH H OH H OH CH₂OH O H H H HO OH H OH H OH

α-D-glucose α-D-glucose

We see that the structure is linked together through carbon 1 of one molecule and carbon 4 of the other. This has been proven rigorously. If the attachment were at any other position, a different disaccharide would result. Also note that spot 1 is an acetal type linkage and is stable and does not change, and that spot 2 is a hemiacetal structure. Therefore, maltose contains two glucoses linked together through the alpha linkage, which is fixed and rigid. However, because it still retains a hemiacetal linkage as shown, maltose is a reducing sugar and will mutarotate (i.e., it can exist in α- and β-forms).

The maltose drawn above is α-maltose since it has the higher (+) rotation. Also, the hemiacetal hydroxyl (at spot 2) is directed downward. If the $-OH$ at spot 2 were sticking up, that structure would have been β-maltose. However, remember that, as long as the structure is maltose, the linkage at spot 1 *must always be* α *and cannot change.*

Maltose is one of the most common reducing disaccharides. When barley is allowed to sprout under certain controlled conditions, maltose is formed. The sprouted barley is known as *malt.* Malt can be used in the manufacture of beer and other alcoholic beverages. The maltose is first hydrolyzed by the enzyme maltase to two molecules of glucose. The glucose is then acted upon by a variety of enzymes, which convert it into alcohol and carbon dioxide.

CELLOBIOSE

Cellobiose is another disaccharide that gives two molecules of D-glucose on hydrolysis. Both maltose and cellobiose, then, are disaccharides containing two D-glucose units. Maltase will not break down cellobiose, but emulsin will. Emulsin is an enzyme capable of breaking down β-glucosidic linkages; thus, cellobiose is a disaccharide that is a β-glucoside.

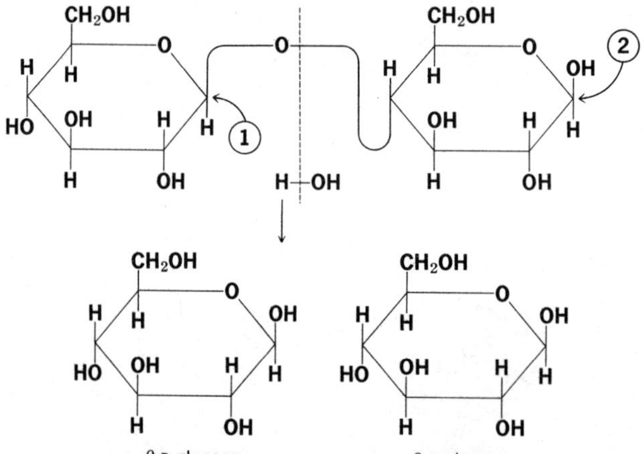

cellobiose ($C_{12}H_{22}O_{11}$)

β-D-glucose β-D-glucose

Note that cellobiose is a β-linked glucoside. Cellobiose has an acetal linkage at spot 1 and is fixed at that spot. However, at spot 2 it has a hemiacetal group. Therefore, cellobiose is a reducing sugar and will mutarotate. In the above form, the $-OH$ at spot 2 aims upward to show one of the two isomers. If the $-OH$ at spot 2 aimed downward, it would show the other isomer. However, so long as the molecule is cellobiose, the *linkage connecting the two glucoses must be* β.

A second glance at the above structure would indicate that the bond to the oxygen atom connecting the two glucoses would be rather peculiar if it went through such contortions.

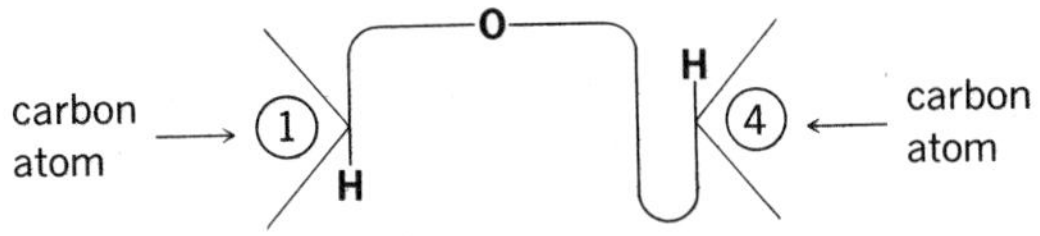

It is quite certain that no bond would really do this. Actually, the molecule of cellobiose is better written to show the customary bonds and the same stereochemistry as follows:

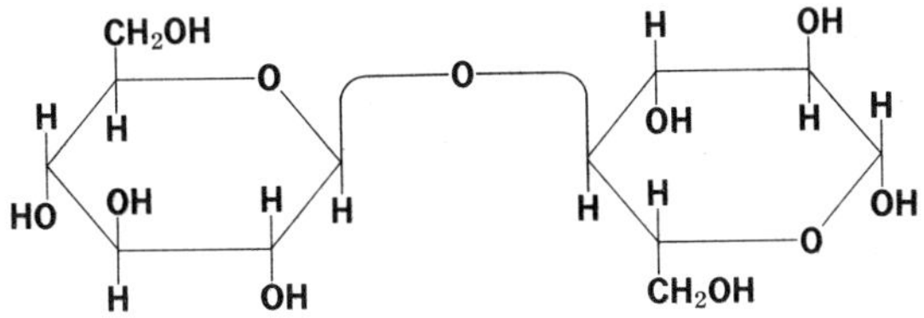

cellobiose

The above structure is a correct way to draw cellobiose. If you compare it with the previous structure of cellobiose, the latter looks as if the glucose on the right-hand side has flipped over. Cellobiose may be prepared by the indirect hydrolysis of cellulose in going through the acetate derivative.

LACTOSE

Lactose, or milk sugar, is a common disaccharide that may be hydrolyzed by dilute acids or certain enzymes into glucose and galactose. Lactase is an enzyme capable of breaking the β-galactoside linkage; therefore, lactose is a disaccharide that is a β-galactoside.

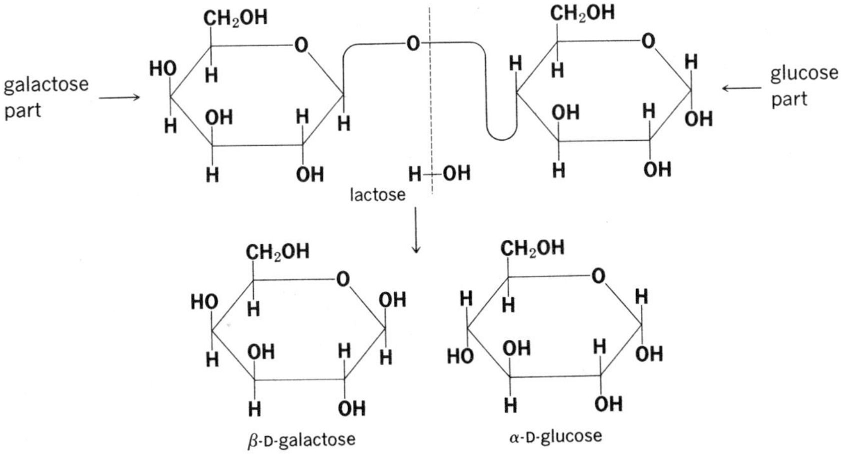

lactose

β-D-galactose

α-D-glucose

Lactose, like cellobiose, is better drawn by flipping over the right-hand part of the molecule to give the correct relationship of the two rings:

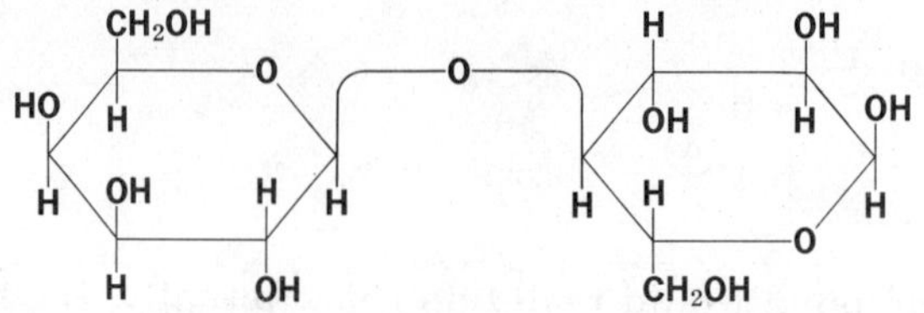

lactose

Remember, as long as the molecule is lactose, it must be β-linked through the galactose acetal linkage. The glucose end contains a hemiacetal group that may exist in a β- or an α-form. Therefore, lactose is a reducing sugar and will mutarotate.

SUCROSE

Sucrose (cane sugar or beet sugar) is the "sugar" of our kitchen and dining table. Since sucrose is very widely distributed in nature in plants, its isolation and manufacture represent a large industry. The important industrial sources of sucrose are sugar cane, sorghum, sugar beet, sugar maple, and the sugar palm; the very pure crystalline sucrose, which is usually encountered, is prepared from the sugar cane and the sugar beet.

Sugar cane is a grass with blades spreading from a jointed stalk. It is grown successfully only in tropical and semitropical countries, which excludes most of the United States. The stalk contains about 14% sucrose, as such. The mature stalk is cut close to the ground and the sugar juice is squeezed out by a rolling machine. Colloidal material and other impurities are removed by a precipitation process, and the sugar solution is then concentrated. The concentrated sugar solution must be decolorized and then evaporated to produce the crystalline material. Sucrose is probably the most readily crystallizable sugar because it can exist in only one form. It does not mutarotate and will not reduce Benedict's solution.

Molasses is the crude, colored sugar solution from which the sucrose cannot be further extracted profitably. Molasses can be used on our eating tables, or as animal food, or in a fermentation process to produce rum. When sucrose is heated to 200°C, decomposition occurs, and the cooled brown product is called caramel.

On hydrolysis, sucrose yields D-glucose and D-fructose. It has been proved that sucrose contains no hemiacetal, which accounts for its nonreducing properties and its nonmutarotation. Sucrose is a β-fructoside as well as an α-glucoside, and our bodies are provided with the enzyme sucrase to hydrolyze this disaccharide.

Acids will hydrolyze sucrose with greater ease than maltose or lactose. When sucrose hydrolyzes, the solution gets sweeter because of the formation of free fructose. An equal mixture of fructose and glucose is about 30% sweeter than sucrose. Jellies (containing sucrose and fruit acids) and some chocolates (containing sucrose and added sucrase) get sweeter in an aging process because of the slow formation of free fructose.

It has been estimated that the average American obtains about 15% of his total caloric intake in the form of sucrose.

Since fructose is a ketose that is a hexose (hexulose), it can exist readily in the hemiketal form. A fructose solution may contain fructose in the pyranose (six-membered ring) form:

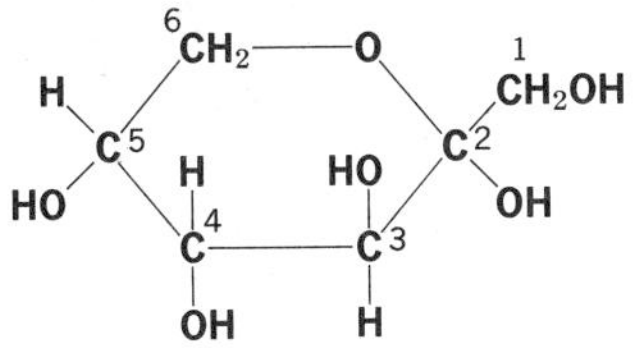

α-D-fructopyranose

It is evident, however, that a five-membered ring, called a furanose ring by its analogy to furan (the familiar five-membered ring compound containing one oxygen), is just as likely to exist, because the hydroxyl on carbon 5 is as close as the hydroxyl on carbon 6 to the carbonyl group. It is indeed this furanose ring that occurs in the fructose part of sucrose. Although fructose may form either the furanose or the pyranose structure, in *chemical synthetic methods* the pyranose form seems to form *preferentially*. Since the fructose part of sucrose occurs *naturally* in the *furanose form,* this odd situation had for years prevented the chemist from synthesizing this naturally abundant chemical. The chemical synthesis of sucrose was achieved in 1953 by a complex series of many steps.

As we did with glucose, let us strip the H and O atoms from fructose except at carbons 2 and 5. Structure I is the open chain form, and structures II and III are the hemiketal furanose forms.

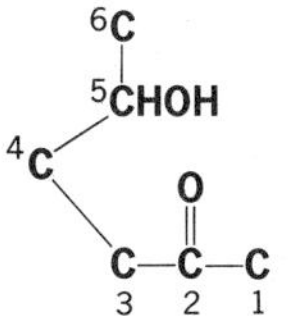

I
open chain form of fructose

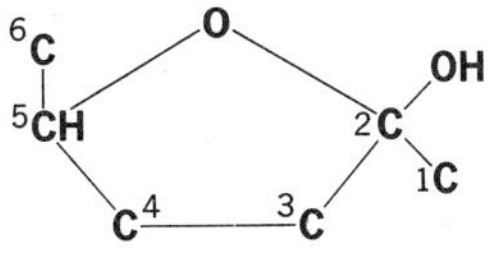

II
hemiketal furanose form of fructose (*β-form*)

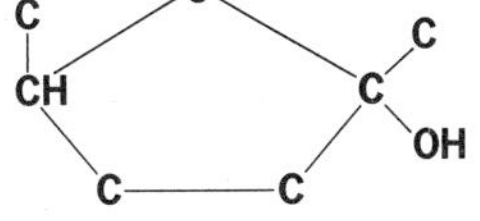

III
hemiketal furanose form of fructose (*α-form*)

A ketal formed from structure II and methanol would be named methyl β-D-fructofuranoside and is shown at structure IV. Instead of methanol, let us take glucose, formulated as $C_6H_{11}O_5$—OH, with the OH as the *hemiacetal hydroxyl.* Let it be still further abbreviated to G—OH, from which structure V is sucrose. Thus, sucrose is a β-fructoside.

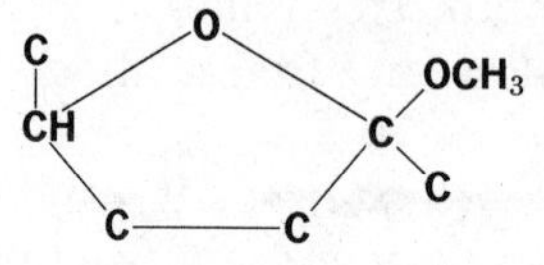

IV

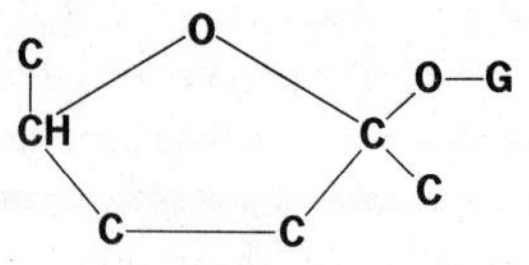

V

Sucrose is also an α-glucoside. The full structure of sucrose, an expansion of structure V, is structure VI. Structure VI, on the left-hand side, shows the β-D-fructofuranoside part in the conventional way. Structure VII shows another way of drawing sucrose; it is structure VI flipped over. Structure VII, on the left-hand side, shows the α-D-glucopyranoside part in the conventional way.

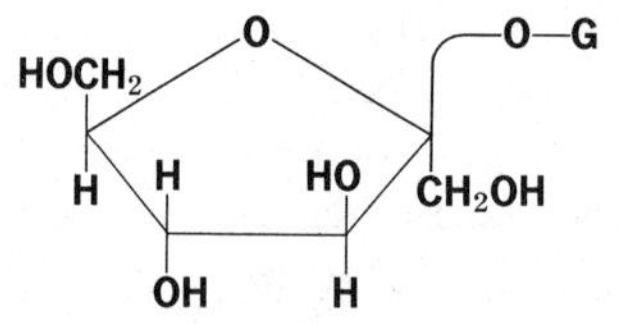

sucrose
VI

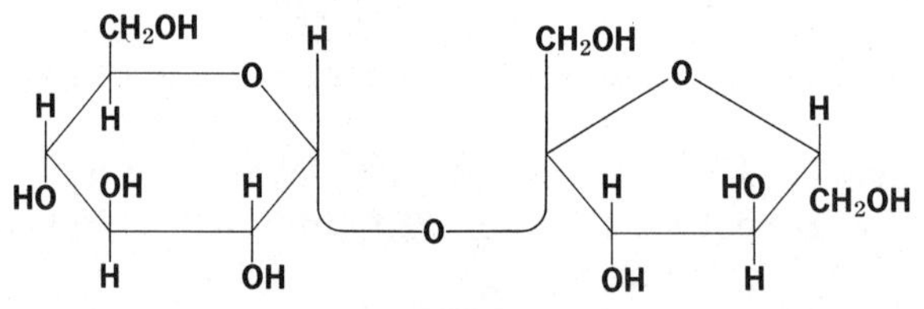

sucrose
VII

Trisaccharides

There are several known trisaccharides, but the most important is raffinose. Raffinose consists of galactose, glucose, and fructose units. Raffinose is a nonreducing sugar that occurs in sugar beets, cottonseeds, soybeans, and other seeds. It is of limited utility to man. A trisaccharide obtained from gentian roots is gentianose, a nonreducing fructose-glucose-glucose combination.

Polysaccharides

Polysaccharides occur abundantly in nature and fulfill a variety of functions. Since these molecules are so large, they are very complex, and much is still to be learned about them. Polysaccharides are not sweet, do not reduce Benedict's solution, do not mutarotate, and are not fermented by common yeast. These large molecules do not form true molecular solutions. It is difficult to classify polysaccharides, but Table 10-3 sets up an arbitrary system dependent upon the uses of these compounds.

Nutrient Polysaccharides

THE STARCHES

Starches constitute the reserve carbohydrate of the plant and are very abundant. Since starch can be hydrolyzed to give glucose, we may call it a natural glucose polysaccharide. Starch occurs as small granules in seeds, roots, and main body of the plant. The size and the nature of the starch granule vary and are dependent upon the source. These granules are amorphous in nature and insoluble in water. When a starch suspension is heated, the granules start to swell; if heating is continued, the materials eventually become a thick pasty mass. The temperature and the length of time required for the starch suspension to become pasty depend on the source of the starch; for example, tapioca starch becomes viscous much more quickly than corn starch.

Table 10-3 Polysaccharides

CLASSIFICATION	USE
nutrient polysaccharides	starch glycogen inulin others that serve as reserve nutrients
both nutrient and structural	pectins plant gums mucilages hemicelluloses, which serve as structural materials as well as nutrients
structural polysaccharides	cellulose chitin others that serve as structural material for plants and invertebrates

When a starch granule bursts, it liberates two distinct types of starch: one that is linear in structure (amylose) and one that is branched (amylopectin). The ratio of these two starch types varies and is dependent on the source; it has been possible to obtain genetic strains of plants, which make one type almost to the exclusion of the other.

Ordinary corn starch is composed of approximately 25% amylose and 75% amylopectin. However, in some hybrid corn, the amylose content has been raised to approximately 80%. Also, in some waxy maize corn, percentages of amylopectin have been determined to be over 95%.

There are various ways to determine the amount of one (i.e., amylose) in the presence of the other. For example, the well-known dark blue iodine-starch test is due to the reaction of iodine with the amylose (iodine does not give a blue color with amylopectin). Also, 1-butanol will almost quantitatively precipitate the amylose, but not the amylopectin, from aqueous solutions. Thus, by correlating the intensity of the color produced in the iodine reaction with the amount precipitated with butanol, one can obtain a rather accurate percentage of amylose.

Both types of starch may form colloidal solutions when cooked, but the amylopectin is stable and remains in "solution." However, the amylose usually crystallizes out on standing. The amylose usually precipitates out of dilute solutions and gels in concentrated solutions. This behavior is valuable in foods such as gum, candies, and puddings where gelation is desired. The nongelling property of amylopectin is also valuable in foods where a clear, viscous thickening agent is desired. Thus, waxy starches are widely used as thickening agents in pies, canned fruits, and vegetables. The waxy starch is usually chemically modified to give it maximum viscosity and freeze-thaw stability.

The greatest use for starch is the coating and sizing of paper to improve the writing qualities. Starch is used to treat textile fibers before they are woven into cloth. This treatment strengthens the fibers so that they can be woven without breaking. Starch is also used in food preparation (pies, gravy, sauces, puddings, etc.). Naturally, much starch is still used in laundering, but with the advent of new fibers and new fabrics, this use is not as important as it used to be.

Amylose is an α-linked 1,4-polyglucoside. The molecule may vary in size from 500 to over 2,000 units. Since the molecule is easily broken down, the large figure is probably a more accurate estimate as to the amylose size (the molecular weight is probably over 100,000). When iodine molecules approach the amylose, the linear molecule coils up like a spring, and the iodine molecules insert themselves inside the coils. The dark blue color is due to the unusually bound iodine molecules inside the starch coils. Apparently, the amylose coils up as the iodine molecules approach; ordinarily, the big molecule is reasonably uncoiled.

linear amylose

Enzymatic and chemical studies have shown amylopectin to be highly branched. The molecule has been shown to be an α-linked 1,4-polyglucoside, but the occurrence of occasional α-linked 1,6-glucoses causes the branching. Amylopectin is a very large molecule with a molecular weight greater than 1 million (see Figure 10-12).

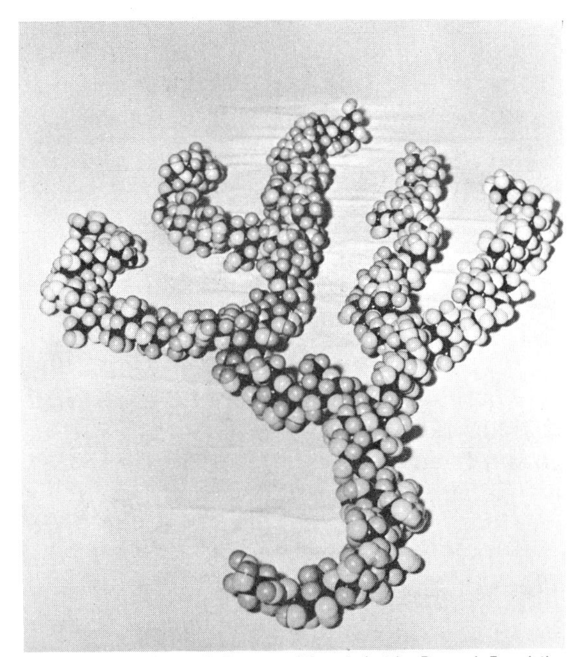

George V. Caesar and Corn Industries Research Foundation

Figure 10-12 Amylopectin.

Amylopectin has been shown to have well over 1,000 glucose residues, and, on an average, to branch every 25 glucose residues.

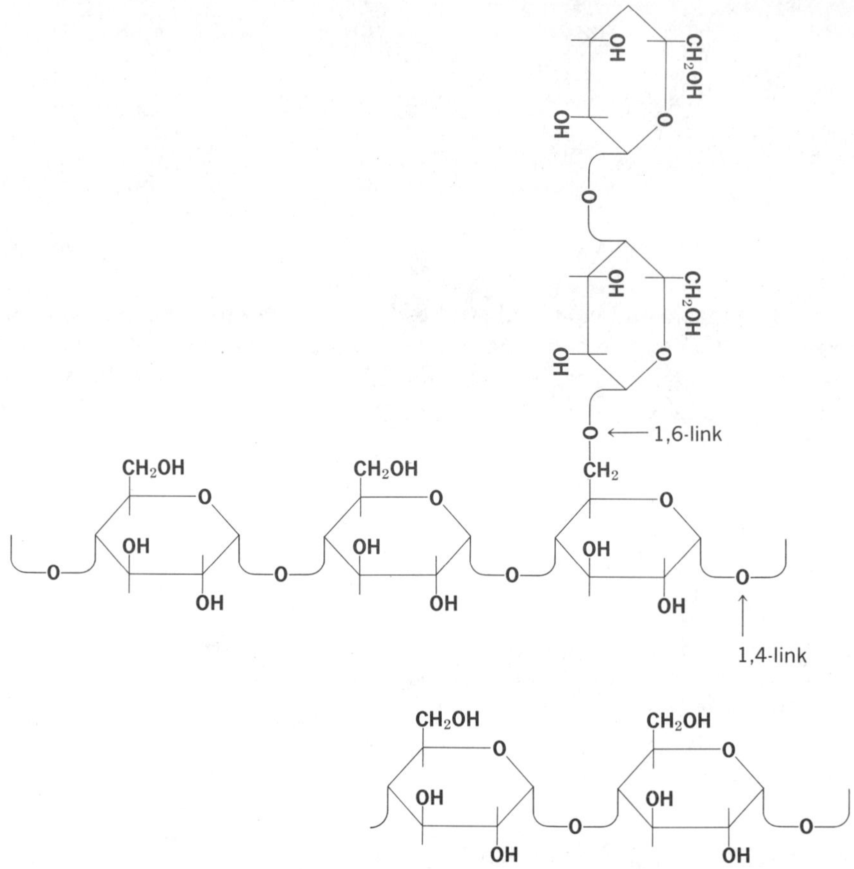

Actually, starch is not 100% pure carbohydrate, for there are small quantities of phosphoric acid bound as the phosphoric acid ester on carbon 6. The phosphoric acid has been shown to be necessary for the conversion of glucose into starch by the enzyme phosphorylase. In certain cereals, for example, sugars are formed and then changed into starch as the grain matures and becomes less sweet. However, in certain fruits, such as the banana, the starch is changed into sugars as the fruit ripens, and it becomes sweeter.

The famous dark blue iodine-starch (amylose) color is stable in the cold but disappears on heating. Heat expels the iodine from the starch complex. When starch hydrolyzes, it first forms dextrins, then maltose, and finally glucose, if the reaction goes to completion. We may follow this reaction by the iodine color test. When the starch is broken down to the dextrin stage, the blue disappears and is replaced by red, which disappears when we get to the maltose stage.

	starch ⟶	dextrins ⟶	maltose ⟶	glucose
Iodine Color	*blue*	*red*	*colorless*	*colorless*

By colorless we mean that the color of the solution is no different from that of an ordinary dilute iodine solution. In the digestive process, ptyalin of the saliva and amylopsin of the pancreatic juice help break down starch into maltose. The amylose is probably *completely* broken down by the body enzymes of the digestive tract into maltose, whereas the amylopectin is probably *not,* because the branching spots would resist hydrolysis.

Rice starch is found in many face powders, and *arrowroot starch* is used in the manufacture of tapioca.

DEXTRINS

Dextrins are glucose polysaccharides of intermediate size in the hydrolysis of starch to maltose. The dextrins may vary in size and may produce different iodine color reactions. The iodine may be deep red (amylodextrin, the largest dextrin), red (erythrodextrin), or colorless (achroodextrins, the shortest and smallest dextrins).

The simple heating of starch produces dextrins. Toasting bread causes the starch on the bread surface to change into dextrins. Because dextrins represent starch already partially hydrolyzed, they are easier to digest than starch. Bread crust and toasted cereals all contain dextrins. Dextrimaltose, which is a mixture of dextrins and maltose, is found in many infant formulas and is easier to digest than starch. Dextrins do not mutarotate, will not reduce Benedict's solution, and are not fermented by common yeast.

Dextrins are used quite extensively in the manufacture of cheap adhesives because of their sticky properties when wet. Such adhesives or gums are used on postage stamps and envelopes.

GLYCOGEN

Glycogen is the animal counterpart of starch and represents the reserve carbohydrate supply. It is found mostly in liver and muscles, but some may be found in some plants and microorganisms.

Glycogen is a very large molecule similar to amylopectin. It is even more highly branched than amylopectin, and its molecular weight is well over 1 million. Liver glycogen may be more than five times as large as muscle glycogen.

Because acid hydrolysis yields only D-glucose, and the amylases, ptyalin and amylopsin, hydrolyze it to maltose in about a 50% yield, glycogen is an α-linked 1,4-glucoside. The branching spots are due to α-linked 1,6-glucosides. Glycogen dissolves in water to form colloidal suspensions, which do not mutarotate, will not reduce Benedict's solution, and will not be fermented by common yeast. Iodine reacts with glycogen to form a red-brown color.

The concentration of glycogen is high (about 6% or higher) in liver and low in muscles (about 1%). However, since there is so much more muscle than liver, there are about 250 g of muscle glycogen and about 110 g of liver glycogen. This amounts to an average of 360 g of glycogen per adult. Glycogen may readily be prepared by the treatment of liver with KOH. Such treatment breaks up the lipids and the proteins and leaves the glycogen essentially intact.

In the body, the processes of breaking down glycogen to D-glucose, and the further oxidation of glucose, release energy the body utilizes.

INULIN

Inulin, instead of starch, is the reserve polysaccharide serving as the source of energy for some plants. Hydrolysis yields mostly D-fructose. It is a β-linked 1,2-fructoside. Inulin forms a colloidal suspension in water, gives no color with iodine, and shows mild reducing properties to Benedict's solution, due to its low molecular weight (estimated at 3,000 to 5,000).

The acid hydrolysis of inulin yields D-fructose, but the amylases do not touch it. Consequently, inulin is of no nutritional value to us. Some lower animals have *inulinase,* an enzyme capable of breaking inulin down.

Inulin is found in the roots of the chicory, dahlia, dandelion, and Jerusalem artichoke. Some other polyfructosides, somewhat similar to inulin, are asparagosin (from asparagus roots), sinistrin (from the sea onion), graminin (from rye), phlein (from tubers of timothy), poan (from roughstalk bluegrass), and tricitin (from couch grass).

LICHENIN

Lichenin is a celluloselike polysaccharide found in mosses and lichens. It can be hydrolyzed to cellobiose by some agents, and completely to D-glucose by others. This indicates many β-D-glucoside linkages. Unlike cellulose, lichenin is soluble in hot water to form a colloidal suspension and, as such, is more readily hydrolyzed than cellulose. The linkages between units are slightly different from those in cellulose, which accounts for the difference in the ease of breakdown of lichenin as compared to cellulose.

Nutrient and Structural Polysaccharides

PECTINS

The pectins are complex polysaccharides found in the cell walls of all young plant tissues and are quite characteristic of the fruits and fleshy roots. A common occurring unit is galacturonic acid. The pectins differ from those hemicelluloses that contain uronic acid parts in that the pectins have a much higher uronic acid content.

The pectins used commercially have a high molecular weight and disperse in water to form viscous colloidal suspensions. The most outstanding property of a pectin is to form a sugar-acid-pectin gel, and such fruit jellies have been known for some time. The uronic acid units in pectins are not all free acids. It has been estimated that the purest commercial pectins contain 10 to 12% methyl ester groups (the acid group has formed a methyl ester). A completely saponified material is called pectic acid, and a partially saponified material is called pectinic acid. The important function of pectin in plants is its cementing action: it appears able to hold the cells together. Kaopectate, useful in stopping diarrhea, is a formulation of pectin and kaolin (clay).

VEGETABLE GUMS AND MUCILAGES

The classification of vegetable gums and mucilages in a separate section from the pectins and hemicelluloses is an indefinite and arbitrary one and is based on the solubility of these gums and mucilages in water. Also, there is no sharp distinction between the gums and the mucilages. The gums may form on the barks of trees either spontaneously in some natural process or as a result of some mechanical injury. Gums usually form clear solutions in water, whereas mucilages do not. The gums are neutral salts of complex polysaccharide acids, containing pentoses, hexoses, and uronic acid residues. The mucilages are also salts of complex polysaccharide acids.

Gum arabic (gum acacia) is obtained from the acacia tree. The gum is used in the candy industry because of its ability to prevent the crystallization of the sugar, which would make the confection uneven. Medically, gum arabic has been administered intravenously to restore the normal colloidal osmotic pressure in the treatment of certain edemas.

Gum tragacanth is obtained from the Asiatic shrubs of the genus *Astragalus*. It has some value as a demulcent.

The mucilages, which are extracted from seeds and seed coverings, form slimy solutions with water. The mucilages usually contain a noncarbohydrate part. In hot water, the mucilages form colloidal suspensions that gel on cooling. One of the best examples of a mucilage is agar-agar, obtainable from seaweed. Agar-agar is of special interest to us because it is used in the preparation of solid culture media in bacteriology. We cannot digest agar-agar because of the lack of a specific enzyme. Therefore, agar-agar is of value in preventing constipation, because it absorbs water to give bulk to the feces and makes the stool softer and more easily eliminated. Petrolagar is a commercial preparation of agar-agar and mineral oil.

HEMICELLULOSES

The hemicelluloses differ significantly from cellulose in that hydrolysis yields monosaccharides other than glucose. The hemicelluloses are more readily hydrolyzed than cellulose and are of some value as plant foods.

Structural Polysaccharides

CELLULOSE

Cellulose is the most widely distributed structural polysaccharide and the most abundant and chemically resistant of all the substances elaborated by living cells. It is the main constituent of all walls of plants. Wood is 40–50% cellulose, cottonseeds 85–90%, and flax, from which linen is made, about 80–90%.

Acid hydrolysis of pure cellulose yields D-glucose exclusively. Enzymatic and chemical studies indicate that the units are β-linked 1,4-glucosides. The structure of cellulose is complex, and the molecular weight of the molecule may be higher than $\frac{1}{2}$ million. Whereas starch consists mostly of α-D-glucosides, cellulose is mostly β-D-glucosides in the form of long chains, which are parallel to each other.

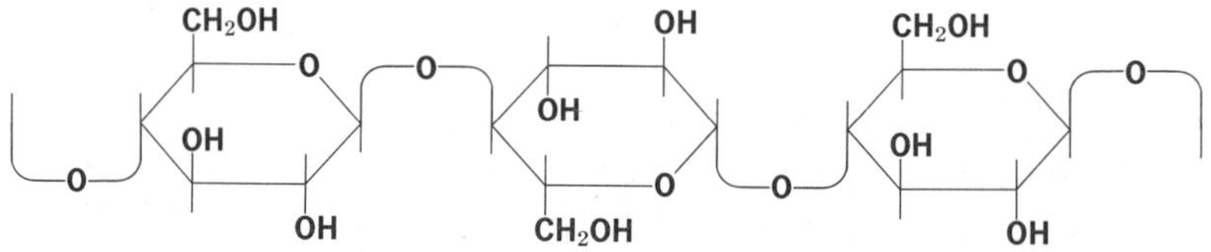

cellulose

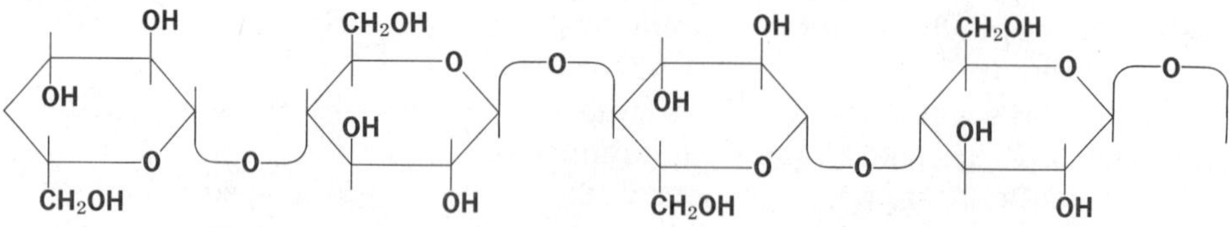

Cellulose is the most stable hexose polysaccharide because it is the only structure in which every adjacent group is in a perfectly alternating fashion. That is, if a bulky group sticks up above the plane of the ring, then the two adjacent bulky groups stick down below the plane of the ring.

This type of structural arrangement gives the least crowding with consequent greater stability.

Cellulose is not soluble in water, will not reduce Benedict's solution, and is not fermented by common yeast. Man apparently lacks the appropriate enzyme necessary to hydrolyze cellulose, and it has no nutritional value to us. Cellulose does have a function in that it provides bulk to the feces, thus preventing constipation. An enzyme, cellulase, is commonly found in many microorganisms, but rarely in animals. Many animals (i.e., herbiverous animals) apparently thrive on cellulose, but the utility of cellulose for these animals is due to the microorganisms that fluorish in their digestive systems.

Mercerization is the process of treating cellulose with a strong base, usually 18% sodium hydroxide. Under these circumstances, the cellulose swells and heat is evolved. This alkali cellulose complex is not very stable, and the addition of water breaks the complex back into the original components. The regenerated cellulose is apparently different from the original material. The new cellulose is stronger, has a greater absorptive capacity for dyestuffs, and is more suitable for textiles.

If a mixture of cellulose and sodium hydroxide is treated with carbon disulfide CS_2, cellulose xanthates are formed. The reaction involves one alcohol group of the cellulose units, the sodium hydroxide, and the carbon disulfide in the following manner (ROH represents the cellulose unit):

$$\underset{\text{cellulose}}{ROH} + \underset{\text{sodium hydroxide}}{NaOH} + \underset{\text{carbon disulfide}}{CS_2} \longrightarrow \underset{\text{sodium cellulose xanthate}}{R{-}O{-}\overset{\overset{\displaystyle S}{\|}}{C}{-}S{-}Na} + H_2O$$

The sodium cellulose xanthate "solution" is called *viscose*. This "viscose solution" is colloidal in nature and has an orange color. In the viscose rayon process, the viscose solution is forced under pressure through small holes in a platinum bar into an acidic solution. This procedure results in the immediate formation of the free cellulose xanthic acid, which is unstable and immediately decomposes to form the cellulose again.

$$\underset{\text{sodium cellulose xanthate}}{R{-}O{-}\overset{\overset{\displaystyle S}{\|}}{C}{-}S{-}Na} + \underset{\text{acid}}{H^+} \longrightarrow \underset{\text{cellulose xanthic acid}}{\left[R{-}O{-}\overset{\overset{\displaystyle S}{\|}}{C}{-}S{-}H\right]} + Na^+$$

$$\left[R{-}O{-}\overset{\overset{\displaystyle S}{\|}}{C}{-}S{-}H\right] \longrightarrow \underset{\text{regenerated cellulose ("rayon")}}{ROH} + CS_2$$

The regenerated cellulose takes the solid form of a thread, corresponding to the diameter of the small hole, and the *rayon* is then wound

I.R.C. Fibers Division, Midland-Ross Corp.

Figure 10-13 A spinnerette. Viscose solution is being forced through tiny holes in nozzle.

up on a spool. The rayon industry arose as a competitor to the silk industry but now must compete with all the new synthetic fibers.

If the viscose solution is forced out through a slit (see Figure 10-13), we obtain a sheet of regenerated cellulose. The sheet may be treated with glycerine to make it pliable, with lacquers to make it water repellent, and with other chemicals to make the surface attractive. Regenerated cellulose sheets (e.g., Cellophane, Visqueen, etc.) find ever increasing usage as transparent protective agents.

A glance at any particular unit of cellulose indicates that, as a maximum, there are three free —OH groups per glucose unit,

CH_2OH

—O—   —O—   OH   OH

glucose unit in cellulose
showing three free —**OH** groups

which means that, as a maximum, any glucose unit may form three alcohol derivatives (i.e., esters). Some of the esters of cellulose are very important commercially. If purified cellulose is almost completely nitrated (almost three nitric ester groups per unit), we obtain *guncotton,* an explosive.

A less highly nitrated cellulose is known as *pyroxylin,* which is used extensively to make lacquers. *Collodion* is a solution of pyroxylin in a mixture of ether and alcohol. When collodion is applied to any surface, the ether and alcohol evaporate quickly and leave a transparent protective coating of pyroxylin. This has been used to protect certain minor wounds. *Celluloid* is a mixture of pyroxylin and camphor.

Cellulose acetate is cellulose in which the alcohol groups have been converted into acetic ester groups by the action of acetic anhydride. Cellulose acetate, like rayon, can be used to make clothes and possesses the advantage over cellulose itself in that the ester is a water repellent. Cellulose acetate is used to make lacquers, plastics, and home motion-picture film, and in the fabrication of some shatterproof glass.

LIGNIN

Lignin is the cementing material found between the cell walls of woody tissue; it gives strength and rigidity to the cell wall. In making paper from wood, the lignin must be removed by dissolving it away. Lignin contains benzene rings, methoxy —OCH_3, and other groups and is an exceedingly complex material. Two of the many compounds isolable from lignin are vanillin and coniferyl alcohol.

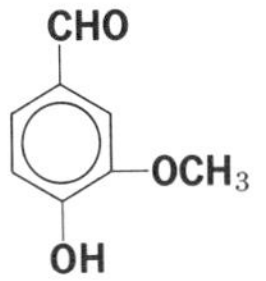

CHO
—OCH_3
OH
vanillin

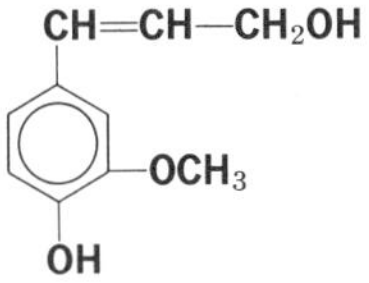

CH=CH—CH_2OH
—OCH_3
OH
coniferyl alcohol

After the lignin has been removed, the wood pulp (mostly cellulose now) is dried and made into appropriate sheets of paper, depending upon the size, color, and quality required.

CHITIN

Chitin is a nitrogen-containing polysaccharide commonly occurring in invertebrate animals. It is found particularly in insects and crustaceans. It may be found in the hard outer portion of the body as armor of protection, such as the protection shell of crabs and lobsters, where it may be mixed with calcium salts, such as the carbonate. Chitin may also occur in the lens of the eye and may line the inner organs or canals of animals. Glucosamine is related to glucose in that the second hydroxyl has been replaced by an amino group. If glucosamine is acetylated, the N-acetylglucosamine is the actual unit out of which chitin is made. The structure of chitin is similar to that of cellulose in that it is a linear, β-linked 1,4 molecule.

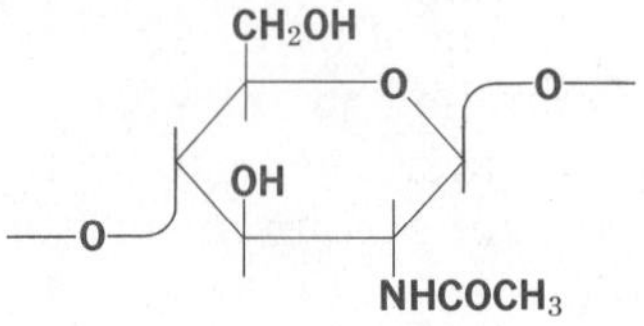

CH_2OH
O O
OH
O
$NHCOCH_3$

the recurring unit in chitin

Chitin is colorless, insoluble in water, and unreactive.

Pyrogens

Pyrogens are toxic products, carbohydrate-like in nature, which produce fever and chills when present in the blood stream. The pyrogens are very complex with a high molecular weight (50,000–100,000). Glucosamine units have definitely been established; sugar alcohols and gluconic acid and similar -onic acids may exist, whereas glucuronic acid and similar -uronic acids very probably are not present.

Pyrogens are elaborated by the fever producing organisms, such as *Eberthella thyphosa, Bacillus subtilis, Proteus vulgaris,* etc. It has been shown that each organism produces its own characteristic pyrogen, although the pyrogens are all generally alike.

Pyrogens are used in the fever treatment of certain diseases and body disorders, such as syphilis, certain allergies, arthritis, malignant hypertension, and status asthmaticus. The object of pyrogen treatment is to produce fever that may destroy the organism causing the disease or alleviate the symptoms. Naturally, in *most* pharmaceutical preparations, it is important that impurities, such as pyrogens, *be absent!* Great care is taken in hospitals to insure the pyrogen-free nature of solutions.

REVIEW QUESTIONS

1. What are the functional groups liable to be found in carbohydrates?
2. What is the difference between a hemiacetal and an acetal?
3. Define the terms monosaccharide, disaccharide, and polysaccharide.
4. What is the difference between a tetrose, a pentose, and a hexose? between an aldose and a ketose? Draw the structures of several pentoses that are aldoses and of several hexoses that are ketoses.
5. Define the terms dextrorotatory and levorotatory.

6. What is the difference between D- and L-sugars?
7. How many isomers are there if we have a tetrose that is an aldose? A pentose that is a ketose? A hexose that is an aldose?
8. Discuss Benedict's test, the Molisch test for a carbohydrate, and Tollens' test. Indicate how the test is performed, how a positive test would be recognized, and what a positive test signifies. Illustrate by a balanced equation Benedict's test for glucose. Name three carbohydrates that do not give a positive Benedict's test.
9. What is meant by the fermentation of glucose? Write a balanced equation illustrating this process. Does it signify a complete oxidation of the glucose? Name two carbohydrates easily fermented. Name three carbohydrates not readily fermented.
10. Discuss mutarotation.
11. What is meant by the term sugar alcohol? Give several examples.
12. What is meant by the term sugar acid? Contrast the structures of -onic acids and -uronic acids.
13. What is meant by photosynthesis? Write an equation illustrating this process. Is this an important reaction?
14. What is meant by a nonreducing sugar? a reducing sugar? Give examples.
15. What is the concentration of glucose in normal human blood? Does this vary? Discuss.
16. What is milk sugar? dextrimaltose? Why is the latter used?
17. What are other names for levulose, dextrose, and common table sugar?
18. How is glucose prepared commercially?
19. May glucose be given intravenously? May sucrose be given intravenously?
20. List the relative sweetness of some of the common sugars.
21. Why is honey so sweet? Why do some candies become sweeter on aging?
22. Defend the statement, "All monosaccharides give a positive Benedict's test, whereas only some of the disaccharides give a positive test."
23. What is the difference between an α- and a β-sugar?
24. What sugars that may be found in urine give a positive Benedict's test?
25. Explain the following: "Sucrose is a β-sugar and we can digest it; cellobiose is a β-sugar and we cannot digest it."
26. Is lactose an ideal sugar for infants? Explain.
27. How is sucrose obtained commercially? Of what use is this sugar?
28. How may polysaccharides be classified?
29. Discuss the structure of starch. How would you completely separate a mixture of glucose and starch? Explain what happens when starch hydrolyzes.
30. Of what use are the dextrins commercially?
31. Discuss glycogen, its chemical composition, and its use in the body.
32. What are the pectins?
33. Contrast starch and cellulose from a chemical viewpoint. Is there any use for either in the diet?
34. Explain: "Elephants can digest cellulose, whereas humans cannot."
35. What is the color test for starch?
36. Identify the following terms: mercerization, cellulose xanthate, and viscose. What are rayon, cellophane, collodion, celluloid, pyroxylin, and cotton?
37. What are lignin and chitin?
38. What are the pyrogens? Have they any use in medicine?

39. Define the terms diastereoisomer and enantiomer.

40. Which of the following would you expect to be optically active?

$CH_3CH(Br)CH_2CH_3$ $CH_3CH(OH)CH_2CH_2CH_3$

$CH_3CH(OH)CH_3$ $HO_2CCH_2CH(OH)CO_2H$

41. Draw all of the possible optical isomers of the following compounds, and mark the asymmetric carbon atom or atoms with an asterisk.

$CH_3CH(OH)\text{—}CH(OH)CH_3$ $HC(=O)\text{—}CHOH\text{—}CH_2OH$ $HOC(=O)\text{—}CHBr\text{—}CH_2\text{—}CH_3$

42. What is the meaning of the following equation?

$$[\alpha]_D^{25°} = +19°$$

11

lipids

Lipids are essential constituents of protoplasm. They occur widely in nature. Probably the most characteristic property of lipids is their *insolubility* in water. Lipids are soluble, however, in "fat solvents," such as ether and chloroform. Lipids are usually lighter than water and tend to float as an insoluble layer on top of a water layer.

Lipids usually have ester groupings in them. They contain carbon, hydrogen, and oxygen (like carbohydrates) and may also contain nitrogen and phosphorus. Since the lipid may contain more hydrogen and less oxygen than a carbohydrate of equal carbon content, the lipid is more reduced than the corresponding carbohydrate and thus has more energy. Because they contain more energy than carbohydrates, lipids are the most economical way to store energy and represent the best reserve energy supply for the body. Other uses for lipids will be discussed in Chapter 18.

Lipids may be classified in the following manner:

Simple lipids: esters of fatty acids and alcohols.

Fats or solid fats: esters of fatty acid and glycerol. These compounds are solid at room temperature (20°C).

Oils or liquid fats: esters of fatty acids and glycerol. These compounds are liquid at room temperature (20°C).

Waxes: esters of long-chain fatty acids and long-chain alcohols. Waxes do not contain glycerol.

Compound lipids: esters of fatty acid and alcohol in combination with other compounds.

Phospholipids: compounds that contain glycerol, fatty acids, phosphoric acid, and nitrogen-containing organic bases.

Glycolipids: compounds that contain fatty acids, an alcohol (not glycerol), a carbohydrate, and a nitrogen-containing organic base. No phosphoric acid is present.

Derived lipids: compounds formed when simple or compound lipids are hydrolyzed. The most common fragments are sterols (complex alcohols).

Simple lipids

Some Oils and Fats

Esters formed from glycerol are called glycerides. All oils and fats are esters of glycerol. When the fatty acids are the same, we call the fat a *simple glyceride.* When the fatty acids are different, we call the fat a *mixed glyceride.* In *nature,* esters of glycerol usually occur with all the —OH groups esterified. Thus, fats and oils are triple esters, because glycerol has three —OH groups.

$$\underset{\text{alcohol}}{R{-}OH} + \underset{\text{acid}}{HO{-}\overset{\overset{\displaystyle O}{\|}}{C}{-}R'} \xrightarrow{H^+} \underset{\text{ester}}{R{-}O{-}\overset{\overset{\displaystyle O}{\|}}{C}{-}R'} + H_2O$$

$$\underset{\text{glycerol}}{\begin{matrix} CH_2OH \\ | \\ CHOH \\ | \\ CH_2OH \end{matrix}} + \underset{\substack{\text{fatty acids} \\ (\textit{all alike})}}{\begin{matrix} HO{-}\overset{\overset{\displaystyle O}{\|}}{C}{-}R \\ HO{-}\overset{\overset{\displaystyle O}{\|}}{C}{-}R \\ HO{-}\overset{\overset{\displaystyle O}{\|}}{C}{-}R \end{matrix}} \xrightarrow{H^+} \underset{\substack{\text{simple glyceride} \\ (\textit{triple ester})}}{\begin{matrix} CH_2{-}O{-}\overset{\overset{\displaystyle O}{\|}}{C}{-}R \\ | \\ CH{-}O{-}\overset{\overset{\displaystyle O}{\|}}{C}{-}R \\ | \\ CH_2{-}O{-}\overset{\overset{\displaystyle O}{\|}}{C}{-}R \end{matrix}} + 3H_2O$$

$$
\begin{array}{llll}
 & \quad\ \ O & & \qquad\quad\ O \\
 & \quad\ \ \| & & \qquad\quad\ \| \\
CH_2OH & HO-C-R & & CH_2-O-C-R \\
| & \quad\ \ O & & | \qquad\quad\ O \\
| & \quad\ \ \| & \xrightarrow{H^+} & | \qquad\quad\ \| \\
CHOH & + HO-C-R' & & CH-O-C-R' + 3H_2O \\
| & \quad\ \ O & & | \qquad\quad\ O \\
| & \quad\ \ \| & & | \qquad\quad\ \| \\
CH_2OH & HO-C-R'' & & CH_2-O-C-R''
\end{array}
$$

glycerol — fatty acids (*all different*) — mixed glyceride

Most naturally occurring oils and fats are mixed glycerides, although some simple glycerides have been isolated and identified. Some formulas of fats are

$$
\begin{array}{l}
CH_2-O-\overset{\overset{O}{\|}}{C}-C_{17}H_{35} \\
| \\
CH-O-\overset{\overset{O}{\|}}{C}-C_{17}H_{35} \\
| \\
CH_2-O-\overset{\overset{O}{\|}}{C}-C_{17}H_{35}
\end{array}
\qquad
\begin{array}{l}
CH_2-O-\overset{\overset{O}{\|}}{C}-C_{15}H_{31} \\
| \\
CH-O-\overset{\overset{O}{\|}}{C}-C_{15}H_{31} \\
| \\
CH_2-O-\overset{\overset{O}{\|}}{C}-C_{15}H_{31}
\end{array}
$$

glyceryl tristearate
(*stearin,* a fat)
m.p. 71.5°C

glyceryl tripalmitate
(*palmitin,* a fat)
m.p. 65.5°C

$$
\begin{array}{l}
CH_2-O-\overset{\overset{O}{\|}}{C}-C_{13}H_{27} \\
| \\
CH-O-\overset{\overset{O}{\|}}{C}-C_{13}H_{27} \\
| \\
CH_2-O-\overset{\overset{O}{\|}}{C}-C_{13}H_{27}
\end{array}
\qquad
\begin{array}{l}
CH_2-O-\overset{\overset{O}{\|}}{C}-C_{11}H_{23} \\
| \\
CH-O-\overset{\overset{O}{\|}}{C}-C_{11}H_{23} \\
| \\
CH_2-O-\overset{\overset{O}{\|}}{C}-C_{11}H_{23}
\end{array}
$$

glyceryl trimyristate
(*myristin,* a fat)
m.p. 56.5°C

glyceryl trilaurate
(*laurin,* a fat)
m.p. 49°C

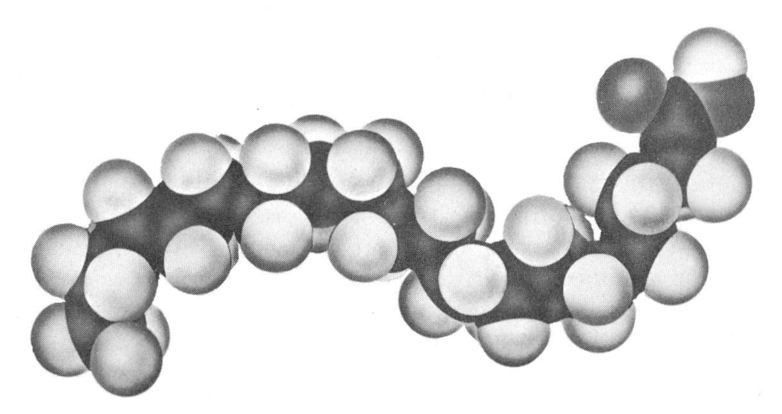

Figure 11-1 A long-chain fatty acid.

The line of demarcation between an oil and a fat is melting point. If the fatty acid part is a saturated long-chain fatty acid, such as palmitic, stearic, myristic, or lauric acid, the glyceride will tend to be solid at room temperature, and we call it a fat. (We see that the melting points vary from about 71°C to about 46°C.)

If the fatty acid part has few carbon atoms, such as butyric acid, the glyceride will tend to be liquid at room temperature, and we call it an oil. For example,

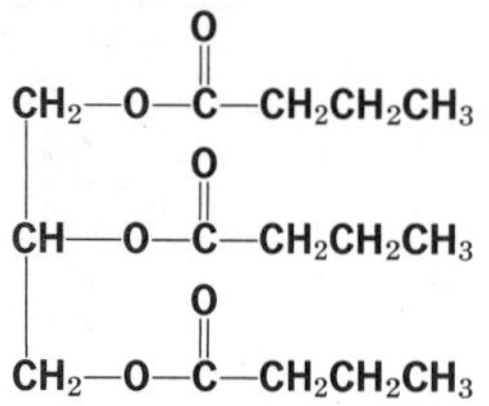

$$\begin{array}{l} CH_2-O-\overset{\displaystyle O}{\overset{\|}{C}}-CH_2CH_2CH_3 \\ | \\ CH-O-\overset{\displaystyle O}{\overset{\|}{C}}-CH_2CH_2CH_3 \\ | \\ CH_2-O-\overset{\displaystyle O}{\overset{\|}{C}}-CH_2CH_2CH_3 \end{array}$$

glyceryl tributyrate
(*butyrin*, an oil)
m.p. −75°C

We see that the melting point of a fat depends on the length of the saturated fatty acid. The presence of a long-chain fatty acid raises the melting point, and the presence of a short-chain fatty acid lowers the melting point of the glyceride. As we have mentioned before, mixed glycerides are the common occurrence in nature, and simple glycerides are the exception. For example, instead of finding glyceryl tristearate and glyceryl tripalmitate, we are more likely to encounter mixed glycerides, such as

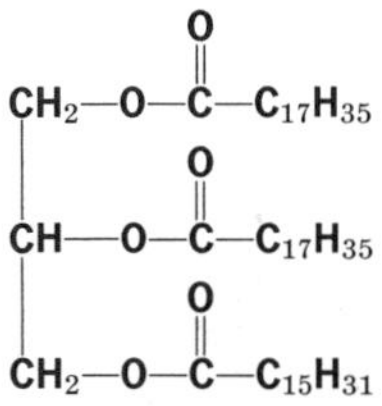

$$\begin{array}{l} CH_2-O-\overset{\displaystyle O}{\overset{\|}{C}}-C_{17}H_{35} \\ | \\ CH-O-\overset{\displaystyle O}{\overset{\|}{C}}-C_{17}H_{35} \\ | \\ CH_2-O-\overset{\displaystyle O}{\overset{\|}{C}}-C_{15}H_{31} \end{array} \qquad \begin{array}{l} CH_2-O-\overset{\displaystyle O}{\overset{\|}{C}}-C_{17}H_{35} \\ | \\ CH-O-\overset{\displaystyle O}{\overset{\|}{C}}-C_{15}H_{31} \\ | \\ CH_2-O-\overset{\displaystyle O}{\overset{\|}{C}}-C_{17}H_{35} \end{array}$$

a mixed glyceride 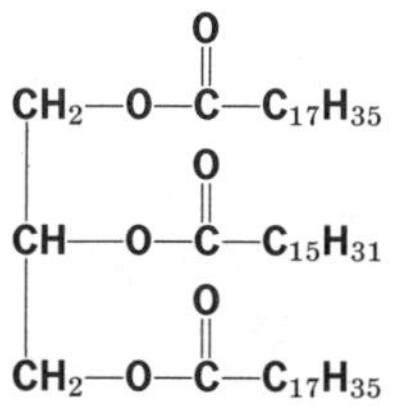 — an isomeric mixed glyceride

as well as mixtures of these two glycerides.

In general, a mixture of various isomeric mixed glycerides has a lower melting point than any of its constituents. This is a common phenomenon, which is true in the majority of cases but not necessarily always correct. Mixtures of isomeric mixed glycerides are indeed common.

In general, the presence of a double bond in the fatty acid part gives an unsaturated fat a melting point lower than that of simlar saturated fat. For example, glyceryl trioleate (olein) is a liquid at room temperature, and we call it an oil. Note that the only difference between olein and stearin is the presence of three double bonds in olein.

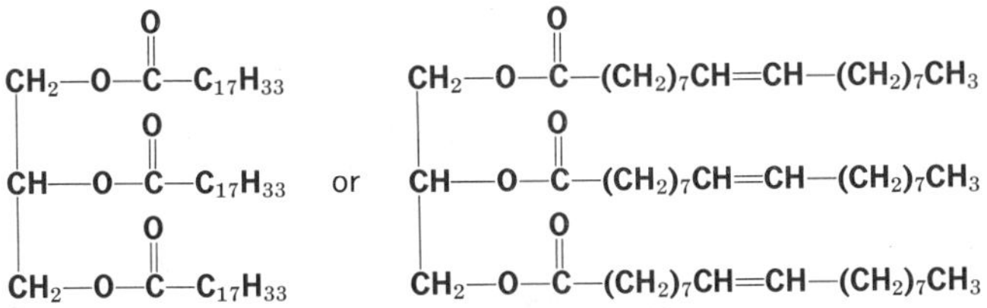

$$\begin{array}{l} CH_2-O-\overset{O}{\overset{\|}{C}}-C_{17}H_{33} \\ | \\ CH-O-\overset{O}{\overset{\|}{C}}-C_{17}H_{33} \\ | \\ CH_2-O-\overset{O}{\overset{\|}{C}}-C_{17}H_{33} \end{array} \quad \text{or} \quad \begin{array}{l} CH_2-O-\overset{O}{\overset{\|}{C}}-(CH_2)_7CH{=}CH-(CH_2)_7CH_3 \\ | \\ CH-O-\overset{O}{\overset{\|}{C}}-(CH_2)_7CH{=}CH-(CH_2)_7CH_3 \\ | \\ CH_2-O-\overset{O}{\overset{\|}{C}}-(CH_2)_7CH{=}CH-(CH_2)_7CH_3 \end{array}$$

glyceryl trioleate (*olein,* an oil)
m.p. −5°C

We can generalize and say that an increase in the number of double bonds present in the glyceride lowers the melting point, as illustrated by

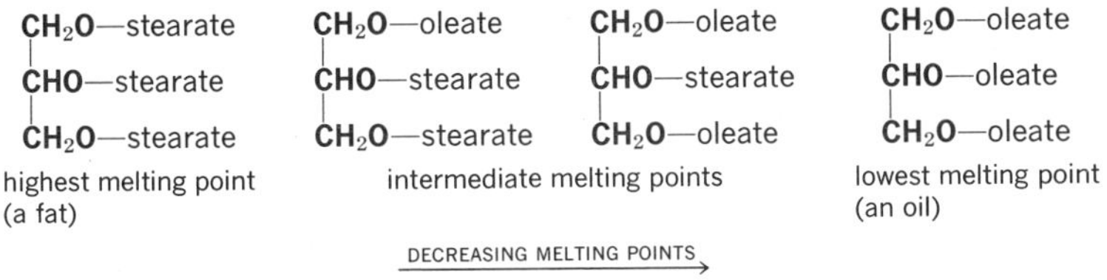

CH_2O—stearate	CH_2O—oleate	CH_2O—oleate	CH_2O—oleate
CHO—stearate	CHO—stearate	CHO—stearate	CHO—oleate
CH_2O—stearate	CH_2O—stearate	CH_2O—oleate	CH_2O—oleate
highest melting point (a fat)	intermediate melting points		lowest melting point (an oil)

DECREASING MELTING POINTS →

Isomerism can also occur when a double bond is present in a long-chain fatty acid. The double bond can occur in many positions. For example,

$CH_3(CH_2)_7CH{=}CH(CH_2)_7COOH$

oleic acid
the double bond is between
carbons 9 and 10

$CH_3(CH_2)_6CH{=}CH(CH_2)_8COOH$

isoleic acid
the double bond is between
carbons 10 and 11

A mixture of glycerides, one containing an unsaturated fatty acid and the other containing the isomeric unsaturated fatty acid (double bond in a different position), tends to have a melting point lower than that of any glyceride containing all of one isomer.

We may also encounter *cis-trans* isomerism. The reader will recall that this possibility exists when we have a double bond. A mixture of *cis* and *trans* isomers in glycerides tends to have a lower melting point than that of a single isomer.

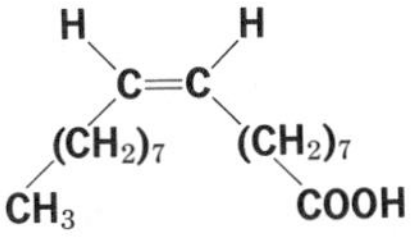

$$\begin{array}{c} H \quad\quad H \\ \diagdown\;\;\diagup \\ C{=}C \\ \diagup\;\;\diagdown \\ (CH_2)_7 \quad (CH_2)_7 \\ CH_3 \quad\quad\quad COOH \end{array}$$

oleic acid (*cis*)

$$\begin{array}{c} COOH \\ (CH_2)_7 \quad H \\ \diagdown\;\;\diagup \\ C{=}C \\ \diagup\;\;\diagdown \\ H \quad\quad (CH_2)_7 \\ \quad\quad\quad CH_3 \end{array}$$

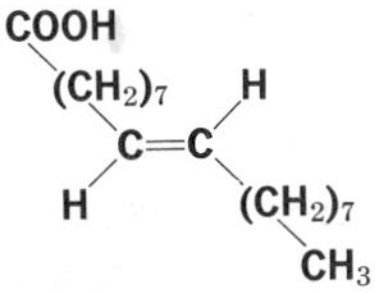

elaidic acid (*trans*)

Actually, elaidic acid does not occur in nature, but it serves as a simple example here. In general, *cis* isomers predominate in nature.

In addition, optical isomerism may complicate the picture, particularly in the hydroxy-fatty acids.

Thus, many factors decrease the melting point of a simple lipid. In some ways, as we shall see later, this is indeed fortunate for us because of the relationship between the melting point of a fat and its digestibility (the lower the melting point of the fat the more digestible it is). As we have seen, oils and fats do not differ chemically; they only differ physically. The chief difference is in the melting point: An oil is a liquid at 20°C, a fat is a solid at 20°C. Oils and fats are usually less dense than water and will float on top of water.

Many naturally occurring liquids called oils, such as oil of cloves, oil of peppermint, and motor oil, are not true lipids and should not be confused with true lipid oils.

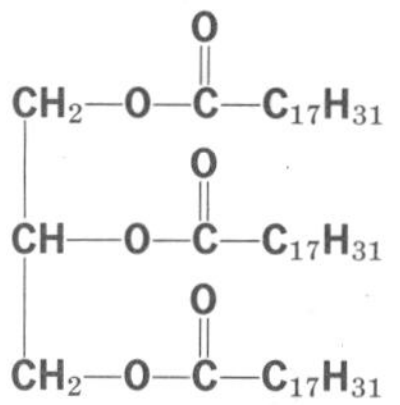

$$\begin{array}{l} CH_2{-}O{-}\overset{\displaystyle O}{\overset{\|}{C}}{-}C_{17}H_{31} \\ | \\ CH{-}O{-}\overset{\displaystyle O}{\overset{\|}{C}}{-}C_{17}H_{31} \\ | \\ CH_2{-}O{-}\overset{\displaystyle O}{\overset{\|}{C}}{-}C_{17}H_{31} \end{array}$$

glyceryl trilinoleate
(*linolein,* an oil)
(each fatty acid has two double bonds)
m.p. 8.9°C

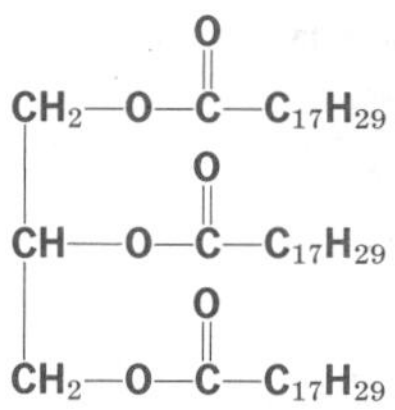

$$\begin{array}{l} CH_2{-}O{-}\overset{\displaystyle O}{\overset{\|}{C}}{-}C_{17}H_{29} \\ | \\ CH{-}O{-}\overset{\displaystyle O}{\overset{\|}{C}}{-}C_{17}H_{29} \\ | \\ CH_2{-}O{-}\overset{\displaystyle O}{\overset{\|}{C}}{-}C_{17}H_{29} \end{array}$$

glyceryl trilinoleneate
(*linolenein,* an oil)
(each fatty acid has three double bonds)

There is a growing tendency among biochemists, food chemists, and nutritionists to avoid terms such as "oils and fats" because of the confusion the word "oil" brings to many minds. A suggested solution is to call any fat that is a solid a *solid fat,* and any oil a *liquid fat.* Instead of speaking of "oils and fats," the modern trend is to speak of "solid fats and liquid fats." Although the new terminology is not universally accepted, you may encounter it in various articles and books.

Reactions

HYDROLYSIS OF SOLID FATS AND LIQUID FATS

Esters may be hydrolyzed by the action of either an acid or a base. If an acid is reacted with an ester, we obtain the free fatty acid and glycerol. If a base is reacted with the ester, we obtain glycerol and the salt of the fatty acid. The former reaction is called *acid hydrolysis;* the latter is called *saponification.*

Acid Hydrolysis:

$$\begin{array}{l} CH_2-O-\overset{O}{\overset{\|}{C}}-C_{17}H_{35} \\ | \\ CH-O-\overset{O}{\overset{\|}{C}}-C_{17}H_{35} \\ | \\ CH_2-O-\overset{O}{\overset{\|}{C}}-C_{17}H_{35} \end{array} \xrightarrow[\text{(H}^+\text{) acid}]{3H_2O} \begin{array}{l} CH_2OH \\ | \\ CHOH \\ | \\ CH_2OH \end{array} + 3C_{17}H_{35}\overset{O}{\overset{\|}{C}}-OH$$

glyceryl stearate — glycerol — stearic acid

Saponification:

$$\begin{array}{l} CH_2-O-\overset{O}{\overset{\|}{C}}-C_{17}H_{35} \\ | \\ CH-O-\overset{O}{\overset{\|}{C}}-C_{17}H_{35} \\ | \\ CH_2-O-\overset{O}{\overset{\|}{C}}-C_{17}H_{35} \end{array} \xrightarrow[\text{base}]{3NaOH} \begin{array}{l} CH_2OH \\ | \\ CHOH \\ | \\ CH_2OH \end{array} + 3C_{17}H_{35}\overset{O}{\overset{\|}{C}}-ONa$$

glyceryl stearate — glycerol — sodium stearate (a soap)

The salt of a long-chain fatty acid is called a soap. The physical and chemical properties of soaps are of particular interest to us. The *free* fatty acids containing over 10 carbon atoms (i.e., lauric and higher) are insoluble in water. We can easily convert a soap into the free fatty acid by treating the soap with a little strong acid, such as sulfuric or hydrochloric. The free fatty acid formed floats on top of the water. For example,

$$C_{15}H_{31}COONa + HCl \longrightarrow C_{15}H_{31}COOH + NaCl$$

sodium palmitate (a soap) — hydrochloric acid — palmitic acid (free fatty acid insoluble in water) — sodium chloride

This means that an ordinary soap will not give suds in acidic water.

Soaps

A soap is a molecule with two very dissimilar ends. The salt end is ionic and tends to dissolve in a polar substance, such as water. We call it the hydrophilic end (loves water). The other end is a hydrocarbon chain that is very insoluble in water (although it is soluble in oils, fats, and other nonpolar solvents). We call it the hydrophobic end (hates water).

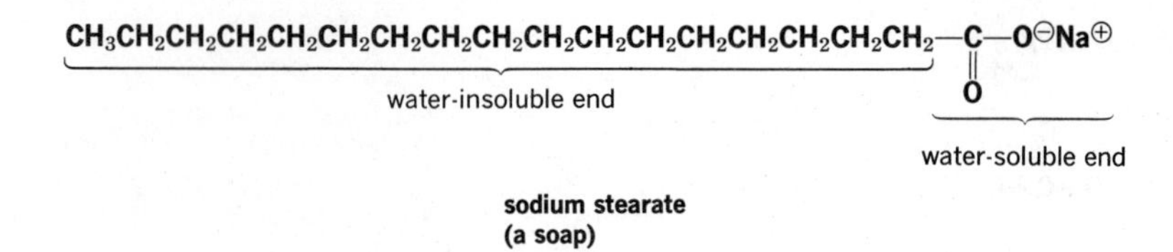

sodium stearate
(a soap)

For simplicity, we shall draw a soap as

The wavy line is the hydrocarbon end, and the dot is the ionic end.

When soap is placed in pure water, suds are formed. Apparently, the soap molecules form aggregates, with the polar ends together and the nonpolar ends jutting out (like the bristles on a circular brush). See Figure 11-2.

Soaps are of value to us because they lower the surface tension of water-insoluble materials, such as oils and fats. Dirt particles in grease and grease itself are then emulsified (i.e., converted into many small globules) by the soap and are conveniently washed away by rinsing with water. See Figure 11-3. As the surface tension is lowered, a smear of grease is converted into globules of grease; the globules are much more easily removed than the smear. Soap helps the globules to remain in that discrete spherical form and keeps them from coming together again and coalescing into large globules.

Sodium soaps are only slightly soluble in water and are called hard soaps. Because it is completely soluble in water, the glycerol can be separated relatively easily from the sodium soap in the saponification process. Thus, sodium soaps contain little or no glycerol. Glycerol, of course, has many commercial uses, as mentioned in Chapter 4.

If one wishes to depress further the solubility of a sodium soap, satu-

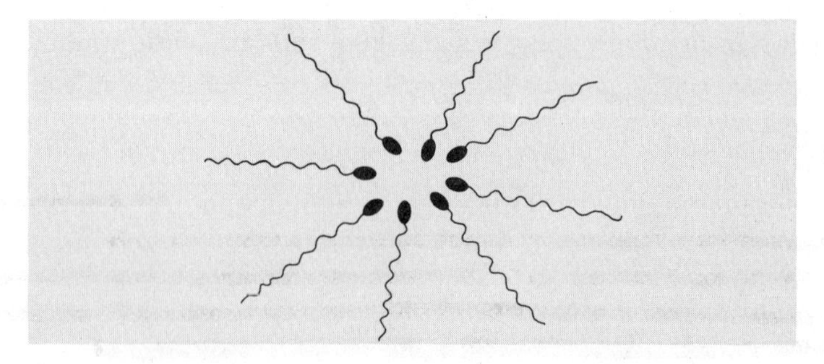

Figure 11-2 Orientation of soap molecules in water to form suds.

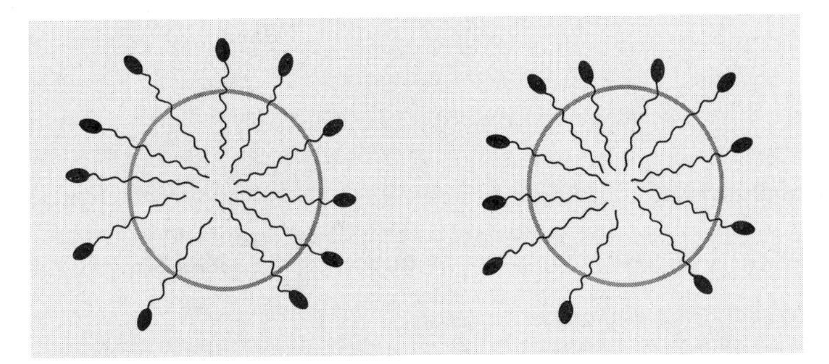

Figure 11-3 Grease particles suspended in water and prevented from coming together. The hydrocarbon tail dissolves in the grease and the ionic end dissolves in the water.

rated salt solution can be added (i.e., salting out process). The salt addition makes the sodium salt of the long-chain fatty acid quite insoluble in water. Thus, a sodium soap *cannot dissolve and will not give suds in strong salt solution.* You may have encountered this phenomenon in trying to produce a lather with a hard soap in ocean water.

The potassium soap is formed when potassium hydroxide is the base used in the saponification process. Potassium soaps are much more soluble in water than sodium soaps and are called soft soaps. Because potassium soaps are quite soluble in water, the glycerol is not easily separated from the soap, and many soft soaps contain a definite amount of glycerol. For example, glycerol is found in many shampoos, shaving creams, and liquid soaps.

Of particular interest is the nature of the water used for soap suds formation. We designate water that contains calcium and magnesium in the form of the bicarbonate temporary hard water.

$Ca(HCO_3)_2$	$Mg(HCO_3)_2$
calcium bicarbonate	magnesium bicarbonate
(soluble in water)	*(soluble in water)*

Heating temporary hard water makes the water soft (i.e., it removes the calcium and magnesium ions from solution).

$$Ca(HCO_3)_2 \xrightarrow{\Delta} CaCO_3\downarrow + CO_2\uparrow + H_2O$$

soluble calcium bicarbonate		calcium carbonate *(insoluble)*	carbon dioxide *(gas)*	water

Permanent hard water usually contains calcium and magnesium sulfates ($CaSO_4$ and $MgSO_4$). The first of these is slightly soluble and the second is very soluble, and both remain *unchanged* in solution, even if the solution is boiled. The calcium and magnesium ions must be removed chemically from permanent hard water to make it soft.

When soap is placed in hard water, that is, water containing calcium and magnesium ions, the insoluble salts of the fatty acids are formed, thus preventing suds formation.

ACTION OF HARD WATER

$2RCOONa$	+	$CaSO_4$	$\longrightarrow$	$(RCOO)_2Ca\downarrow$	$+ Na_2SO_4$
a soap *(somewhat soluble)*		calcium sulfate *(slightly soluble)*		calcium salt of fatty acid *(insoluble)*	

Under these circumstances, the soap must react with the calcium ions until all the calcium ions have been removed from solution in the form of an insoluble calcium salt of a fatty acid. When the water is calcium ion free (i.e., when the water is soft), the soap will form suds. This process, of course, is very wasteful, because the first portion of the soap is used to soften the water and not to produce suds. In launderies and similar places that use much soap, such waste would cost millions of dollars a year if the water were not softened by a cheaper process.

METHODS OF SOFTENING PERMANENT HARD WATER

1. Use of washing soda. Sodium carbonate (Na_2CO_3 or washing soda) is used to precipitate the calcium ion out of solution.

Na_2CO_3	+	$CaSO_4$	$\longrightarrow$	$CaCO_3\downarrow$	+	Na_2SO_4
washing soda *(soluble)*		calcium sulfate *(soluble)*		calcium carbonate *(insoluble)*		sodium sulfate *(soluble)*

The washing soda softens the water by precipitating the calcium in a relatively cheap process. Borax ($Na_2B_4O_7 \cdot 10H_2O$) is also used extensively in water softening because it forms insoluble calcium borate.

2. Use of an agent to form complexes with the calcium ions. The agents are frequently called sequestrants. The complexes may be soluble in water but they can effectively tie up the calcium ion so that *none is available for calcium salt formation with the soap.* Thus, the soap will form suds, and the water has been softened. Various complex phosphates have been used for this purpose; substances such as sodium hexametaphosphate and sodium tetraphosphate are cheap and effective.

Many organic chemicals are effective in holding a metallic ion inactive in solution, and these are called chelates (Greek: *kelos* meaning claw). A familiar chelating agent is Versene. Versene unites with calcium ions to form a soluble calcium complex from which *very, very few* calcium ions are available to interfere with suds formation. We can illustrate the Versene reaction as follows:

$$\begin{matrix} NaO-\overset{O}{\overset{\|}{C}}-CH_2 & & CH_2-\overset{O}{\overset{\|}{C}}-ONa \\ & \diagdown N-CH_2-CH_2-N \diagup & \\ HO-\underset{O}{\underset{\|}{C}}-CH_2 & & CH_2-\underset{O}{\underset{\|}{C}}-OH \end{matrix} \xrightarrow{Ca^{++}} \begin{matrix} NaO-\overset{O}{\overset{\|}{C}}-CH_2 & & CH_2-\overset{O}{\overset{\|}{C}}-ONa \\ & \diagdown N-CH_2-CH_2-N \diagup & \\ \underset{O}{\underset{\|}{C}}-CH_2 & & CH_2-\underset{O}{\underset{\|}{C}} \\ \diagdown O-Ca-O \diagup & & \end{matrix} + 2H^+$$

Versene
(*soluble in water*)

calcium-Versene complex
(*soluble, very stable*)

We see that the calcium ion is now chelated or "tied up" and is not available to destroy the sudsing process. Milk scums and the scum in bathtubs and sinks usually contain insoluble calcium salts; a substance like Versene can dissolve the salts effectively by removing the calcium ion from the precipitates to form the soluble calcium-Versene complex ion. An amazing illustration is the treatment of an eggshell with Versene. When treated with Versene, the shell becomes soft and spongy as the rigid calcium salts dissolve. Versene has proved successful in the preparation of certain bone tissue sections because the calcium salts in the bone slowly dissolve, exposing the noncalcium part of the bone tissue. Versene also finds use in the quick determination of the hardness of water in a rapid, easy titration method.

3. *Use of ion exchangers.* Some insoluble solid chemicals have ions adhering to their surface. When soluble ions are washed over these chemicals, the ions from the insoluble surface may be exchanged with the soluble ions. These useful chemicals are called ion exchangers. A convenient ion exchanger is sodium zeolite.

$NaAlSiO_4$
sodium aluminum silicate
(*sodium zeolite*)

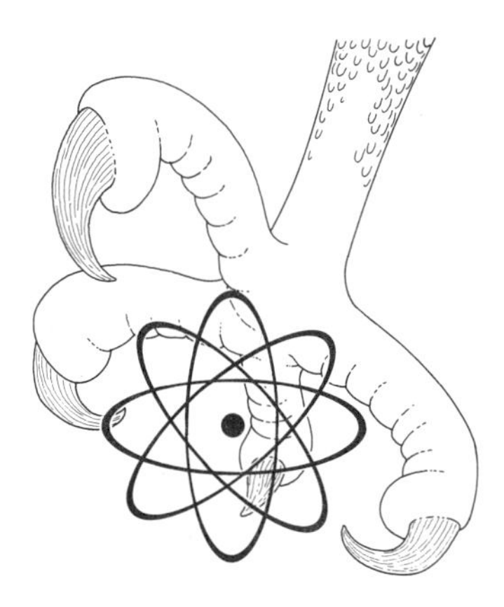

Figure 11-4 Action of a chelate.

If hard water containing calcium ions is passed over solid sodium zeolite, the sodium and calcium ions exchange in the following fashion:

Ca^{++}	+	$2NaAlSiO_4$	$\longrightarrow$	$Ca(AlSiO_4)_2$	+	$2Na^+$
calcium ions in hard water passing over the ion exchanger		ion exchanger having sodium ions on the surface of the insoluble solid		ion exchanger now having calcium ions sticking to the insoluble solid surface		soft water leaving the ion exchanger

As the above equation indicates, the calcium ions are removed, and the water leaving the ion exchanger is softened. The zeolite can be reconditioned by an ion-exchanger process. If a concentrated sodium chloride solution is slowly flushed up through the spent zeolite, the calcium ion is washed out and the sodium ion is put back. This is essentially the reverse process of the softening of water.

$Ca(AlSiO_4)_2$ +	$2NaCl$	$\longrightarrow$	$2NaAlSiO_4$	+ $CaCl_2$
spent zeolite	salt solution		reconditioned zeolite	

In many towns where the water is particularly hard, water entering homes may be passed through a tank containing a sack of this sodium zeolite, which, of course, must regularly be changed and reconditioned.

THE GERMICIDAL PROPERTY OF SOAPS

This is a rather controversial point. Soaps are by no means complete or general germicides; apparently, they are very selective in their action. Soaps may kill certain organisms readily and may not injure others. Certainly, evidence shows that soaps have some germicidal properties. Certain soaps have detoxifying properties. *Sodium ricinoleate,* for example, is effective in detoxifying diphtheria and tetanus toxins, probably by an absorption phenomenon, which is related to the surface-tension-lowering properties of the soap.

Castor oil contains ricinoleic acid that is undoubtedly converted into sodium ricinoleate in the intestines, which are basic (pH, 7–8). Castor oil, then, probably serves a dual function as a laxative and a detoxifier.

Tincture of green soap is used extensively in medicine. It is an alcoholic solution of a potassium soap and combines the germicidal properties of the alcohol and the soap. In addition, the cleansing properties of the soap make this an effective solution. Modern soaps, in many instances, contain special germicidal agents that make the soap effective in destroying most microorganisms.

Detergents

Like soaps, many detergents owe their cleansing properties to the fact that they are anionic (i.e., the negative ion has the sudsing properties). In addition, some detergents may be cationic (i.e., the positive ion has the

Table 11-1 Classification of detergents

anionic detergents	sulfates of long-chain alcohols sulfonates of aromatic compounds miscellaneous sulfates and sulfonates
cationic detergents	quaternary ammonium salts
non-ionic detergents	certain polyethers

sudsing properties) or non-ionic (i.e., the detergent does not ionize). See Table 11-1. Cationic and anionic cleansing agents are not compatible because they combine to form an insoluble precipitate.

Detergents, like soaps, owe their efficiency to their ability to lower the surface tension of water-insoluble materials. Because the chemist can greatly modify the detergent structure, a great variety of detergents are available today, each one with some special property. In addition, the hardness of the water does not seriously affect the sudsing and cleansing properties of the detergents.

ANIONIC DETERGENTS

1. Sulfates of fatty alcohols. ($ROSO_2ONa$), where R is at least 12 carbons. An important example of this type of detergent is lauryl alcohol, which may be obtained from cocoanut oil:

$$C_{12}H_{25}OSO_2ONa$$
sodium lauryl sulfate

2. Sulfonate of aromatic hydrocarbons. This type has an interesting history. Propylene was polymerized to form a tetramer.

$$4C_3H_6 \xrightarrow{\text{polymerize}} C_{12}H_{24}$$

The $C_{12}H_{24}$ has one double bond and, of course, is a nonlinear molecule. The tetramer was condensed with benzene to form an alkyl derivative of benzene:

$$C_6H_5\text{-}H + C_{12}H_{24} \xrightarrow{\text{condense}} C_6H_5\text{-}C_{12}H_{25}$$

The derivative was sulfonated by sulfuric acid,

$$C_6H_5\text{-}C_{12}H_{25} + H_2SO_4 \longrightarrow C_{12}H_{25}\text{-}C_6H_4\text{-}SO_2OH$$

and the product was converted into its sodium salt.

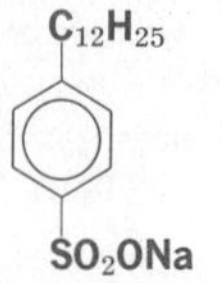

$$C_{12}H_{25}-C_6H_4-SO_2ONa$$

Sodium dodecyl benzene sulfonate

(Remember, this is not a normal dodecyl, but a branched-chain dodecyl.) This was, at one time, the most widely used detergent. However, it was noted that the water-treatment plants had mountains of suds, and nearby streams likewise had a surprisingly large head of suds. These unpleasant sights were caused by the difficulty encountered by microorganisms involved in water-treatment plants. The microorganisms could not easily chemically degrade the detergents because of the branched side chain attached to the benzene ring. We say that the detergent was not readily biodegradable.

Many objections to this detergent were raised, and laws were passed outlawing its use. As a result, this detergent is now made *using a straight-chain dodecyl group* (derived from a fatty acid), and detergents of this type *can be* chemically degraded by microorganisms without much difficulty.

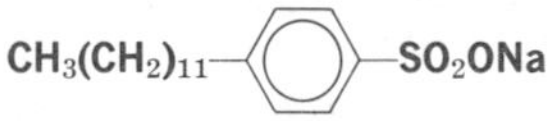

$$CH_3(CH_2)_{11}-C_6H_4-SO_2ONa$$

sodium *n*-dodecyl benzene sulfonate
currently used in great quantity as a detergent
called *LAS* (*linear alkylate sulfonate*) and *biodegradable*

3. *Miscellaneous sulfate and sulfonate.* Many different kinds exist: for example, alkyl sulfonate, sulfated esters, sulfate amides, and sulfonate amides. They are unstable in acidic or basic mediums but are particularly unaffected by hard water.

CATIONIC DETERGENTS

These detergents are called invert soaps, because their sudsing properties reside in the positive and not the negative ion as in soaps.

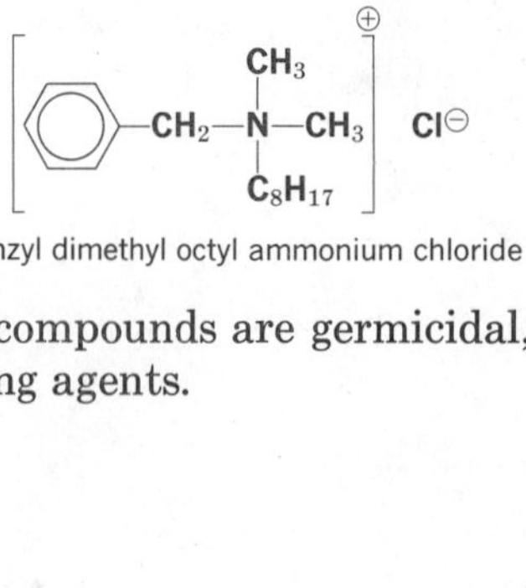

$$\left[C_6H_5-CH_2-N(CH_3)_2(C_8H_{17})\right]^{\oplus} Cl^{\ominus}$$

benzyl dimethyl octyl ammonium chloride

These compounds are germicidal, unaffected by hard water, and also good cleansing agents.

NON-IONIC DETERGENTS

These are modified ethers and possess excellent soil removal and grease emulsification properties accompanied by low foam. An example is

$$R{-}(O{-}C_2H_4)_n{-}OH$$

where R is phenyl, ethyl, or a similar group.

Hydrogenation of oils

If a glyceride contains several double bonds in the fatty acid parts, it is probably a liquid at room temperature, and we classify it as an oil or liquid fat. Hydrogenation is the addition of hydrogen, in the presence of a catalyst, to a double bond, thus converting the double bond into a single bond. By the hydrogenation process, the double bonds of an unsaturated glyceride can be removed one at a time and the melting point of the lipid raised. Thus, a liquid fat can be converted into a solid fat.

$$\begin{array}{l} CH_2{-}O{-}\overset{\overset{\large O}{\|}}{C}{-}(CH_2)_7CH{=}CH{-}(CH_2)_7CH_3 \\ | \\ CH{-}O{-}\overset{\overset{\large O}{\|}}{C}{-}(CH_2)_7CH{=}CH{-}(CH_2)_7CH_3 \\ | \\ CH_2{-}O{-}\overset{\overset{\large O}{\|}}{C}{-}(CH_2)_7CH{=}CH{-}(CH_2)_7CH_3 \end{array} \xrightarrow[\text{catalyst}]{3H_2} \begin{array}{l} CH_2{-}O{-}\overset{\overset{\large O}{\|}}{C}{-}(CH_2)_7CH_2{-}CH_2{-}(CH_2)_7CH_3 \\ | \\ CH{-}O{-}\overset{\overset{\large O}{\|}}{C}{-}(CH_2)_7CH_2{-}CH_2{-}(CH_2)_7CH_3 \\ | \\ CH_2{-}O{-}\overset{\overset{\large O}{\|}}{C}{-}(CH_2)_7CH_2{-}CH_2{-}(CH_2)_7CH_3 \end{array}$$

glyceryl trioleate (an oil) — glyceryl tristearate (a solid fat)

Lard is rendered hog's fat and is a cheap, useful product in cooking. Because lard comes from living sources, its composition varies. Hydrogenated oils are products produced industrially to imitate lard, and, because the reaction is controlled by the chemist, it may be stopped at any stage of the reduction.

Commercially, liquid unsaturated fat is introduced into a huge sealed vat, and hydrogen gas is introduced into the oil under pressure and in the presence of a catalyst, usually nickel. The mixture is stirred. As the reaction proceeds, the melting point rises and the mixture gets thicker. The increase in viscosity is a good clue to the extent of the reduction and when the reaction should be stopped. In this way, a product of consistent quality may be produced.

If all the double bonds were reduced, the final product would be too high in melting point and too brittle. In practice, a few double bonds are left to make the product soft and pliable. Crisco and Spry are hydrogenated oils commonly found in stores.

In recent times, reports have stated that the use of *unsaturated liquid lipids* in cooking may lessen the chance of a coronary attack, and, thus, there has been an increase in the use of liquid fats in cooking.

Test for Oils and Fats

Glycerol is a substance common to all oils and fats. Because it has three —OH groups, the molecule is sensitive to oxidation and heat. The body can effectively oxidize it to produce energy. When glycerol is heated, it loses two molecules of water to form acrolein or acrylaldehyde.

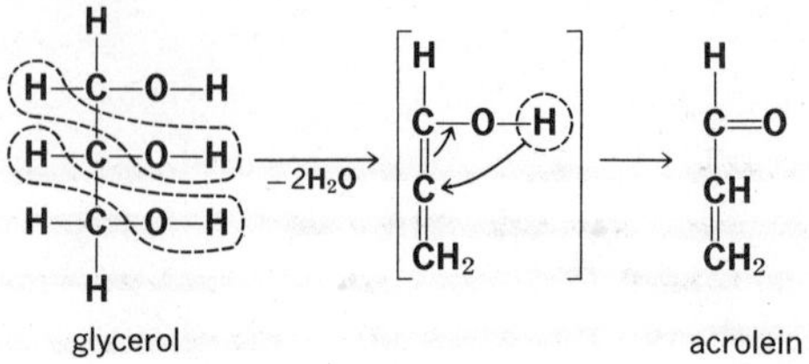

$$\underset{\text{glycerol}}{\text{H—C(H)(OH)—C(H)(OH)—C(H)(OH)—H}} \xrightarrow{-2H_2O} \left[\text{H—C—O—H} \;\; \text{C} \;\; \text{CH}_2\right] \longrightarrow \underset{\text{acrolein}}{\text{H—C=O, CH=CH}_2}$$

In the presence of any mild dehydrating agent, such as potassium acid sulfate $KHSO_4$, the dehydrating process proceeds at a lower temperature. One is aware of acrolein because of its sharp, biting odor. Whenever fat is cooked at too high a temperature, (e.g., frying bacon too hot or overcooking pork), the decomposition of the glycerol is evident from the development of the acrolein odor. Because all oils and fats contain glycerol, this is a convenient test for the presence of these compounds.

Occurrence of Oils and Fats

The glycerides in plants are liquids. The glycerides found in animals are, however, mostly low-melting solids or solids of such a melting point as to be half solid and half liquid at body temperature. As indicated before, the melting point of fat depends, among other things, on the length of the fatty acid. Lard (hog fat) melts at 28°C; beef fat melts at 46°C; and sheep fat melts at 51°C. Of course, the melting point of fat varies in the different parts of the body. Fats must be free flowing in muscle and regions of activity, or muscle action and motion will be impeded.

The glycerides near an important active site, such as heart muscle, have a lower melting point than other glycerides, which, for example, are used as body insulating fat or protective fat. Some correlation exists between the deposition of fat in active body centers and the degree of unsaturation of the fatty acids in the fat. Activity and unsaturation seem to go hand in hand. This is true because the unsaturated glycerides are more chemically active, are more easily oxidized, and can enter more readily into metabolic reactions.

Diet has some influence on the type of fat deposited in the body. For example, when hogs are fed large quantities of feed containing liquid glycerides, the hog fat becomes soft, and the melting point of the deposited glycerides is definitely lowered.

MILK AND RELATED PRODUCTS

Milk is one of the most important foods in the human diet because it has many components essential to growth and well being. Table 11-2 gives the average composition of milk.

Mammalian milk will settle out and form two layers. The top layer is the *cream.* It is difficult to purchase such milk (cream-top) in a store these days, since most milk is homogenized. *Homogenized milk* is a milk product mechanically treated to alter its physical properties with reference to the appearance of the fat globules. In part, the United States Public Health Service defines homogenized milk as milk treated to ensure breakup of the fat globules to the extent that, after 48 hours of storage, no visible cream separation occurs. When milk is homogenized, the fat particles are broken up, and the milk is forced under high pressure (i.e., pressure of 2,000 to 4,000 pounds per square inch) through a very small orifice. In the process, the milk fat globules are reduced to the diameter of the orifice, and the very small fat particles no longer form a separate cream layer but remain dispersed.

Cream (or *sweet cream*) is the portion of milk, rich in butterfat, that is separated from the milk by centrifugal force, or that rises to the surface on standing.

The Food and Drug Administration defines cream as the butterfat portion of the milk that contains *at least 18% butterfat.*

Light cream (table cream or coffee or tea cream) must contain at least 18% and not more than 30% butterfat. This may be homogenized cream, which does not whip easily. *Light whipping cream* must contain not less than 30% nor more than 36% butterfat. This type of cream is usually not homogenized and whips readily. *Heavy whipping cream* must contain at least 36% butterfat and, on occasion, may contain as much as 50% butterfat.

A typical light cream contains about 20.00% fat, 3.0% protein, 4.0% lactose, 0.6% ash, and about 72% water. Physically, cream is a suspension of fat particles in water. *Half and half* is a mixture of about 50% cream and 50% milk and, as such, has about 12% fat.

Skim milk is defined as milk from which a sufficient portion of the fat has been removed so that the fat content is below 3.25%. Since many people are "calorie conscious," it is possible to buy "milk" with 2% fat and

Table 11-2 Average composition of milk

CONSTITUENT	%	CONSTITUENT	%
water	87.3	albumin	0.6
fat	3.7	lactose	4.8
casein	2.9	ash (minerals)	0.7

less. *In practice,* skim milk has almost all the fat removed, and a typical analysis would show 0.2% fat, 3.5% protein, 5.0% lactose. 0.8% ash, and 90.5% water.

Butter must contain not less than 80% butterfat. When cream is churned, the fat globules coalesce and form progressively larger globules. The globules finally get large enough to form a large, visible, insoluble mass called butter. Whereas cream is a colloidal dispersion of fat particles in water, butter has the inverted system of water particles suspended in fat. A typical creamery butter analysis might show 81% fat, 1% protein, 2.4% salt, and 15.6% water. A typical analysis for fatty acids in butter might show

oleic acid	38%
palmitic acid	26%
stearic acid	10%
myristic acid	8%
lauric acid	4%
linoleic acid	4%
capric acid	3%
butyric acid	3%

and small quantities of caproic, caprylic, and other acids

Margarine is a product, analogous to butter, prepared by churning and blending the lipids mostly from *plant origin.* The precipitated lipid is identical to butter except that it lacks vitamins and has little color. When the proper vitamins are added, margarine is of comparable nutritional value.

Buttermilk is the liquid left when the butter precipitates out during the churning process. A typical chemical analysis shows 0.5% fat, 3% protein, 5% lactose, 0.7% ash, and 90.8% water. As you can see, buttermilk is low in fat because almost all the fat has been precipitated in the butter. If you compare the composition of buttermilk with that of skim milk, you see that they are almost identical: They are both low in fat. For every 100 pounds of butter produced, 166 pounds of buttermilk are obtained. Most *genuine buttermilk* is *not* used for human consumption. Most of the buttermilk available for food purposes is known as *cultured buttermilk,* which is made by souring pasteurized or partly skimmed milk.

Cheese is the food product made by precipitating proteins from milk. The coagulation may be accomplished by various means, such as enzyme action or fermentation. The cheese or curd may be "modified" by heat, pressure, additional fermentation, molds, etc. There are hundreds of cheeses, and these vary considerably in lipid content, depending on their source.

A typical *"American" cheddar cheese* is made from whole milk. As the curd coagulates, it brings down with it the lipid that may be present (cheddar analysis: 37% water, 33% fat, 24% protein, and 6% ash.)

A *cottage cheese* is prepared from skimmed milk. As the protein is curdled, there is little fat to be dragged down (cottage cheese analysis: 70% water, 1.0% fat, 25% protein, and 21% ash). For this reason, calorie watchers have long favored this type of cheese.

A *cream cheese* may be prepared by whole milk greatly *enriched* with cream. In the coagulation process such a cheese would drag down most of the fat present (cream cheese analysis: 43% water, 40% fat, 14% proteins, and 3% ash). Because the particles of cream cheese are very fine, it is very digestible. Thus, cream cheese is the most fattening of the cheeses.

Cheeses may be hard or soft, with or without gas holes, ripened by molds or bacteria, etc.

Whey is the liquid left after the cheese has been coagulated. From every 100 pounds of milk used in the manufacture of cheddar cheese, we obtain 10 pounds of cheese and 90 pounds of whey. Characteristically, whey contains very little protein and little fat (typical analysis: 93% water, 0.3% fat, 1.0% protein, 5% lactose, and 0.7% ash). A number of products may be prepared from whey, and it is the principal commercial source of lactose.

Classification of Vegetable Oils

From Table 11-3 we see that the drying oils contain the greatest amount of unsaturation. Usually, the more unsaturated an oil is, the better drying oil it is (there are exceptions). The greater the unsaturation, the

Table 11-3 Classification of vegetable oils

CLASSIFICATION	EXAMPLES
Nondrying oils containing large quantities of oleic acid	palm oil cocoanut oil olive oil peanut oil date oil rice oil
Semidrying oils containing mainly oleic and linoleic acids	corn oil cottonseed oil wheat oil sesame oil Brazil nut oil soybean oil rapeseed oil
Drying oils containing mainly linoleic and linolenic acids	linseed oil tung oil poppyseed oil hempseed oil walnut oil sunflower oil

greater the *tendency* for the oil to absorb oxygen from the air and to polymerize to a hard, stable, insoluble film. Drying oils are valuable in the paint and varnish industry.

Some paints contain a mixture of drying oils and pigments, and some varnishes contain a mixture of drying oils and resins. When a paint or varnish containing a drying oil is exposed to the air, oxygen is absorbed by the drying oil, and, in a complex series of reactions, the molecules react to form huge molecules. In this way, the drying oil becomes a hard and brittle film and is therefore a convenient way of coating and protecting surfaces.

Oil cloth is woven canvas coated with linseed oil. Linoleum is made by cementing cork particles with thickened linseed oil and resin.

Drying oils are usually obtained by squeezing the oils from the seeds or by extracting the oils by means of fat solvents. Because the drying of an oil is an exothermic process (i.e., heat is evolved), spontaneous combustion can occur. An oily (polyunsaturated lipid) rag slowly absorbs oxygen from the air in the drying process and gives off heat. If ventilation is poor, the heat formed increases the temperature of the oil until it is hot enough to spontaneously catch fire. For this reason, clothes and rags wet with linseed oil should never be sealed in closets or kept in drawers.

Rancidity

Rancidity occurs when a lipid becomes unpleasant in odor and taste. We recognize two types of rancidity: hydrolytic and oxidative.

Hydrolytic rancidity occurs when the lipid is hydrolyzed to glycerol and the free fatty acids. This will be objectionable *only* when the free fatty acid possesses an unpleasant odor. In other words, the bad effect is limited to the small carbon-containing fatty acids, which, as mentioned before, are extremely unpleasant in aroma. Hydrolytic rancidity presents a problem of great importance in the dairy industry, because dairy products, such as milk, cream, and butter, contain lipids that have appreciable quantities of butyric and other acids with objectionable aromas.

In the normal digestive process, an enzyme, lipase, converts the lipid into the free fatty acid and glycerol. Traces of any lipase, of course, would greatly accelerate the hydrolytic rancidity process. If we had a lipid such as glyceryl stearate, hydrolysis would not produce any unpleasant aroma, because glycerol and stearic acid do not possess any strong aromas.

Oxidative rancidity is the formation of unpleasant aromas due to an oxidation reaction and may occur with any unsaturated lipid. It is a very complex reaction, which is not perfectly understood, but it is similar in many respects to the drying of an oil. The key reaction is the absorption of oxygen at the allylic position to form a hydroperoxide. (The allylic carbon is the carbon next to the double-bond carbon. The allylic position is an active spot.)

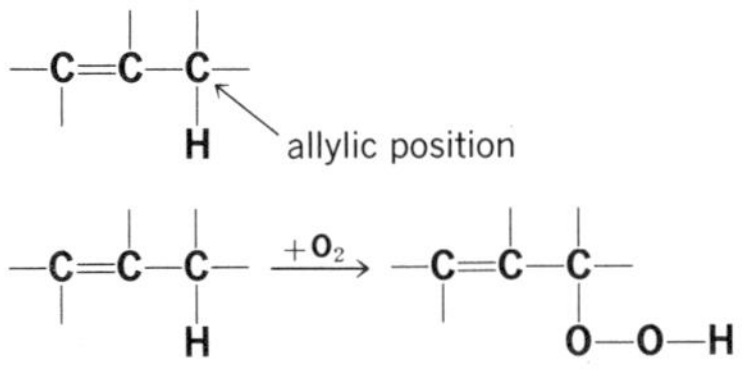

```
     |   |
 —C=C—C—
  |     |↖
        H  allylic position

     |   |                 |   |
 —C=C—C—  —+O₂→  —C=C—C—
  |     |           |     |
        H                 O—O—H
                   a hydroperoxide
```

When two or more double bonds exist (e.g., linoleic, linolenic, etc.), they may shift to become conjugated, which then causes the molecule to undergo 1,4-butadiene-type polymerization. In addition, substituted ethylene oxide groups may be formed, glycols may be formed, and one molecule may become attached to another, which may become attached to another, etc., until the final molecules are giant in size and very insoluble. Such a sequence of reactions may be involved in the drying of an oil.

In oxidative rancidity, many of the preceding reactions occur. In addition, the acids break at or near the double bonds to form fragment acids, much smaller in size. These smaller acids may have objectionable aromas.

For example, suppose a C_{12} acid (containing one double bond) is one of the acids attached to glycerol. Such an acid would not be objectionable in aroma. If this acid cleaved, by oxidative rancidity, to form a C_6 acid, then an objectionable odor would be present.

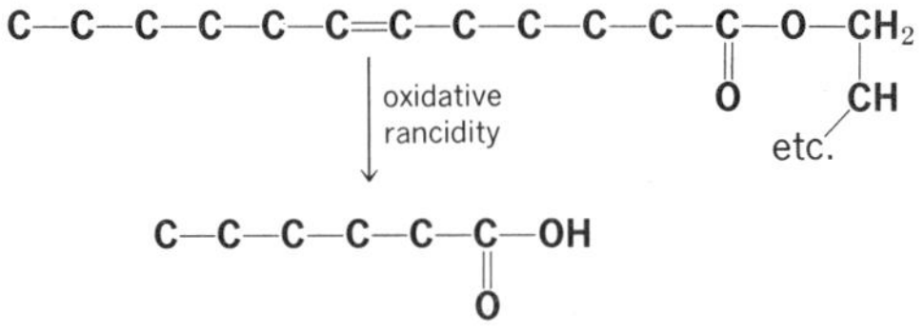

```
C—C—C—C—C—C=C—C—C—C—C—C—O—CH₂
                        ‖      |
        | oxidative     O      CH
        | rancidity       etc./
        ↓
    C—C—C—C—C—C—OH
              ‖
              O

    caproic acid
    (objectionable aroma)
```

In the food industry, where unsaturated lipids are present in many of the foods, oxidative rancidity is a problem of great concern. If it occurred, we would not want to eat the food and would call it "spoiled."

Oxygen, of course, is necessary for the oxidative process, and the reaction is also catalyzed by moisture, light, heat, and traces of metals. The presence of an antioxidant prevents this type of rancidity and protects the lipid from oxidation. An efficient antioxidant would have to be more easily oxidized than the oils. Various synthetic and natural antioxidants are used in industrial processes. Read the labels on food packages and see how many antioxidants are present in our foodstuffs to keep the food from spoiling.

TESTS FOR RANCIDITY

The best test for rancidity is the Kreis test. One milliliter of HCl (specific gravity 1.19) is added to 1 ml of the suspected oil in a large test tube. The tube is closed with a rubber stopper and shaken vigorously for 30 seconds. Then, 1 ml of 0.1% solution of phloroglucinol in ether is added, and the tube is closed again and shaken.

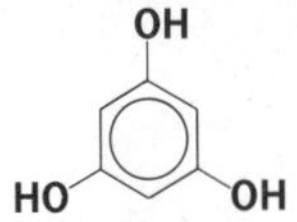

OH

HO OH

phloroglucinol

A red or pink color in the acid layer denotes rancidity. The Kreis test is not infallible, but it is reasonably accurate. A positive test means that epihydrin aldehyde was formed in an oxidative process from glycerol.

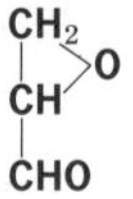

CH_2
$>O$
CH
|
CHO

epihydrin aldehyde

Another test for oxidative rancidity is to mix the suspected oil with a potassium iodide, KI, solution and titrate the liberated iodine with sodium thiosulfate $Na_2S_2O_3$. The greater the amount of oxygen absorbed, the greater the amount of iodine liberated and the more sodium thiosulfate necessary in the titration process.

Chemical Constants

Many times the chemical and physical properties of lipids can be expressed in terms of certain constants, which immediately tell us something about the lipid in question. A few of these constants are indicated below.

ACID VALUE

The acid value is a number that indicates the amount of free acid present in the lipid. It is the number of milligrams of potassium hydroxide KOH required to neutralize the free fatty acid in 1 gram of the lipid tested. Acid value is particularly useful in determining the extent of hydrolytic rancidity.

SAPONIFICATION NUMBER

The saponification number tells us something about the molecular weight of the fatty acid in the lipid. It is the number of milligrams of KOH required to saponify 1 gram of oil or fat. The higher the saponification number, the lower the molecular weight.

Unsaponifiable matter, as the name implies, is the lipid material that resists hydrolysis with a base. The most important of these are the sterols.

The volatile fatty acids are those acids that can be separated from the hydrolyzed fat or oil by steam distillation. The volatile fatty acids are those from butyric to lauric. Butyric acid is of interest because of its occurrence in butter fat.

ACETYL NUMBER

The *acetyl number* is defined as the number of milligrams of KOH required to neutralize the acetic acid obtained by saponifying 1 gram of acetylated fat. The determination is a measure of the free —OH groups present in the lipid. Castor oil, for example, which contains a high percentage of the hydroxy acid ricinoleic acid, has a high acetyl number.

IODINE NUMBER

The *iodine number* is the number of grams of iodine absorbed by 100 grams of lipid. It is a good measure of the degree of unsaturation of the fatty acids. Actually, free iodine does not react with double bonds; therefore, iodine bromide IBr or iodine chloride ICl, is more conveniently used.

Iodized acids, oils, and fats are useful contrast media in roentgenography (see Figure 11-5).

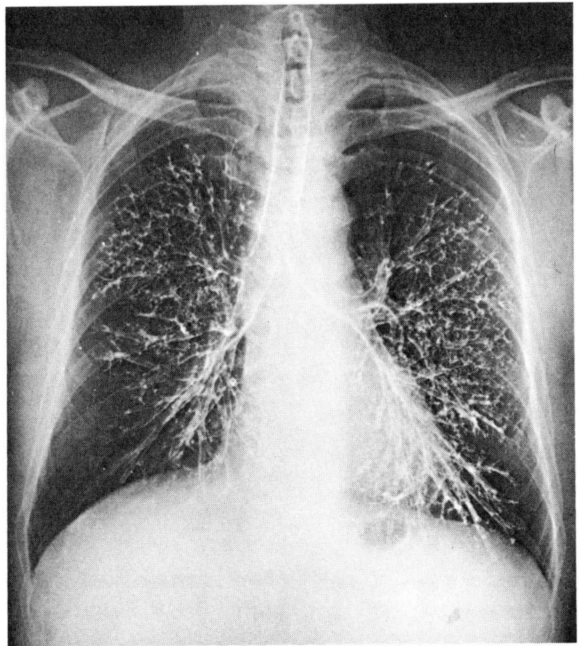

John G. Maurer, Loyola University

Figure 11-5 X ray showing iodized material, Lipiodol (iodized poppy seed oil) has been used (by spraying into the breathing system) as a contrast medium in roentgenology.

Calcium iodobehenate, $(C_{21}H_{42}ICOO)_2Ca$, containing 23.5% iodine; iodostarine ($C_{18}H_{32}O_2I_2$), containing 47.5% iodine; Oridine, (calcium salt of iodized fatty acids from cottonseed oil and containing about 24% iodine); and calcium iodostearate $(CH_3(CH_2)_7CHI(CH_2)_8COO)_2Ca$, containing about 27% iodine, can be administered in tablet form.

Iodized poppy-seed oil (lipiodol), containing either 40% or 10.5% iodine; ethyl iodobrassidate $C_{21}H_{39}I_2COOC_2H_5$, containing 41% iodine; and Riodine, which is iodized castor oil containing about 17% iodine, are useful iodized esters.

If, for example, a bronchiectasis is suspected, lipiodol can be sprayed into the lungs, and subsequent flouroscopy and x-ray pictures can tell if the lung passages are open and normal. Other iodides are useful. Urokon Sodium, a substance of low toxicity, is opaque to x rays. When injected intravenously, it is excreted by the kidneys, giving the diagnostician a clear picture of the urinary system on an x-ray film.

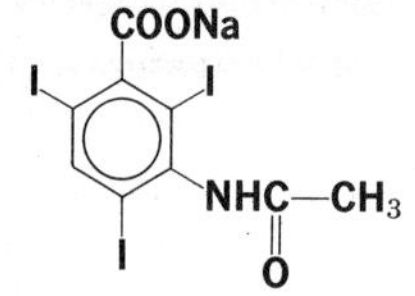

COONa, I, I, NHC—CH$_3$, I, O

Urokon Sodium

Waxes

The waxes are esters, but, unlike fats and oils, they are usually esters of long-chain alcohols and long-chain acids. Occasionally an alcohol with two —OH groups is encountered, but this is not the usual case. Table 11-4 lists some of the commonly met alcohols.

Some of the commonly met acids are

myristic	$C_{13}H_{27}COOH$
palmitic	$C_{15}H_{31}COOH$
carnaubic	$C_{23}H_{47}COOH$
cerotic	$C_{25}H_{51}COOH$
melissic	$C_{29}H_{59}COOH$

Some typical formulas and names of waxes are

lauryl myristate	$C_{13}H_{27}COOC_{12}H_{25}$
cetyl palmitate	$C_{15}H_{31}COOC_{16}H_{33}$
carnaubyl carnaubate	$C_{23}H_{47}COOC_{24}H_{49}$
myricyl melissate	$C_{29}H_{59}COOC_{30}H_{61}$

Waxes are very insoluble in water, are usually quite unreactive chemically, and are often soft and pliable. Waxes are, therefore, excellent protective agents. They are found on surfaces of feathers and hair and help keep them soft and pliable. Because they are very insoluble in water, waxes

Table 11-4 Commonly met alcohols

ALCOHOL	FORMULA	OCCURRENCE
lauryl alcohol	$C_{12}H_{25}OH$	cuticle wax of Cascara sagrada
myristyl alcohol	$C_{14}H_{29}OH$	sperm head oil
cetyl alcohol	$C_{16}H_{33}OH$	spermaceti
stearyl alcohol	$C_{18}H_{37}OH$	spermaceti
carnaubyl alcohol	$C_{24}H_{49}OH$	wool fat
ceryl alcohol	$C_{26}H_{53}OH$	beeswax, cuticle wax, wool fat
myricyl alcohol	$C_{30}H_{61}OH$	carnauba wax, beeswax, sugar cane wax
incarnatyl alcohol	$C_{34}H_{69}OH$	beeswax

are not wetted and help animals to swim and live in the water. Wax coatings on fruits protect them from moisture loss and from foreign organism invasion. In humans, the sebaceous glands secrete a wax that is an ester of cholesterol, which keeps the skin soft and pliable.

Spermaceti is a wax found in the head of the sperm whale and is mostly cetyl palmitate. This wax is used in making candles. Beeswax is mostly myricyl palmitate, but many other waxes are also found in beeswax. Carnauba wax, found in the carnauba palm of Brazil, is used to make varnishes and other protective agents. Wool wax (lanolin) is obtained from wool and is found in many ointments, salves, and creams used on the skin. Lanolin approximates the natural skin wax.

Compound lipids

Phospholipids or *phosphotides* are found in every living cell. We shall concern ourselves with three types.

1. The cephalins. The cephalins contain the base β-hydroxyethylamine.

$CH_3CH_2NH_2$
ethylamine

$HO—CH_2CH_2NH_2$
β-hydroxyethylamine

2. The lecithins. The lecithins contain the base choline, which is a quaternary ammonium salt.

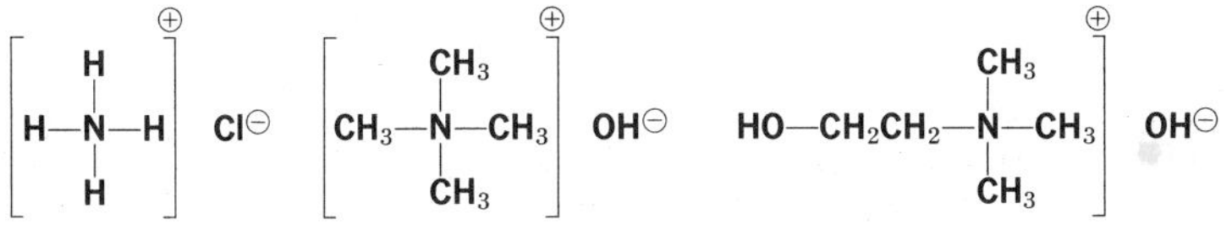

$$\left[\begin{array}{c} H \\ | \\ H—N—H \\ | \\ H \end{array}\right]^{\oplus} Cl^{\ominus} \qquad \left[\begin{array}{c} CH_3 \\ | \\ CH_3—N—CH_3 \\ | \\ CH_3 \end{array}\right]^{\oplus} OH^{\ominus} \qquad \left[\begin{array}{c} \qquad\qquad\qquad CH_3 \\ \qquad\qquad\qquad | \\ HO—CH_2CH_2—N—CH_3 \\ \qquad\qquad\qquad | \\ \qquad\qquad\qquad CH_3 \end{array}\right]^{\oplus} OH^{\ominus}$$

ammonium chloride

tetramethylammonium hydroxide

β-hydroxyethyltrimethylammonium hydroxide (*choline*)

3. *The sphingomyelins.* The sphingomyelins are distinguished from lecithins and cephalins by the absence of glycerol in the molecule. In sphingomyelins, the glycerol has been replaced by sphingosinol.

```
CH3—(CH2)12—CH=CH—CH—CH—CH2
                   |   |   |
                   HO  NH2 OH
```

sphingosinol

In cephalins and lecithins, the nitrogen and phosphorus ratio is 1:1, whereas in sphingomyelins, the ratio is 2:1.

We distinguish between α- and β-forms of compound lipids depending on where the phosphoric acid group is attached.

```
          O
          ||
CH2—O—C—R
|         O
|         ||
CH—O——C—R
|         O
|         ||
CH2—O—P—O—CH2CH2NH2
          |
          OH
```

an α-cephalin

```
          O
          ||
CH2—O—C—R
|         O
|         ||
CH—O——P—O—CH2CH2NH2
|         |
|         OH
|         O
|         ||
CH2—O—C—R
```

a β-cephalin

```
          O
          ||
CH2—O—C—R
|         O
|         ||
CH—O——C—R                     ⊕
|         O             CH3   ┐
|         ||            |     |
CH2—O—P—O—CH2CH2N—CH3 |  OH⊖
          |             |     |
          OH            CH3   ┘
```

an α-lecithin

```
          O
          ||
CH2—O—C—R                        ⊕
|         O             CH3      ┐
|         ||            |        |
CH—O——P—O—CH2CH2N—CH3 |  OH⊖
|         |             |        |
|         OH            CH3      ┘
|         O
|         ||
CH2—O—C—R
```

a β-lecithin

In nature, the α- and β-forms occur together. It is reported that egg lecithin occurs predominately in the β-form, whereas liver lecithin contains about 50% α- and 50% β-lecithin. Brain lecithin and brain cephalin occur mostly in the α-form. It is usually an easy task to separate the lipids of a naturally occurring substance (after it has been dried) from the carbohydrate and protein parts by a simple ether extraction. However, to separate the simple lipids from the compounds lipids, and then to completely separate the various members of each group, presents an almost impossible task.

Lecithins

The lecithins are the best-known examples of phospholipids. It has been shown that lecithin contains saturated as well as unsaturated fatty acids. The unsaturated fatty acids are extremely important from the standpoint of health and normal metabolism. More will be said on this subject in Chapter 18. For example, it has been reported that the phospholipid fatty acids from the serum of eczematous infants seem to be less unsaturated than those from normal infants.

Lecithin is a clear, waxlike material, which turns yellow quickly on exposure to air. Lecithin is easily hydrolyzed into various fragments, and it is possible to selectively hydrolyze various portions of the molecule.

Of particular interest is the action of the enzyme lecithinase-A to form a lysolecithin, which is illustrated as follows:

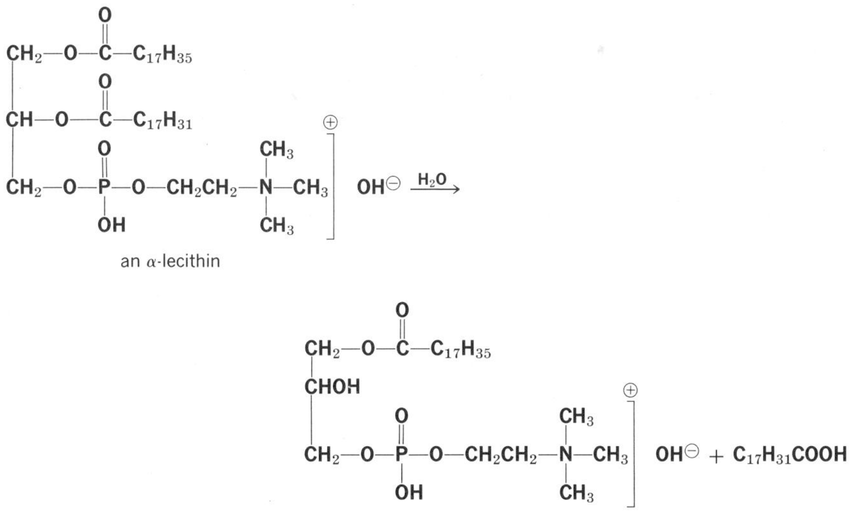

$$\left[\begin{array}{l} CH_2{-}O{-}\overset{\overset{O}{\|}}{C}{-}C_{17}H_{35} \\ | \\ CH{-}O{-}\overset{\overset{O}{\|}}{C}{-}C_{17}H_{31} \\ | \\ CH_2{-}O{-}\underset{\underset{OH}{|}}{\overset{\overset{O}{\|}}{P}}{-}O{-}CH_2CH_2{-}\underset{\underset{CH_3}{|}}{\overset{\overset{CH_3}{|}}{N}}{-}CH_3 \end{array}\right]^{\oplus} OH^{\ominus} \xrightarrow{H_2O}$$

an α-lecithin

$$\left[\begin{array}{l} CH_2{-}O{-}\overset{\overset{O}{\|}}{C}{-}C_{17}H_{35} \\ | \\ CHOH \\ | \\ CH_2{-}O{-}\underset{\underset{OH}{|}}{\overset{\overset{O}{\|}}{P}}{-}O{-}CH_2CH_2{-}\underset{\underset{CH_3}{|}}{\overset{\overset{CH_3}{|}}{N}}{-}CH_3 \end{array}\right]^{\oplus} OH^{\ominus} + C_{17}H_{31}COOH$$

a lysolecithin

action of Lecithinase-A

A lysolecithin is an active hemolytic agent. It acts on isolated muscle and causes, among other effects, contractures, fibrillations, increased inhibition of water, loss of potassium ion, and excitability. Lysolecithin also attacks the capillary endothelium and causes hemorrhage of the lungs.

Snake venom is a mixture, chiefly of proteins, varying in composition from species to species, and over 300 species are distributed throughout the world. The amount of venom ejected by a snake may be a few drops or as much as two cubic centimeters in a single strike.

Many snake venoms contain lecithinase-A. Another common toxic principle has a powerful effect on nerve tissue and produces a curare-like effect as well as paralysis. Also present in snake venom may be principles capable of coagulating blood. This is why a person who has been bitten on the hand, for example, may spit up blood from ruptured capillaries in the lungs, become paralyzed, and die of blood coagulation.

Antivenin is a specially prepared horse serum, which is the only specific treatment for poisonous snake bite. Prompt injection of sufficient antivenin prevents death in most patients and relieves pain and other local and general symptoms.

Commercially, lecithin is conveniently prepared from soybeans. Some of the fatty acids isolated from soybean lecithin are stearic, palmitic, oleic, linoleic, and linolenic acids. Lecithin has important commercial uses due in part to the excellent emulsifying properties of this phospholipid. Large amounts of lecithin are used in the manufacture of chocolate candies, cookies and cakes, and oleomargarine.

THE CHOLINE PART

Choline, by itself, is a very strong base, comparable to sodium hydroxide. Choline and its related compounds are very important both physiologically and pharmacologically.

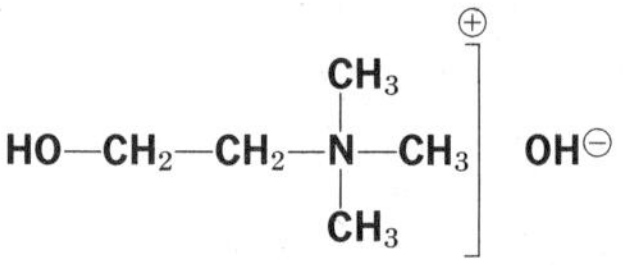

$$\left[HO{-}CH_2{-}CH_2{-}\overset{\displaystyle CH_3}{\underset{\displaystyle CH_3}{N}}{-}CH_3\right]^{\oplus} OH^{\ominus}$$

choline

$$\left[CH_3{-}\overset{\displaystyle O}{\overset{\|}{C}}{-}O{-}CH_2{-}CH_2{-}\overset{\displaystyle CH_3}{\underset{\displaystyle CH_3}{N}}{-}CH_3\right]^{\oplus} OH^{\ominus}$$

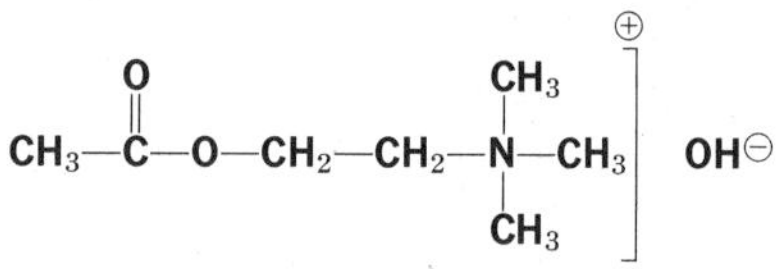

acetylcholine

Choline is important because of its participation in vital body processes, and also from a nutritional point of view. It has been classified as one of the B vitamins, because, if eliminated from the diet of rats, chickens, and dogs, and if certain other precursors are also eliminated, pathological conditions such as fatty livers and hemorrhage of the kidney may occur.

Choline is a vasodepressor agent. Acetylcholine, which is the acetate ester of choline, is 100,000 times more powerful than choline in causing a fall in blood pressure. Acetylcholine is involved in the stimulation of organs by nerves. In the parasympathetic nervous system, the terminal ganglia are very near to the organs innervated. The part of the nerve attached to the muscle tissue is called the end organ. When the nerve is stimulated, the end organ liberates acetylcholine, which produces a powerful stimulus in the muscle. It is believed that acetylcholine is present in the nerve tissue in a physiologically inactive, nondiffusible form. When stimulated, the nerve converts the inactive acetylcholine into the active form, which can diffuse into the muscle tissue and elicit the proper response. The presence of large amounts of acetylcholine in muscle tissue for a long period of time could be serious.

Fortunately, the body is provided with cholinesterase, a specific enzyme that hydrolyzes acetylcholine into choline and acetic acid.

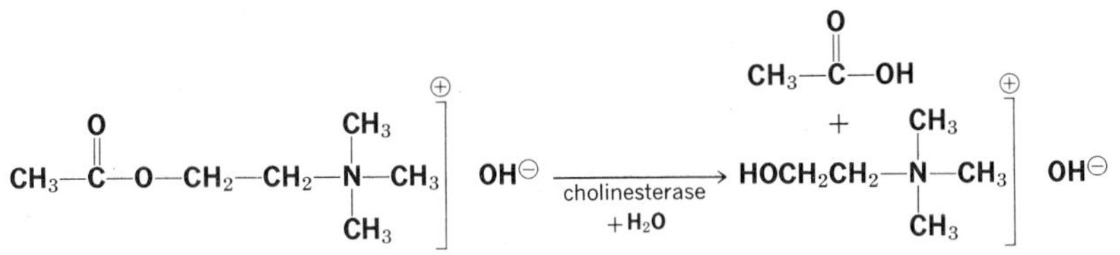

$$CH_3-\overset{\overset{\displaystyle O}{\|}}{C}-O-CH_2-CH_2-\overset{+}{\left[\overset{\overset{\displaystyle CH_3}{|}}{\underset{\underset{\displaystyle CH_3}{|}}{N}}-CH_3\right]} OH^{\ominus} \xrightarrow[+H_2O]{\text{cholinesterase}} CH_3-\overset{\overset{\displaystyle O}{\|}}{C}-OH + HOCH_2CH_2-\overset{+}{\left[\overset{\overset{\displaystyle CH_3}{|}}{\underset{\underset{\displaystyle CH_3}{|}}{N}}-CH_3\right]} OH^{\ominus}$$

Because choline is so much weaker than acetylcholine, the powerful stimulus is stopped. Cholinesterase appears to exist in tissues especially where acetylcholine may be liberated, and the enzyme can effect the hydrolysis very rapidly. Whenever cholinesterase is inactivated (e.g., physostigmine can inactivate the enzyme), the action of the acetylcholine is prolonged and intensified. This is the basis for the parasympathomimetic action of physostigmine.

The action of acetylcholine is usually evanescent because of its quick hydrolysis in the body.

Neurine, which is dehydrated choline, is a very toxic substance.

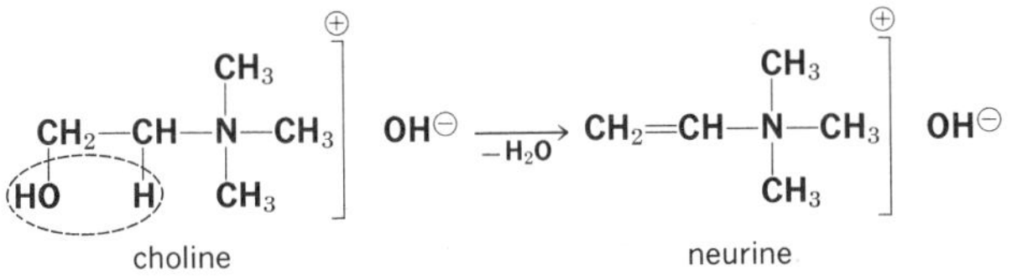

$$\underset{\text{choline}}{\underset{\underset{\displaystyle HO}{|}}{CH_2}-\underset{\underset{\displaystyle H}{|}}{CH}-\overset{+}{\left[\overset{\overset{\displaystyle CH_3}{|}}{\underset{\underset{\displaystyle CH_3}{|}}{N}}-CH_3\right]} OH^{\ominus}} \xrightarrow[-H_2O]{} \underset{\text{neurine}}{CH_2{=}CH-\overset{+}{\left[\overset{\overset{\displaystyle CH_3}{|}}{\underset{\underset{\displaystyle CH_3}{|}}{N}}-CH_3\right]} OH^{\ominus}}$$

When putrefying bacteria act on choline, neurine is formed.

During World War II, *nerve gas,* an essentially odorless, colorless gas, which is particularly deadly when either inhaled, absorbed through the skin, or consumed with food, was developed but apparently never used. A typical nerve gas formula is

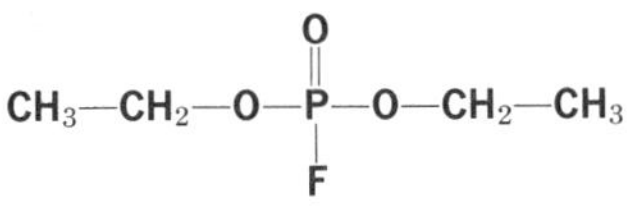

$$CH_3-CH_2-O-\overset{\overset{\displaystyle O}{\|}}{\underset{\underset{\displaystyle F}{|}}{P}}-O-CH_2-CH_3$$

diethyl fluorophosphate

The chief damage of nerve gas is its combination with the enzyme cholinesterase, to render the enzyme ineffective. With cholinesterase inactivated, the acetylcholine cannot be hydrolyzed back to choline and acetic acid. The accumulated acetylcholine increases salivary and sweat gland secretions and excites the muscles into continuous activity. This leads to muscular fatigue, exhaustion, and eventually paralysis and death. Other nerve gases since developed are reported to be even more deadly. *Atropine,* a drug that tends to dry up gland secretions, may be of some help in a mild case of nerve gas poisoning. It is fortunate that a 100% effective antidote, called PAM, has been perfected against nerve gas.

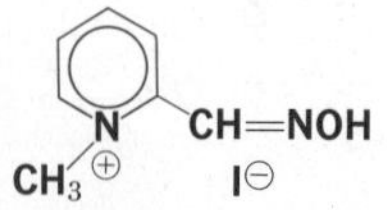

$$\text{(pyridinium ring)}\ \overset{\oplus}{N}(CH_3)\text{—}CH{=}NOH\quad I^{\ominus}$$

2-pyridine aldoxime methiodide (PAM)

PAM seems capable of removing the nerve gas from cholinesterase, and so releases cholinesterase to perform its usual function of hydrolyzing acetylcholine.

Cephalin

The chief difference between cephalin and lecithin lies in the nitrogen-containing base part. Cephalin contains β-hydroxyethylamine, whereas lecithin contains choline. Cephalin, which occurs predominately in the brain (hence, its name), may also contain the hydroxy amino acid, serine, in place of the β-hydroxyethylamine.

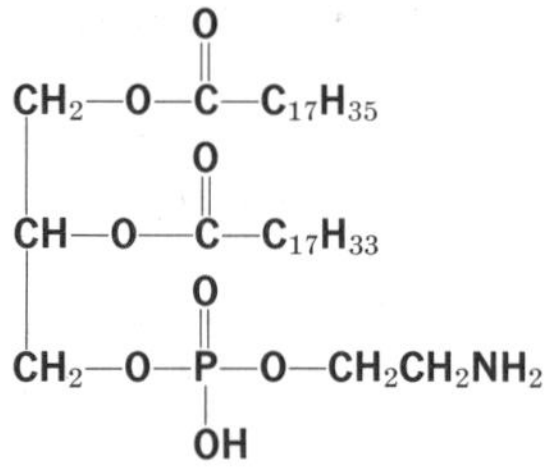

$$\begin{array}{l} CH_2\text{—}O\text{—}\overset{O}{\overset{\|}{C}}\text{—}C_{17}H_{35} \\ | \\ CH\text{—}O\text{—}\overset{O}{\overset{\|}{C}}\text{—}C_{17}H_{33} \\ | \\ CH_2\text{—}O\text{—}\underset{OH}{\underset{|}{\overset{O}{\overset{\|}{P}}}}\text{—}O\text{—}CH_2CH_2NH_2 \end{array}$$

an α-cephalin containing β-hydroxyethylamine

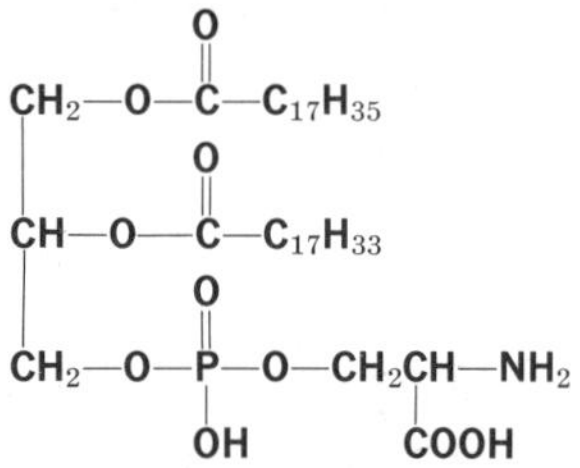

$$\begin{array}{l} CH_2\text{—}O\text{—}\overset{O}{\overset{\|}{C}}\text{—}C_{17}H_{35} \\ | \\ CH\text{—}O\text{—}\overset{O}{\overset{\|}{C}}\text{—}C_{17}H_{33} \\ | \\ CH_2\text{—}O\text{—}\underset{OH}{\underset{|}{\overset{O}{\overset{\|}{P}}}}\text{—}O\text{—}CH_2\underset{COOH}{\underset{|}{CH}}\text{—}NH_2 \end{array}$$

an α-cephalin containing serine

Cephalins are very difficult to isolate in a high state of purity and quickly oxidize in the air, becoming dark in color. Lysocephalin (i.e., cephalin with the unsaturated acid removed), contrary to lysolecithin, possesses no hemolytic power. Cephalins supposedly play an important role in blood clotting.

Sphingomyelins

Sphingomyelins contain sphingosinol (or sphingosine), a nitrogen-containing dialcohol. There is no glycerol in sphingomyelins. Instead of

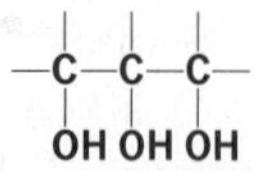

$$\text{—}\underset{OH}{\underset{|}{\overset{|}{C}}}\text{—}\underset{OH}{\underset{|}{\overset{|}{C}}}\text{—}\underset{OH}{\underset{|}{\overset{|}{C}}}\text{—}$$

glycerol skeleton

we have

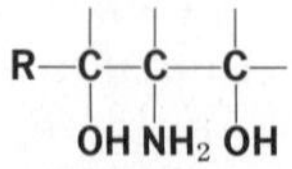

$$R\text{—}\underset{OH}{\underset{|}{\overset{|}{C}}}\text{—}\underset{NH_2}{\underset{|}{\overset{|}{C}}}\text{—}\underset{OH}{\underset{|}{\overset{|}{C}}}\text{—}$$

sphingosinol skeleton

Sphingosinol has the structure

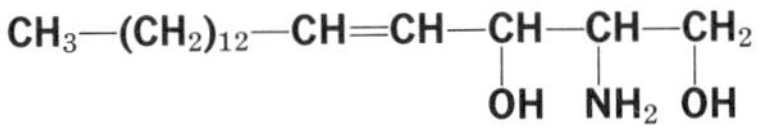

$$\begin{array}{l} CH_3{-}(CH_2)_{12}{-}CH{=}CH{-}\underset{\displaystyle OH}{\underset{|}{CH}}{-}\underset{\displaystyle NH_2}{\underset{|}{CH}}{-}\underset{\displaystyle OH}{\underset{|}{CH_2}} \end{array}$$

sphingosinol

In addition to sphingomyelins, cerebrosides and gangliosides also contain sphingosinol, and, hence, the group mentioned may be classified as sphingolipids.

On hydrolysis, sphingomyelins yield sphingosinol, phosphoric acid, choline, and a fatty acid. At least three different fatty acids have been isolated from sphingomyelins: stearic, lignoceric $CH_3(CH_2)_{22}COOH$, and nervonic $CH_3(CH_2)_7CH{=}CH(CH_2)_{12}CH_2COOH$ acids.

We can now indicate the structure of a sphingomyelin:

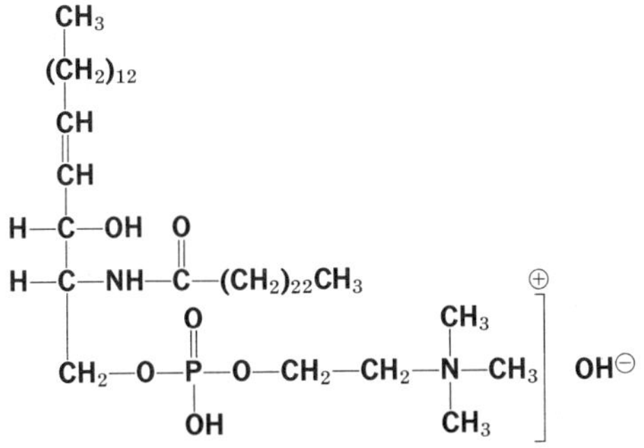

$$\begin{array}{l}
\quad CH_3 \\
\quad | \\
\quad (CH_2)_{12} \\
\quad | \\
\quad CH \\
\quad \| \\
\quad CH \\
\quad | \\
H{-}C{-}OH \quad O \\
\quad | \qquad\qquad \| \\
H{-}C{-}NH{-}C{-}(CH_2)_{22}CH_3 \\
\quad | \\
\quad CH_2{-}O{-}\underset{\displaystyle OH}{\underset{|}{\overset{\displaystyle O}{\overset{\|}{P}}}}{-}O{-}CH_2{-}CH_2{-}\left[\underset{\displaystyle CH_3}{\underset{|}{\overset{\displaystyle CH_3}{\overset{|}{N}}}}{-}CH_3\right]^{\oplus} OH^{\ominus}
\end{array}$$

a sphingomyelin

In Niemann-Pick's disease, sphingomyelins accumulate in the liver, brain, and spleen.

Myelin is a sheathlike structure that surrounds the nerve axon, somewhat like insulation around a wire. It is not known exactly why lipids in myelin are "metabolically inert," whereas lipids in gray matter metabolize readily, but it is suspected that this may be due to the presence of more long-chain, more saturated fatty acids than in gray matter lipids. Myelin contains cholesterol, sphingomyelins, and other phospholipids.

GLYCOLIPIDS

When glycolipids are hydrolyzed, they yield a sugar molecule, a fatty acid, and sphingosinol. The sugar molecule is usually galactose. The only variation in the various glycolipids is in the fatty acid part. Four fatty acids have been isolated from glycolipids: lignoceric, cerebronic or phrenosinic, nervonic, and oxynervonic acids.

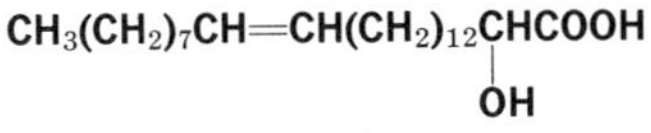

$$CH_3(CH_2)_7CH{=}CH(CH_2)_{12}\underset{\displaystyle OH}{\underset{|}{C}}HCOOH$$

oxynervonic acid

$$CH_3(CH_2)_7CH_2CH_2(CH_2)_{12}\underset{\displaystyle OH}{\underset{|}{C}}HCOOH$$

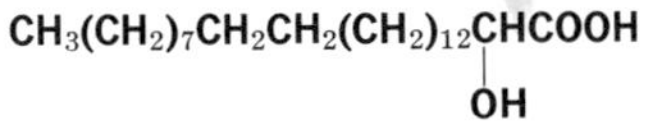

cerebronic acid

Galactose, an aldohexose, has the formula

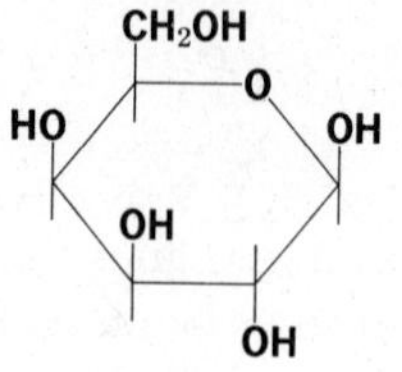

β-galactose

In a glycolipid, a β-galactose is linked to the sphingosinol and may be represented as

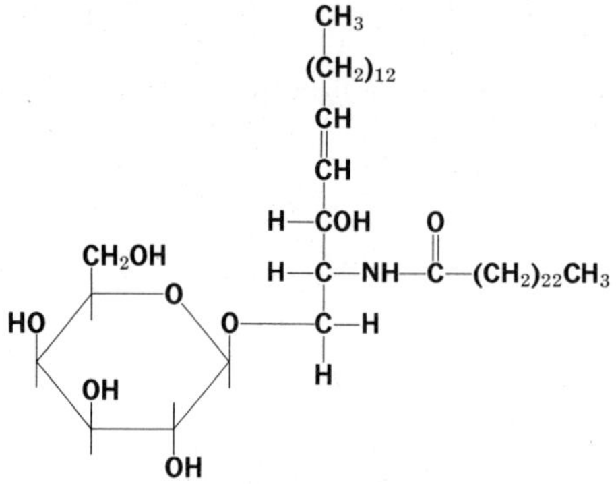

kerasin, an β-galactoside

Kerasin is reported to contain lignoceric acid, phrenosin contains phrenosinic or cerebronic acid, nervon contains nervonic acid, and oxynervon contains oxynervonic acid.

The glycolipids, often called cerebrosides, are found especially in the brain and nervous tissue but are probably a general component of all cells. The glycolipids have been isolated also from fungi, oak wood, and seeds.

The presence of galactose in the glycolipid suggests that milk sugar is indeed quite important in the diet of infants and children during the development of nervous and brain tissue. However, no definite relationship between a mental deficiency and a deficiency of milk in the diet of an infant has been proved conclusively. Apparently, glucose can be changed into galactose in the body.

In Gaucher's disease, the amount of cerebrosides in the liver and spleen is greatly increased.

Derived lipids

Steroids

The steroids (also called sterids) are among the most important physiologically active compounds in the body. From a chemical standpoint they are very complicated, and numerous outstanding chemists have contributed to the elucidation of the chemical structure. The many years of work culminated in the awarding of the Nobel Prize in 1928 to Wieland and Windaus. It is interesting that the actual structure proposed by these German Scientists was wrong, and it was not until 1932 that British (Rosenheim and King) and German (Wieland and Dane) scientists independently arrived at the correct structure almost simultaneously.

Very small amounts of steroids can accomplish profound changes in living organisms. Consequently, a very small steroid deficiency or excess may cause damage to the body.

Some of the important compounds containing the steroid nucleus are bile acids, the cardiac-active substances, sex hormones, vitamin D, adrenal cortex hormones, and steroid saponins.

Cholesterol (meaning solid bile) is the most abundant steroid in the body and is found especially in the brain, spinal cord, and nerve tissues. It is widely distributed throughout the body in the blood stream, as well as in the tissues.

The basic chemical nucleus of the steroids is the cyclopentanophenanthrene ring system.

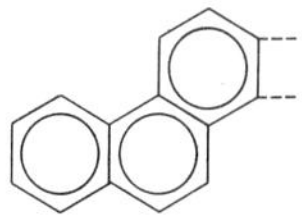

phenanthrene

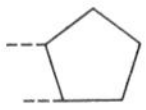

cyclopentano group

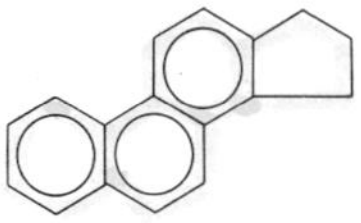

cyclopentanophenanthrene

The steroids, however, usually contain the cyclopentanophenanthrene ring system in a state of complete or partial hydrogenation.

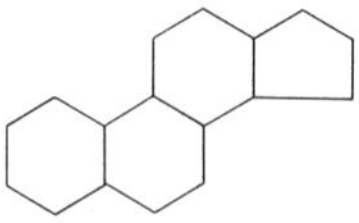

completely hydrogenated cyclopentanophenanthrene
(*perhydrocyclopentanophenanthrene*)

Some steroids may contain two aromatic rings (e.g., equilenin):

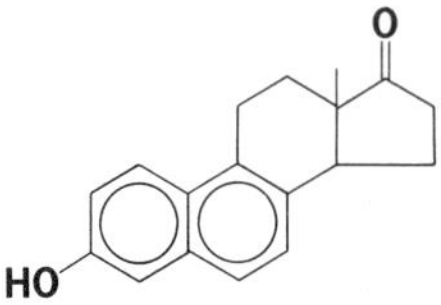

O

HO

equilenin

Some may contain one aromatic ring (e.g., estrone):

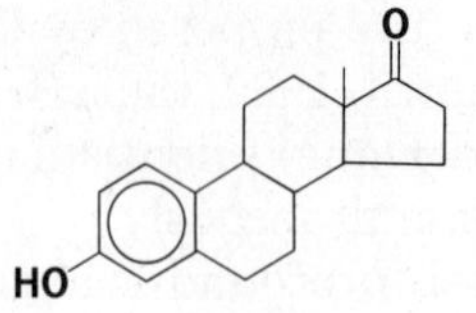

HO
O
estrone

More frequently, however, the steroids contain only an occasional double bond, such as in progesterone.

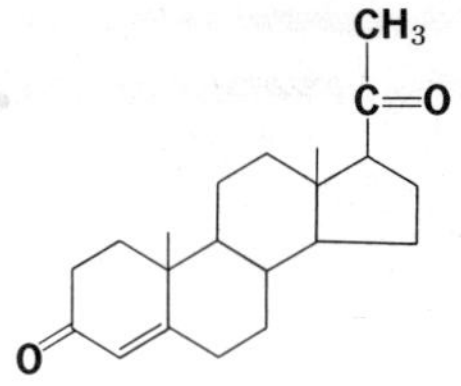

CH_3
C=O
O
progesterone

Cholesterol has an —OH group in the molecule, as well as one double bond. Because there are so many carbons, the numbering system of cholesterol, which is the system used for all steroids, is indicated below:

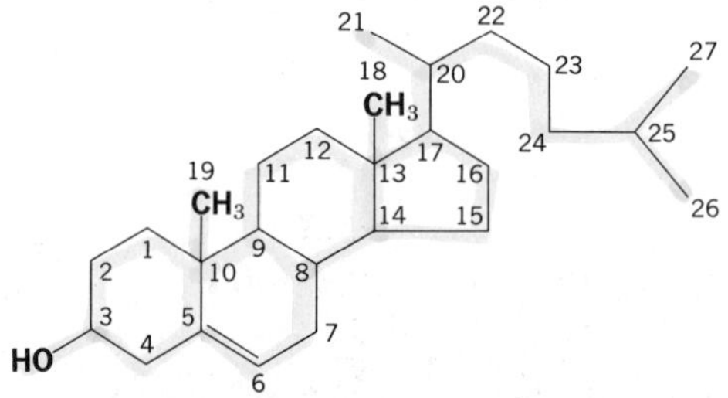

HO
CH_3
CH_3
cholesterol and steroid numbering system

The two methyl groups, carbons 18 and 19, are called the bridgehead or angular methyl groups and are characteristically met in the steroid series. The long chain of carbon atoms coming out of carbon 17 is called the side chain. Although a complicated molecule, cholesterol possesses all the properties of an unsaturated alcohol. The double bond can readily be reduced, and the alcohol group can be esterified or oxidized to a ketone group, because cholesterol is a secondary alcohol.

If a chemist reduces the double bond in cholesterol, he obtains cholestanol.

HO — cholesterol $\xrightarrow{+2H}$ HO — cholestanol

It is interesting that cholesterol, which is excreted in bile, is reduced in the *intestines* by microbial enzymes to *coprosterol.* Coprosterol and cholestanol are stereochemical isomers and are identical except for the hydrogen at carbon 5: In coprosterol, the carbon 5 hydrogen juts above the plane of the rings; in cholestanol, the carbon 5 hydrogen lies below the plane of the rings.

Inspection of the steroid nucleus will show that many carbon atoms are asymmetric, and, thus, there are many isomers.

HO

The nine dots indicate asymmetric carbon atoms of cholestanol. This means 2^9 or 512 isomers. Cholesterol (which does not have an asymmetric carbon atom at carbon 5) would have 2^8 or 256 isomers. Fortunately, certain isomers seem to predominate, and only a few of the many possible isomers are ever met.

Naturally, to synthesize cholesterol, a chemist would have to prepare the one correct isomer out of the 256 possible ones. Woodward accomplished this remarkable feat in 1955.

Chemical & Engineering News

Figure 11-6 Robert Woodward

Cholesterol is found in the bile liquid and is an elimination product. If the cholesterol crystallizes, it may form small stonelike balls, which are difficult to eliminate, and surgery may be necessary to remove them from the gall bladder. Gall stones are very painful and, in addition, may block the normal bile liquid flow, causing a jaundice condition.

The blood serum of normal individuals contains about 0.20 g of total cholesterol (i.e., cholesterol and esters of cholesterol) per 100 ml. Of this total cholesterol, about 27% is free cholesterol. The Liebermann-Burchard test for cholesterol is performed as follows: A solution of a small crystal of cholesterol in acetic anhydride is treated with 3 to 4 drops of concentrated sulfuric acid; or, cholesterol dissolved in chloroform is treated with acetic anhydride and sulfuric acid. A positive test is given by a series of bright color changes. Cholesterol is conveniently determined quantitatively by the Schoenheimer-Sperry method. Blood serum is extracted with acetone-alcohol, and the free cholesterol is precipitated by digitonin, a saponin $C_{56}H_{92}O_{29}$.

Bile Acids

To see the relationship between cholesterol and bile acids, we need only remove three carbon atoms from the side chain of cholestanol and oxidize the end carbon to an acid.

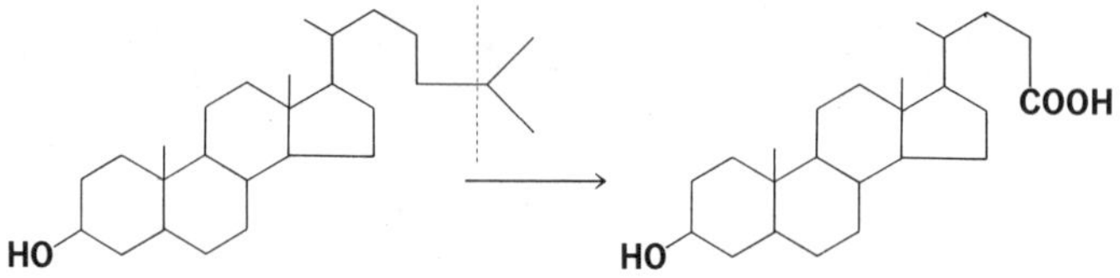

HO

cholestanol

→

COOH

HO

a bile acid
(*lithocholic acid*)

Cholic acid, lithocholic acid (above), and desoxycholic acid are important bile acids.

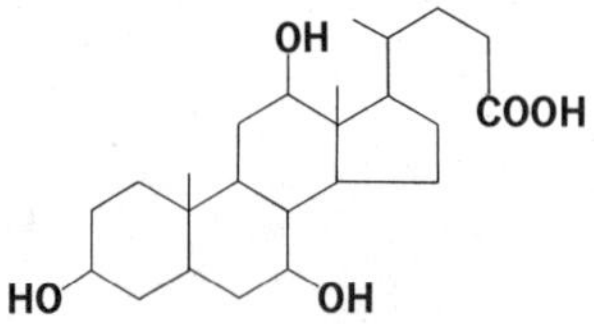

OH COOH

HO OH

cholic acid

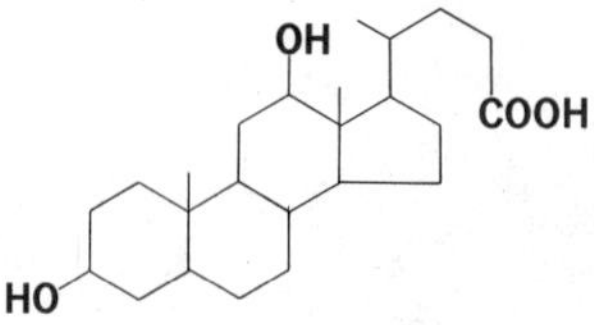

OH COOH

HO

desoxycholic acid

The bile acids are, of course, found in bile. Bile salts are the sodium salts of combined bile acids and amino acids. Glycocholic acid is made up of cholic acid and glycine.

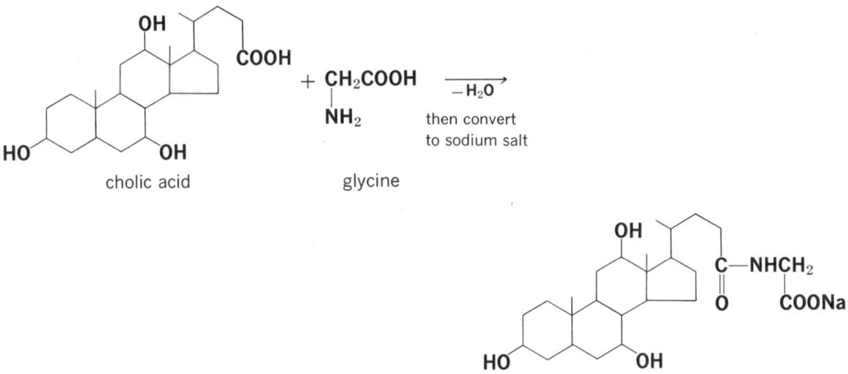

cholic acid + $CH_2(NH_2)COOH$ (glycine) $\xrightarrow{-H_2O}$ then convert to sodium salt

glycocholic bile salt ($C{=}O$—$NHCH_2COONa$ side chain)

Taurocholic acid is made up of cholic acid and taurine.

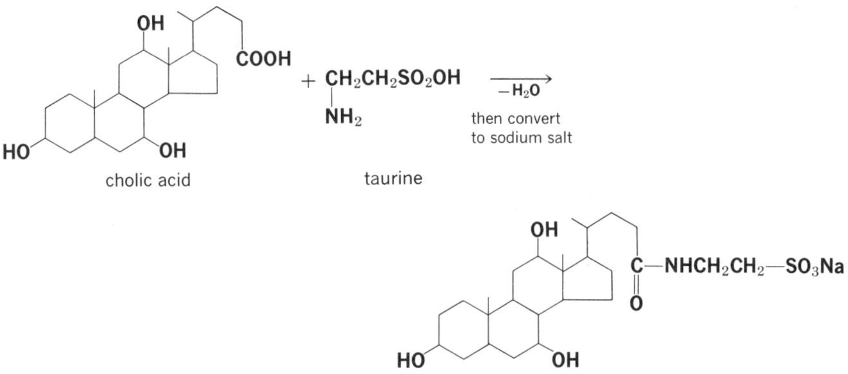

cholic acid + $CH_2(NH_2)CH_2SO_2OH$ (taurine) $\xrightarrow{-H_2O}$ then convert to sodium salt

taurocholic acid bile salt ($C{=}O$—$NHCH_2CH_2$—SO_3Na side chain)

The bile salts are very important in the digestion and assimilation of lipids in the intestines. They are also necessary for the proper assimilation of the fat-soluble vitamins, A, D, E, and K. This will be discussed in more detail in Chapter 18.

Adrenal Cortex Hormones

Investigations into the constitution of the adrenal cortex resulted in the discovery of many different crystalline compounds that possessed steroid structures and were physiologically active in prolonging the life of adrenaloctomized animals. Many important physiological properties are attributed to the adrenal cortex hormones.

Many workers were involved in the isolation of these compounds, and originally these substances were characterized by letters of the alphabet, that is, compounds A, E, D, S, etc. The crude extract is called cortin. The adrenal cortex hormones contain only two carbon atoms in the side chain and all are unsaturated ketones. Some of the more important compounds of this series are

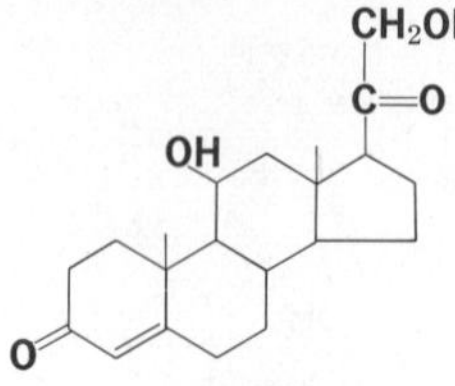

CH_2OH / C=O / OH

corticosterone
(*compound H*)

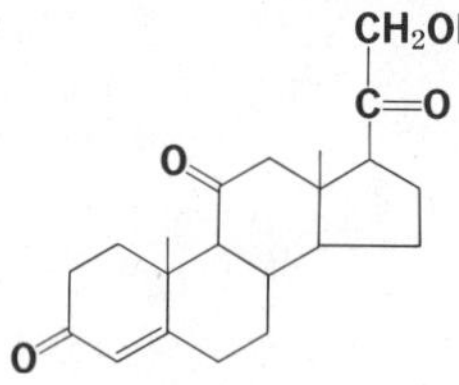

CH_2OH / C=O / O

dehydrocorticosterone
(*compound A*)

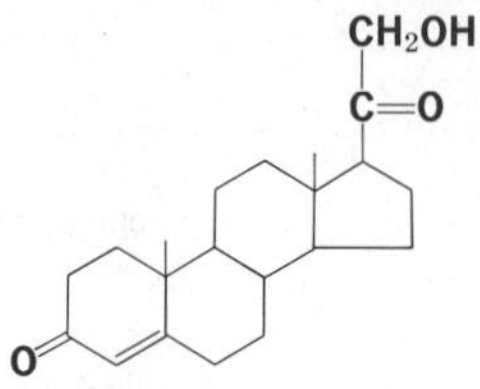

CH_2OH / C=O / O

desoxycorticosterone
(*compound Q*)

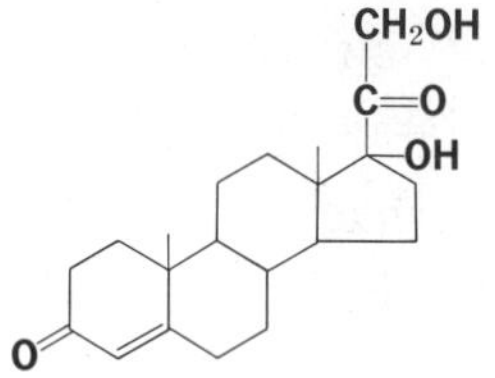

CH_2OH / C=O / OH / O

17-hydroxydesoxycorticosterone
(*compound S*)

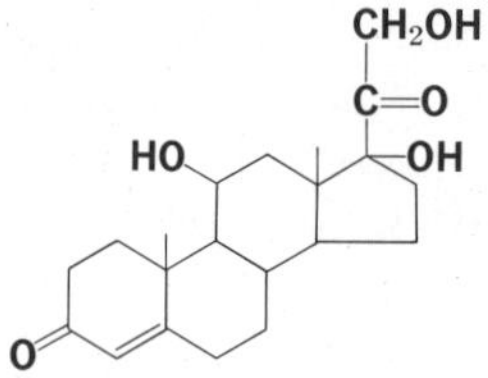

CH_2OH / C=O / HO / OH / O

17-hydroxycorticosterone
(*compound F*)

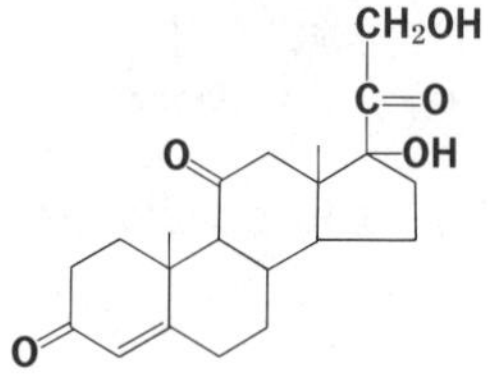

CH_2OH / C=O / O / OH / O

17-hydroxydehydrocorticosterone
(*compound E*)

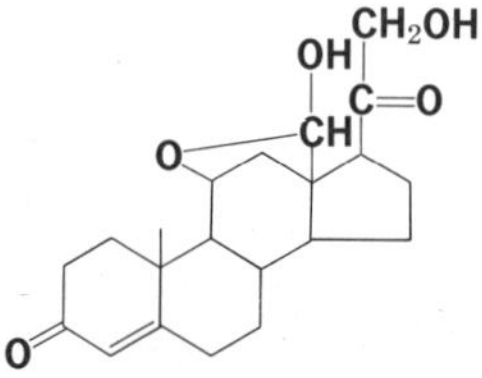

CH_2OH / OH / C=O / CH / O / O

aldosterone

The important physiological activities of these compounds are complex and will be discussed in Chapter 22.

The Sex Hormones

The male and female sex hormones, although they occur in minute quantities in the organism, have profound effects. These hormones control the growth and physiological function of the reproductive organs and are responsible for the development of the male and female secondary sex characteristics.

The male hormones are called *androgens;* testosterone is the prime androgen. Androsterone is a closely related androgen.

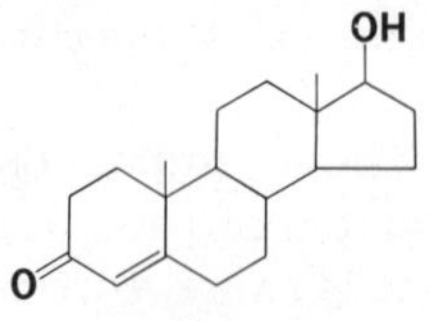

OH / O

testosterone

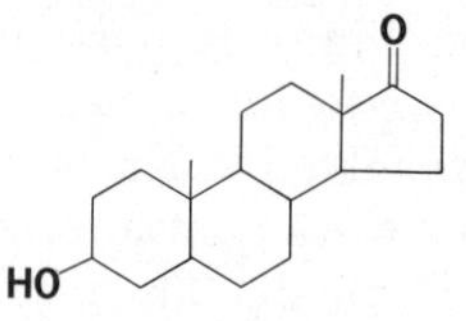

O / HO

androsterone

androgens

There are two types of female sex hormones: *estrogens* and *progestational hormones*. The principal progestational hormone is progesterone.

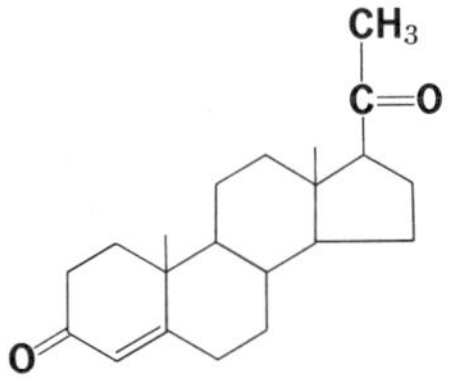

progesterone

The principal estrogen is estradiol. Estrone and estratriol (estriol) are related estrogens.

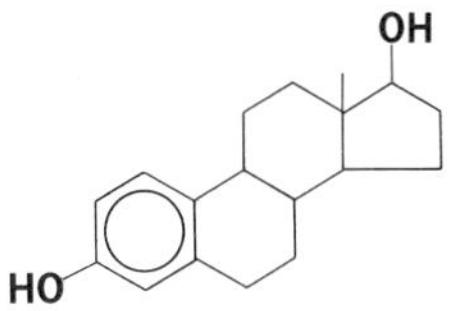

estradiol 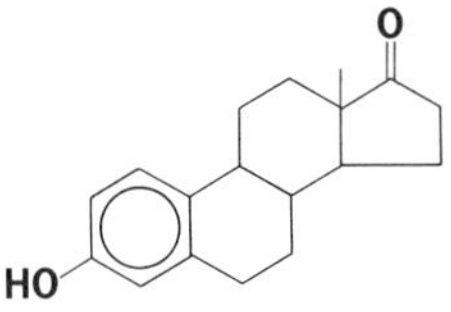 estrone 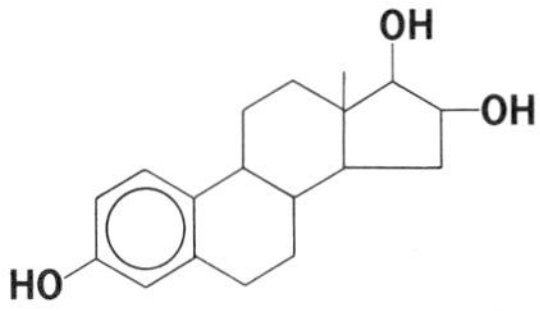 estriol

estrogens

Stilbestrol is representative of a number of synthetic products that are not steroids but possess estrogen activity.

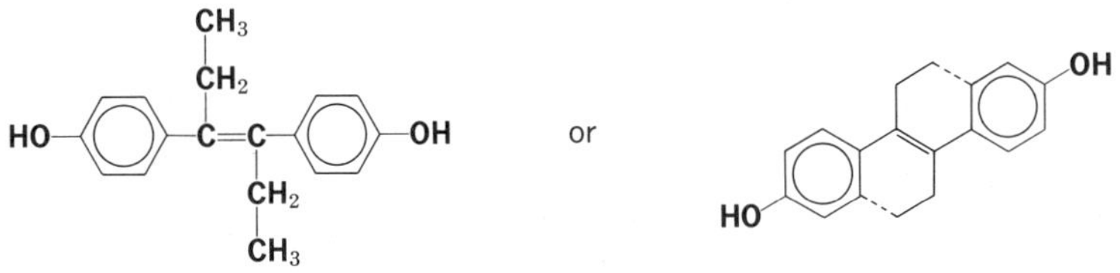

or

stilbestrol

When stilbestrol is drawn as indicated on the above right, one can see how closely it imitates the steroid type structure.

Vitamin D

Certain irradiated oils were found to prevent rickets. The substance first isolated turned out to be a mixture (vitamin D_1). Vitamin D_2 is formed when ergosterol is irradiated, and vitamin D_3 is formed when 7-dehydrocholesterol is irradiated. Vitamin D_3 is superior to D_2 in human therapy.

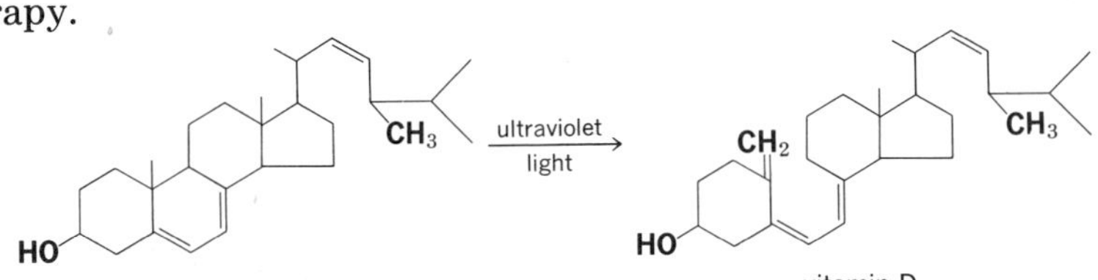

ultraviolet light

ergosterol

vitamin D_2 (*calciferol*)

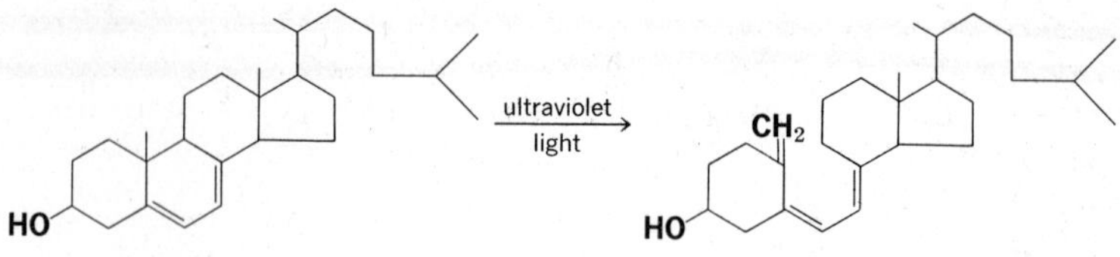

HO — 7-dehydrocholesterol —(ultraviolet light)→ vitamin D_3 (CH_2, HO)

The chemical difference between vitamins D_2 and D_3 is in the side chain. For further information on vitamin D, see Chapter 21.

Cardiac-active Substances

Two groups of these naturally occurring steroids can exert a specific and powerful action on the cardiac muscle of man and animals. The first group, found in bark and seeds and synthesized by plants, is called cardiac glycosides. The second group, found in the skin secretions of toads and elaborated by that organism, is called toad poisons. These cardiovascular substances are very important pharmocologically and are unrivaled in the treatment of congestive heart failure. A small amount of one of these substances exerts beneficial action on the diseased heart, whereas a large amount causes death. For example, most patients who require digitalis to maintain adequate heart activity require the drug for the remainder of their lives. The dosage must be carefully prescribed by a physician.

CARDIAC GLYCOSIDES

The cardiac glycosides contain a sugar part and a nonsugar part (i.e., aglycone or genin). The genin part is steroidal in nature. Digitalis is the dried leaf of the common and beautiful foxglove plant *Digitalis purpurea.* The seeds and leaves of other digitalis species also contain active cardiac substances. Digitoxin is the principle cardiac glycoside in digitalis. The sugar part is digitose, and the genin part is digitoxigenin. The two parts are attached through the 3 —OH group.

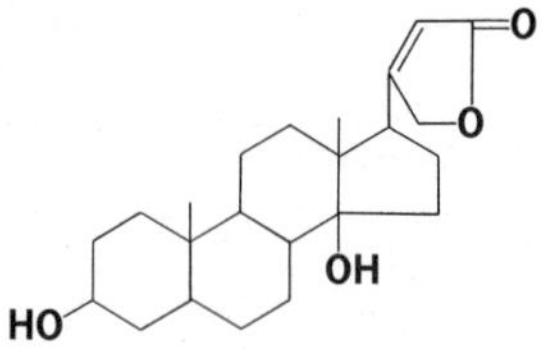

HO, OH, O, =O

digitoxigenin

Squill (*Scilla maritima*), the bulb of the "sea onion," contains scillaren-A. The sugar attached at carbon 3 contains glucose and rhamnose.

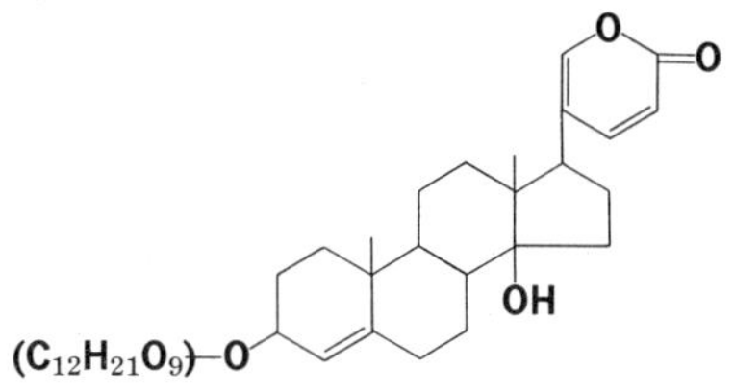

scillaren-A

It is employed as an expectorant, a cardiac stimulant, and a diuretic. The side chain is a six-membered ring lactone containing two conjugated double bonds.

The seeds and bark of the *Strophanthus* species, such as *Strophantus kombé, hispidus,* and *gratis,* are known to contain poisonous substances. Strophanthidin is a representative genin from *S. kombé.*

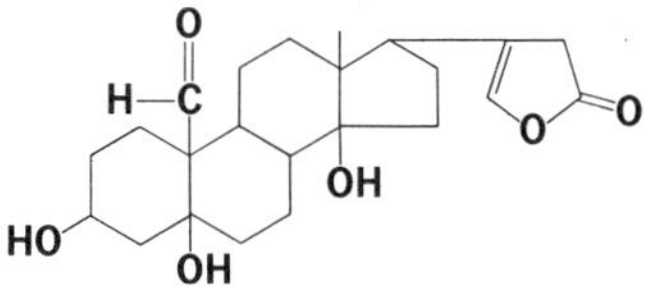

strophanthidin

The side chain is a five-membered ring lactone containing one double bond. Another interesting feature is the presence at carbon 10 of an aldehyde group instead of the customary methyl group.

TOAD POISONS

The poisonous secretions of the toad can be obtained from either the dried skin or the living animal. The bulk of the venom is located behind the eye in the parotid gland. Apparently, the toad makes no use of its own poison, either in self-defense or in body function. In small quantities, the venom has digitalis-like activity; in high quantities, it is lethal. A typical steroid part of a toad poison is bufogenin-B.

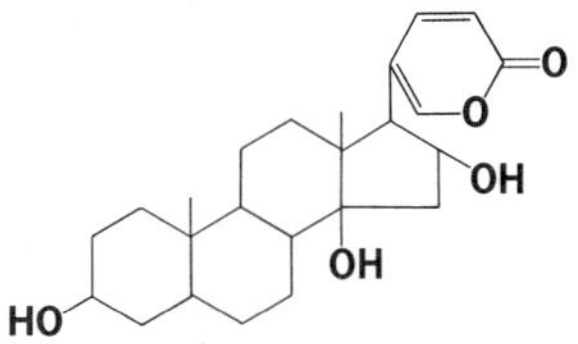

bufogenin-B

Steroid Saponins

Steroid saponins (soap former) is the name given to a group of plant glycosides that have the property of forming a soapy lather in water. Although somewhat similar to the cardiac glycosides, the saponins are differentiated because of their different physiological activity. Digitonin is a typical saponin. Diosgenin, a saponin, is formulated as follows:

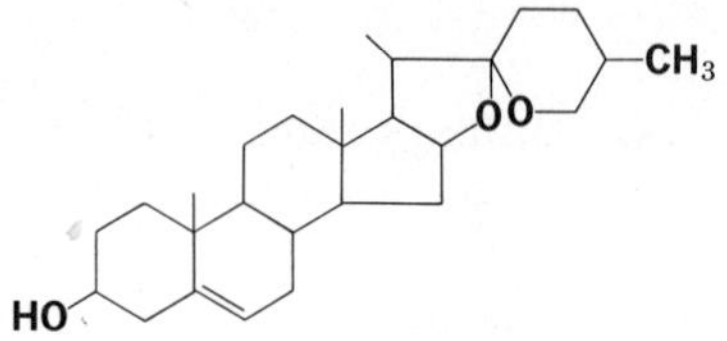

diosgenin

Particular attention has been drawn to the saponins because of the possibility of degrading them into useful steroidal hormones (i.e., sex hormones and adrenal cortex hormones). Progesterone and cortisone can be made from diosgenin.

REVIEW QUESTIONS

1. How may lipids be classified?
2. Write representative structures of several fats and oils.
3. What is the essential difference between a fat and an oil?
4. Write several equations illustrating the saponification of an oil or a fat.
5. Define the terms hard soap and soft soap.
6. Write an equation for the formation of a soap. Name all compounds.
7. What is the difference between "hard water" and "soft water"? What is the difference between "permanent hard water" and "temporary hard water"?
8. Discuss by means of equations the various ways of softening hard water.
9. Discuss the germicidal properties of soaps. Of what use are soaps? Write the formula for a detergent. What advantages do detergents have over ordinary soaps? What are invert soaps?
10. Discuss the test for a fat, the test for oxidative rancidity, and the Liebermann-Burchardt test. Indicate how the tests are performed, how a positive test would be recognized, and what a positive test would signify.
11. Write an equation illustrating the hydrogenation of an oil.
12. Identify paint, varnish, oil cloth, and linoleum.
13. Define the term rancidity. What is the difference between oxidative and hydrolytic rancidity?
14. Of what use are iodinated oils in medicine?
15. What is spontaneous combustion?
16. Write the chemical formulas for several waxes. Of what use are waxes in the body?
17. What are the significant chemical differences between phospholipids and glycolipids?

18. Discuss the chemical effect of an injection of snake venom into the blood stream.
19. Identify chemically lecithin, cephalin, choline, and acetylcholine. What function does acetylcholine have in the body?
20. Identify cholinesterase.
21. Discuss the effect of nerve gas on the body.
22. What is the basic structure of all steroids?
23. What is the relationship between cholesterol and the bile acids, adrenal cortex hormones, male and female sex hormones, vitamin D, cardiac active substances, toad poison, and steroid saponins?
24. What is the relationship between stilbestrol and estradiol?
25. Classify the following lipids:

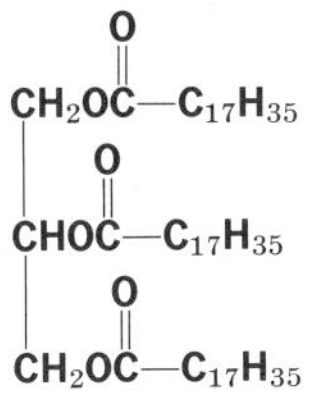

(a)

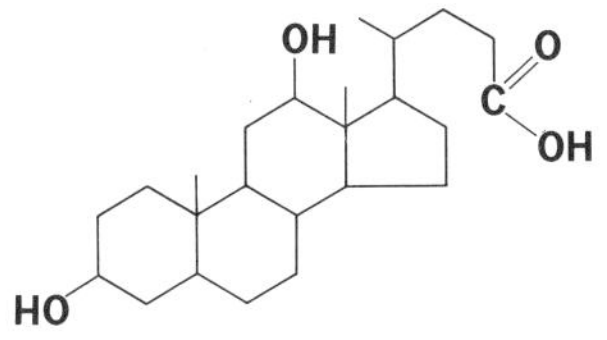

(b)

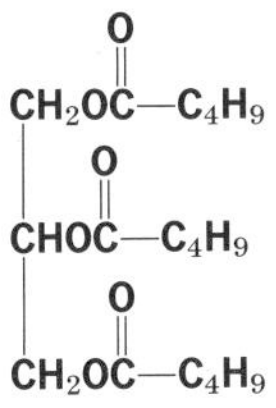

(c)

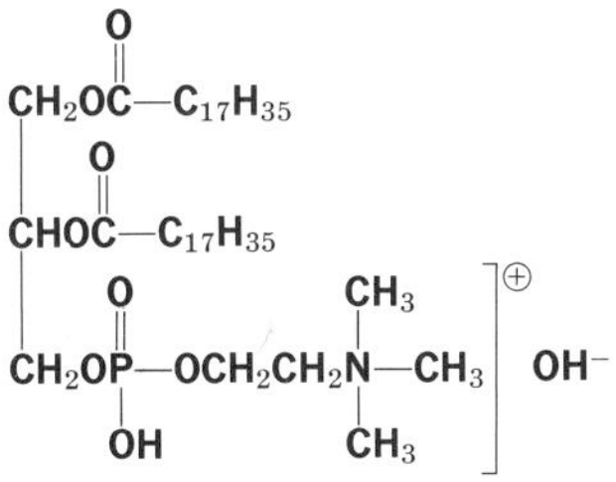

(d)

12

proteins and enzymes

The proteins probably represent the most important group of compounds in biochemistry, inasmuch as they are a major constituent of every living cell. Animals could not survive on a *protein-free* diet of lipids, carbohydrates, minerals, and vitamins, but theoretically they could survive on a carbohydrate- and lipid-free diet of proteins, minerals, and vitamins.

Proteins, like carbohydrates and lipids, contain carbon, hydrogen, and oxygen; in addition, they *always* contain nitrogen and may also contain sulfur, phosphorus, and traces of other elements. Proteins represent the principal source of nitrogen intake for the animal organism.

Although we can readily write the formulas for most carbohydrates and lipids, we can do this for very few proteins because of the complexity and large size of protein molecules. We know, however, that proteins are made up of certain units called *alpha-amino acids* (α-amino acids). For a certain protein we can ascertain which amino acids are present, and how many there are of each, but we generally do not know the arrangement of each amino acid with respect to the others.

Table 12-1 Typical analyses

SOURCE	C(%)	H(%)	N(%)
fibrin	54.56	6.90	15.72
egg albumin	54.48	7.01	15.70
serum albumin	54.84	7.09	15.82
zein	55.23	7.26	16.13
dog hemoglobin	54.57	7.11	16.38
casein	53.13	7.06	15.78

All proteins are characterized by having approximately 55% carbon, 7% hydrogen, and 16% nitrogen. The nitrogen content of pure proteins seldom varies far from 16% and thus represents a criterion for judging purity. Because 16% nitrogen represents pure protein, we can estimate the protein content of a mixture by multiplying the N% by 6.25.[1] There are other ways, of course, of determining the purity of proteins.

Table 12-1 gives some typical analyses.

Table 12-2 lists some proteins with their molecular weights.

Because the α-amino acids are the primary building units of proteins, we should familiarize ourselves with some of their formulas. The α-amino acids may be written in the general manner as

$$R-\underset{NH_2}{\overset{H}{C}}-COOH \quad \{\alpha \text{ carbon atom}$$

Only the R group varies in the building blocks of proteins. This variation is indeed of great significance. Note that the α carbon atom of every α-amino acid is *asymmetric,* with the exception of the acid with R=H. Table 12-3 lists some of the common α-amino acids found in proteins.

Table 12-3 lists the more important α-amino acids. A complete list of all known α-amino acids from proteins would, however, contain approxi-

Table 12-2 Protein molecular weights

PROTEIN	SOURCE	MOLECULAR WEIGHTS OBTAINED FROM SEDIMENTATION VELOCITY
lactoglobulin	cow's milk	34,000
pepsin	pig's stomach	35,500
hemoglobin	human blood	63,000
edestin	hempseed	303,000
hemocyanin	homarus blood	752,000
hemocyanin	helix blood	6,630,000
virus	tobacco mosaic	40,000,000

[1] 16% nitrogen × 6.25 = 100% protein, and, for example, 8% nitrogen × 6.25 = 50% protein.

Table 12-3 Common α-amino acids

1. **R** = an aliphatic hydrocarbon radical
   1. glycine (Gly) (**R** = **H**—)
   2. alanine (Ala) (**R** = CH_3—)
   3. valine (Val) (**R** = isopropyl) $\left(\begin{matrix} CH_3 \\ \quad CH- \\ CH_3 \end{matrix}\right)$
   4. leucine (Leu) (**R** = isobutyl) $\left(\begin{matrix} CH_3-CH-CH_2- \\ \quad\ | \\ \quad\ CH_3 \end{matrix}\right)$
   5. isoleucine (Ileu) (**R** = secondary-butyl) $\left(\begin{matrix} CH_3-CH_2-CH- \\ \qquad\qquad | \\ \qquad\qquad CH_3 \end{matrix}\right)$
2. **R** = an aromatic hydrocarbon radical
   1. phenylalanine (Phe) (**R** = benzyl) $\left(C_6H_5-CH_2-\right)$
3. **R** = a radical containing an aliphatic —**OH** group
   1. serine (Ser) (**R** = $HO-CH_2-$)
   2. threonine (Thr) $\left(\begin{matrix} R = CH_3-CH- \\ \qquad\qquad | \\ \qquad\qquad OH \end{matrix}\right)$
4. **R** = a radical containing an aromatic hydroxyl group
   1. tyrosine (Tyr) $\left(R = HO-C_6H_4-CH_2-\right)$
5. **R** = some sulfur-containing group
   1. cysteine (CySH) (**R** = $HS-CH_2-$)
   2. methionine (Met) (**R** = $CH_3-S-CH_2CH_2-$)
   3. cystine (CyS) $\left(\begin{matrix} R = S-CH_2- \\ \quad\ | \\ \quad\ S-CH_2- \end{matrix}\right)$ $\left(\begin{matrix} \text{cystine itself is} \\ S-CH_2-CH-COOH \\ |\qquad\qquad | \\ |\qquad\qquad NH_2 \\ S-CH_2-CH-COOH \\ \qquad\qquad | \\ \qquad\qquad NH_2 \end{matrix}\right)$
6. **R** = an acidic group (contains —**COOH**)
   1. aspartic acid (Asp) $\left(\begin{matrix} R = COOH \\ \qquad | \\ \qquad CH_2- \end{matrix}\right)$
   2. glutamic acid (Glu) $\left(\begin{matrix} R = COOH \\ \qquad | \\ \qquad CH_2CH_2- \end{matrix}\right)$

(Continued).

Table 12-3 (Continued)

7. **R** = a nitrogen-containing basic group (contains —**NH**$_2$)
   1. arginine (Arg) (**R** = $H_2N-\underset{\underset{NH}{\|}}{C}-NH-CH_2CH_2CH_2-$)
   2. lysine (Lys) (**R** = $H_2N-CH_2CH_2CH_2CH_2-$)
8. **R** = a group containing a heterocyclic ring
   1. tryptophane (Try) (**R** = indole ring with N–H, attached via $-CH_2-$)
   2. proline[a] (Pro) CH_2-CH_2, CH_2, C, COOH, N, H, H ← actual formulas
   3. hydroxyproline[a] (Hypro) ↓ H, HO—C—CH_2, COOH, CH_2, C, H, N, H
   4. histidine (His) (**R** = N, CH_2-, N, H)

[a] Strictly speaking, proline and hydroxyproline are imino acids rather than amino acids.

mately 30 acids. A single typical protein may contain 300 to 400 amino acids, which indicates the complexity of such a molecule. If we investigate the properties of the α-amino acids, we may understand more about the properties of proteins.

Acidic and Basic Properties of Amino Acids

The amino acids are unique in that they contain the carboxyl group (—COOH, an acidic group) and the amino group (—NH_2, a basic group) in the same molecule. We have learned that acids and bases react to form salts and water. For this reason, we would expect the addition of either an acid or a base to an amino acid to yield a salt and water. A substance that can react with either an acid or a base to form a salt is called *amphoteric*. Amino acids are excellent examples of amphoteric substances.

The amphoteric nature of amino acids may be indicated as follows:

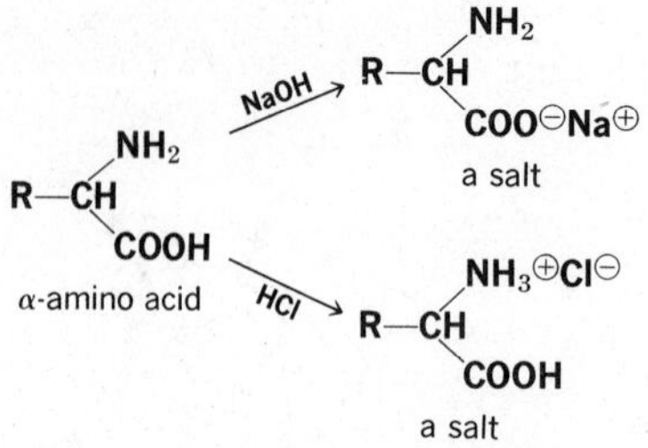

$$R{-}CH(NH_2)COOH \;(\alpha\text{-amino acid}) \xrightarrow{NaOH} R{-}CH(NH_2)COO^{\ominus}Na^{\oplus} \;(\text{a salt})$$

$$R{-}CH(NH_2)COOH \;(\alpha\text{-amino acid}) \xrightarrow{HCl} R{-}CH(NH_3^{\oplus}Cl^{\ominus})COOH \;(\text{a salt})$$

You may have wondered why an α-amino acid, which contains acidic and basic groups within the same molecule, does not react with itself. Evidence shows that amino acids *do* react with themselves to form *inner salts* or *zwitterions.*

Instead of writing

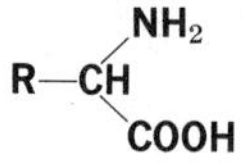

$$R{-}CH(NH_2)COOH$$

it would be more correct to write

$$R{-}CH(NH_3^{\oplus})COO^{\ominus}$$

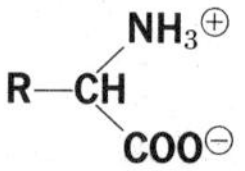

a zwitterion

Amino acids, in general, are insoluble in organic solvents and soluble in water, have high melting points, and migrate under the influence of an electric current. This information and other evidence indicate that amino acids and proteins are polar in nature.

It probably would be more correct to write the amphoteric equations as follows:

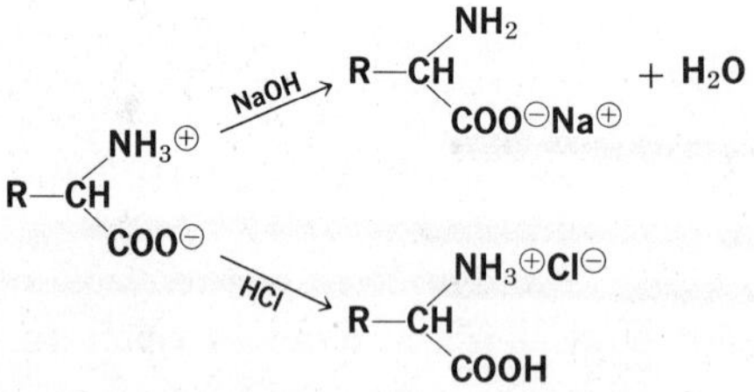

$$R{-}CH(NH_3^{\oplus})COO^{\ominus} \xrightarrow{NaOH} R{-}CH(NH_2)COO^{\ominus}Na^{\oplus} + H_2O$$

$$R{-}CH(NH_3^{\oplus})COO^{\ominus} \xrightarrow{HCl} R{-}CH(NH_3^{\oplus}Cl^{\ominus})COOH$$

The determination of the acidity and basicity of the —COOH and the —NH_2 groups in amino acids presents a problem, because the two groups are always interacting. To measure the actual acidity of an amino acid, one "ties up" the basic group and renders it nonbasic; thus, the effect of the

—COOH group is isolated, and the actual acidity can be determined. This is conveniently done by the *Sorenson method* (*Formol titration*). Formaldehyde reacts with amines to give a *nonbasic* nitrogen-containing group.

$$R{-}CH(NH_2)(COOH) + O{=}CH_2 \xrightarrow{-H_2O} R{-}CH(N{=}CH_2)(COOH)$$

nonbasic nitrogen (N=CH₂)

actual acidity of acid group determined by titration or other means (COOH)

To measure the basicity of an amino group, one "ties up" the acid group as a neutral group; thus, one can determine the actual basicity of the basic amino group by itself. In this method, the acid group is converted into a neutral ester group.

$$R{-}CH(NH_2)(COOH) + H{-}O{-}R' \longrightarrow R{-}CH(NH_2)(COOR')$$

free isolated basic group (NH_2)

neutral ester group ($COOR'$)

By techniques such as the above, we can accurately measure the acidity of every acid group and the basicity of every basic group in every α-amino acid. In particular, acids with more than one acid group (e.g., aspartic and glutamic) and acids with more than one basic group (e.g., lysine and arginine) have been carefully evaluated.

The Charge on Amino Acids and Proteins

Any discussion of amino acids and proteins, as can now be seen, is intrinsically involved with charged particles. The *isoelectric point* of amino acids and proteins is reached when the sum of the positive charges is *exactly* equal to the sum of the negative charges.[2] Under these circumstances, the amino acid or proteins will not migrate to either the positive or the negative pole. This is a very important point in the precipitation of proteins.

[2] The pH at which a dipolar ion does not migrate in an electrical field is called the *isoelectric point.* In water and in the absence of other solutes, this pH is also the *isoionic point,* that is, the pH at which the number of positive ions equals the number of negative ions. In salt solutions or in solutions containing ions other than those derived from the amphoteric polyelectrolyte, some of the ionizable groups of the amphoteric polyelectrolyte may be electrically neutralized by the other ions present. In this case, there will be a difference between the value for the isoelectric point and that for the isoionic point. This may be of special significance for proteins. For simplicity, however, we shall use the term isoelectric point in this text.

Let us examine aspartic acid, from the viewpoint of a charged particle.

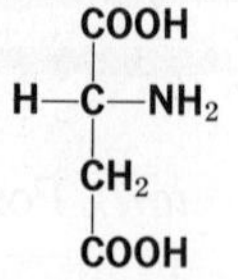

$$\begin{array}{c} COOH \\ | \\ H-C-NH_2 \\ | \\ CH_2 \\ | \\ COOH \end{array}$$

aspartic acid

In aspartic acid we have two acid groups and one basic group. This means that we can have an ion like

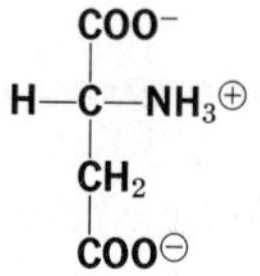

$$\begin{array}{c} COO^- \\ | \\ H-C-NH_3^{\oplus} \\ | \\ CH_2 \\ | \\ COO^{\ominus} \end{array}$$

In this ion we find two negative charges and one positive charge (the net overall charge is -1). To bring the aspartic acid ion to its isoelectric point, we must carefully add just enough acid to neutralize it.

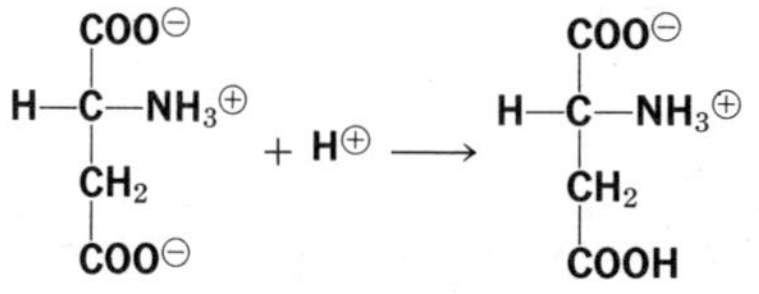

$$\begin{array}{c} COO^{\ominus} \\ | \\ H-C-NH_3^{\oplus} \\ | \\ CH_2 \\ | \\ COO^{\ominus} \end{array} + H^{\oplus} \longrightarrow \begin{array}{c} COO^{\ominus} \\ | \\ H-C-NH_3^{\oplus} \\ | \\ CH_2 \\ | \\ COOH \end{array}$$

at isoelectric point

Under these circumstances, the amino acid ion has been converted into a neutral zwitterion.

Lysine can exist in the following form:

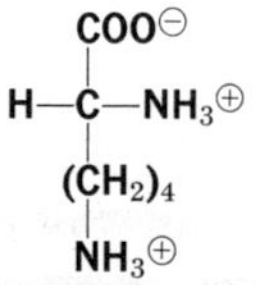

$$\begin{array}{c} COO^{\ominus} \\ | \\ H-C-NH_3^{\oplus} \\ | \\ (CH_2)_4 \\ | \\ NH_3^{\oplus} \end{array}$$

lysine

We see that lysine has two positive charges and one negative charge. This means the net overall charge is $+1$. To bring this positively charged particle to its isoelectric point, we must add just enough base to produce a neutral salt.

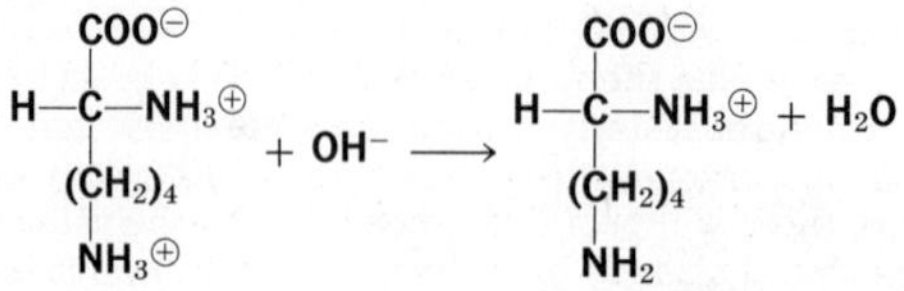

$$\begin{array}{c} COO^{\ominus} \\ | \\ H-C-NH_3^{\oplus} \\ | \\ (CH_2)_4 \\ | \\ NH_3^{\oplus} \end{array} + OH^- \longrightarrow \begin{array}{c} COO^{\ominus} \\ | \\ H-C-NH_3^{\oplus} \\ | \\ (CH_2)_4 \\ | \\ NH_2 \end{array} + H_2O$$

at isoelectric point

Under these circumstances, the amino acid ion has been converted into a neutral zwitterion. The foregoing serves as a simple explanation of a complicated subject.

Structure of Proteins

The *peptide* linkage is formed when two α-amino acids are combined with the elimination of a molecule of water in the following way.

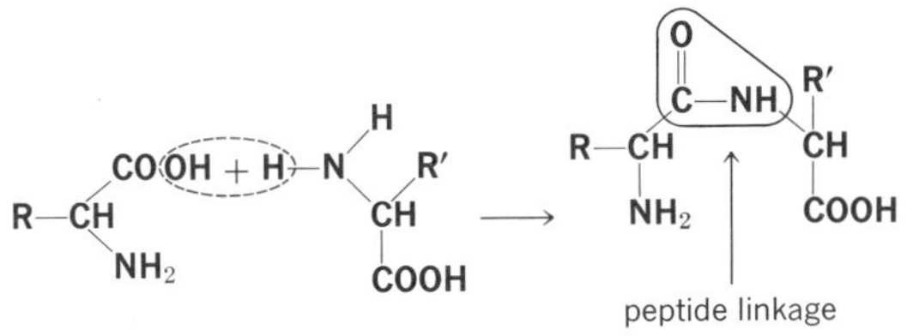

peptide linkage

In the above illustration, we have produced a dipeptide (two α-amino acids). Proteins are polypeptides (i.e., they contain many peptide linkages), and in a typical protein there can be 300 or more peptide linkages.

Let us illustrate the protein structure by the formation of a tetrapeptide (i.e., it contains four α-amino acids).

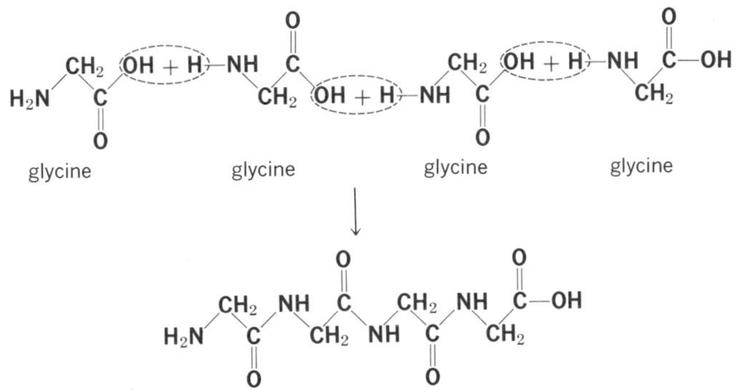

glycine glycine glycine glycine

glycyl-glycyl-glycyl-glycine
(*a tetrapeptide*)

We have picked the simplest possible example because glycine is the simplest α-amino acid. Let us illustrate the general structure for any protein, whereby any of the α-amino acids listed earlier in the chapter could be used.

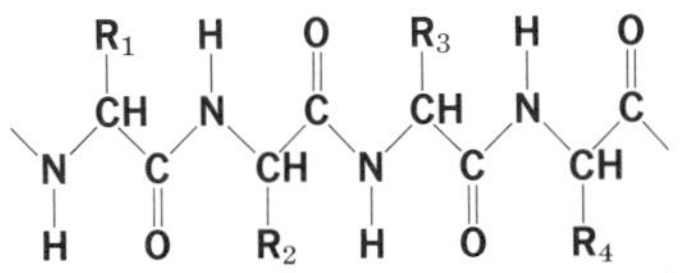

general structure for any protein

To be even more specific, let us suppose we have a tetrapeptide wherein

$R_1 = CH_3$—(alanine)

$R_2 = HO—CH_2$—(serine)

$R_3 =$ COOH
|
CH_2—(aspartic acid)

$R_4 = H_2N—(CH_2)_4$—(lysine)

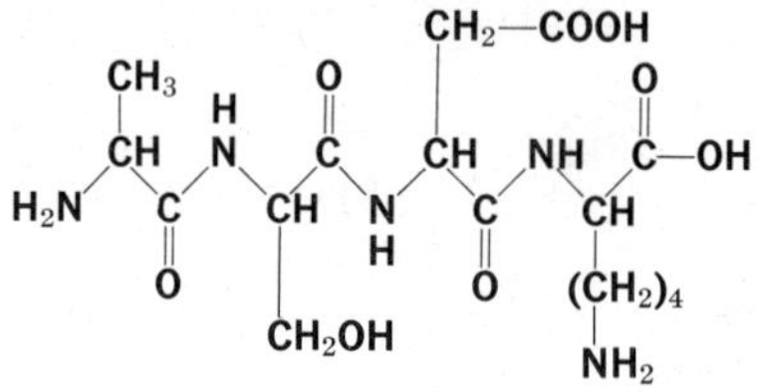

alanyl-seryl-aspartyl-lysine

You can appreciate the complexity of proteins when you realize that a typical protein of about 300 amino acids may contain about 20 different amino acids, which can be arranged in an astronomical number of ways.

In a few unusual proteins where the number of amino acids is small, we can actually write the structure of the molecule in detail. For example, gramacidin-S seems to be a dimer of the following structure. (In this unusual case, the phenylalanine is reported to be D-form and not the usual L-form.)

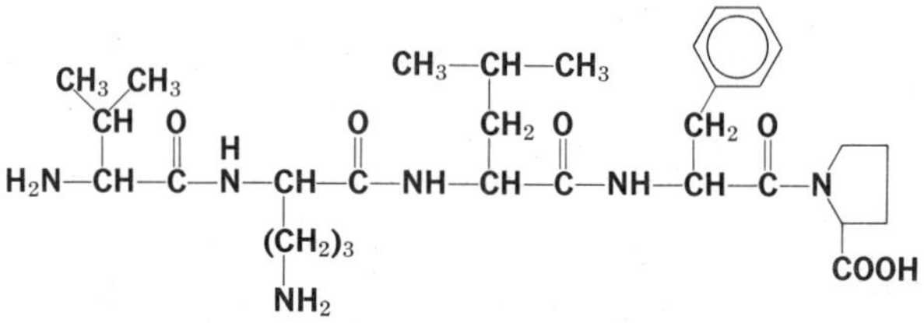

valyl-ornithyl-leucyl-phenylalanyl-proline
gramacidin-S

Glutathione is a tripeptide possessing the following structure:

$$H-\underset{NH_2}{\overset{COOH}{C}}-CH_2CH_2-\overset{O}{\overset{\|}{C}}-NH-\underset{CH_2SH}{CH}-\overset{O}{\overset{\|}{C}}-NH-CH_2COOH$$

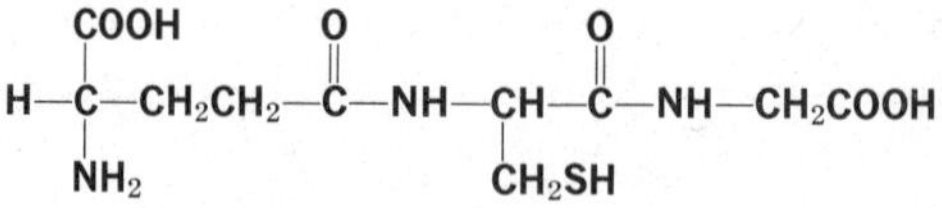

glutathione
(*glutamyl-cysteinyl-glycine*)

This is a common substance present in all cells and probably involved in intermediary protein metabolism. The —SH group can be involved in reversible oxidation-reduction systems.

$$2R-SH \rightleftharpoons R-S-S-R + H_2$$

One of the truly remarkable achievements of chemistry has been the work of F. Sanger in elaborating the structure of insulin. Insulin, the hormone responsible for the regulation of glucose metabolism in the body, is a protein containing 51 amino acid residues (see Figure 12-1). The molecule was found to be built of two polypeptide chains bound together by —S—S— bridges of cystine residues. These bridges could be broken by oxidation, and two fractions (A and B) were obtained, which represented the two separated chains. In this process, the R—S—S—R′ linkage becomes R—SO_3H and R′—SO_3H. Fraction A consists of 21 residues and has no basic amino acids. Fraction B contains 30 residues and has basic amino acids.

Each fraction was then subjected to partial hydrolysis with acid. The resulting small peptides were fractionated by paper chromatography and other techniques, and their structures were investigated. From the results, certain sequences were deduced as being present in insulin. The peptides arising from the action of various proteolytic enzymes were next studied, and, from their structures, the amino acid sequences in the two chains of insulin were shown to be

Fraction A: Glycine, isoleucine, valine, glutamic acid, glutamic acid, cystine-SO_3H, cystine-SO_3H, alanine, serine, valine, cystine-SO_3H, serine, leucine, tyrosine, glutamic acid, leucine, glutamic acid, aspartic acid, tyrosine, cystine-SO_3H, aspartic acid.

Fraction B: Phenylalanine, valine, aspartic acid, glutamic acid, histidine, leucine, cystine-SO_3H, glycine, serine, histidine, leucine, valine, glutamic acid, alanine, leucine, tyrosine, leucine, valine, cystine-SO_3H, glycine, glutamic acid, arginine, glycine, phenylalanine, phenylalanine, tyrosine, threonine, proline, lysine, alanine.

Chains A and B are held together by —S—S— linkages.

We are all familiar with the multitude of uses of silk as a fiber, and are probably also impressed by the tremendous utility and serviceability of nylon. *Nylon* is a huge synthetic molecule, very similar to the silk protein molecule.

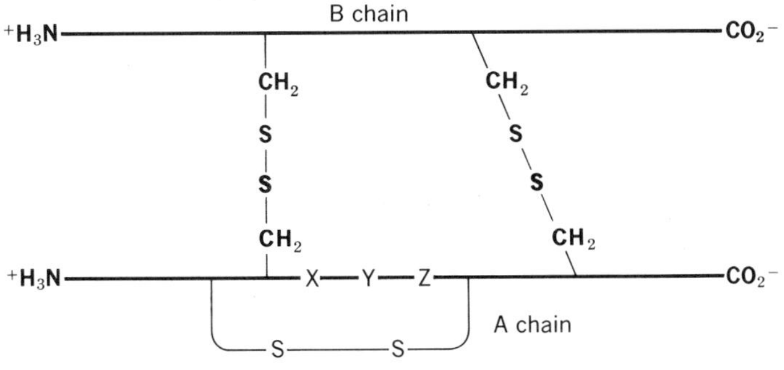

Figure 12-1 The primary structure of insulin. (© 1967 by Harcourt, Brace & World, Inc. Reproduced from *General Chemistry* by M. A. Paul, E. J. King, and L. H. Farinholt, by permission of the publishers.)

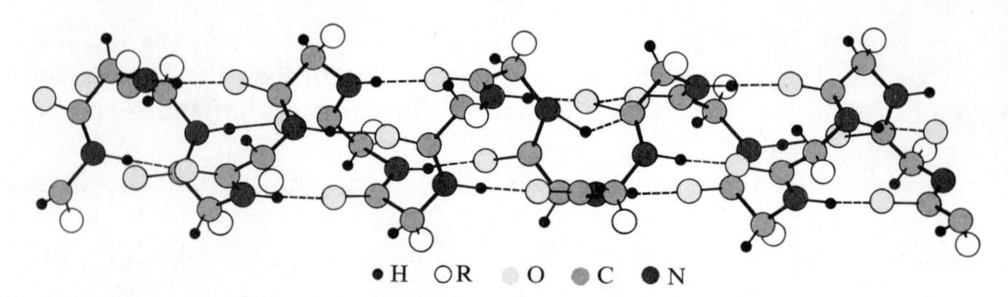

Figure 12-2 The alpha helix proposed by Pauling and Corey for polypeptide chains. (© 1967 by Harcourt, Brace & World. Reproduced from *General Chemistry* by M. A. Paul, E. J. King, and L. H. Farinholt, by permission of the publishers.)

One type of nylon is made from adipic acid and hexamethylene diamine. The nylon molecule has peptide linkages and is fibrous in nature, just like its silk counterpart. Although nylon is not a protein, it is a very good imitation of nature's handiwork. See facing page.

In addition to recognizing the arrangement of the α-amino acids held together by peptide bonds, we also know that the polypeptide chain assumes a helical structure (see Figure 12-2).

In the helical structure, weak hydrogen bonds hold sections of the helix together.

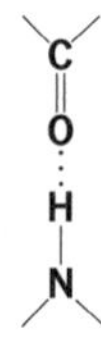

hydrogen bond between one carbonyl group of a peptide linkage and between an —**NH**— group of another peptide linkage.

Also, acid groups and basic groups interact, when stereochemically possible, to form a saltlike linkage, which strengthens the helix.

Finally, as the helix structure develops, the total structure may be exceedingly complicated and may resemble a ball of yarn, in which the thread is the chain of α-amino acids.

Protein complexity is further augmented by the fact that the R groups are so different in nature. The R groups may contain acid groups, basic groups, hydroxyl groups, sulfhydryl groups (HS—), etc., and *these* groups can interact. Because we generally do not know the exact arrangement of the amino acids, we can only guess the extent of the R group interaction. If we assume that the protein molecule is a huge mass of amino acids, undoubtedly many of the R groups are free and "jut out" from the main protein body. The R groups are of great importance because they carry the charges. Let us *represent* the protein moiety as a sphere (for convenience) and the various R groups as uneven spots on the surface of the sphere. See Figure 12-3.

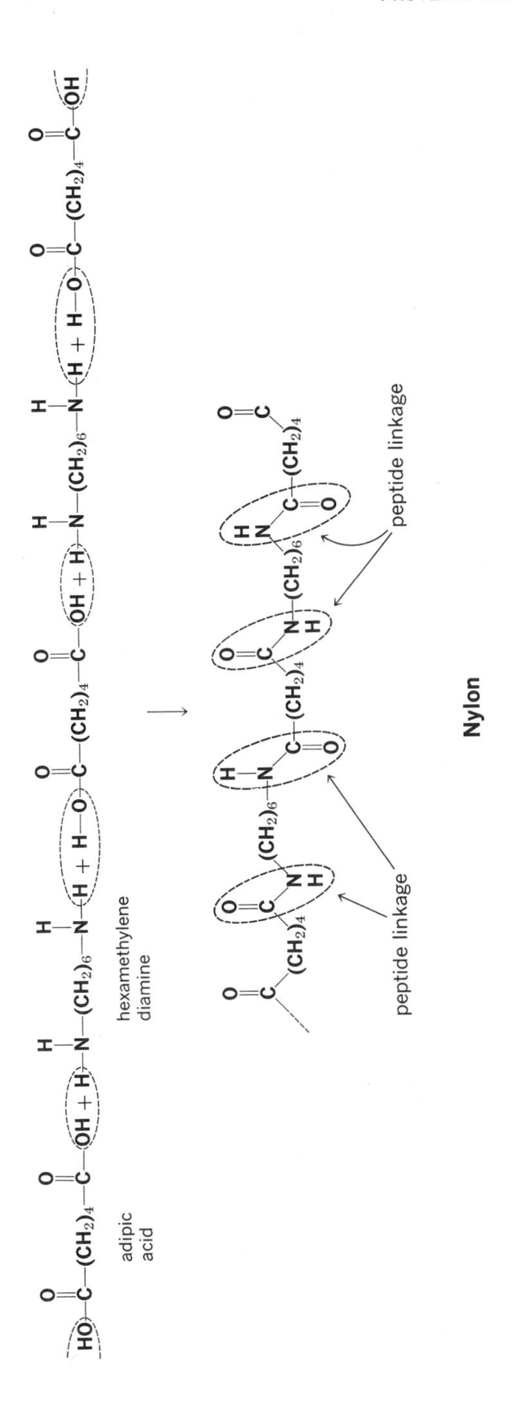
adipic
acid
hexamethylene
diamine
peptide linkage
peptide linkage
Nylon

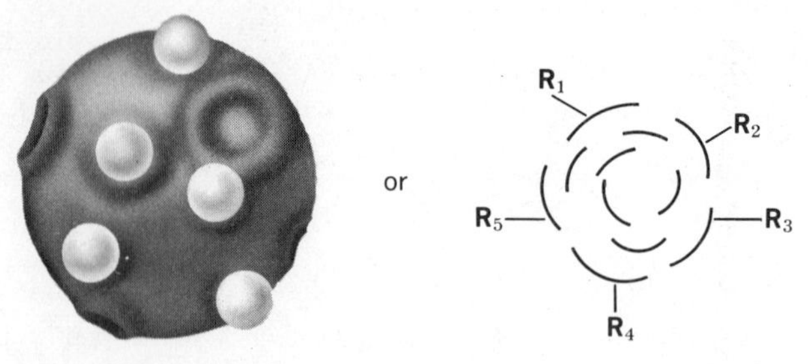

Figure 12-3 Protein molecule.

In normal proteins, the amino acids can be combined in an infinite number of ways, and it is indeed surprising that nature should ever synthesize, twice in succession, proteins that are alike.

For a very simple example, let us suppose that a protein had five R groups jutting out and that three of these were carboxyl groups and two were amino groups. For example,

H_2N— —COOH
—NH_2
HOOC— —COOH

This would probably be better represented in the ionic form.

$H_3\overset{\oplus}{N}$— —$COO^{\ominus}$
—$NH_3^{\oplus}$
$^{\ominus}OOC$— —$COO^{\ominus}$

In the above molecule, there are three (−) charges and two (+) charges. The net overall charge of this protein would be −1. (It would migrate towards the + pole.)

Colloidal Protein Particles

Proteins are excellent examples of colloidal matter. Protein molecules are very large; that is, they are large enough to be in the colloidal range. They are protected by the *electrical charges* on the various R groups and by the *solvent molecules* (H_2O) that permeate the surface and surround the colloidal protein molecules. Because *like charges repel each other,* two like charged particles are not apt to come together and coalesce to form a larger, precipitated particle.

Because the surface is polar in nature, the molecule has a special exterior layer of polar water molecules. The surface water molecules have an organized structure, like ice, and yet are in liquid form. The special surface water layer on a protein acts like a bumper of an automobile and physically prevents the large protein molecules from coming together.

Proteins are most likely to precipitate at the isoelectric point, because the net overall charge is zero and this protection is gone. The majority of the proteins in the body have a net overall negative charge. The addition of an acid to such a charged protein would tend to lower the excess negative charge and bring the colloidal particle to the isoelectric point, at which it may readily precipitate. This is why many natural proteins become insoluble when they are acidified (e.g., casein in milk, albumin in eggs, etc.).

By adding sufficient acid we may completely *change* the net overall charge of a negatively charged protein to that of a positively charged particle. In so doing, we pass through the isoelectric point. If we quickly pass over this sensitive point, the colloidal particle is again protected by electrical charges, this time of a different sign. See Figure 12-4.

Precipitation of Proteins

To precipitate proteins, we must in some way remove the protective electrical charges and/or the protective solvent molecules.

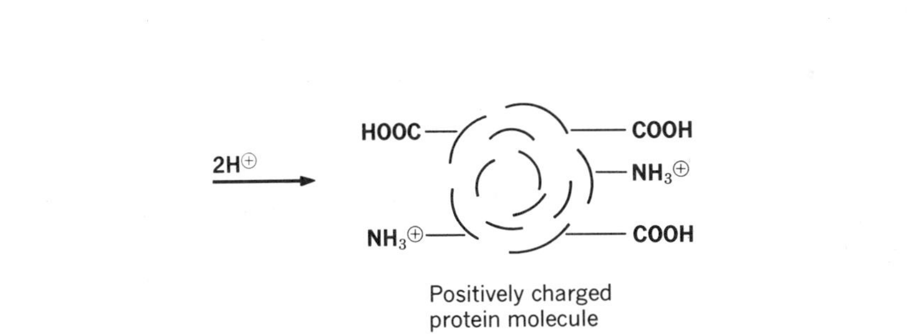

$^{\ominus}OOC$, $COO^{\ominus}$, $NH_3^{\oplus}$, $COO^{\ominus}$, $NH_3^{\oplus}$

Negatively charged protein molecule

$\xrightarrow{H^{\oplus}}$

$HOOC$, $COO^{\ominus}$, $NH_3^{\oplus}$, $COO^{\ominus}$, $NH_3^{\oplus}$

Protein molecule at the isoelectric point

$\xrightarrow{2H^{\oplus}}$

$HOOC$, $COOH$, $NH_3^{\oplus}$, $COOH$, $NH_3^{\oplus}$

Positively charged protein molecule

Figure 12-4 Transfer from a negative to a positive protein.

ACTION OF HEAT

When a solution of colloidal protein particles is heated to boiling, coagulation usually occurs. The temperature at which coagulation occurs is almost as sharp as a melting point. When a protein is heated, it first undergoes *denaturation.* Denaturation is a process whereby the protein molecule undergoes a change in which its chemical, physical, and biological properties are altered but its actual chemical composition remains the same. In this process, no amino acids are split off, and the charge on the molecule stays the same. Denaturation may be considered a breaking of some of the weak internal bonds or a reorientation of the large protein molecule, much as in the opening or unraveling of a long chain of atoms and the closing of the chain in a different position. Denaturation is necessary but not sufficient for the formation of a coagulum. For this reason, when working with proteins, one tries to avoid heat, which might change the protein without precipitating it. Once denaturation has occurred, continued heating causes the flocculation of the protein. (The flocculum may or may not be soluble in water, depending on the pH of the solution.) Continued heating of the flocculum causes the formation of the coagulum, which is completely insoluble in water. In heating a colloidal protein molecule, *the water content changes,* and the decrease in this protective agent also contributes to the precipitation of the protein.

All microorganisms are proteinlike in character. The flaming of the mouth of a test tube or the autoclaving of equipment results in the precipitation and death of any proteinlike organisms that may be present and thus sterilizes the material. Cooking food often results in the precipitation of proteins (e.g., preparing hard-boiled eggs). Many times, one tests a solution for proteins by the application of heat to see if anything precipitates (e.g., heating urine samples to test for foreign protein).

ACTION OF ALCOHOL

If alcohol is added to a protein solution, the protein coagulates. The presence of the alcohol *changes the water content* of the protein molecule and thereby decreases its solubility and causes the formation of the coagulum. Seventy percent alcohol is an effective sterilizing agent because it destroys the microorganisms, by penetrating them and causing denaturation. Higher concentrations of alcohol (e.g., 95%) render the proteins insoluble, without apparently causing denaturation. Thus, 95% alcohol may precipitate microorganisms without destroying them. For this reason, 70% alcohol is used extensively in medical work.

ACTION OF SALT SOLUTIONS

The addition of salt solutions *changes the water content* of the proteins and thereby decreases the solubility. This process is known as salting out. Ammonium sulfate, $(NH_4)_2SO_4$, is a commonly used salting-out agent. In the process, proteins apparently are not denatured. A protein (colloid) so precipitated may be separated from the salt (crystalloid) by dialysis, and the purified protein thus obtained is still the same in all respects (including biological activity) and will dissolve again in pure water. This method is used extensively in the isolation of biologically active proteins. The solubility of proteins in salt solutions varies considerably. Some proteins are quite soluble in fairly concentrated salt solutions, whereas others are easily precipitated by only small additions of salt. Some classifications of proteins are based on their solubilities in salt solutions.

ACTION OF HEAVY METAL SALTS

Salts of mercury, silver, lead, and other heavy metals have been known for a long time to be very poisonous. These salts are also quite effective in killing microorganisms. Heavy metal salts precipitate proteins by forming insoluble proteinates and thus account for the above-mentioned facts.

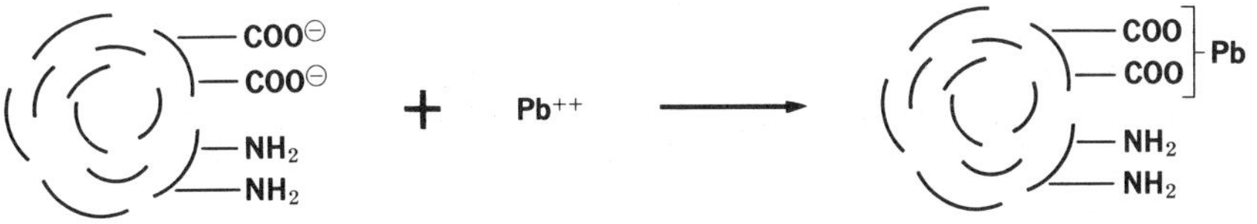

$COO^{\ominus}$, $COO^{\ominus}$, NH_2, NH_2 $\;+\;$ Pb^{++} $\longrightarrow$ COO, COO] Pb, NH_2, NH_2

Insoluble lead proteinate

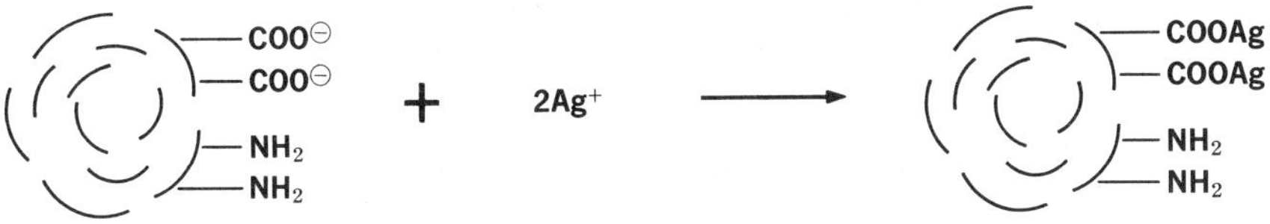

$COO^{\ominus}$, $COO^{\ominus}$, NH_2, NH_2 $\;+\;$ $2Ag^{+}$ $\longrightarrow$ $COOAg$, $COOAg$, NH_2, NH_2

Insoluble silver proteinate

Because the majority of naturally occurring proteins are negatively charged, the above reactions can be visualized also as a neutralization process (i.e., a process that destroys the protective charges on the colloidal particles). If, however, the protein is positively charged, the heavy metal ions (also positively charged) cannot destroy the protective charges, and the proteins remain in solution.

In the not too distant past, chemotherapy was concerned, to a great extent, with giving a sick patient just enough heavy metal ion to kill the disease organism but not the patient. This was frequently an unsatisfactory process. If heavy metal salts are accidently taken into the body, important proteins are precipitated and destroyed, which accounts for the toxic effects of these salts. An efficient antidote for the heavy metal ion, which has been taken internally, is to give the patient egg white or another available naturally negatively charged protein. This precipitates the heavy metal ion before too much damage has been done. This procedure is usually followed by the administration of an emetic to remove the precipitated heavy metal proteinate. Silver salts such as Argyrol, used in the treatment of nose and throat infections, and silver nitrate, used to prevent gonorrhea infections in the eyes of newborn infants, are used extensively. Mercuric chloride is a disinfectant commonly used in biological laboratories.

Inorganic mercury compounds, such as mercuric chloride, $HgCl_2$ (corrosive sublimate), furnish many mercuric ions; hence, the poisonous effects. Mercurous chloride, Hg_2Cl_2 (calomel), is *insoluble* in water, furnishes *few* mercury ions, and thus is not so poisonous.

Many organic compounds containing mercury are known, and these, in general, furnish very few mercury ions and, hence, can be taken internally as diuretics.

ALKALOIDAL REAGENTS AND LARGE NEGATIVE IONS

If the protein has a net overall positive charge, precipitation may occur by the addition of a large negative ion, such as the tungstate ion WO_4^{--} or ferrocyanide ion $Fe(CN)_6^{4-}$.

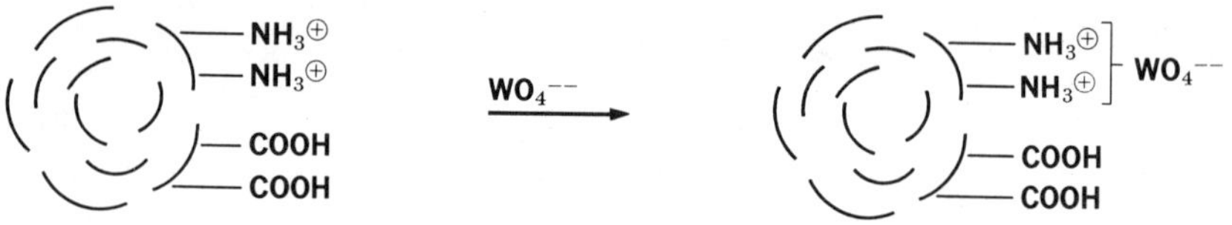

$NH_3^{\oplus}$, $NH_3^{\oplus}$, $COOH$, $COOH$ $\xrightarrow{WO_4^{--}}$ $[NH_3^{\oplus}, NH_3^{\oplus}]\ WO_4^{--}$, $COOH$, $COOH$

Positively charged protein

An insoluble protein salt, protein tungstate

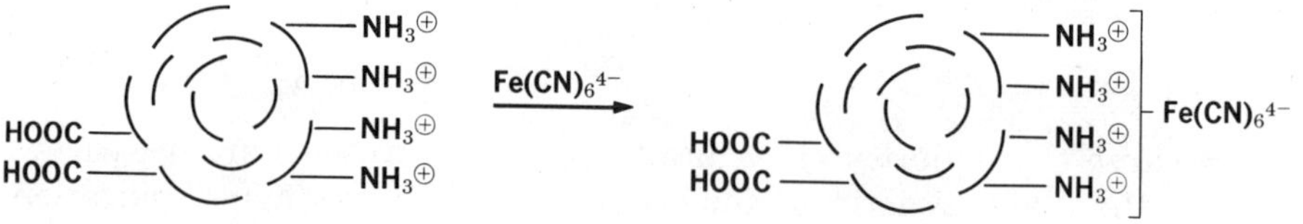

$HOOC$, $HOOC$, $NH_3^{\oplus}$, $NH_3^{\oplus}$, $NH_3^{\oplus}$, $NH_3^{\oplus}$ $\xrightarrow{Fe(CN)_6^{4-}}$ $HOOC$, $HOOC$, $[NH_3^{\oplus}, NH_3^{\oplus}, NH_3^{\oplus}, NH_3^{\oplus}]\ Fe(CN)_6^{4-}$

Positively charged protein

An insoluble protein salt, protein ferrocyanide

If the protein has a net overall negative charge, no precipitation will occur if the tungstate ion is added. The protein in blood can be conveniently and completely precipitated by the tungstate ion. Because blood is alkaline in character (i.e., protein has a negative charge), the solution must be made acidic (i.e., protein charge now positive) before the tungstate ion is added, to insure proper conditions for precipitation. This may also be regarded as a neutralization of the protective positive charge and removal of the electrical protection of the colloidal particles.

If the protein is acidic, many other reagents are also commonly used. Substances such as tannic acid, trichloroacetic acid, phosphotungstic acid, and phosphomolybdic acid will also precipitate proteins.

Tannic acid has enjoyed some success as a precipitant in the treatment of burns. Its efficiency is limited because its effectiveness depends on the pH. Tannic acid has little effect on intact skin, but when used in the absence of protective epidermis (i.e., when used on a bad burn), a protective protein film is precipitated that prevents contact with atmospheric oxygen, stops the loss of body fluids, and thus eases the pain and serves as a temporary skin. Nowadays, pressure bandaging technique has replaced, to a large extent, tannic acid treatments.

General Test For All Proteins

BIURET TEST

All types of proteins give this test. In fact, all polypeptides containing more than one peptide linkage will react positively. The substance, biuret, is derived from a condensation of two urea molecules and gives a positive test, since biuret also has the peptide linkage.

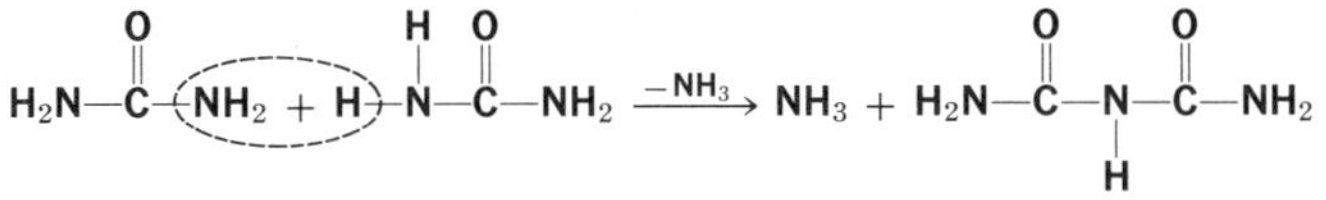

$$H_2N-\overset{O}{\overset{\|}{C}}-NH_2 + H-\overset{H}{\overset{|}{N}}-\overset{O}{\overset{\|}{C}}-NH_2 \xrightarrow{-NH_3} NH_3 + H_2N-\overset{O}{\overset{\|}{C}}-\underset{H}{\underset{|}{N}}-\overset{O}{\overset{\|}{C}}-NH_2$$

urea urea biuret

In performing the test, a strong solution of sodium hydroxide is added to the protein solution to be tested. After mixing thoroughly, a dilute solution of copper sulfate is added. A blue-violet (sometimes pink) color is indicative of a positive test.

Other Tests

NINHYDRIN REACTION

The ninhydrin reagent contains triketohydrindene hydrate.

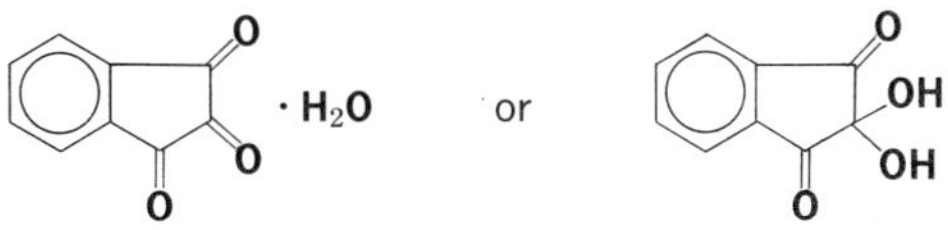

[structures: indane-1,2,3-trione $\cdot H_2O$ or 2,2-dihydroxyindane-1,3-dione]

triketohydrindene hydrate

If the solution to be tested contains at least one free $—NH_2$ group and one free —COOH group, a positive test (i.e., a test with the color ranging from clear deep blue to a violet-pink) will be observed. This very delicate test works for proteins, polypeptides, and even free amino acids, with proline and hydroxyproline as exceptions (red color).

MILLON'S TEST

This is a specific test for the hydroxyphenyl group in the protein molecule.

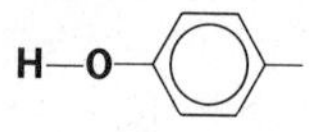

$$H—O—C_6H_4—$$

p-hydroxyphenyl group

The hydroxyphenyl group is commonly found in the amino acid tyrosine.

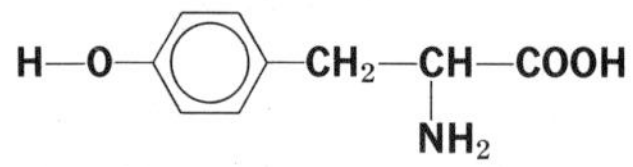

$$H—O—C_6H_4—CH_2—CH(NH_2)—COOH$$

tyrosine

Millon's reagent contains mercuric nitrate $Hg(NO_3)_2$ and mercuric nitrite $Hg(NO_2)_2$. When the reagent is added to a protein solution, a white precipitate (mercuric salt) is formed. When the test is positive, additional heating causes the precipitate to turn a flesh color. An excess of the reagent should be avoided.

XANTHOPROTEIC ACID TEST

This is a specific test for aromatic rings that are easily *nitrated* (such as rings in tryptophane, tyrosine, and phenylalanine). The reagent is concentrated nitric acid. The addition of any acid would have some precipitating action on normally basic proteins, but nitric acid produces some additional reactions. When a positive reaction occurs, the following is observed: When nitric acid is added to the protein solution to be tested, a precipitate is formed that changes to a yellow solution when heated. The addition of ammonium hydroxide to the basic point causes the solution to turn orange. The xanthoproteic acid test is performed by students many times, unintentionally, when nitric acid is spilled on the skin.

HELLER RING TEST

This test is commonly performed on urine to detect the presence of albumin (a protein). The condition of albumin in urine is known as *albuminuria.* A positive test may mean that the body is not functioning properly. This test is routinely performed in urinalysis. The reaction is observed by adding concentrated nitric acid slowly down the side of a test tube containing the urine sample to be tested. A white or yellow zone of precipitated and nitrated albumin, formed at the junction of the two liquids, is indicative of a positive test.

Some Quantitative Tests

The tests just mentioned are qualitative in nature: They tell us what groups are present, but not how much of each. We shall briefly mention several routinely run tests that are quantitative in nature.

VAN SLYKE

This test determines the amount of amino nitrogen present. In this procedure, the amino nitrogen is converted into nitrogen gas, by action of nitrous acid. The volume of the nitrogen gas can be conveniently measured, and the percentage of amino nitrogen can then be easily calculated.

$$\underset{}{R{-}NH_2} + \underset{\text{nitrous acid}}{HNO_2} \longrightarrow \underset{\text{gas}}{N_2\uparrow} + R{-}OH + H_2O$$

KJELDAHL

This test determines the percentage of nitrogen in certain samples. It is not applicable to all nitrogen-containing compounds but works well for proteins. Heterocyclic ring nitrogens, as well as some others, may give erroneous results (low). In this method, the protein is digested with concentrated sulfuric acid and a catalyst. This converts the nitrogen into a form such that, when the solution is made basic with concentrated sodium hydroxide, ammonia is liberated. The ammonia is blown out of the reaction vessel by steam into a definite amount of known acid. By titration, one can quickly discover how much acid is left and calculate the amount of ammonia that must have entered the acid solution. Once the ammonia is known, the amount of nitrogen in the original sample can easily be calculated.

DUMAS

This is a general method for determining the percentage of nitrogen in all samples, regardless of how the nitrogen is bound in the compound. In this method, the sample is mixed with copper oxide catalyst at high temperatures in an atmosphere of carbon dioxide. This procedure converts all the nitrogen into nitrogen gas, the volume of which can be conveniently measured.

Classification of proteins

Various systems of classification can be applied to proteins, but most of these systems were conceived about a half century ago and, in many cases, leave much to be desired. In general, the classifications are based on variations in solubility, which depends on many factors, one of the more important being the environmental salt concentration. We shall avoid this

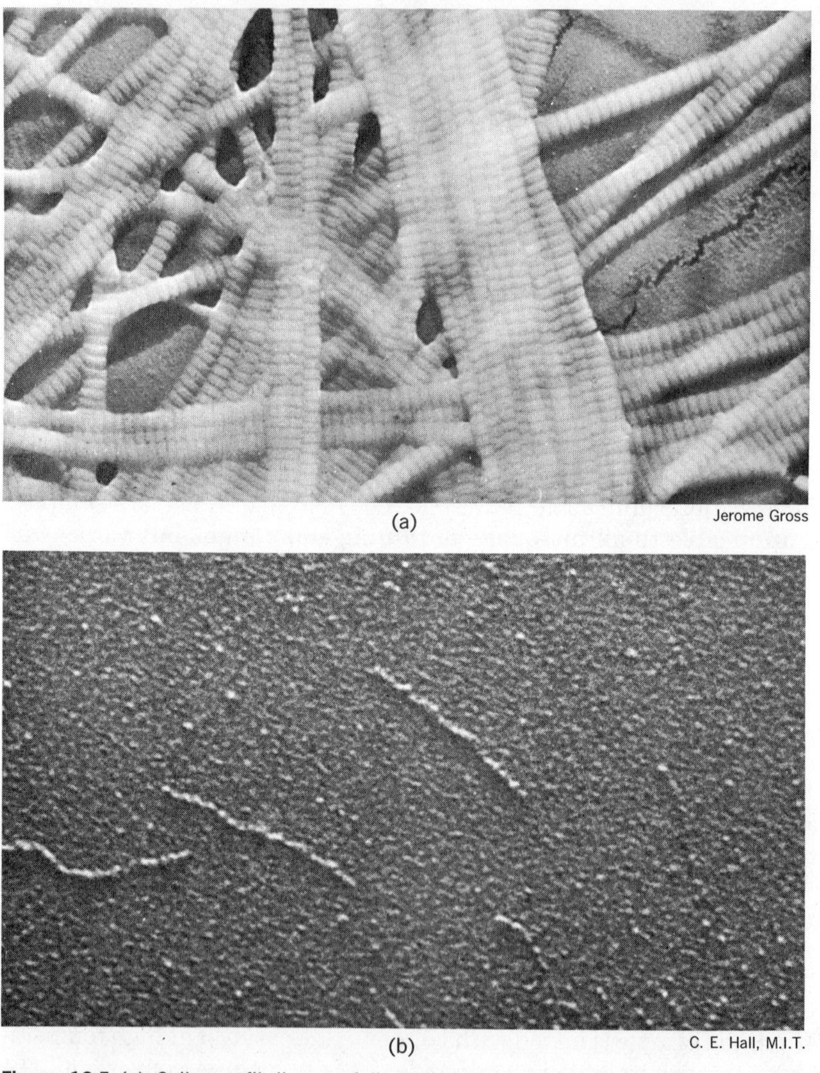

(a) Jerome Gross

(b) C. E. Hall, M.I.T.

Figure 12-5 (a) Collagen fibrils, carefully pulled away from human skin, show bands spaced about 700 A apart. (Electron Micrograph, magnification 28,000 diameters.) (b) Collagen molecules in an electron micrograph enlarged 162,500 ×. They are 2,800 to 2,900 A long and 14 to 15 A wide.

strict classification and discuss some of the important topics from a practical viewpoint.

Proteins may be considered the building material of tissue, and, accordingly, a valid classification of tissue protein is made dependent on its physical nature. We may call some proteins *fibrous* and some *globular*. A fibrous protein, as the name implies, is stringy and elongated, as, for example, the protein in silk, and keratin in hair and wool (see Figure 12-5). The globular proteins are not necessarily spherical, although their asymmetry is less than that of the fibrous proteins. Typical globular proteins are the globulins and others we shall mention.

Some proteins have been classified as *simple, conjugated,* and *derived.* Here again, some questions can be raised. A simple protein is one that yields only α-amino acids on hydrolysis. It is hard to believe that these proteins are not combined with something in the body. Therefore, the distinction may be artificial, because the proteins isolated and investigated chemically in the test tube are perhaps not in an identical state with those active in the body or living organism.

Conjugated proteins yield α-amino acids and something else upon hydrolysis. There are no limits as to what the other portions of the molecule may contain, which emphasizes the versatility of proteins.

Derived proteins are natural proteins in some state of partial or almost complete hydrolysis. Derived proteins are then breakdown products of proteins. Here again, one may question the validity of calling these fragments proteins. The following contains some of the more commonly encountered classes of proteins and some important examples of each.

ALBUMINS

The best examples are egg albumin, isolable from the white of the eggs, and serum albumin, isolable from blood serum. Both are relatively easy to obtain and have been prepared in a high degree of purity as crystalline material. Egg albumin and serum albumin contain carbohydrate residues and are therefore typical conjugated proteins. Proteins conjugated with carbohydrates are called glycoproteins. Other examples of albumins are lactalbumin from milk and leucosin from wheat. Some of the soft tissues of the body are composed of albumins. Albumins are readily soluble in water and are readily coagulated by heat.

GLOBULINS

Globulins have been isolated from vegetable sources and also from muscle tissue, blood serum, and other biological fluids. The fibrinogen of blood and the myosin of muscle are globulins. At death, the muscle myosin coagulates to form a hard material, resulting in *rigor mortis.* The duration of this coagulation process varies depending on the circumstances of death. Many of the soft tissues of the body are composed of globulins. Whey from cheese, excelsin from brazil nut, pomelin from orange seeds, and edestin from Indian hempseed are globulins. Squash and pumpkin seeds yield globulins. Seeds, in general, are rich in proteins. Globulins are insoluble or very slightly soluble in water, but their solubility is greatly increased by the addition of salts, such as sodium chloride. The globulins are readily coagulated by heat.

PROLAMINES

The prolamines are obtainable from all cereal grains (with the exception of rice). The name is given to this group because of the unusually large amount of proline formed on hydrolysis. Some examples are gliadin from wheat and rye, zein from maize, and hordein from barley.

ALBUMINOIDS

The *albuminoids* are a heterogeneous class containing many proteins that are difficult to classify. The albuminoids do not occur in the vegetable kingdom. Proteins from silk, wool, hair, skin, nails, horns, quills, and bone matrix are albuminoids. Spongin, the skeletal proteins of sponges and coral, is classified in this group. The albuminoids are found in certain connective body tissues and as such are divided into three classes:

Elastins, the main protein of yellow connective tissue, are present in arteries, tendons, and other elastic tissue. The elastins are not convertible into gelatins.

Keratins are the main proteins of wool, hair, quills, hoofs, finger nails, etc. These proteins are high in the sulfur-containing α-amino acid, cystine.

Collagens are the main proteins of white connective tissue. More than half the total protein in mammals is collagen. Collagens are *insoluble* in water and quite *resistant* to animal digestive enzymes. There has been great interest centered in collagen because, when this protein is boiled in water, the insoluble protein is converted into the soluble form, called *gelatin.* Purified gelatin, being a modified natural protein, is useful as a food. Food gelatin prevents formation of large ice crystals in frozen desserts and also renders milk more digestible by preventing the formation of large casein curds by gastric juice with the accompanying occlusion of fat. Powdered gelatin, sugar, and solids from evaporated fruit juice, colors, and flavors are the ingredients of the popular dessert powders. Technical gelatin has a variety of uses, including the manufacture of adhesives and glue and the making of colloidal protectors of silver salts employed in photography.

Certain gelatin preparations, which have been very highly purified, are useful in surgery in that the material may be left in the body to fill holes left by removal of considerable portions of body tissues (e.g., injuries from accidents, war wounds, etc.). The gelatin, being a protein, acts as a simple replacement for the removed proteins and becomes the new connective tissue.

PROTAMINES

The protamines are found in ripe sperm cells and are characterized by being smaller than the usual protein. Some protamines vary in molecular weight between 3,000 to 10,000. Salmine, for example, is found in ripe salmon sperm, and clupeine is found in herring sperm. *Insulin,* which is classified as a hormone, is a protein secreted in the body. In treating diabetes, insulin injections cause a rapid decrease in blood sugar and produces many undesirable side effects. However, when *protamines* and *zinc* are combined with insulin, they form the zinc-protamine-insulin complex, which is somewhat insoluble and consequently not easily or quickly absorbed. When this complex is injected, the effect of the insulin is more even, and the duration of the effect of the drug is longer. The injection does not cause a rapid decrease in blood sugar, and thus larger doses of insulin can be injected.

HISTONES

Histones are soluble in water and contain large amounts of lysine and arginine. Histones occur in large amounts in certain glandular tissue, such as the pancreas and the thymus.

Conjugated Proteins

THE CHROMOPROTEINS

These are typical conjugated proteins that contain a coloring group. The coloring group is known as the prosthetic group and is nonprotein in nature. The red hemoglobin is probably the best-known chromoprotein. Globulin is the protein part, and heme is the coloring part. Apparently four heme groups are connected to each globulin molecule. Heme contains iron in the ferrous state. Chlorophyll, the green coloring substance in plants, contains a prosthetic group remarkably similar to heme. One of the big differences is that chlorophyll contains magnesium, whereas heme contains iron.

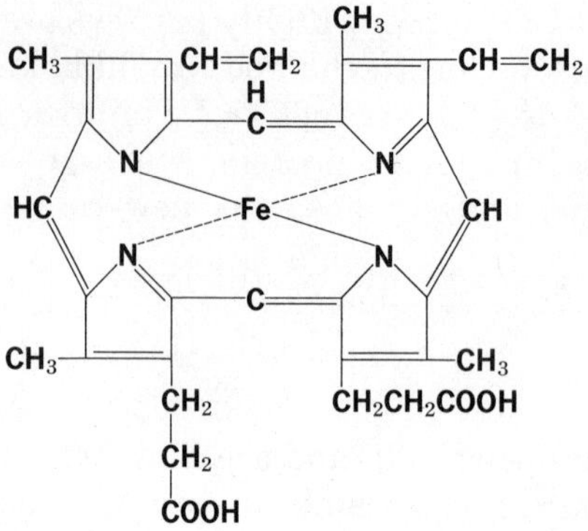

heme

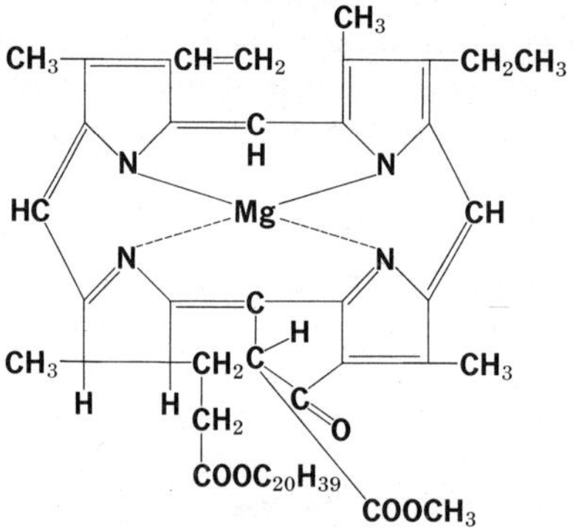

chlorophyll a

The main function of hemoglobin is to carry oxygen, which was breathed in, to the tissue of the body, via the blood stream. The hemoglobin combines with the oxygen in the lungs to form oxyhemoglobin, which is a loosely combined compound. The oxyhemoglobin then goes to all the parts of the body and liberates the oxygen to the tissues, which need the oxygen for energy-producing purposes. Hemoglobin is synthesized in the red bone marrow, liver, and spleen, and traces of cobalt, manganese, and copper are essential catalysts for hemoglobin formation.

Hemoglobins from different species differ in their crystalline form and can be easily differentiated by microscopic examination. The difference is due to the different globulins in the various species. The heme part, however, is *identical* in each species.

Chlorocruorin is the green oxygen-containing pigment found in the blood of polychaete worms. The coloring group is related to heme, but it is not heme. Erythrocruorin is the red oxygen-containing pigment obtained from certain worms. Hemocyanins are very large conjugated proteins characterized by containing *copper*. Hemocyanins are found in the blood of the squid, octopus, lobster, oyster, and mollusk. The oxygen-containing capacity of the hemocyanins is about one-fourth that of hemoglobin.

MELANO PROTEINS

Melanin is the dark pigment found in the basal layer of the epidermis. Melanin is synthesized in the melanoblasts from tyrosine.

HO–C_6H_4–CH_2–CH(NH_2)–COOH $\xrightarrow[\text{steps}]{\text{several}}$ indole 5,6-quinone $\longrightarrow$ melanin

tyrosine — indole 5,6-quinone

In a series of oxidation steps, tyrosine is oxidized to indole 5,6-quinone (an orthoquinone), which may be spontaneously oxidized to melanin (exact structure unknown). Skin color depends upon the distribution of melanoblasts and the melanin. In *albinos,* either melanin-forming cells or the enzyme involved in the oxidation of tyrosine (see above) may be absent.

Darkening of the human skin may be caused by the ultraviolet irradiation of tyrosine. It has been discovered that the monobenzyl ether of hydroquinone can effect depigmentation of the skin. The ether has been used as an *antioxidant* in rubber goods, but it has been recommended that its use be discontinued. However, some dermatologists have reported that the ether is useful in removing skin blotches. It is believed that the monobenzyl ether of hydroquinone prevents the formation of the basic skin pigment, melanin.

FLAVOPROTEINS AND GLYCOPROTEINS

The *flavoproteins* contain riboflavin, one of the B-vitamins, and are involved in many enzymatic reactions, usually oxidations. *Luciferase* is an interesting flavoprotein that catalyzes the absorption of oxygen by certain species and thus produces luminescence. The light produced by the firefly, the glowworm, and photogenic bacteria is due to luciferase.

Glycoproteins are conjugated proteins, which on hydrolysis yield carbohydrates in addition to amino acids. Mucin, the glycoprotein found in saliva, is characterized by its slippery texture. Heparin, the anticoagulant involved in blood clotting, is also a glycoprotein.

PHOSPHOPROTEINS

Phosphoproteins are conjugated proteins that yield phosphoric acid, as well as amino acids, on hydrolysis. This is perhaps an arbitrary class, because many other conjugated proteins also yield phosphoric acid. For example, the nucleoproteins and the lipoproteins yield phosphoric acid on hydrolysis but are classified differently because of the importance of their nonprotein part. The two important phosphoproteins are casein, obtained from milk, and vitellin, isolable from egg yolk. Casein is the characteristic protein of the milk of all mammals. More will be stated concerning the use and properties of casein in Chapter 14.

LIPOPROTEINS

Some proteins are conjugated to certain lipids, such as cephalins, lecithins, and steroids. Lipoproteins is a general name, and perhaps lecithoprotein and cephaloprotein may be more descriptive. More will be said about the lipoproteins in the discussion of the mechanism of blood clotting in Chapter 20.

NUCLEOPROTEINS

The nucleoproteins are conjugated proteins, and the nonprotein part is the nucleic acid. The nucleic acid may be regarded as cylindrical in shape, with the protein surrounding the nucleic acid like a glove (see Figure 12-6).

Viruses are nucleoproteins that have been shown to have unusual characteristics. The molecules are so large that they are actually visible by means of the electron microscope. The molecular weights vary from about 2 to 70 million. Viruses, when purified, are crystalline in nature, indicating single *inanimate* chemical entities. Viruses are capable of infecting a host, *reproducing* at the expense of the host, and often killing the host. This latter characteristic indicates that viruses are *living* organisms. This raises the question: Are viruses living organisms or nonliving matter? Viruses and genes have a striking resemblance in that both are protein in nature and can be altered to produce a mutant substance.

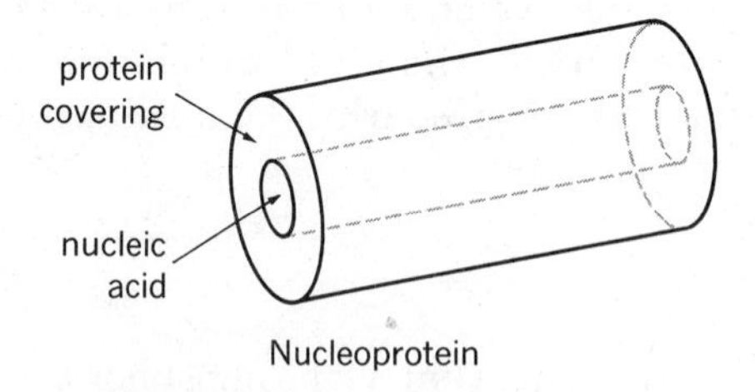

Figure 12-6 Nucleoprotein.

Many of the serious diseases of man are caused by viruses. Such conditions as influenza, poliomyelitis, and virus pneumonia are caused by these nucleoproteins. Much work has been done to learn more about viruses and thus be able to prevent and cure the virus diseases. Some success has been encountered in treating certain strains of virus with chemicals that destroy its disease-producing properties, so that it may be used as a vaccine. The main difficulty in trying to destroy viruses in living tissue by chemotherapy is that the tissue itself is full of other nondisease nucleoproteins. To destroy a virus in the host, one must possess some superselective agent that will destroy only the virus nucleoprotein. A *bacteriophage* is a virus that infects bacteria.

Nucleic Acids

Two types of nucleic acids occur in every living cell. Deoxyribonucleic acid, abbreviated DNA, is a constituent of cell nuclei and is responsible for the transfer of genetic information. Ribonucleic acid, abbreviated RNA, is located chiefly in the cytoplasm outside the nucleus and is responsible for the synthesis of proteins.

Both DNA and RNA are very large molecules containing special nitrogen bases, phosphoric acid, and a pentose. In DNA, the pentose is β-2-deoxy-D-ribose.

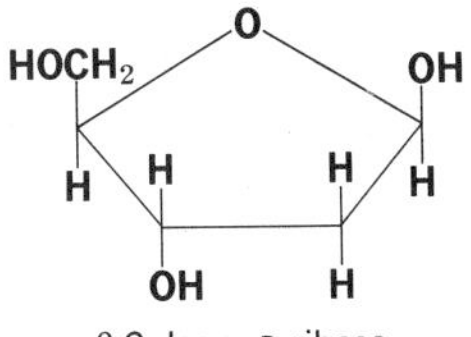

O
$HOCH_2$ OH
H H H H
OH H

β-2-deoxy-D-ribose

In RNA, the pentose is β-D-ribose.

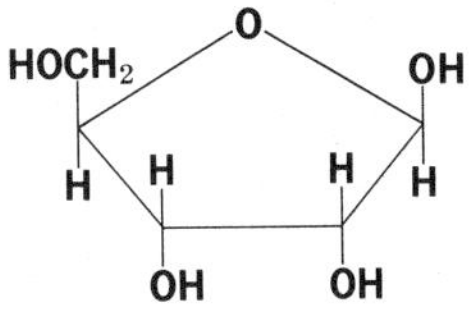

O
$HOCH_2$ OH
H H H H
OH OH

β-D-ribose

In DNA and RNA, we have a long chain of alternating pentose and phosphoric acids, with the base attached to each pentose.

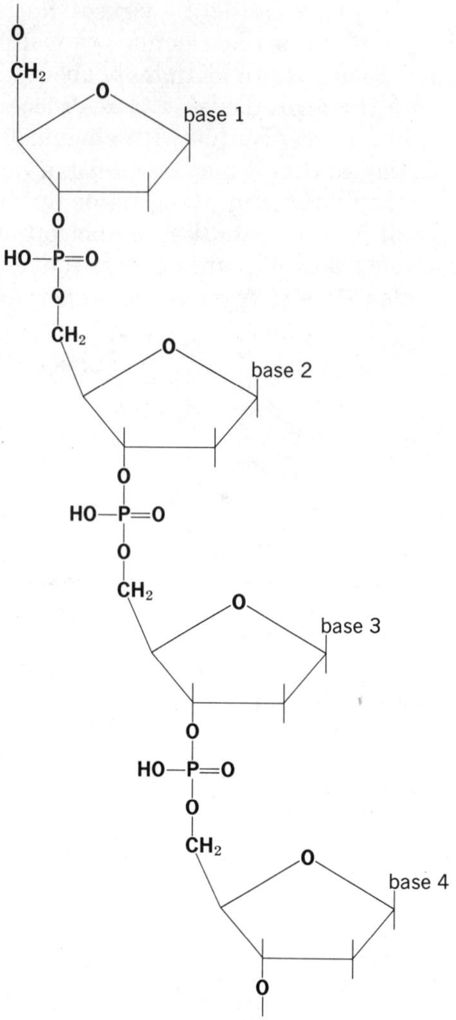

simple features of
RNA and DNA structures

THE ORGANIC BASES

The organic bases in nucleic acids are usually purines or pyrimidines.

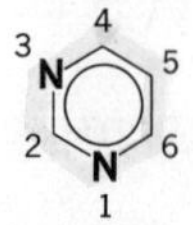

pyrimidine

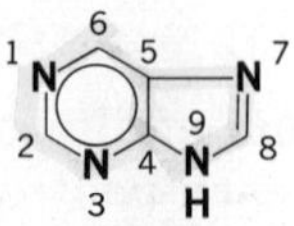

purine

Whenever an oxygen atom is present in these nitrogen heterocyclic systems in a position *next* to the nitrogen hetero-atom, the molecule can exist in two different forms: the enol and keto forms.

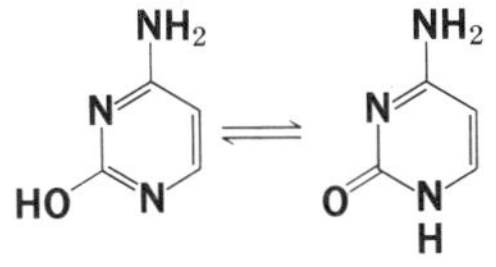

enol form keto form

cytosine

Note that the hydrogen atom on the hydroxyl group in spot 2 (i.e., the enol form) moves over to the nitrogen in spot 1 (i.e., the keto form). Remember that this hydrogen may jump back to its original position to produce the enol form.

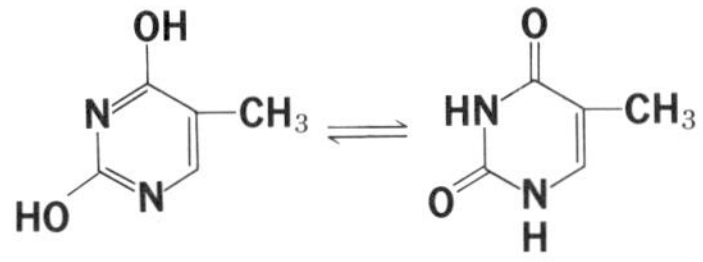

enol form keto form

thymine

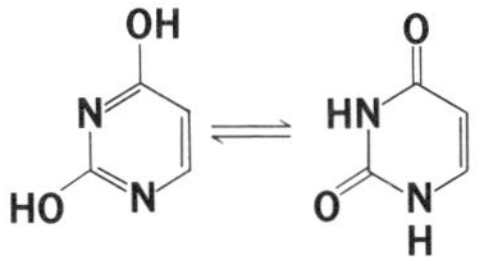

enol form keto form

uracil

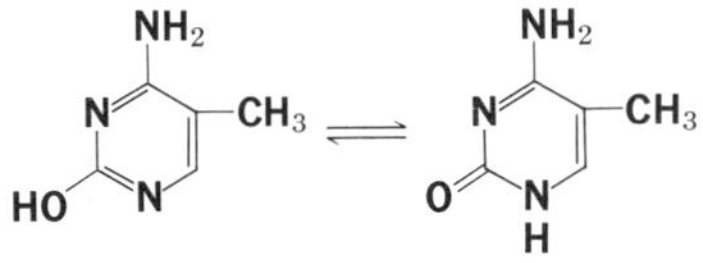

enol form keto form

5-methylcytosine

In nucleic acids, cytosine, thymine, and uracil are of great importance, and 5-methylcytosine is of lesser importance.

We find a similar situation in the purine systems.

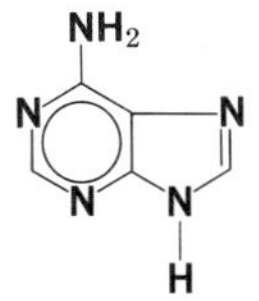

adenine

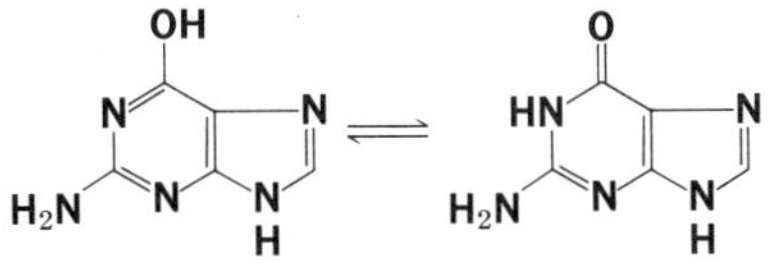

enol form keto form

guanine

In man, it is interesting that uracil is an end metabolic product of pyrimidines, and uric acid is the end metabolic product of purines.

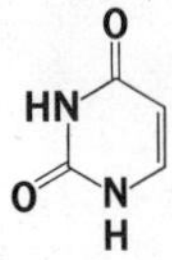

uracil 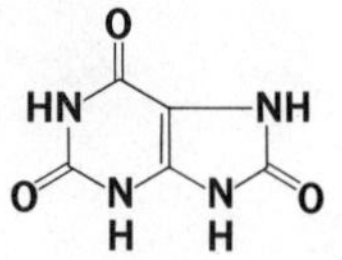 uric acid

The purines, adenine and guanine, are found in both DNA and RNA. The pyrimidine, cytosine, is also found in both RNA and DNA. However, the fourth organic base varies with the different nucleic acids: RNA contains uracil, whereas DNA contains thymine. Occasionally, bases other than the ones discussed above are found in nucleic acids.

NUCLEOSIDES

A nucleoside is the combination of the pentose and the nitrogen base.

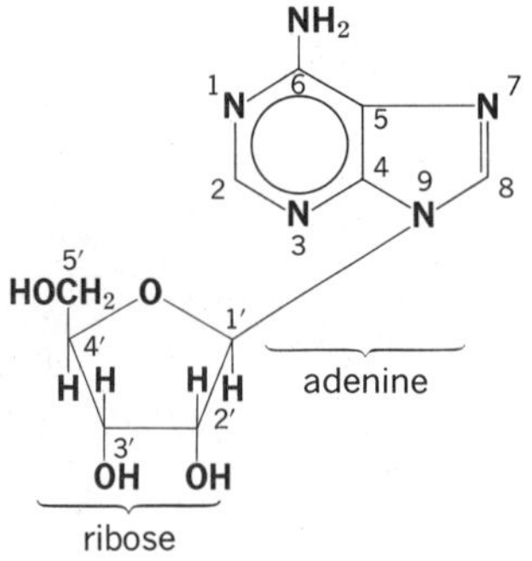

ribose adenine

adenosine

Note that the linkage from the carbohydrate is β and that the linkage is between nitrogen 9 of the purine and OH—1′ of the pentose. We use prime numbers for the carbohydrates and regular numbers for the nitrogen base so that there will be no possibility of confusion.

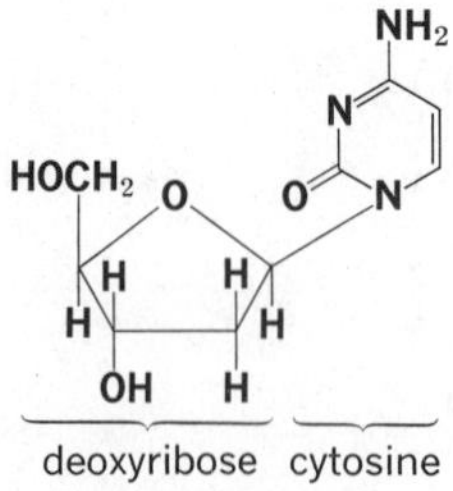

deoxyribose cytosine

deoxycytidine

Table 12-4 Common nucleosides

Combination	*Name*
RIBOSIDES	
adenine-ribose	adenosine
guanine-ribose	guanosine
cytosine-ribose	cytidine
uracil-ribose	uridine
thymine-ribose	thymine ribonucleoside or thymine-riboside
DEOXYRIBOSIDES	
adenine-deoxyribose	deoxyadenosine
guanine-deoxyribose	deoxyguanosine
cytosine-deoxyribose	deoxycytidine
uracil-deoxyribose	deoxyuridine
thymine-deoxyribose	thymidine

Note that the linkage from the deoxycarbohydrate is still β and that the linkage is between the keto form of the pyrimidine, spot 1, and carbon 1′ of the deoxypentose.

Table 12-4 lists the accepted names for the common nucleosides.

NUCLEOTIDES

A nucleotide is a phosphate ester of a nucleoside. If you examine the structural formula of adenosine, you see that the ribose part has *three* free —OH groups (2′, 3′, and 5′). This means that the phosphate ester may be attached in any of these positions, and, indeed, all have been found in nature.

In the deoxyadenosine, only *two* free —OH groups remain (3′ and 5′), and, indeed, phosphate esters at both positions have been isolated. Names such as adenylic acid, guanylic acid, uridylic acid, cytidylic acid, and thymidylic acid are used to identify the phosphate esters of the nucleosides.

If a nucleotide is treated with a base, the phosphoric acid is easily removed to leave the base-sugar combination (nucleoside). If the nucleotide is treated with acid, however, the nitrogen base is split off to leave the sugar-phosphate combination. The purine nucleosides are easily hydrolyzed in acid; the pyrimidine nucleosides are slowly hydrolyzed in acid.

One can determine whether one is dealing with a DNA molecule or a RNA molecule by using the furfural test on the carbohydrate. Recall that a pentose and HCl yields furfural, whereas a deoxypentose does not give furfural.

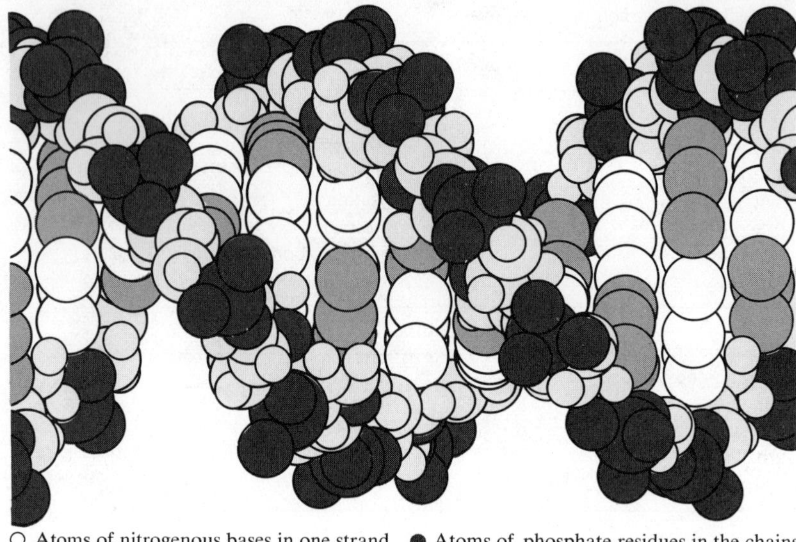

Figure 12-7 Two-stranded DNA. The double helix model of Watson and Crick. Adopted from "Single-stranded DNA," by Robert L. Sinsheimer. Copyright © July 1962 by Scientific American, Inc. All rights reserved.

THE STRUCTURE OF DNA AND RNA

An important observation concerning the ratio of the bases of DNA led to the elucidation of the structure.

It was observed that the adenine and thymine occurrence in DNA was essentially equal. It was also deduced that the 1:1 ratio meant that the two are chemically close to one another and, in fact, at least loosely attached to one another. The two bases are loosely held together by two hydrogen bonds.

CH_3 O ·········· H—N (2.85 A)
N—H ·········· N (2.90 A)

A = angstrom unit
the dotted lines indicate the two hydrogen bonds holding the adenine and thymine together

It was also observed that cytosine and guanine occurred in a 1:1 ratio, and that probably 3 hydrogen bonds held the bases together in the latter case.

the dotted lines indicate the three hydrogen bonds holding the cytosine and guanine together

X-ray work by Wilkens revealed the atomic distances (in angstrom units A) between the hydrogen bonded atoms in DNA and showed that they are all almost identical and that the base pairs really *fit together,* as shown on the above drawings. This led Watson and Crick to propose their famous model of DNA.

According to this concept, two parallel chains of polynucleotides are wound into a helix. The bases are pointed internally towards the axis and are paired together as shown in Figure 12-7.

The spatial configuration of RNA is probably similar to that of DNA, with respect to the helix and base pairings, but it is not as yet so clearly elucidated because it has been more difficult to obtain pure, undegraded samples of RNA than of DNA.

The ribosomes, or ribonucleoprotein particles, are apparently involved in protein synthesis (see Figure 12-8).

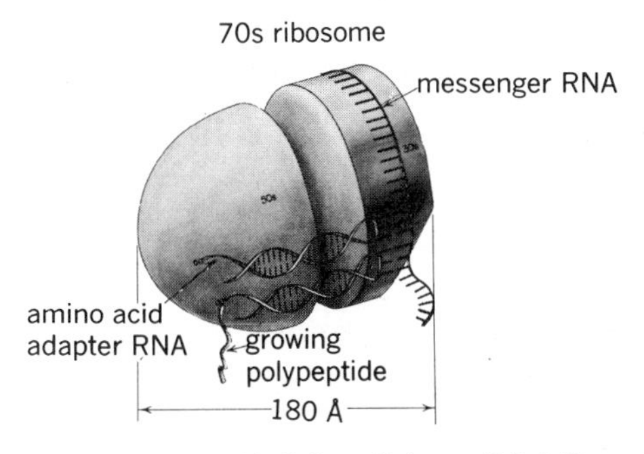

Figure 12-8 Ribosome. (G. Zubay, *Science,* Vol. 140, pp. 1092–1095, 7 June 1963. © 1963 by The American Association for the Advancement of Science.)

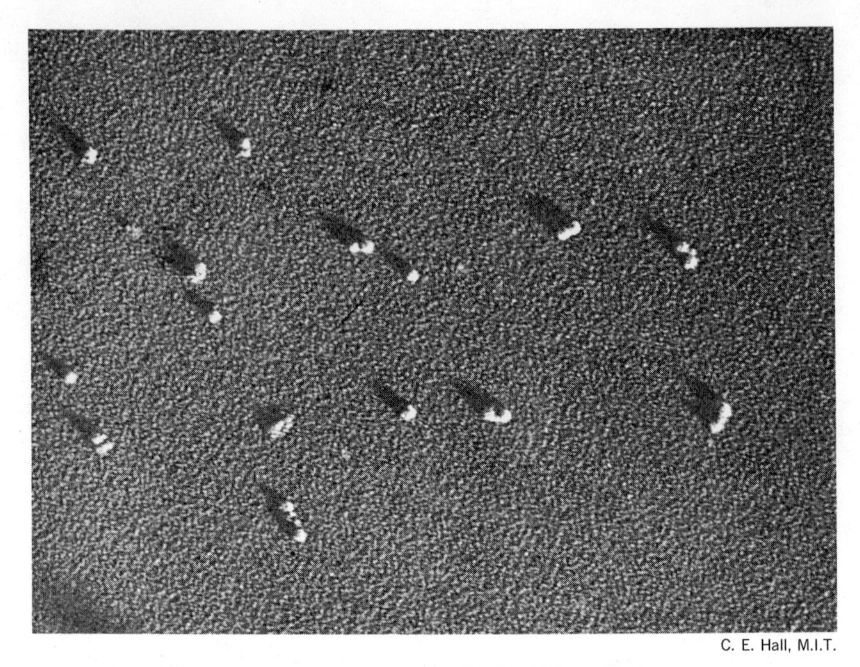

C. E. Hall, M.I.T.

Figure 12-9 Ribonucleoprotein particles from *Escherichia coli.* Magnification 100,500 ×.

A *group* of ribosomes actively involved with the soluble RNA and engaged in protein synthesis is called a *polysome.* (See Figures 12-9 and 12-10.)

The ribosomes have a molecular weight of about 3 million and an average diameter of about 150 A. Most of the RNA is associated with ribosomes. About 10% of the RNA is in the form of a low molecular weight structure (molecular weight about 30,000), and this smaller, *soluble* RNA is called soluble RNA (sRNA) or transfer RNA (tRNA).

According to current theory, the soluble RNA chain wraps itself around the ribosomes, and the arrangement of the bases in the RNA determines the arrangement of the α-amino acids in the protein being synthesized.

It is believed that three consecutive bases in the RNA form a "codon," or coding unit, which determines a particular α-amino acid (see Figures 12-11 and 12-12). As the RNA goes over the surface of the ribosomes, it "spells" out the arrangement of the α-amino acids of a protein being synthesized, just as the sheet of music going through the player piano determines the notes of the piano to be pressed.

All the inherited information concerning the protein to be made in our bodies resides in the DNA molecules, which transmit it to the RNA molecules, which in turn transmit it to the soluble RNA molecules, which are involved in making our own individual kinds of proteins.

Derived Proteins

Derived proteins are proteins that have been altered in some way so that the chemical, physical, and biochemical properties are now different. Among the more interesting of the derived proteins are those that have been exposed to hydrolytic reactions. The hydrolysis may proceed partially or completely and may be represented roughly by

proteins ⟶ proteoses ⟶ peptones ⟶ polypeptides ⟶ α-amino acids

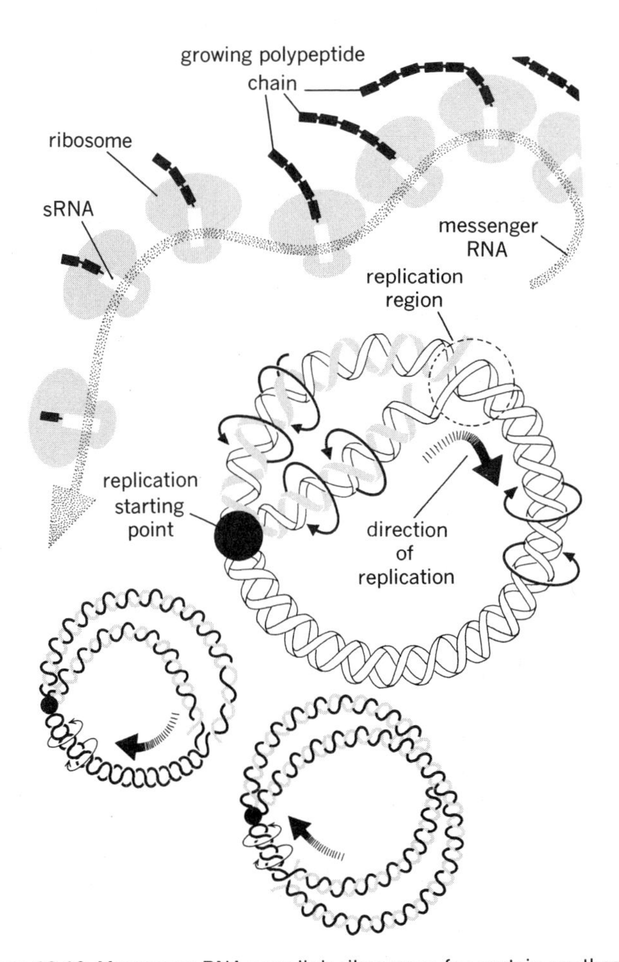

Figure 12-10 Messenger RNA may link ribosomes for protein synthesis.

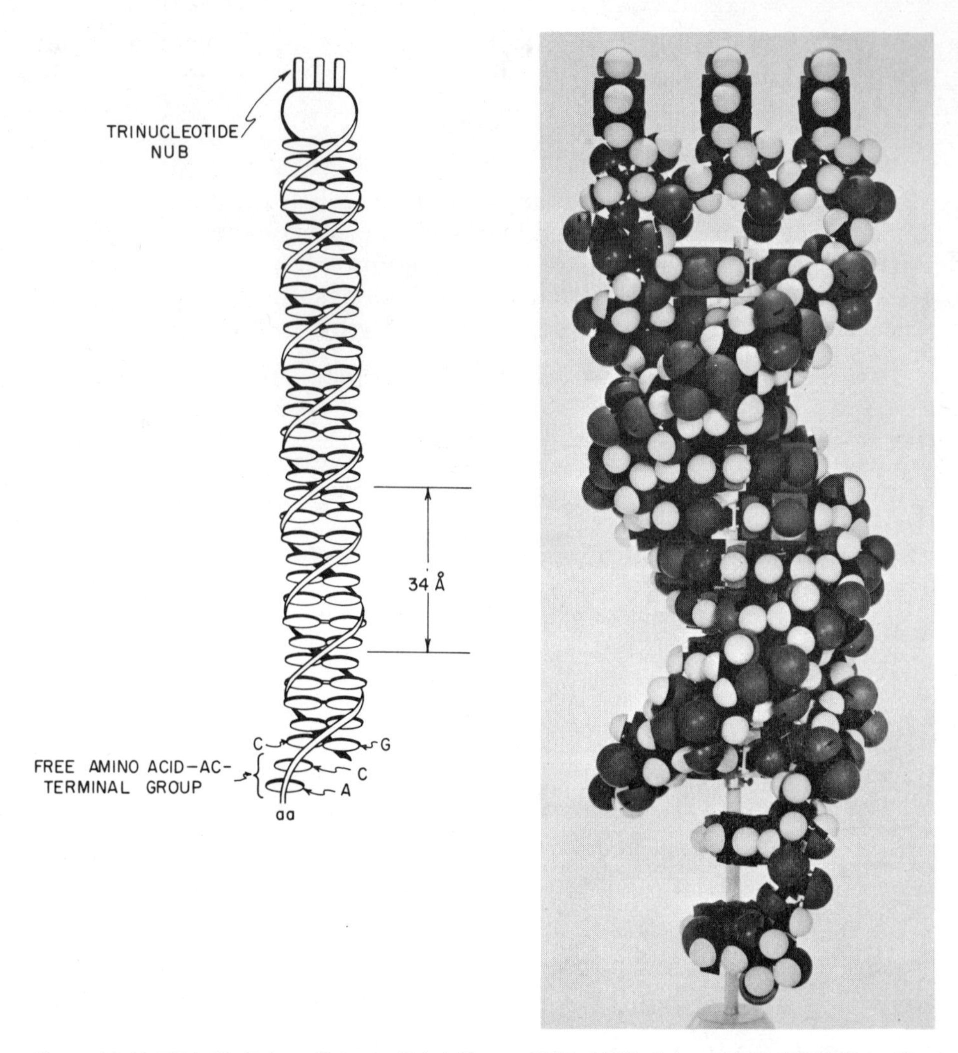

Figure 12-11 RNA (G. Zubay, *Science,* Vol. 140, pp. 1092–1095, 7 June 1963. © 1963 by The American Association for the Advancement of Science.)

This hydrolysis scheme is exactly the path followed in the body in the digestive process. For proteins to be properly assimilated, they must be broken down to the simple units, α-amino acids. As the digestive process continues, the proteins get small and smaller, passing through the various stages indicated above, until the actual amino acids are formed. The body performs this hydrolysis because the protein, proteoses, etc., are too large to be absorbed through the intestinal membrane. When the amino acids are formed, they can be easily absorbed into the blood stream and sent to the proper site to be resynthesized into proteins. Other reactions may occur; these will be discussed in Chapter 19.

Obviously, proteoses would be easier to digest than proteins, because the proteoses are already partially broken down. Also, peptones would be easier to digest than proteoses, because peptones are still further broken down. If the amino acids themselves were eaten, no digestive action would be necessary, for the amino acids are ready to be assimilated. In preparing nutrient broth for bacteria, one often uses peptones so that the organisms do not have to work hard to hydrolyze the peptones and consequently grow faster and easier.

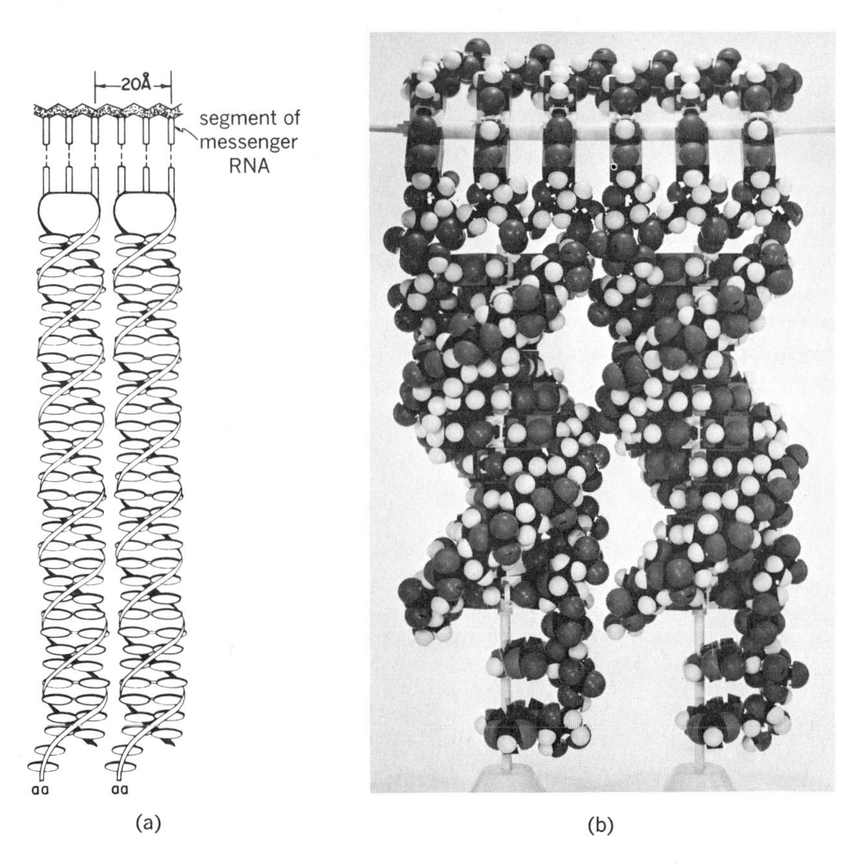

Figure 12-12 (a) Proposed structure for adapter-RNA—messenger-RNA complex. (b) A space-filling molecular model. (G. Zubay, *Science,* Vol. 140, pp. 1092–1095, 7 June 1963. © 1963 by The American Association for The Advancement of Science.)

Foreign Proteins

Foreign proteins are proteins not normally present in the body; these proteins are called antigens. The foreign protein may enter the body by inhalation or by subcutaneous, intraperitoneal, or intravenous injection. After the foreign protein is introduced into the body, four general types of reactions may occur, depending on the biological circumstances. A substance produced as a response to the antigen is called an antibody.

THE HEMOLYTIC REACTION

When red blood cells of an animal are injected into the blood stream of an animal of a different species in a series of shortly spaced injections, the injected animal acquires the ability to dissolve the foreign blood corpuscles. The foreign protein, antigen, has caused the injected animal's blood to form antibodies, which can dissolve the invading substance. In certain criminal cases, this test may be of interest in detecting whether a suspected blood stain is human. The test can be conveniently carried out in a test tube.

THE PRECIPITIN REACTION

When the initial injection of the foreign protein is followed in short intervals by injections of increasing dosages, the injected blood serum acquires the property of precipitating the particular foreign protein. The foreign protein, antigen, has caused the injected subject's blood to form protective antibodies, which can now precipitate and destroy the invading substance. This is the basis of immunotherapy.

THE COMPLEMENT REACTION

In order that a reaction may occur between an antibody and its antigen, an additional factor known as the complement is generally necessary. The antibody is relatively heat stable, and the complement is destroyed by heating to 55°C. The complement fixation test is the basis of the famous Wasserman test for syphilis.

The patient's serum is first heated to destroy the complement and is then mixed with the antigen. Because the patient's complement has been destroyed, *even if antibodies were present in the patient's serum,* no precipitin or hemolytic reaction can occur. Next, complement is added to the test solution in the form of normal whole serum. If the patient's serum originally contained the specific antibodies, then a precipitin or hemolytic reaction will occur. Since this sometimes may not be too obvious to behold, an additional series of tests is usually run to double-check the reaction.

ANAPHYLAXIS

If a small amount of a foreign protein somehow gets into the body and a rather long period of time (i.e., two weeks or longer) elapses before the second dose enters, anaphylaxis may occur. (The intervening time is called the incubation period and varies depending upon the amount of the initial dose.) The initial dose is called the sensitizing dose, and the second dose is called the intoxicating dose, which may result in anaphylaxis. In anaphylaxis, the following symptoms may be apparent: lowered blood pressure, irregular breathing, disturbed blood and protein chemistry, and violent contractions of bronchiae, uterus, stomach, intestines, and bladder. Essentially, all these symptoms may also be caused by an injection of histamine. Gelatin is one of the few proteins that do not produce anaphylaxis.

It is believed that the body, when injected with foreign proteins in regular doses, develops antibodies to somehow destroy these invaders. However, when only a single dose is given, instead of developing protective antibodies, the body develops sensitized antibodies, which react later with the intoxicating dose of the foreign protein to liberate a substance that causes anaphylaxis symptoms. The substance released is probably histamine. The histamine is probably produced by the removal of carbon dioxide from histadine, a naturally occurring amino acid.

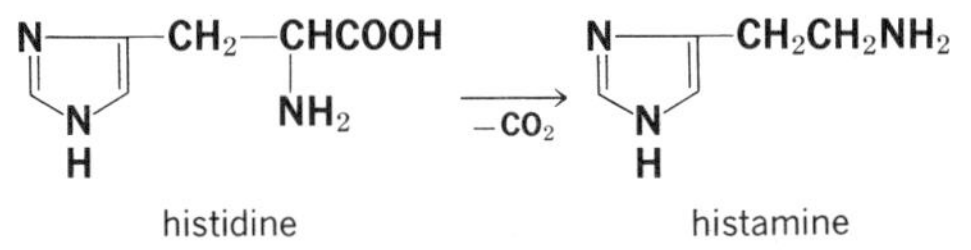

$$\text{(imidazole ring, N–H)}-CH_2-CH(NH_2)COOH \xrightarrow[-CO_2]{} \text{(imidazole ring, N–H)}-CH_2CH_2NH_2$$

histidine histamine

An allergy, a term employed to designate hypersensitivity, is a form of anaphylaxis. The antigen producing the allergic reaction is called an allergen. The allergen is usually protein in nature but may contain carbohydrate and even lipid material. Some people may exhibit allergic reactions even to nonprotein substances, such as drugs.

The allergic response and the site of reaction depends on the particular allergen and the chemical nature of the allergen. The commonly met allergens are the epidermals (e.g., scales, dander of hairs of animals, or feathers of birds), pollens (e.g., ragweed, grass, or trees), fungi and molds, foods, drugs, and dust.

The commonly reported symptoms are irritated conjuctiva, irritated mucous membranes of the nose and throat, asthma, hives and other skin disorders, and sneezing. With allergic patients, the procedure is first to discover the cause of the allergy. This may be done by skin testing, a procedure in which the suspected allergen is placed on a small scratch. If the patient is allergic to this allergen, a wheal, that is, a small raised reddened area, develops. From the size and shape of the wheal, it is possible to predict something of the allergy condition.

Once the allergen is discovered, the obvious approach is for the patient to avoid the allergen. This may be possible with foods, feathers, etc., but it is not too practical with the airborne inhalants, where perhaps a change of climate might be effective. To treat an allergy patient, desensitization treatments may be used. In desensitization, the allergen is injected into the body in increasing doses at regular intervals until proper protective antibodies have been established. In this way, one may become permanently cured. However, this technique does not always work.

Temporary relief may be obtained by using the antihistamines. An antihistamine, as the name implies, counteracts the effect of a histamine.

The general formula of an antihistamine is

$$R—X—\overset{\beta}{C}—\overset{\alpha}{C}—N\langle$$

R = some ring group such as benzene, pyridine, or thiophene
X = an oxygen, nitrogen, or carbon atom

A few examples are

Benadryl: $(C_6H_5)_2CH—O—CH_2CH_2—N(CH_3)_2$

Pyribenzamine: $(C_5H_4N)(C_6H_5CH_2)N—CH_2CH_2—N(CH_3)_2$

Histadyl (*Thenylene*): $(C_5H_4N)(C_4H_3SCH_2)N—CH_2CH_2—N(CH_3)_2$

Trimeton: $(C_6H_5)(C_5H_4N)CH—CH_2CH_2—N(CH_3)_2$

The efficiency of these drugs varies with the test method employed.

Recently, considerable publicity was given to the antihistamines because of their reputed ability to prevent colds. This was shown to be untrue. Often allergic symptoms are almost identical to those of a common cold. In fact, when some people think they have colds, they are showing simple manifestations of an allergic attack. The antihistamines would be of some use to these people.

Enzymes

Enzymes are the catalysts usually encountered in biochemical reactions. They are organic in nature, elaborated by living cells, but capable of action outside these cells. An enzyme is a substance that alters the speed of a biochemical reaction. We assume that a biochemical reaction proceeds normally at a relatively slow rate and that in the presence of the proper enzyme, the velocity is greatly changed. When one becomes aware of the variety and number of chemical reactions occurring in living organisms, one soon becomes impressed at the versatility and scope of these important catalysts.

The material the enzyme activates is called the substrate. If, for example, an enzyme causes an ester to be hydrolyzed, the ester is the substrate. Enzymes are usually named according to the substrate with the ending -ase; that is, sucrase acts on sucrose, lactase acts on lactose, maltase acts on maltose, lipase acts on lipids, etc.

The enzyme may also be named according to the type of reaction it causes: for example, oxidation (oxidase), dehydrogenation (dehydrogenase), hydrolysis (hydrolase), etc. Some enzymes named before any formal system was adopted retain their old fashioned names, such as pepsin, rennin, trypsin, and ptyalin. Table 12-5 gives an abridged classification of enzymes.

Specificity of Enzyme Action

Enzymes are amazingly specific in their action. In fact, for every reaction taking place in protoplasm, there appears to be an enzyme that catalyzes this reaction. For example, the enzyme lactase catalyzes the hydrolysis of lactose. Lactase is of no use in hydrolyzing any other similar disaccharide; the enzyme is specific *for that one reaction,* the hydrolysis of lactose.

Chemical Nature of Enzymes

All the enzymes isolated so far can be classified as proteins, and many are conjugated proteins. One of the criteria for judging the purity of an enzyme is its physical state. An enzyme that can be obtained in a crystalline state is presumably chemically pure. Further evidence for the protein-like character of enzymes is the colloidal nature of these biochemical catalysts. Enzymes form colloidal solutions in water and do not pass through a dialyzing membrane. They migrate under the influence of an electrical current, which indicates that they are protected by electrical charges. They can be destroyed by heat, which indicates a solvent protection. Enzymes contain protein molecules associated with other groups,

Table 12-5 An abridged classification of enzymes

NAME	OCCURRENCE	SUBSTRATE	END PRODUCTS
carbohydrases		*carbohydrates*	*hydrolytic products*
1. amylases		starch	maltose
a. ptyalin	saliva	starch	maltose
b. amylopsin	pancreatic juice	starch	maltose
c. diastase	plants	starch	maltose
2. lactase	intestinal juice	lactose	glucose and galactose
3. maltase	intestinal juice	maltose	glucose
4. sucrase	intestinal juice	sucrose	glucose and fructose
5. zymase	yeast	sugars	ethyl alcohol and CO_2
6. hyaluronidase[a]	bacteria, snake venom	hyaluronic acid	glucuronic acid, N-acetyl glucosamine
glucosidases		*glucosides*	*sugars*
1. emulsin	plants	β-glucosides	sugars
2. maltase	yeast	α-glucosides	sugars
esterases		*esters*	*acids and alcohols*
1. lipases		fats	fatty acids and glycerol
a. steapsin	pancreatic juice	fats	fatty acids and glycerol
b. vegetable lipase	castor bean	fats	fatty acids and glycerol
c. gastric lipase	gastric juice	fats	fatty acids and glycerol
2. phosphatase	tissues	organic phosphates	phosphoric acid, etc.
3. cholinesterase	brain and muscle	acetylcholine	choline and acetic acid
nucleases		*nucleic acids, derivatives*	*hydrolytic products*
1. nucleicacidase	intestinal juice	nucleic acid	nucleotides
2. nucleotidase	intestinal juice	nucleotides	nucleosides and H_3PO_4
3. nucleosidase	tissues	nucleosides	sugars and purines
deaminases		*amino compounds*	
1. urease	soybeans	urea	CO_2 and NH_3
peptidases		*peptides*	*simpler peptides, amino acids*
1. aminopolypeptidase	intestines	polypeptides	simpler peptides, amino acids
2. carboxypolypeptidase	pancreas	polypeptides	simpler peptides, amino acids
3. prolinase	intestines	polypeptides containing proline	amino acids, simpler peptides
4. dipeptidase	intestines	dipeptides	amino acids
proteases		*proteins*	*hydrolytic products*
1. pepsin	gastric juice	proteins	proteoses and peptones
2. trypsin	pancreatic juice	proteins	proteoses, peptones, polypeptides
3. chymotrypsin	pancreatic juice	proteins	proteoses, peptones, polypeptides
4. rennin	gastric juice	casein	paracasein
5. papain[b]	papaya	proteins	polypeptides
oxidases			
1. catalase	plant and animal tissues	H_2O_2	molecular oxygen
2. uricase	animal tissues	uric acid	allontoin
3. dehydrogenase	tissues	organic compounds	oxidation products
4. tyrosinase	potato and mushroom	tyrosine	black pigments

[a] Hyaluronidase is an enzyme known as the "spreading factor." This enzyme acts by breaking down hyaluronic acid, an important component in the jellylike mass that holds the tissue cells together. This hastens the spread of liquids through the body.

[b] Found in meat tenderizers.

which are nonprotein in nature, such as metals, vitamins, and carbohydrates, depending upon the particular enzyme. These nonprotein groups, the prosthetic groups, are often of greater interest than the protein part. This will be discussed later in the chapter.

Conditions For Enzyme Activity

Many factors influence enzyme activity.

TEMPERATURE

Enzymes respond, to a limited extent, to the rule that an increase in temperature usually increases the rate of reaction. However, this rule must be modified because enzymes are protein in character and are permanently destroyed by high temperatures. Thus, at a high temperature, that is, a temperature around the boiling point of water, enzymes become completely inactivated. Dry heat does not completely destroy an enzyme. If an enzyme is put into a dry test tube and the tube is immersed in a beaker of boiling water, the enzyme, when brought back to room temperature, retains a fair share of its original activity. Low temperatures, such as freezing temperatures, generally inactivate an enzyme, but this loss of activity may be only temporary, since a return of the enzyme to the starting temperature causes the return of enzyme activity. From the foregoing, it is apparent that if low and high temperatures inactivate enzymes, the enzyme must possess its greatest activity at some intermediate temperature. Such a condition does indeed exist, and we call this the *optimum temperature*. The optimum temperature for enzymes is, in general, about 37–45°C. This, fortunately, is in the realm of body temperature. Each enzyme has its characteristic optimum temperature.

THE pH EFFECT

The hydrogen ion concentration is of extreme importance in enzyme activity. Extreme acidity or alkalinity usually causes irreversible destruction of the enzyme, due probably to the hydrolysis or denaturation of the protein part of the molecule. Exposure to lesser degrees of acidity or alkalinity may cause reversible inactivation in some cases. This may be regarded as a change of the sign of the electrical charges protecting the protein molecule. Returning to the original pH, the enzyme may reacquire its original electrical protection and consequently its activity, provided that no denaturation has occurred. The pH at which a particular enzyme possesses its greatest activity is known as the optimum pH. Each enzyme has its characteristic optimum pH, as can be seen in Figure 12-13.

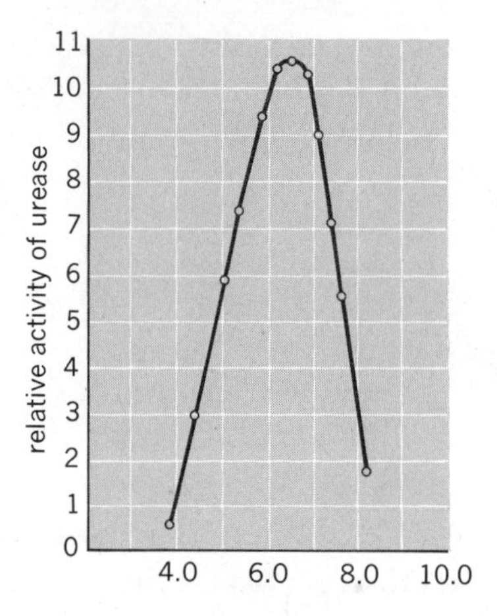

Figure 12-13 The activity of urease as a function of the pH.

It is a pleasant circumstance that most enzymes in our bodies are found in solution at almost the optimum pH.

CONCENTRATION FACTOR

With a highly purified enzyme, the initial rate of the catalyzed reaction is directly proportional to the enzyme concentration over a wide range: the more enzyme, the faster the reaction. An impure enzyme may contain inhibitors so that an increase in the enzyme concentration only slightly increases the rate of reaction. With the concentration of the enzyme and all other conditions except the concentration of the substrate (the substance upon which the enzyme acts) constant, it is known that the initial rate of the reaction increases with an increase in substrate concentration up to a certain maximum, but with high substrate concentrations, no further increase in the rate is obtained.

In general, enzymes tend to be inactivated by strong light. Ultraviolet light is especially effective in destroying enzyme activity. X-rays may or may not destroy enzymes, depending on the circumstances. The presence of salts may alter enzyme activity by precipitating the enzyme, due to its protein nature.

Enzyme Composition and Mechanism of Activity

Some enzymes are inactive when produced by the cells and rely upon some activating influence to bring them to maximum activity. The inactive form of the enzyme is called the *zymogen* or *proenzyme,* and the activating substance is known as the *activator* or *kinase.* Customarily we refer to inorganic substances as activators and organic substances as kinases. For example, hydrochloric acid activates pepsinogen into active pepsin. We call the hydrochloric acid the *activator*. Enterokinase converts inactive trypsinogen into active trypsin. We call the enterokinase a *kinase,* because it is organic in nature.

We have mentioned previously that the prosthetic group, which is nonprotein in nature, is often of great importance. This prosthetic group is referred to as the *coenzyme*. Coenzymes, being nonprotein in nature, may not be destroyed by heat. Neither the coenzyme nor the protein part is active independently; both must be present before activity is observed. Investigations into the nature of enzymes have given us the following information.

A catalyst does not last forever because it becomes inactivated by some means. This inactivation may be complex or simple. Enzyme inactivation may be rather simple. Because enzymes are protein in part, they are subject to the many reactions that denature or destroy proteins. As the protein part of the enzyme is slowly destroyed and broken down, the body tends to eliminate in some way the leftover coenzyme. This means that the body is constantly in need of more coenzyme (even if it may be a very, very small amount), so that the cells can resynthesize the necessary enzyme.

Discoveries have shown that the coenzyme part often contains a vitamin group. (Vitamins will be discussed in Chapter 21.) It is known that the body requires in the diet each day a certain amount of a vitamin to maintain a normal healthy condition. It is logical that these vitamins are necessary to replenish the body store of coenzymes so that the proper whole enzyme may be present and function as needed. A vitamin deficiency, then, means that an enzyme deficiency exists. When an enzyme is missing, some vital reaction, normally occurring in the body, ceases to consummate, and this manifests itself in many of the conditions known to us as vitamin deficiencies.

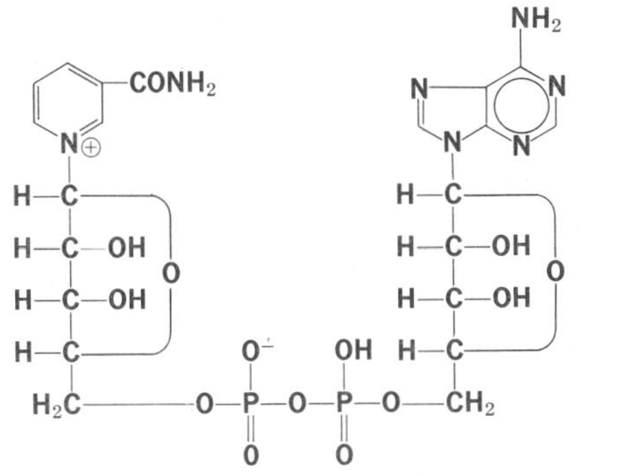

a coenzyme containing nicotinamide, one of the B vitamins

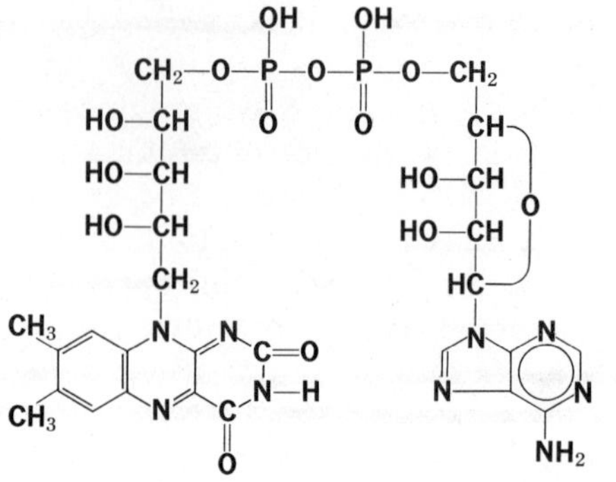

a coenzyme containing riboflavin, one of the B vitamins

REVIEW QUESTIONS

1. Of what are proteins composed? What are the usual percentages of carbon, hydrogen, and nitrogen in proteins?
2. Contrast the molecular weight of proteins with the molecular weights of various common electrolytes such as $NaCl$, $NaHCO_3$, NaH_2PO_4.
3. Define amphoteric. Give an example.
4. What is a zwitterion?
5. How is it possible to independently determine the acidity of the acid groups and the basicity of the amino group in the α-amino acids?
6. What is meant by the isoelectric point?
7. What is meant by protein structure specificity?
8. What evidence indicates that protein molecules are colloidal in nature?
9. Discuss proteins from the standpoint of composition and factors influencing stability and instability. What are the effects of pH change, solvent change, and temperature change?
10. Discuss the various ways of precipitating proteins and how these methods work.
11. Discuss the Heller ring tests, Millon's test, Biuret test, Xanthoproteic acid test, and Ninhydrin reaction. Indicate how the tests are performed, how a positive reaction would be recognized, and what a positive test would signify.
12. Discuss the Van Slyke, Kjeldahl, and Dumas quantitative methods.
13. What are some of the ways of classifying proteins? Give several examples of each.
14. Give examples of a simple protein, a conjugated protein, and a derived protein.
15. Distinguish between fibrous and globular proteins.
16. Identify rigor mortis, gelatin, collagen, silk, and nylon.
17. What are some of the coloring groups found in chromoproteins?
18. Discuss the structure and composition of nucleoproteins.
19. Discuss viruses.
20. Define the term foreign protein? What can happen when a foreign protein enters the body?

21. Discuss the hemolytic reaction, the precipitin reaction, the complement reaction, and anaphylaxis.
22. What is the basic structure common to many antihistamines?
23. Is there any relationship between enzymes, viruses, and nucleoproteins?
24. What is the relationship between an enzyme and a vitamin?
25. What is the general ending in naming of enzymes? Is the name of the enzyme a clue to its activity? Discuss the specificity of enzyme action.
26. What are some of the conditions necessary for optimum enzyme activity? What are the effects of changing temperature, pH, and concentration on enzyme activity?

13

digestion in the mouth

Digestion

Digestion is the process whereby complex food molecules are broken down by chemical action into simple molecules that can be absorbed by the body.

Very large molecules, such as starch, proteins, and fat, are insoluble in water. Because they can form colloidal solutions, these molecules may appear to be soluble, but they are unable to pass through the small holes of a semipermeable membrane. Most of the absorption of digested (hydrolyzed) food material occurs in the intestines.

We can summarize digestion as follows: Food molecules are too big to pass through the digestive tract wall and must be broken down. After the molecules are broken down, they are absorbed. Generally, the absorbed material is resynthesized into large molecules in the body. The digestive tract wall acts like a typical semipermeable membrane (see Figure 13-1)

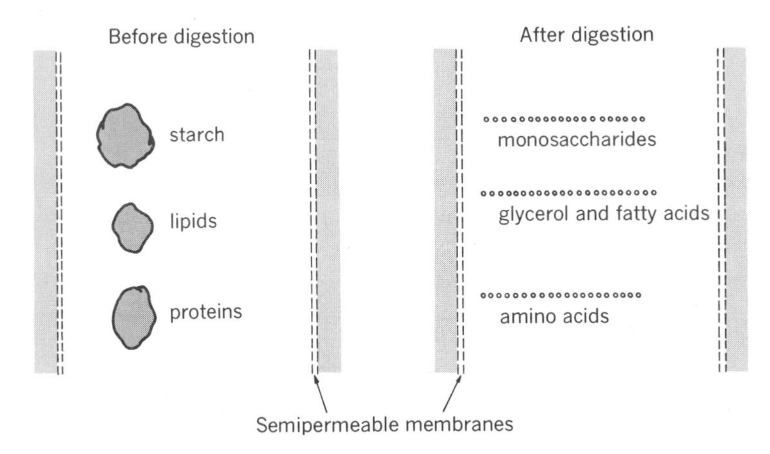

Figure 13-1 Before and after digestion.

and is a barrier that prevents large molecules from coming into the circulatory fluids of the body and the large molecules in the circulatory fluids from leaving the body. Small molecules, such as glucose, are in the simplest form and can be assimilated without any digestive action.

We may regard digestion as a process that renders food particles suitable for absorption. In bacteria, absorption takes place throughout the entire surface of the organism. In man, digestion takes place in the digestive tract (i.e., mouth, stomach, and intestines), and absorption takes place primarily in the intestines.

Digestion in the Mouth

THE TEETH

The primary function of the teeth is to help in the physical breakdown of food in the mouth. Unchewed food remains in the stomach much longer than chewed food. In essence, chewing the food causes it to exhibit more surface and consequently be more easily susceptible to digestive enzyme attack.

The central portion of the tooth is called the pulp cavity and contains the nerves and blood vessels, which service the tooth. The main body of the tooth is made of dentine, a substance that resembles bone. Outside the dentine and above the gum line is a white substance known as enamel. Below the gum line, the dentine is covered by a material called cementum.

Both dentine and enamel are chemically similar to bone, and enamel is the hardest material formed in the body. Dentine, cementum, and enamel are composed of inorganic material embedded in a protein matrix (mostly collagen). See Figure 13-2.

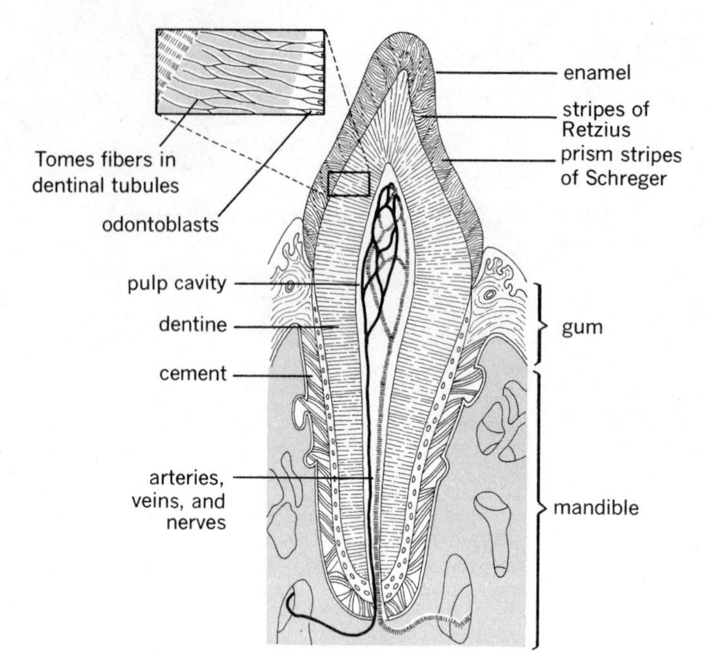

Figure 13-2 Longitudinal section of incisor tooth.

When the enamel surface of the tooth is etched by a trace of acid, the physical nature of the organic and inorganic material is clearly visible under high magnification (see Figure 13-3).

Chemically, the inorganic portions of dentine, enamel, and cementum are composed of ionic crystals of apatite $Ca(OH)_2 \cdot 3[Ca_3(PO_4)_2]$ accompanied by traces of fluorapatite $CaF_2 \cdot 3[Ca_3(PO_4)_2]$, chlorapatite $CaCl_2 \cdot 3[Ca_3(PO_4)_2]$, and dahllite $CaCO_3 \cdot 3[Ca_3(PO_4)_2]$. Fluorapatite, the principle fluorine-containing compound in the body, is an extremely hard substance. As a general rule, the higher the concentration of apatite crystals, the harder the tissue.

In the formation of a tooth, calcium phosphate precipitates from blood serum and carries with it some organic material. This process accounts for the combination of organic and inorganic material in the tooth.

Although the fluoride ion is poisonous (because it is an enzyme inhibitor) in appreciable concentrations, a minute supply in the diet of a growing child seems to prevent dental caries (i.e., tooth decay). This is obviously involved in the deposition of fluorapatite in the teeth. The fluoride ion content of drinking water varies from about 0 to 5 parts per million. Some cities with a low fluoride content in their water have added the ion to make the concentration 1.2 parts per million. This predisposes the child to produce a proper amount of fluorapatite. If the fluoride ion concentration is too high, the enamel becomes malformed. We refer to this condition as

Figure 13-3 Etched surface of a tooth. (From Scott, *et al., Mineral Metabolism,* New York: Academic Press, Inc., Vol. IB, p. 683.)

mottled teeth. Mottled teeth have discolored areas and are porous, brittle, and chalky.

The protective action of fluorapatite can be seen in Figure 13-4. Nonfluorosed teeth dissolve rapidly at a pH of 5.2, whereas fluorosed teeth are quite stable at this pH. Fluorosed teeth will dissolve, however, at a pH of 4.7.

When caries-susceptible rats were fed a 65% sucrose solution, they developed dental caries in all their teeth. When the same number of susceptible rats were fed the same diet by a stomach tube, they did not

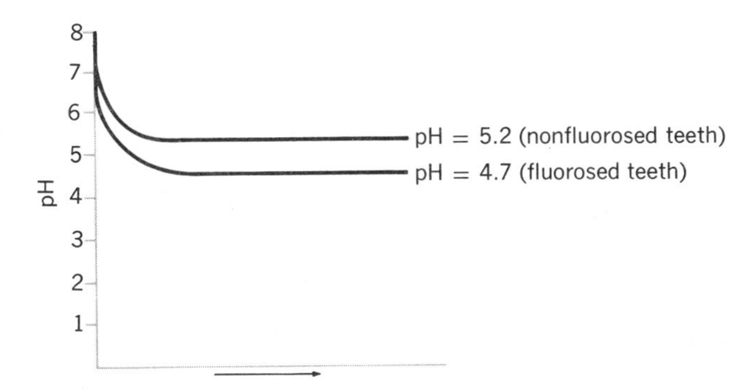

Figure 13-4 Solubility of Ca^{++} from enamel.

develop caries. From this and other evidence, it is fairly clear that dental caries are caused by the action of bacterial enzymes on carbohydrates in the mouth to form acids. These acids, such as lactic, pyruvic, acetic, propionic, butyric, formic, and phosphoglyceric, will attack the enamel and move toward the pulp, if sufficient osmotic pressure is built up with respect to the circulatory fluids in the pulp. The enamel then acts like an osmotic membrane.

Considerable attention has been given recently to materials that prevent enzyme action, particularly the enzymes responsible for converting carbohydrates into acids. The enzyme inhibitors are called antienzymes. Some of these antienzymes are found in toothpastes today.

Naturally, bacteria in the mouth play an important role in dental decay. Caries-immune individuals (i.e., people without any dental decay) usually have an exceptionally low oral bacterial count. This is apparently due to the presence in their saliva of a protein fraction which has some bactericidal properties.

Many substances have been used to prevent and delay dental caries. Both fluoride paste (i.e., sodium fluoride or sodium silicofluoride applied to the teeth directly by the dentist) and stannous fluoride (i.e., applied to the teeth via some toothpastes) alter the surface of the enamel and make it more resistant to acid attack.

SALIVA

Saliva is secreted by the parotid, the submaxillary, and the sublingual glands (see Figure 13-5). About 1,500 ml of saliva are secreted daily by a normal person. Saliva is over 99% water, but the small amount of solids in this liquid is very important. Saliva, when nonstimulated, is essentially neutral, with a pH of about 7.0. This may be regarded as a neutral protective action for the teeth. When stimulated by the presence of food or by the thought, sight, or smell of food, the saliva is acidic, with a 6.5–6.8 pH range. The optimum pH of activity of ptyalin, an enzyme in saliva, is 6.6. Therefore, it seems that the slight acidity of saliva produces the most active ptyalin. Saliva contains mucin, a conjugated protein (glycoprotein), composed of carbohydrate and protein. Mucin's chief function is to make the saliva slippery. Mucin is therefore a mechanical aid to swallowing. Mineral salts in the saliva constitute the buffer systems of the mouth. The buffer systems consist of H_2CO_3 and $KHCO_3$, the carbonate buffers; KH_2PO_4 and K_2HPO_4, the phosphate buffers; and potassium mucinate, the protein buffer. The buffers tend to prevent the mouth from becoming too acidic and consequently are natural protective agents against dental caries. They also try to keep the pH of saliva around 6.6 and thus aid in the production of the most active ptyalin. People with an insufficient supply of saliva, and consequently insufficient buffers, usually suffer from extensive tooth decay.

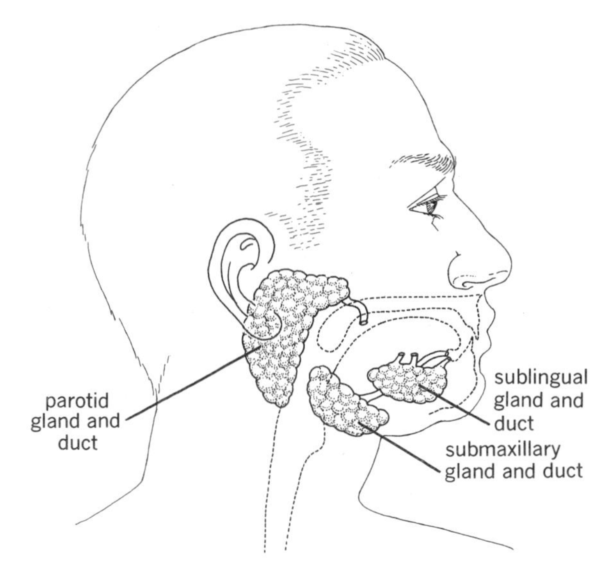

Figure 13-5 Salivary glands in the face.

Ptyalin is the most important enzyme in the mouth. Ptyalin is an amylase; it acts on starch (amylum). By ptyalin action, starch is broken down through the various dextrins to form maltose. This action may be considered a hydrolysis reaction in that water is added to the starch molecule as each maltose molecule is removed.

We may represent the hydrolysis reaction as

$$\begin{aligned}
\text{starch} + \text{water} &\longrightarrow \text{amylodextrin} + \text{maltose}\\
\text{amylodextrin} + \text{water} &\longrightarrow \text{erythrodextrin} + \text{maltose}\\
\text{erythrodextrin} + \text{water} &\longrightarrow \text{achroödextrin} + \text{maltose}\\
\text{achroödextrin} + \text{water} &\longrightarrow \text{maltose} + \text{maltose}
\end{aligned}$$

We have indicated only four steps, but, because of the size of the starch molecule, many reactions of the type illustrated must occur. Ptyalin is active within the 4–9 pH range, with the maximum activity occurring at pH 6.6. The pH of the stomach is 1–2. The stomach acidity is such that ptyalin activity is quickly inhibited and permanently destroyed. However, because it takes time for the gastric juice to bring all the stomach contents to a 1–2 pH, it is estimated that ptyalin may act in the stomach for about 10 minutes after the food has been swallowed. Obviously, proper and careful digestion of the food would insure the greatest ptyalin activity and would ease the subsequent digestive process.

After one has finished eating, the bacterial enzymes in the mouth act upon the food residues to produce the acids, mentioned previously, which cause dental caries. It has been shown that the maximum acidity is reached within 10–15 minutes. For the best oral hygiene, one should brush one's teeth immediately after a meal. If this is done, dental caries would be greatly decreased. If it is not convenient to brush the teeth after the meal, rinsing the mouth carefully with water is somewhat effective.

Digestion during food preparation

In many instances, the preparation and cooking starts the digestive process by causing some chemical change to occur or by making it easier for some chemical change to occur in the food molecules. For example, the preparation of toast and heating of starch in general cause the starch to change partially to dextrins. Cooking also helps break the starch granules so that the amylases can more readily attack the polysaccharide. Cooking meat causes collagen to change to gelatin, a process whereby tough meat is tenderized.

REVIEW QUESTIONS

1. Define digestion.
2. Why must we digest certain foods?
3. Of what function are the teeth in the digestive process? Discuss the chemical composition of the teeth. Define dentine, enamel, cementum, and pulp cavity. Of what use is the fluoride ion in the diet of growing children? What evidence is there to support the claims that a fluorosed tooth is less susceptible to dental caries?
4. Discuss the chemical composition of saliva. What is its pH range, how is it stimulated, and from where does it come? What is the function of saliva in the digestive process?
5. Discuss the action of ptyalin.
6. What is mucin?
7. Discuss the effect of brushing one's teeth in preventing dental caries.

14

digestion in the stomach

After the food has been swallowed, it passes through the esophagus to the stomach. The fundus is the large main part of the stomach and is attached to the esophagus. The part of the stomach connected to the duodenum is called the pyloric portion and is a narrow constricted region. See Figure 14-1.

The muscular walls of the stomach can expand, for example, when the stomach has received the entire meal, and contract, for example, in the emptying process of passing the partially digested food to the duodenum. In addition to being a digestive organ, the stomach may be considered a storage organ, because undigested food may remain there for several hours. The length of time food remains in the stomach is in part a function of the type of food eaten. For example, fatty foods, in general, are harder to digest than carbohydrates, and, consequently, fatty foods remain in the stomach longer than carbohydrates.

Digestion in the stomach is accomplished by gastric juice. About 2 to 3 liters of gastric juice are secreted daily by a normal adult. Appar-

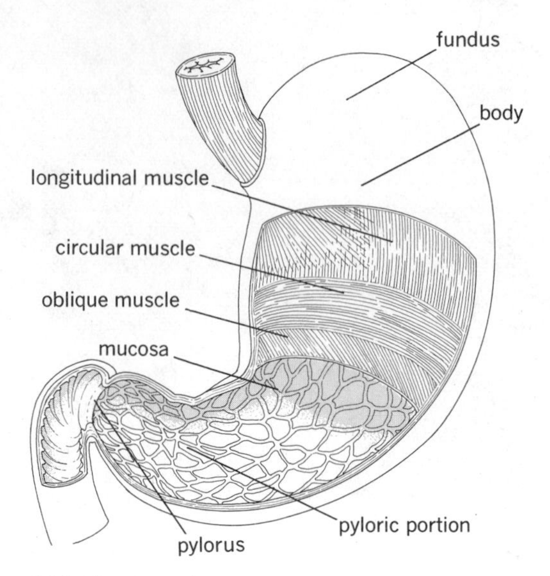

Figure 14-1 The stomach.

ently there is a constant gastric juice flow, because there always appears to be some liquid in the stomach. However, when food enters the mouth, or often when one thinks of, smells, or sees food, the nervous stimulus causes a marked increase in the gastric juice flow. It has been theorized that this nervous stimulus causes the production of a hormone known as gastrin, which stimulates the production of gastric juice. Normal gastric juice is a light-colored, thin fluid, which is very acidic.

Gastric juice contains several substances, the most important of which is the proenzyme pepsinogen. When pepsinogen is converted by hydrocholoric acid into the active enzyme, pepsin, a powerful proteolytic enzyme (i.e., an enzyme capable of hydrolyzing proteins) is formed. For this reason, the chemical action on proteins is the most important digestive reaction occurring in the stomach. Pepsinogen is secreted by the chief cells. (See Figure 14-2.) The conversion of pepsinogen into pepsin in the stomach is caused by free hydrochloric acid, but it has been shown that other acids can accomplish this transformation.

$$\underset{\text{inactive proenzyme}}{\text{pepsinogen}} \xrightarrow[\text{activator}]{\text{HCl}} \underset{\text{active proteolytic enzyme}}{\text{pepsin}}$$

Although pepsin is a powerful proteolytic enzyme, it does not digest proteins to α-amino acids, but instead it chemically transforms proteins into proteoses and peptones.

proteins $\xrightarrow{H_2O}$ proteoses $\xrightarrow{H_2O}$ peptones
(digestive action of pepsin)

It is indeed an amazing coincidence that pepsin is most active at a 1.5–2.0 pH and that the stomach is the only place in the body with such marked acidity. The hydrochloric acid catalyzes the formation of the pepsin and assures its proper activity. It also acts as a chemical barrier, killing many pathogenic organisms and preventing many intestinal infections.

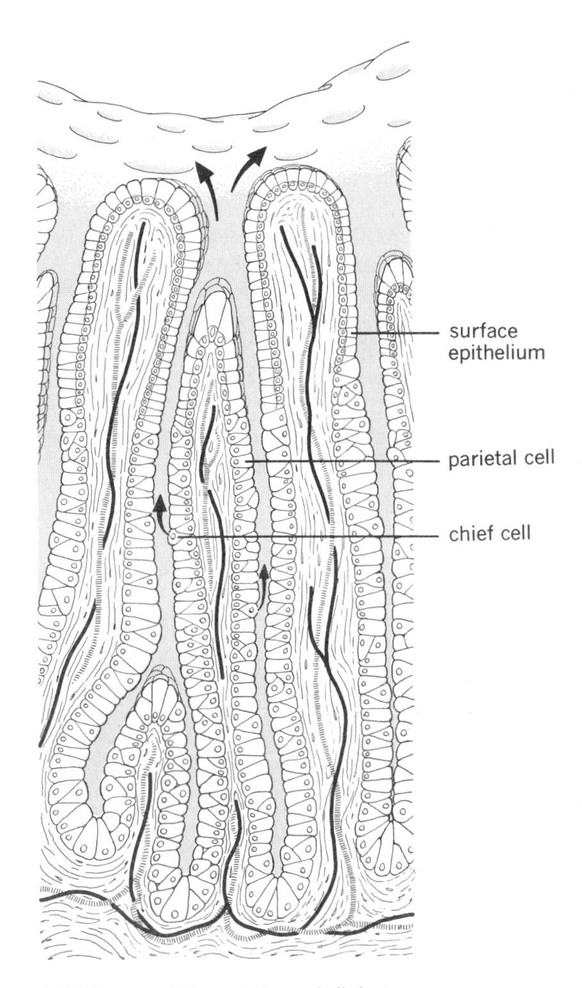

Figure 14-2 Cross section of stomach lining.

Origin of Gastric Acidity

Although most of the body and its circulating fluids are neutral, slightly acidic, or slightly basic, the fluid secreted by the stomach is exceptional because it is markedly acidic. The exact origin of this acidity has always been a subject of controversy.

Undoubtedly the HCl is generated by the *parietal cells* of the stomach mucosa. Very probably the chloride ion passes from the blood stream to the parietal cell and is secreted in the gastric juice. The exact method of hydrogen ion formation is not known, but it may take place by the dissociation of carbonic acid in the parietal cells, which preferentially secrete the H^+ in the gastric juice. The HCO_3^- then migrates into the blood stream to replace the chloride ion and maintain ionic equilibrium. The bicarbonate ions tend to increase the basicity of the blood stream.

As the gastric juice is secreted, the blood stream tends to become slightly more basic than normal. This is especially true after a meal and produces a pleasant satisfied feeling known as the alkaline tide, which sweeps over the body. For example, urine is usually acidic; however, shortly after a meal, it might be alkaline.

Because considerable free strong acid is in the gastric juice, undoubtedly some hydrolysis of disaccharides, such as sucrose, maltose, and lactose, occurs.

$$\text{sucrose} \xrightarrow[+H_2O]{(HCl)} \text{glucose} + \text{fructose}$$

$$\text{maltose} \xrightarrow[+H_2O]{(HCl)} \text{glucose} + \text{glucose}$$

$$\text{lactose} \xrightarrow[+H_2O]{(HCl)} \text{galactose} + \text{glucose}$$

However, this chemical action depends on many factors, the most important of which is the length of time the food remains in the stomach. In general, we can say that the free hydrochloric acid, as such, produces some digestive action but that it is not a major factor itself in the hydrolysis of the large food particles.

In medical practice, it is often an important diagnostic tool to determine the stomach acidity. This determination can be done by titration of removed gastric juice with standardized dilute alkali. If we use phenolphthalein as the indicator (phenolphthalein changes color at a pH of about 9), we can determine the total acidity. If we use Töpfer's reagent as the indicator (Töpfer's reagent changes color at a pH of about 3–4), we can determine the free hydrochloric acid.

Because pepsin is a powerful proteolytic enzyme and the tissues of the stomach wall are protein, the question arises, why does the stomach juice not digest the stomach wall itself? We know that a normal healthy individual's stomach is intact and that something must prevent this destructive action. Two explanations have been given. First, the stomach wall is definitely basic during the digestive process and, hence, would inhibit pepsin activity. Second, there may be a substance known as an antienzyme in the stomach wall, and this substance also inactivates the pepsin.

Hyperacidity

A gastric ulcer is the wearing away of the stomach wall. How this is caused is a controversial point. We cannot say definitely whether an excess of hydrochloric acid causes the ulcer, or whether the presence of the ulcer causes the formation of an excess of hydrochloric acid. However, it is a fact that an ulcer patient does exhibit a greater acidity (i.e., hyperacidity) in the stomach than normal, and usually a hypersecretion of gastric juice.

There is also the possibility that the pepsin may actually be hydrolyzing the protein in the stomach wall. Perhaps people who are highly nervous are prone to develop ulcers because of the increased nerve stimulus and the resultant increased flow of highly acidic gastric juice.

Any chemical agent that stops the nervous stimulus of the gastric juice or stops the hydrochloric acid from becoming too concentrated would possibly relieve or cure an ulcer. Removing the free hydrochloric acid would not only remove an irritating substance from the tender exposed tissues of an ulcer patient, but would also inhibit the conversion of pepsinogen into the active pepsin. Milk is a commonly used liquid, alkaline in nature, that tends to relieve discomfort in ulcer patients.

Drugs like atropine tend to block the nerve stimulus down the vagus nerve and reduce both gastric motility and secretions. Some compounds in the group of quaternary amines have shown promise of blocking this nerve stimulus. When this is done by a drug, we may call it a "chemical vagatomy." Pro-Banthine is a quaternary amine that exhibits this blocking action and may be taken orally. Pamine (i.e., the methyl bromide salt of scopolamine) is about as effective as Pro-Banthine in relieving stomach and duodenal ulcers.

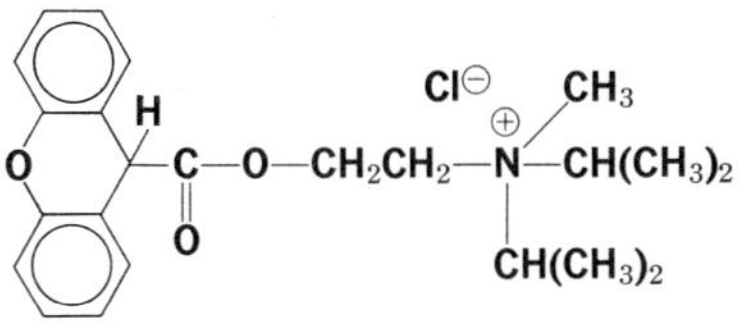

$$\text{(xanthenyl)}\,\text{CH}-\underset{\|}{\overset{}{C}}(=O)-O-CH_2CH_2-\overset{\oplus}{N}(CH_3)(CH(CH_3)_2)_2\;Cl^{\ominus}$$

Pro-Banthine
(a quaternary ammonium salt)

In certain serious cases, the vagus nerve must be interrupted surgically (i.e., a surgical vagotomy) to stop this relentless and uncontrolled stimulus of acidic gastric juice.

Hypoacidity occurs when an unusually small amount of hydrochloric acid is secreted in the gastric juice. This usually indicates stomach cancer but may also occur in pernicious anemia.

Gastric Lipase

The gastric juice also contains an enzyme capable of acting on lipids. This lipase is weak, but it does cause some hydrolysis of the following nature.

$$\begin{array}{l} CH_2{-}O{-}\overset{\overset{\large O}{\|}}{C}{-}R \\ | \\ CH{-}O{-}\overset{\overset{\large O}{\|}}{C}{-}R \\ | \\ CH_2{-}O{-}\overset{\overset{\large O}{\|}}{C}{-}R \end{array} \xrightarrow[\text{gastric lipase}]{+3H_2O} \begin{array}{l} CH_2OH \\ | \\ CHOH \\ | \\ CH_2OH \end{array} + 3RCOOH$$

an oil or fat → glycerol + fatty acid

Because the gastric lipase is most active at a pH of 5, and because the stomach juice has a pH of 1–2, we see that there is very little chance for lipase activity. In addition, the insoluble lipids are often not in the best physical form for digestion. Some finely emulsified fats may undergo a limited amount of hydrolysis of the type illustrated. In general, we can say that there is a very small amount of lipase activity in the stomach.

The Rennin Question

Rennin is a proteolytic enzyme found in the gastric juice secretions of certain young mammals. Commercial rennin (rennet) is prepared from calves' stomachs. There is considerable doubt as to whether an adult's gastric juice contains any rennin, and some doubt if any rennin is even present in an infant's stomach.

When rennin is added to milk, a precipitate is formed. The rennin converts the milk protein, casein, into paracasein, which reacts with the calcium ions present in milk to form insoluble calcium paracaseinate.

$$\underset{\textit{soluble}}{\text{casein}} \xrightarrow{\text{rennin}} \underset{\textit{soluble}}{\text{paracasein}} \xrightarrow{Ca^{++}} \underset{\textit{insoluble}}{\text{calcium paracaseinate}}$$

If oxalated milk (i.e., milk plus oxalic acid) is treated with rennin, no curd is formed because the oxalate ion has effectively removed the calcium ions as insoluble calcium oxalate CaC_2O_4, which furnishes very few calcium ions. However, if calcium ions are later added to such a solution, a clot forms immediately. The calcium paracaseinate clot is composed of small globules and consequently is easier to digest than a larger globule of material. Rennet junkets are given to children because the coagulated protein in that form is easily digested in the stomach and eases the subsequent intestinal digestive process.

Rennin has an optimum 6.0–6.5 pH. For this reason, rennin would not be too effective in the stomach, which has a 1–2 pH during the digestive process.

Acids also coagulate casein by bringing it to its isoelectric point, pH 4.7. Casein, when precipitated as such, is chemically and physically different from the calcium paracaseinate curd. Casein, curdled at the isoelectric point, is a heavy, large clot and not a calcium salt. The curdling or souring of milk is due to the action of bacteria on the milk, causing the formation of lactic acid, which brings the casein to its isoelectric point.

Rennin has about six times the coagulating power of pepsin. However, the hydrochloric acid and pepsin in the stomach can adequately cause the precipitating and hydrolysis of the proteins in milk.

Evacuation of the Stomach Contents

As the digestive process continues in the stomach, the contents become liquefied. The liquefied material is called *chyme*. When the contents are properly liquefied, the muscular contractions of the stomach wall force them toward the pyloric opening and, by peristaltic waves, into the duodenum.

REVIEW QUESTIONS

1. Discuss the production, flow, and amount of gastric juice secreted daily by a normal adult.
2. What is believed concerning the hormonal control of the production of gastric juice? What compounds are known to exist in gastric juice?
3. What are pepsinogen and pepsin? Discuss their digestive action.
4. What is the pH of gastric juice? What is the optimum pH range for pepsin?
5. Show how the acidity of the gastric juice may be created.
6. What is meant by the alkaline tide?
7. How effective is gastric lipase? Illustrate its function by an equation.
8. What is the optimum pH range for lipase?
9. Of what function is rennin? What is meant by oxalated milk? What is the optimum pH range for rennin?
10. Compare the physical and chemical appearance of calcium paracaseinate with that of precipitated casein itself.
11. What is chyme?

15

digestion in the intestines

The first twelve inches of the small intestines are called the duodenum. It is truly an important organ, because so much digestion occurs in this relatively small region. The duodenal secretions are also involved in the elimination of waste products, particularly when the kidneys are impaired. Thus, it is very important that the bowels of patients who suffer from a kidney disease be kept open. Many drugs and metal ions, when injected into the body, are secreted along with the regular duodenal liquids and in this way make their way out of the body.

As the chyme is metered out into the duodenum in small portions, by means of the pyloric sphincter, it is quickly mixed with the flow of pancreatic, bile, and intestinal juices, because the pancreatic and bile ducts are only a few inches away from the pylorus. (See Figure 15-1.) These juices are alkaline and neutralize the acidity of the chyme; thus, they make the intestines alkaline. Because the pancreatic, bile, and intestinal juices are very important, although not completely independent of one another, we shall discuss them one at a time.

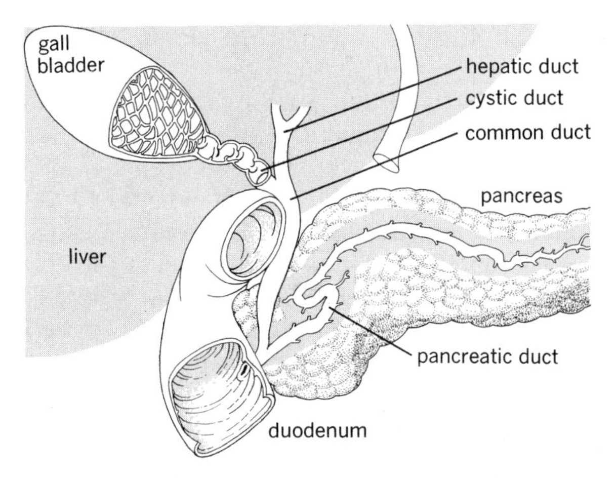

Figure 15-1 Relationship of the liver, the pancreas, and the duodenum.

Pancreatic Secretion

Two substances are involved in the production and flow of pancreatic juice. The first of these is a protein hormone found in the duodenal mucosa. Under the influence of chyme and the free hydrochloric acid from the stomach, the hormone, *pancreatic secretion,* is quickly carried through the blood stream to the pancreas, where it stimulates the flow of pancreatic juice. The pancreatic juice that flows through the pancreatic duct is proportional to the pancreatic secretin carried to the pancreas. The second hormonal substance, known as *pancreozymin,* is not well characterized as yet. This hormone is found in the duodenal tissues but not in the mucosa. Its function is to stimulate the production of the pancreatic juice. Thus, pancreozymin causes the pancreas to produce the necessary enzymes, and pancreatic secretin causes the actual flow of these enzymes into the duodenum.

Activated pancreatic juice is probably one of the most potent digestive juices available in the body. The liquid contains some potentially powerful enzymes and also a high proportion of sodium bicarbonate $NaHCO_3$ and disodium hydrogen phosphate Na_2HPO_4. These basic salts render the juice quite alkaline, within the 7.5–8.0 pH range.

Activated pancreatic juice contains trypsin, chymotrypsin, carboxypeptidase, amylopsin (an amylase), and steapsin (a lipase). Other enzymes, such as lactase and maltase, may be present in trace quantities. In addition, certain enzymes, not yet characterized, are capable of hydrolyzing certain proteoses, peptones, and polypeptides.

Both trypsin and chymotrypsin are secreted as the inactive proenzymes trypsinogen and chymotrypsinogen, respectively. These are rapidly activated by the enzyme *enterokinase* in the intestinal mucosa.

The enterokinase catalyzes the conversion of trypsinogen to trypsin, which in turn converts chymotrypsinogen into chymotrypsin.

$$\text{trypsinogen} \xrightarrow{\text{enterokinase}} \text{trypsin}$$

$$\text{chymotrypsinogen} \xrightarrow{\text{trypsin}} \text{chymotrypsin}$$

Both trypsin and chymotrypsin have an optimum pH of 8.0. The proteolytic enzymes trypsin and chymotrypsin are similar in their activity in that they both hydrolyze proteins to the proteose-peptone stage. Trypsin and chymotrypsin are not substitutes for one another and often enhance each other's activity by complementary activity; that is, one starts acting where the other left off. One of the very obvious differences between the two is that chymotrypsin is a more powerful milk coagulant.

The proteolytic enzymes each hydrolyze specific peptide bonds. Trypsin hydrolyzes peptide bonds between arginine and any other α-amino acid and peptide bonds between lysine and any other α-amino acid. For example,

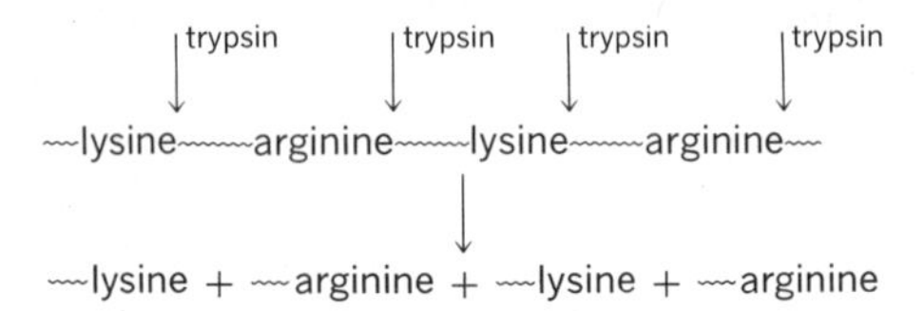

Chymotrypsin hydrolyzes peptide bonds between tryptophane and other α-amino acids, between phenylalanine and other α-amino acids, and between tyrosine and other α-amino acids; these are the major sites of attack.

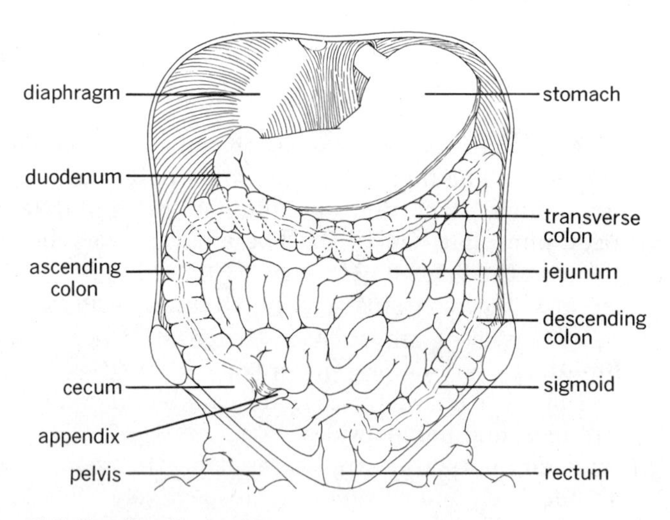

Figure 15-2 The digestive tract.

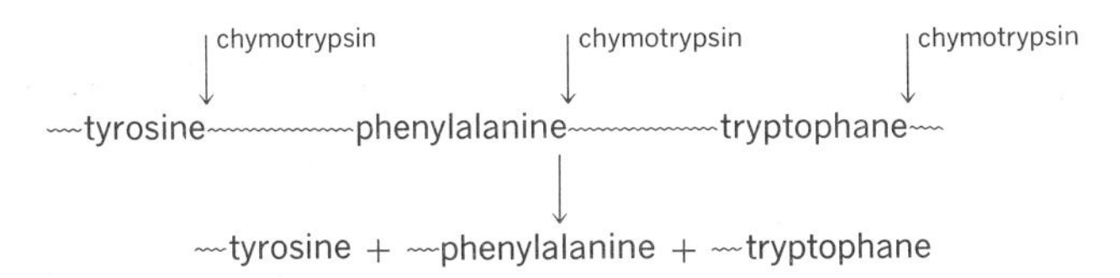

Chymotropsin may also hydrolyze some bonds involving leucine, methionine, asparagine, and histidine.

Pepsin, *a proteolytic enzyme of the stomach,* hydrolyzes peptide bonds at tryptophane, phenylalanine, tyrosine, methionine, and leucine; that is,

pepsin pepsin pepsin pepsin

~leucine~tyrosine~methionine~tryptophane~

↓

~leucine + ~tyrosine + ~methionine + ~tryptophane

An enzyme formerly known as erepsin has now been shown to contain many different enzymes, each one acting upon a particular substrate. "Erepsin" activity is concerned with the hydrolysis of proteoses, peptones, and polypeptides to α-amino acids. We now know that "erepsin" is a mixture of peptidases.

Carboxypeptidase is one of the identified constituents of erepsin. It hydrolyzes peptides by removing the last amino acid group.

$$\sim NH{-}CHR{-}CO{-}NH{-}CHR'{-}CO{-}NH{-}CHR''{-}COOH$$

$$\downarrow + H_2O$$

$$\sim NH{-}CHR{-}CO{-}NH{-}CHR'{-}COOH + R''{-}CH(NH_2){-}COOH$$

$$\downarrow + H_2O$$

$$\sim NH{-}CHR{-}COOH + NH_2{-}CHR'{-}COOH$$

$$\downarrow + H_2O$$

etc.

ACTION OF CARBOXYPEPTIDASES

The other constituents of erepsin have similar activity to carboxypeptidase.

The chief carbohydrate-hydrolyzing constituent of pancreatic juice is the pancreatic amylase known as amylopsin. This enzyme has an optimum pH of 7.1, and its activity is almost identical to that of ptyalin, except that amylopsin is so powerful that it will even hydrolyze raw or uncooked starch.

$$\text{starch} \xrightarrow[+H_2O]{\text{amylopsin}} \text{dextrins} \xrightarrow[+H_2O]{\text{amylopsin}} \text{maltose}$$

The important lipolytic enzyme present in the pancreatic juice is known as steapsin (pancreatic lipase). As the pancreatic juice enters the intestines, the inactive proenzyme prolipase is converted into the active steapsin. Many catalysts can effect this conversion into the active enzyme. Bile salts, for example, are efficient activators. Steapsin hydrolyzes the emulsified fat into fatty acids and glycerol.

$$\begin{array}{l} CH_2-O-\overset{\overset{O}{\|}}{C}-R \\ | \\ CH-O-\overset{\overset{O}{\|}}{C}-R \\ | \\ CH_2-O-\overset{\overset{O}{\|}}{C}-R \\ \text{a fat or oil} \end{array} \xrightarrow[\text{steapsin}]{+3H_2O} \begin{array}{l} CH_2OH \\ | \\ CHOH \\ | \\ CH_2OH \\ \text{glycerol} \end{array} + \begin{array}{c} 3R-\overset{\overset{O}{\|}}{C}-O^-\,Na^+ \\ \text{fatty acid salts} \end{array}$$

(basic conditions of duodenum)

From the foregoing it is apparent that the pancreatic juice is a powerful digestive juice, because it contains enzymes capable of hydrolyzing the three important groups of compounds in food; carbohydrates, lipids, and proteins.

Intestinal Secretion

The intestinal juices are secreted mostly in the duodenum, although some are secreted in the jejunum and ileum. The glands of Brunner and Lieberkühn and the mucous glands of the intestinal mucosa are responsible for the production of this juice. The control of the intestinal juice secretion is not clearly understood. There appear to be two types of secretions. One secretion is independent of the food intake and occurs about every two hours. This juice is low in digestive power but apparently is important for the normal functioning of the bowel. The second juice is apparently stimulated by the presence of chyme in the duodenum and has mild digestive power. This digestive juice is mildly alkaline and contains peptidases, carbohydrases, phosphatase, nucleases, and enterokinase.

Enterokinase is the important kinase that activates the inactive trypsinogen to trypsin in the pancreatic juice.

The carbohydrases are sucrase, maltase, and lactase. These act chemically on the proper disaccharides as follows:

$$\text{sucrose} + H_2O \xrightarrow{\text{sucrase}} \text{glucose} + \text{fructose}$$

$$\text{maltose} + H_2O \xrightarrow{\text{maltase}} \text{glucose} + \text{glucose}$$

$$\text{lactose} + H_2O \xrightarrow{\text{lactase}} \text{glucose} + \text{galactose}$$

Sucrase acts best at a 5–7 pH, maltase at a 7 pH, and lactase at a 5.4–6.0 pH. Maltase and sucrase are the most abundant carbohydrases. Lactase has its greatest concentration in the intestinal juices of young mammals. In adult mammals, the quantity of lactase decreases and its activity diminishes.

PEPTIDASES

Various peptidases, such as amino-polypeptidase and dipeptidase, in intestinal juice affect the hydrolysis of polypeptides to free amino acids. From our knowledge of the peptidases, we are sure that proteins must be broken down to α-amino acids before they can be absorbed. The chemical action of the peptidases is similar to that previously illustrated (carboxypeptidase) and can be represented in a similar fashion. Peptidases complete the digestion of proteins and yield free α-amino acids.

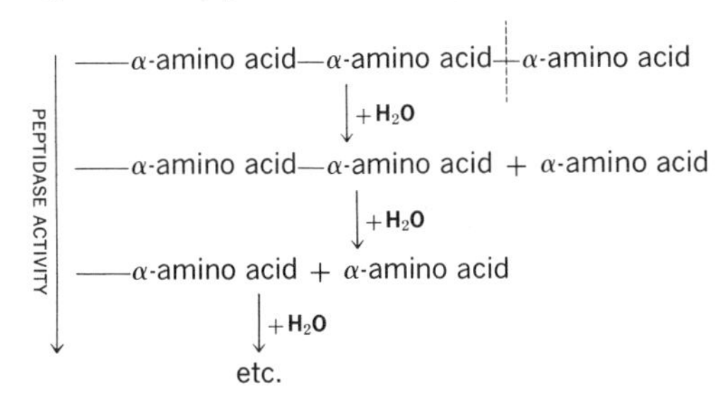

The peptidases are most active at a 7–8 pH and thus are in the perfect medium for maximum activity.

The nucleases and phosphatase are responsible for the hydrolysis of nucleoproteins into their respective units. This can be represented as shown in Figure 15-3.

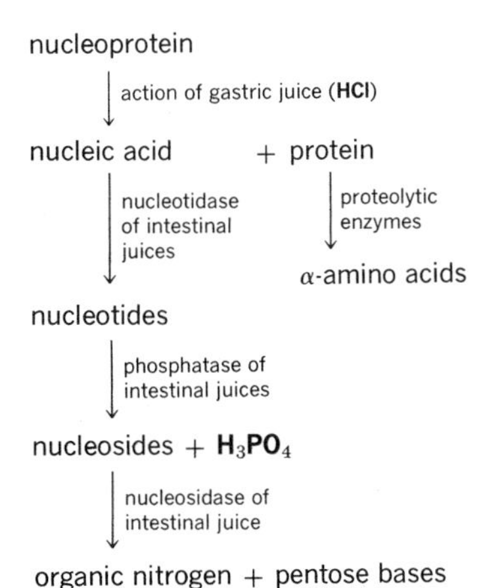

Figure 15-3 Digestive action of nucleoproteins.

Phosphatase is most active at a pH of 8.6 and can function properly in the duodenum.

Bile

Bile juice is produced by the liver. This alkaline liquid (7.7–8.6 pH) is bitter in taste and varies in consistency and color (e.g., it varies from brown to green). There appears to be a continuous flow of bile (about 500–1,000 ml daily), which varies according to the diet. In general, protein foods cause a greater production of bile than carbohydrates.

When food enters the duodenum, the hormone *secretin,* which we have previously discussed, also stimulates the liver to increase bile production to aid in the digestive process. In addition, the presence of food in the duodenum causes the hormone *cholecystokinin* in the duodenal mucosa to make the gall bladder secrete a liquid into the duodenum. The gall bladder liquid is more viscous than liver bile and contains more salts. The gall bladder does not seem to be a simple reservoir for bile. Substances in the bile that are of value to the body are reabsorbed in the gall bladder, and there is an absorption of water, which results in the concentration of the bile. The gall bladder also excretes certain substances into the bile liquid and thereby acts as an excretion organ.

Strictly speaking, bile has little digestive power itself, although it is a great aid in digestion. In cases of infection of the gall bladder or formation of gall stones (crystalline cholesterol), operative removal of the gall bladder (i.e., cholecystectomy) does not adversely affect the digestion in most subjects, although these people usually watch their diet.

Bile juice may be regarded as a secreting and an excreting liquid. The *bile salts* are a secretion useful in the digestive process and are reabsorbed in the body and return to the liver. *Cholesterol* and *bile pigments* may be regarded as excretions as they leave the body.

BILE SALTS

The bile salts (see Chapter 11) are chiefly the sodium salts of taurocholic acid and glycocholic acid. Some potassium salts also may occur to a limited extent. These salts are distinctly alkaline and control the pH of bile. The bile salts may be regarded as secretions that play an important part in the digestive process. Bile salts are valuable for the following reasons:

1. They help activate steapsin by converting the inactive prolipase into the active steapsin.
2. They help emulsify lipid particles so that the steapsin can properly function and hydrolyze these lipids to glycerol and fatty acid salts. Without proper emulsification, the digestion of lipids would be greatly hindered.

3. Usually the fatty acid salts produced in the saponification reaction are not too soluble in water. This low solubility renders their absorption quite difficult. The bile salts combine with the fatty acid salts to form more soluble substances, which can now be properly absorbed. Once absorbed, the bile salts separate from the fatty acids and are returned to the liver to be used again.
4. The fat-soluble vitamins A, D, E, and K could not be properly absorbed in the body if the bile salts did not emulsify the fat particles. Thus, we may regard the bile salts as instrumental in the assimilation of the fat-soluble vitamins.

CHOLESTEROL

The cholesterol in bile may be considered an excretion. The body is an efficient producer of cholesterol, which is synthesized from acetic acid. In addition, much cholesterol enters the body in the diet. Surplus cholesterol is excreted in bile. Some gall stones are almost pure cholesterol. In the intestines, the double bond of cholesterol is reduced, and it is coprostanol that is found in the feces.

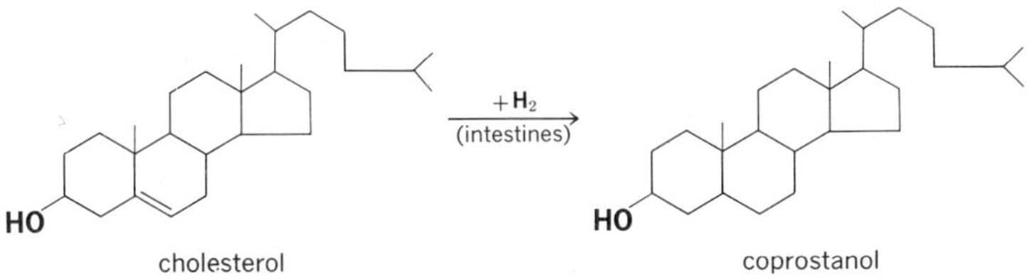

HO — cholesterol $\xrightarrow[\text{(intestines)}]{+H_2}$ HO — coprostanol

BILE PIGMENTS

Hemoglobin is the main pigment of blood. It is composed of the protein globulin and the prosthetic coloring group heme. Heme contains iron.

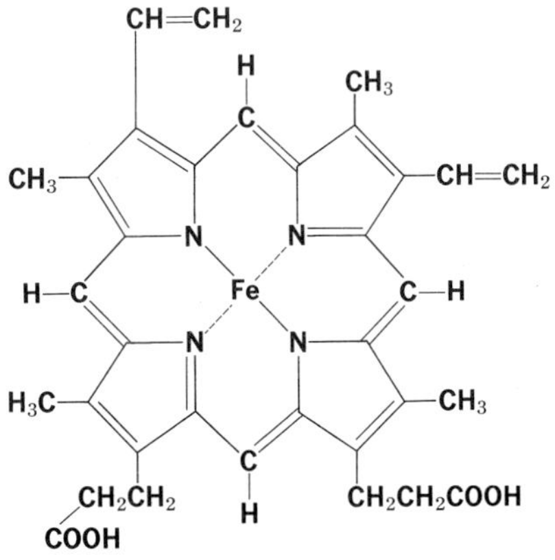

heme

The average life of a red blood cell is about four months. This means that there is a constant turnover of heme in the body. While some heme is being synthesized, some heme is being destroyed and eliminated as bile pigment. The body tries to be economical in this destruction process, in that it tries to save as much iron as possible. The body is about 85% efficient in saving the iron, which means that about 15% of the iron is lost. It is this 15% that must be replenished in the diet in a normal adult (about 12 mg of iron daily).

When the iron is removed from the heme, we call the residue a protoporphyrin. In a simple oxidation process, the protoporphyrin is oxidized to bilirubin, a yellow pigment.

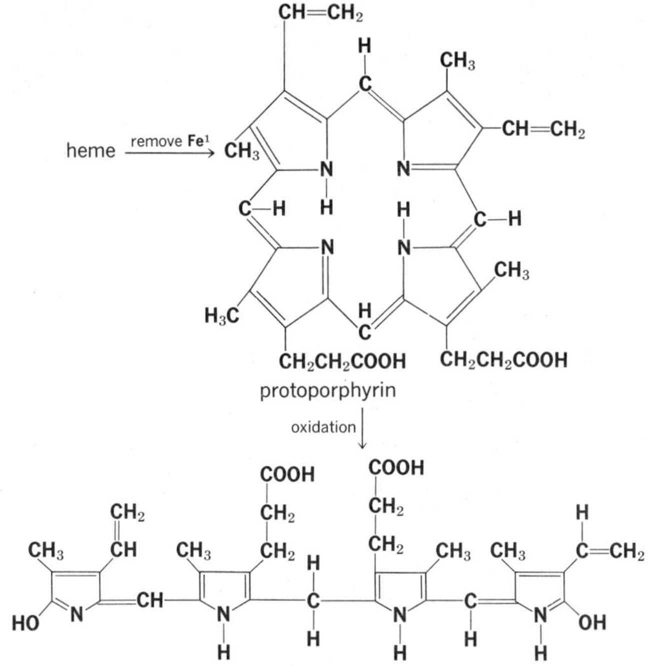

heme $\xrightarrow{\text{remove Fe}^{1}}$

protoporphyrin

oxidation ↓

bilirubin

Bilirubin, the pigment excreted in bile juice, is a sensitive compound and can easily be oxidized and reduced.

In the intestines, bilirubin is reduced to a colorless compound, *mesobilirubinogen*. Mesobilirubinogen is then transformed by further reductions and oxidations into urobilinogen, stercobilinogen, urobilin, and stercobilin.

Biliverdin is green, and stercobilin is brown. Stercobilin is the pigment normally found in feces and is responsible for its characteristic color.

[1] Most of the iron lost each day is secreted with the bile fluid and eventually leaves the body in the feces (10 mg daily). A negligible amount of iron is excreted in urine (1–2 mg daily).

The occasional production of green feces is due to biliverdin produced abnormally.

Urochrome is the pigment responsible for the color of urine. Urochrome contains urobilin or urobilinogen and a peptide fragment.

Jaundice is a condition resulting from the abnormal accumulation of bile pigment in the blood, and the skin becomes yellow. This occurs when there is a bile obstruction, or when the liver function is impaired, or when red blood cells are being destroyed more rapidly than normal.

Although it occurs mainly in the liver, the conversion of hemoglobin to bilirubin may take place in other tissues. When tissue is injured, the blood escapes and clots. The characteristic black-and-blue mark indicates the conversion of hemoglobin to bilirubin. At first, a bluish-red color is observed; then, yellow, green, and brown colors may also be observed. In this way, all the bile pigments may be observed visually.

REVIEW QUESTIONS

1. What is meant by the duodenum? By what physical mechanism does food enter the duodenum in the process of digestion?
2. Generally, what is the pH of the material entering the duodenum?
3. Generally, what is the pH of the material passed from the duodenum?
4. What is meant by the term "pancreatic secretion"? Discuss the hormonal control of the production and secretion of pancreatic juice.
5. What is the pH of the pancreatic juice? What substances in the juice are responsible for this pH?
6. What enzymes or proenzymes are found in the pancreatic juice? Use equations to illustrate the function of each enzyme.
7. Identify trypsin, chymotrypsin, carboxypeptidase, erepsin, amylopsin, and steapsin. What are the optimum pH ranges for these enzymes?
8. Discuss the origin, content, and production of intestinal secretion.
9. Identify enterokinase, sucrase, maltase, lactase, phosphatase, and peptidase. Illustrate the activity of these enzymes by appropriate equations.
10. What is the pH range of the intestinal digestive juices?
11. What are the optimum pH ranges for the enzymes in the intestinal juice?
12. Discuss the pH range, color, amount of flow, and chemical composition of bile. Discuss the hormonal control of the production and flow of bile.
13. What are gall stones? Why has bile been considered a secreting and an excreting liquid?
14. What are the bile salts? Enumerate their functions.
15. What is cholesterol? How is it formed in the body, and in what form is it excreted?
16. What are the bile pigments? How are they formed?
17. What are heme, protoporphyrin, bilirubin, biliverdin, stercobilin, and urobilinogen?
18. What is jaundice?

16

putrefaction and detoxication

It is believed that most of the absorption of digested food material occurs in the small intestines. Little food remains to be absorbed when the contents of the small intestines reach the large intestines.

Absorption may be considered a function of the surface. The small intestines are well suited to this absorption phenomenon because of the large number of *villi* that project into the lumen of the intestines. Most absorption takes place by means of these villi. A lacteal is a vessel running through the center of a villus, and each lacteal is surrounded by a network of capillaries. Absorption occurs through the semipermeable membrane walls of each villus into the lacteals and capillaries through which flow the circulating fluids of the body. See Figure 16-1.

As the contents of the small intestines enter the large intestines, the material is still in a semifluid state of about the same consistency as chyme and now contains undigested food and the remains of digestive juices. Essentially no digestive juice is secreted in the large intestines, although some mucous is secreted. Much of the water of the large intestinal contents is gradually absorbed, and a more solid material, known as *feces,* is produced.

It is highly significant that about 20–30% of the solids of fecal matter consists of bacteria, mostly dead. The colon bacteria reproduce rapidly, are very active chemically, and are usually killed by the chemical products they produce. Because feces always contain some live bacteria, they represent a source of possible contamination.

Due to the strong acidity of the stomach, few microorganisms survive, and the stomach and duodenum are essentially sterile. Microorganisms fluorish in the intestines, particularly the colon, because it is a favorable medium for growth. The bacteria flora are abundant because of the slight alkalinity of the intestines due to the juices that entered the duodenum and neutralized the acidity of chyme.

A newborn infant, particularly one delivered via the Caesarean route, normally is free of bacteria. The feces of a newborn infant are known as *meconium* and consist of desquamated cells of the alimentary tract and skin, lanugo hairs, fatty material from the vernix caseosa, amniotic fluid, and various intestinal secretions. Its dark color is thought to be due to bile pigments. One of the very noticeable differences between meconium and ordinary feces is the odor. Meconium has no odor, because there has been no bacterial action.

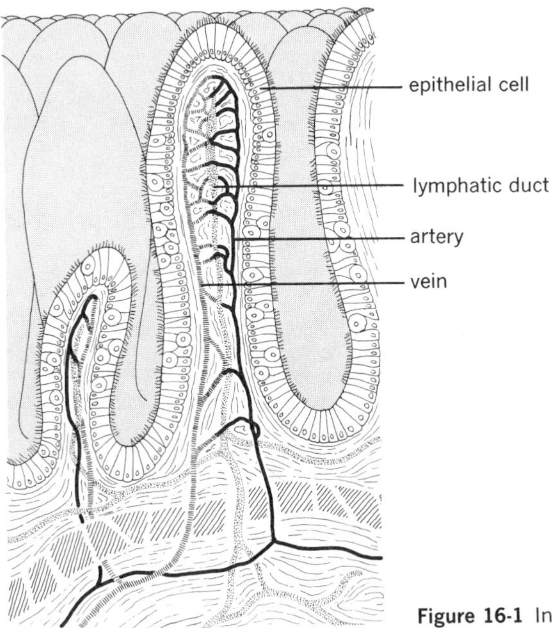

Figure 16-1 Intestinal villi.

Gaseous Products

Various gases are among the compounds produced by intestinal bacteria. The fermentation of carbohydrates produces odorless carbon dioxide and almost odorless methane. By the action of bacteria on proteins, the odorless nitrogen and hydrogen are formed with the very odoriferous hydrogen sulfide and related organic sulfur products. Much of the nitrogen expelled originates from the air swallowed while eating. Not all the gaseous products are expelled from the rectum; some hydrogen sulfide and related sulfur compounds are absorbed into the blood stream and are exhaled in the breath. This is in part responsible for a halotosis condition.

Putrefaction

By putrefaction we mean the production of objectionable products by action of bacteria on proteins. These products are usually toxic and have unpleasant odors. Some of the possible products are illustrated below.

Formation of cadaverine and putrescine:

$$\begin{array}{c} CH_2NH_2 \\ | \\ CH_2 \\ | \\ CH_2 \\ | \\ CH_2 \\ | \\ H-C-NH_2 \\ | \\ COOH \end{array} \xrightarrow[-CO_2]{\text{decarboxylation}} \begin{array}{c} CH_2NH_2 \\ | \\ CH_2 \\ | \\ CH_2 \\ | \\ CH_2 \\ | \\ CH_2NH_2 \end{array} + CO_2$$

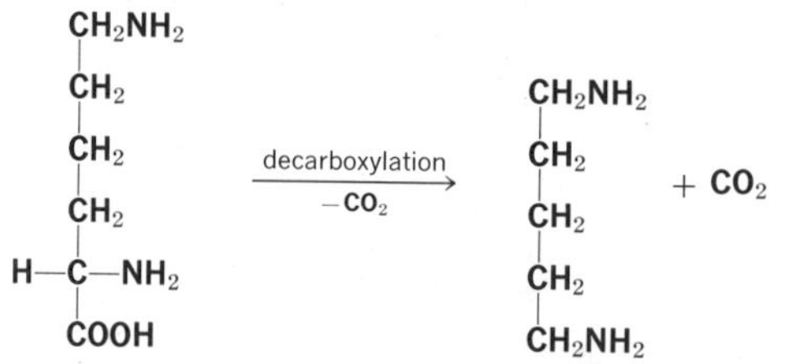

lysine (*an essential α-amino acid*) — cadaverine

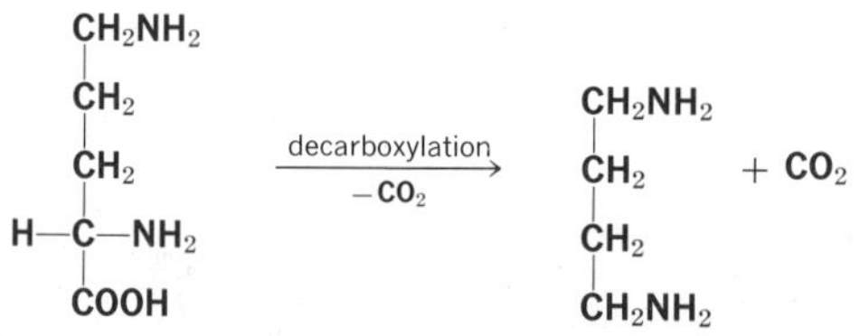

$$\begin{array}{c} CH_2NH_2 \\ | \\ CH_2 \\ | \\ CH_2 \\ | \\ H-C-NH_2 \\ | \\ COOH \end{array} \xrightarrow[-CO_2]{\text{decarboxylation}} \begin{array}{c} CH_2NH_2 \\ | \\ CH_2 \\ | \\ CH_2 \\ | \\ CH_2NH_2 \end{array} + CO_2$$

ornithine (*found in animal tissue*) — putrescine

As the names suggest, cadaverine and putrescine are associated with the odor of decaying or putrefying flesh and are particularly nauseating.

Benzoic acid, an irritating acid, may be formed from phenylalanine by oxidation of the carbon residue attached to the benzene ring.

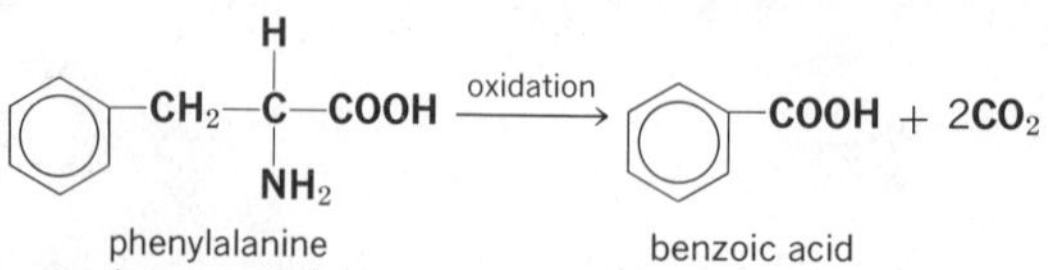

$$C_6H_5-CH_2-\overset{\displaystyle H}{\underset{\displaystyle NH_2}{C}}-COOH \xrightarrow{\text{oxidation}} C_6H_5-COOH + 2CO_2$$

phenylalanine (*an essential α-amino acid*) — benzoic acid

Tyrosine may give rise to many objectionable products, as indicated.

$$HO-C_6H_4-CH_2-CH(NH_2)-COOH \xrightarrow[-CO_2]{\text{decarboxylation}} HO-C_6H_4-CH_2CH_2NH_2$$

tyrosine (*one of the commonly met α-amino acids*) — tyramine

degradation at b → phenol (*carbolic acid*) toxic (C_6H_5OH)

degradation at a → para-cresol (*found in lysol*) toxic ($HO-C_6H_4-CH_3$)

Tryptophan gives rise to two commonly met objectionable products as follows:

tryptophan (*an essential α-amino acid*) $\xrightarrow{\text{degradation at a}}$ skatole (CH_3-indole)

tryptophan $\xrightarrow{\text{degradation at b}}$ indole

Both skatole and indole possess nauseating odors and are chiefly responsible for the characteristic odor of feces.

The decarboxylation of the commonly met α-amino acid histidine results in the formation of the highly potent histamine.

$$\text{H-N(imidazole)}-CH_2-CH(NH_2)-COOH \xrightarrow{-CO_2} \text{N(imidazole)}-CH_2CH_2NH_2$$

histidine — histamine

The sulfur-containing α-amino acids cysteine, cystine, and methionine yield by degradation processes mercaptans and related products.

$$\begin{array}{l} CH_2{-}S{-}CH_3 \\ | \\ CH_2{-}\underset{NH_2}{\overset{H}{C}}{-}COOH \xrightarrow{\text{degradation}} CH_3SH \end{array}$$

methionine → methyl mercaptan

$$H{-}\underset{COOH}{\overset{CH_2-S-H}{C}}{-}NH_2 \xrightarrow{-CO_2} \begin{array}{l} CH_2{-}S{-}H \\ | \\ CH_2NH_2 \end{array} \xrightarrow{-NH_3} CH_3CH_2SH$$

(cysteine also → H_2S)

cysteine → ethyl mercaptan

The mercaptans are among the most objectionable of all organic compounds from an odor standpoint. Their skunk-like odor is due to a great extent to the volatile mercaptans.

Detoxication

From the foregoing it would appear that the intestines are a chemical factory producing toxic products. This is true inasmuch as many toxic products are produced, but most of them are formed in very small quantities.

Nevertheless, some compounds are so toxic that minute quantities represent a threat to the body health; these dangerous compounds must be rendered nontoxic or detoxified. The detoxication process is usually a chemical one carried out principally by the liver, with the kidney and other tissues playing possible minor roles. The detoxified products are usually excreted in urine by the kidneys.

The way the body detoxifies a compound depends to a large extent on the chemical nature of the toxic material.

It must be mentioned that the term detoxication may in some cases be a misnomer, because some of the toxic products are chemically changed into other compounds, which still may be toxic. Usually, however, the toxicity is *decreased* by the chemical action; hence, the origin of the word detoxication.

DETOXICATION OF ACIDS BY COMBINATION WITH α-AMINO ACIDS

As shown before, benzoic acid may be produced from phenylalanine by bacteria action. Benzoic acid also occurs in our food. A large amount of benzoic acid is knowingly used as a food preservative, because it appears that man can detoxify essentially unlimited quantities of this acid. The combination of benzoic acid and glycine yields hippuric acid. The normal amount of hippuric acid excreted daily is about 1 gram. By eating a special diet, the hippuric acid output can be increased to 5 or 10 grams. Experiments have shown that almost all the ingested benzoic acid is excreted within a 12-hour period.

$$C_6H_5COOH + H_2N{-}CH_2COOH \longrightarrow C_6H_5{-}CO{-}NH{-}CH_2COOH + H_2O$$

benzoic acid glycine hippuric acid

Benzoic acid may also be detoxified as the glucuronate.

Salicylic acid, which may be taken in large quantities in the form of the salicylates (i.e., aspirin), is apparently detoxified in a manner similar to benzoic acid. The combination of salicylic acid and glycine yields salicyluric acid.

$$HO{-}C_6H_4{-}CO{-}OH + H_2N{-}CH_2COOH \longrightarrow HO{-}C_6H_4{-}CO{-}NH{-}CH_2COOH + H_2O$$

salicylic acid glycine salicyluric acid

Salicylic acid may also be excreted as the glucuronate and in other chemical modifications.

To illustrate further the generality of the reaction, we see that nicotinic acid can be excreted as nicotinuric acid, although most of it is eliminated as trigonelline (see end of chapter).

$$C_5H_4N{-}CO{-}OH + H_2N{-}CH_2COOH \longrightarrow C_5H_4N{-}CO{-}NH{-}CH_2COOH + H_2O$$

nicotinic acid glycine nicotinuric acid

Glycine is not the only α-amino acid used by the body in detoxication reactions. Glutamic acid, ornithine, and cysteine are known to react with toxic acids and similar compounds to render them more or less innocuous.

DETOXICATION BY FORMATION OF SULFATES

Indole is rendered nontoxic by oxidation to indoxyl, which reacts with sulfuric acid, formed by oxidation of some of the sulfur compounds in the body (e.g., cysteine, methionine, and cystine). The product excreted in the urine is indican, a potassium salt.

indole $\xrightarrow{\text{oxidation}}$ indoxyl (3-OH indole, N–H)

$$\text{indoxyl} + H_2SO_4 \xrightarrow{} \text{indoxyl hydrogen sulfate (–O–}SO_2OH) \xrightarrow{K^+} \text{indican (–}OSO_2OK)$$

(H_2SO_4 ↑ oxidation from (S))

indoxyl — indoxyl hydrogen sulfate — indican

Indoxyl has also been isolated as the glucuronate.

Skatole behaves in a manner similar to indole and forms skatoxyl, analogous to indoxyl.

Some phenol may be excreted as a sulfate salt.

$$C_6H_5OH + H_2SO_4 \longrightarrow C_6H_5OSO_2OH$$

phenol — phenyl hydrogen sulfate

$$C_6H_5OSO_2OH \longrightarrow C_6H_5OSO_2OK$$

potassium phenyl sulfate

Phenol, however, is more commonly excreted as the glucuronate.

DETOXICATION BY FORMATION OF GLUCURONATES

Combinations with glucuronic acid are extremely common.

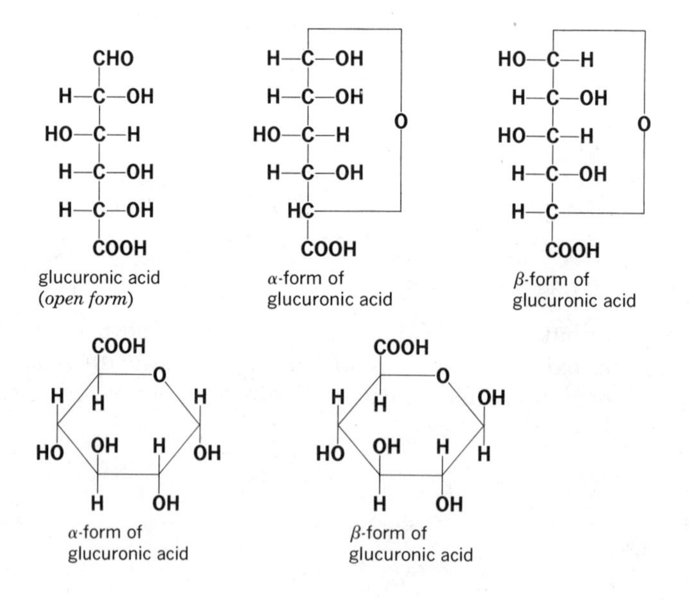

glucuronic acid (*open form*) — α-form of glucuronic acid — β-form of glucuronic acid

α-form of glucuronic acid — β-form of glucuronic acid

As we have mentioned before, compounds like phenol, indoxyl, salicylic acid, benzoic acid, and many others are also excreted as glucuronates.

We shall use benzoic acid and phenol to illustrate glucuronate formation.

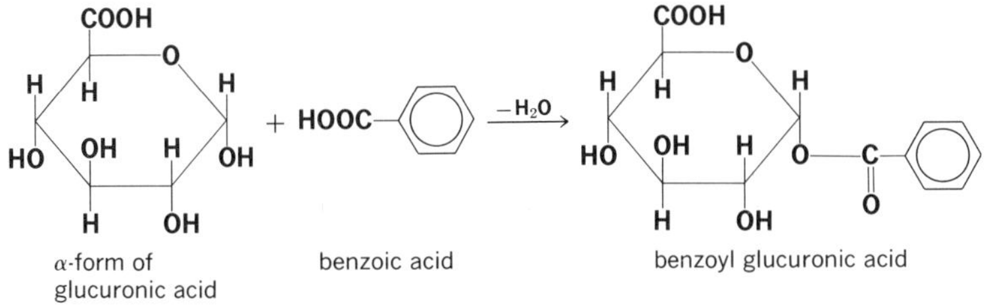

COOH, O, H, H, H, HO, OH, H, OH, H, OH + HOOC–C$_6$H$_5$ $\xrightarrow{-H_2O}$ (glucuronic acid ring)–O–C(=O)–C$_6$H$_5$

α-form of glucuronic acid — benzoic acid — benzoyl glucuronic acid

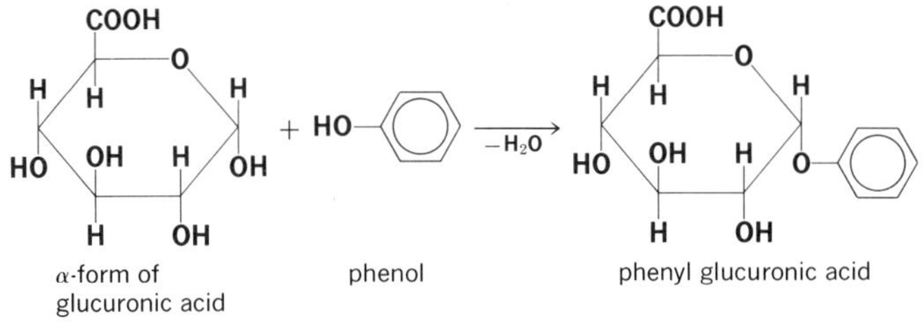

COOH, O, H, H, H, HO, OH, H, OH, H, OH + HO–C$_6$H$_5$ $\xrightarrow{-H_2O}$ (glucuronic acid ring)–O–C$_6$H$_5$

α-form of glucuronic acid — phenol — phenyl glucuronic acid

It has been shown that many of the female sex hormones are eliminated, to a large extent, as glucuronates. Also, many drugs are handled in this manner. Compounds such as chloral hydrate, menthol, turpentine, camphor, and even the sulfa drugs can be eliminated to a certain extent as glucuronates.

OXIDATIVE DETOXICATION

Compounds such as cadaverine and putrescine are detoxified by oxidative degradation.

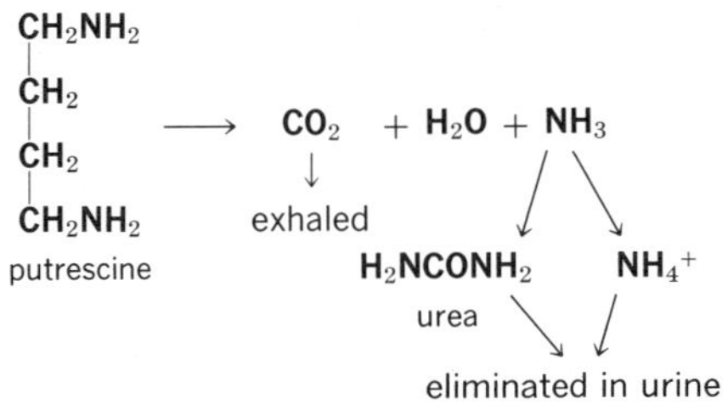

$$CH_2NH_2\text{–}CH_2\text{–}CH_2\text{–}CH_2NH_2 \longrightarrow CO_2 + H_2O + NH_3$$

putrescine

CO_2 ↓ exhaled

NH_3 → H_2NCONH_2 (urea) and NH_4^+ → eliminated in urine

Benzene can be oxidized, and the ring may be opened.

benzene $\xrightarrow{\text{oxidation}}$ muconic acid (HOOC–CH=CH–CH=CH–COOH)

benzene $\xrightarrow{\text{oxidation}}$ phenol

but more commonly, benzene is oxidized to phenol and detoxified as the sulfate or glucuronate. Substituted benzenes can be oxidized to substituted benzoic acids.

toluene (C_6H_5–CH_3) $\xrightarrow{\text{oxidation}}$ benzoic acid (C_6H_5–COOH)

m-xylene $\xrightarrow{\text{oxidation}}$ *m*-methylbenzoic acid

Acetanilide may be oxidized to *p*-acetylaminophenol.

acetanilide (H–N(–C_6H_5)–C(=O)–CH_3) $\xrightarrow{\text{oxidation}}$ *p*-acetylaminophenol (*p-hydroxyacetanilide*)

Also, some aldehydes and alcohols can be oxidized to acids.

benzaldehyde (C_6H_5–CHO) $\xrightarrow{\text{oxidation}}$ benzoic acid (C_6H_5–C(=O)–OH)

β-phenylethylalcohol (C_6H_5–CH_2CH_2OH) $\xrightarrow{\text{oxidation}}$ phenylacetic acid (C_6H_5–CH_2COOH)

Generally, it may be stated that aliphatic compounds are more easily oxidized than aromatic compounds.

DETOXICATION BY REDUCTION

Nitro compounds and similar nitrogen derivatives can be detoxified by reduction. This reduction may be accompanied by other reactions.

$$R{-}NO_2 \xrightarrow{\text{reduction}} R{-}NH_2$$

nitrobenzene (NO_2) → *p*-aminophenol (NH_2, OH) (excreted either as sulfate or glucuronate)

METHYLATIVE DETOXICATION

Many basic nitrogen heterocycles are methylated.

pyridine → N-methylpyridinium ($N^{\oplus}$–CH_3) $OH^{\ominus}$

quinoline → N-methylquinolinium ($N^{\oplus}$–CH_3) $OH^{\ominus}$

nicotinic acid (COOH) → trigonelline ($COO^{\ominus}$, $N^{\oplus}$–CH_3)

REVIEW QUESTIONS

1. Discuss the absorption of digested food material.
2. Discuss the formation of feces. What is known about the bacterial content of feces? What is meconium?
3. What is meant by putrefaction?
4. Discuss the formation of gaseous products in the intestines.
5. What are cadaverine and putrescine? How can they be formed?
6. How can benzoic acid and carbolic acid be formed in putrefaction?

7. What are skatole and indole? How can they be formed in the putrefactive process?
8. What are the mercaptans? How can they be formed in the putrefactive process?
9. Define detoxication. List several ways that detoxication can occur and give examples.
10. What is hippuric acid? Show how it can be formed.
11. What is indican? Show how it can be formed.
12. Give examples to show detoxication by formation of glucuronates.

17

absorption and metabolism of carbohydrates

By *metabolism* we mean the chemical changes digested food molecules undergo after absorption into the body. We know something about the metabolic changes in the body, but we can only guess at many of them. We are hindered in our learning because we cannot see inside the functioning body the way we can see inside a test tube. We must use heavy isotopes, radioactive isotopes, and material sliced from living tissue to obtain information; because this may be indirect evidence, it is sometimes misleading. Despite these handicaps, much has been learned concerning the chemical reactions occurring normally in the body and the chemical reactions that may be responsible for or that may be a result of abnormal circumstances.

In the digestive process, carbohydrates are hydrolyzed to monosaccharides, which are soluble in water and are absorbed through the intestinal mucosa into the blood stream. In our everyday life, the principal carbohydrates in the diet are starch, glucose, sucrose, and lactose. Complete hydrolysis of these carbohydrates produces the monosaccharides glucose,

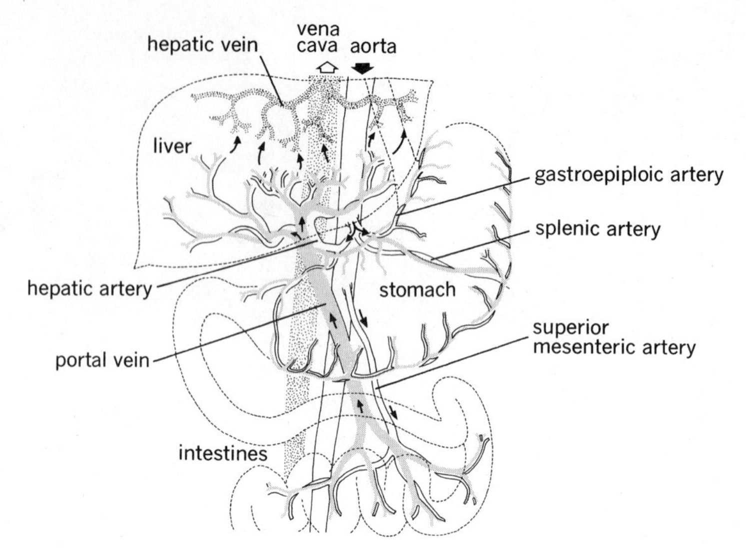

Figure 17-1 Portal circulation.

galactose, and fructose, which are carried directly to the liver by the portal circulation (see Figure 17-1). In the liver, the three monosaccharides may be converted into one simple sugar, glucose, the primary monosaccharide of the blood stream and body.

The primary function of carbohydrates in living organisms is to serve as a source of energy for biological systems. Carbohydrates, however, may serve other functions (see Figure 17-2).

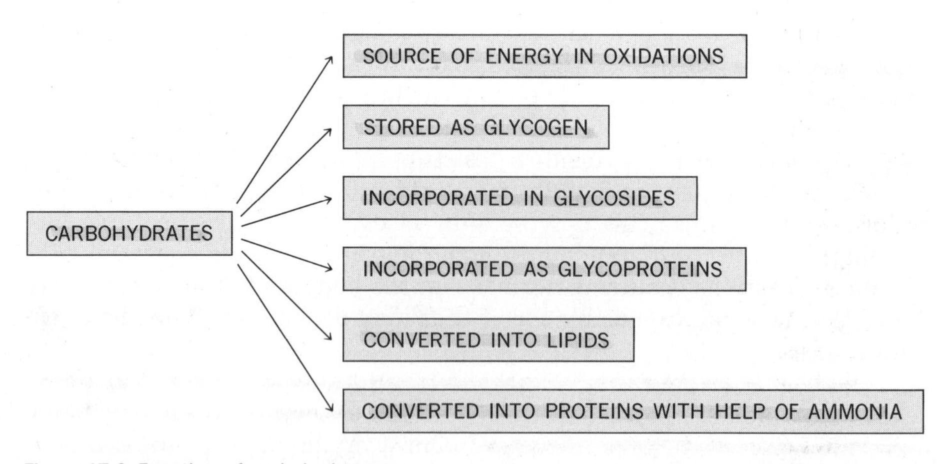

Figure 17-2 Function of carbohydrates.

Glycogen-Glucose Relationships

Glycogen is the reserve carbohydrate of the body. Glycogen has been called animal starch, because starch is the reserve carbohydrate of plants.

The liver and muscles store the glycogen. The liver stores about 6% glycogen by weight, and the muscles store about 0.5% glycogen by weight. Because the body has much more muscle than liver, approximately 250 g of glycogen is stored in the body muscles and approximately 110 g is stored in the liver. The approximately 360 g of glycogen represent about 1,500 kilocalories[1] of available energy, or approximately one-half the daily energy requirements for a man.

The sugar that leaves the liver to circulate in the blood stream through the body is the monosaccharide glucose. The glucose goes to whichever part of the body needs it. Under normal circumstances, the glucose concentration of any one person remains remarkably constant. Because individuals vary in chemical makeup, we regard the glucose concentration as normal if it is in the 90–110 mg per 100 ml of blood range. Some sources regard the 80–120 mg of glucose per 100 ml of blood range as normal, thus indicating the actual variation one finds in comparing one person to another.

Many factors regulate the amount of sugar in the blood. First, we have the interconversion of blood sugar and liver glycogen. This is a reversible reaction.

$$\text{liver glycogen} \underset{\text{glycogenesis}}{\overset{\text{glycogenolysis}}{\rightleftharpoons}} \text{blood sugar}$$

When blood sugar is needed, liver glycogen breaks down. If some extra glucose is available, it may be reconverted into liver glycogen.

In addition, blood sugar forms muscle glycogen. This is essentially an irreversible process, because muscle glycogen does not form blood glucose but instead forms lactic acid.

$$\text{blood glucose} \longrightarrow \text{muscle glycogen}$$

The rates at which the carbohydrates are oxidized, converted into fat, etc., also govern the concentration of the blood glucose. In addition, the pancreas, adrenals, pituitary, and thyroid hormones play a dominant role in influencing the blood sugar level. See Figure 17-3.

[1] A calorie is a unit of heat; it is the heat required to raise the temperature of 1 gram of water 1 degree centigrade. Nutritional requirements are usually expressed in large calories called kilocalories. Energy changes in chemical reactions are usually expressed in small calories. One kilocalorie equals 1,000 small calories.

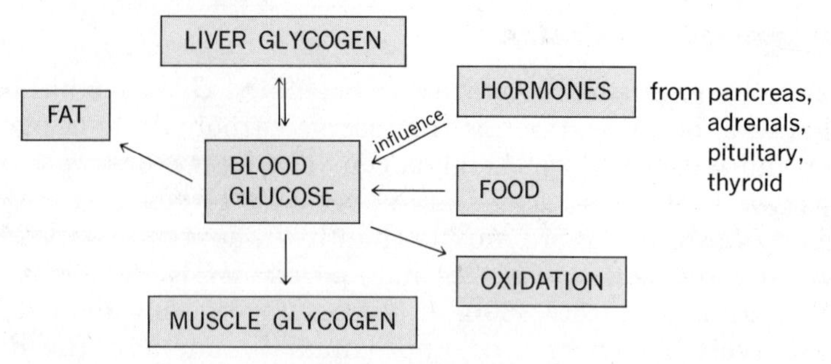

Figure 17-3 Factors influencing blood glucose levels.

Renal Threshold

Under normal circumstances, urine contains a negligible amount of glucose. The glucose in the blood filters through the glomerular membrane of the kidney and is again reabsorbed in the tubules. This is a very select process. If the reabsorption process is hindered in any way, or if the concentration of glucose in the blood becomes so high that the reabsorption process cannot recover all the glucose, the glucose appears in the urine. The *renal threshold* for glucose, or sugar threshold, is the concentration of glucose in the blood at which sugar "spills" over or appears in the urine. This may occur when the glucose concentration is about 140–160 mg per

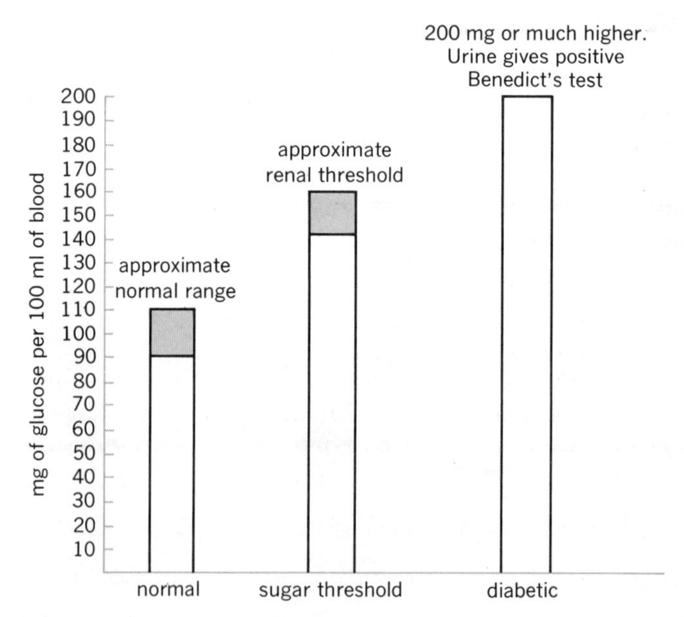

Figure 17-4 Concentration of sugar glucose in the blood.

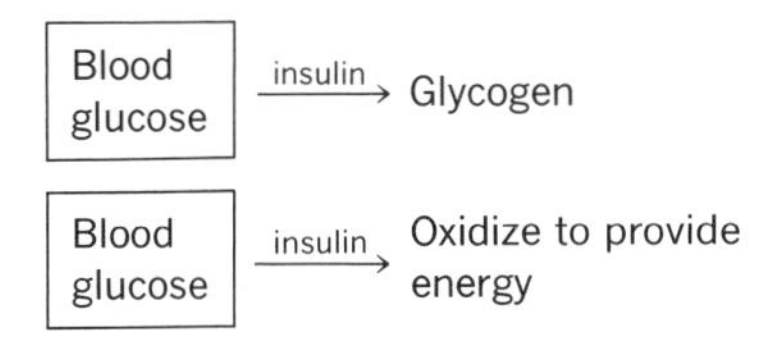

Figure 17-5 Insulin action.

100 ml of blood. An increase in the concentration of glucose past the 160 mg level will raise the glucose level in the urine.

Because glucose is a reducing sugar, one can easily detect its presence by Benedict's test. A high glucose concentration gives a more positive Benedict's test. This is estimated by observing the color intensity of the cuprous oxide (Cu_2O) precipitate. See Figure 17-4.

Insulin Control of Carbohydrate Metabolism

Insulin is a protein hormone, secreted by the pancreas, which markedly affects the blood glucose level. This is accomplished in two ways: by regulating the liver glycogen-glucose interconversion and by regulating the utilization of the glucose (oxidation). The insulin increases the liver glycogen, and possibly the muscle glycogen, at the expense of the blood sugar. The insulin increases the oxidation of the glucose and thus removes the blood sugar. *In essence, insulin tends to lower the blood sugar level.*

If, for some reason, the pancreas does not function properly and does not secrete enough insulin, a diabetic condition may result. Apparently a diabetogenic, or diabetes-producing, factor from the pituitary becomes prominent, and this protein hormone works in the opposite direction to insulin.

The diabetogenic factor tends to increase the conversion of liver glycogen into blood sugar and to inhibit the oxidation of blood sugar. In effect, the diabetogenic factor results in the increased production of blood glucose (see Figure 17-6).

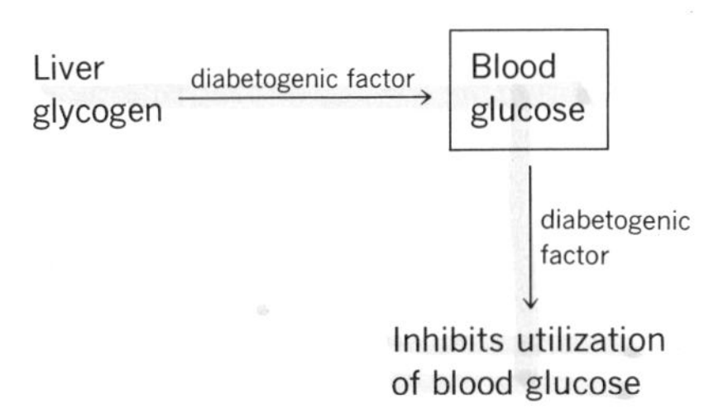

Figure 17-6 Diabetogenic factor.

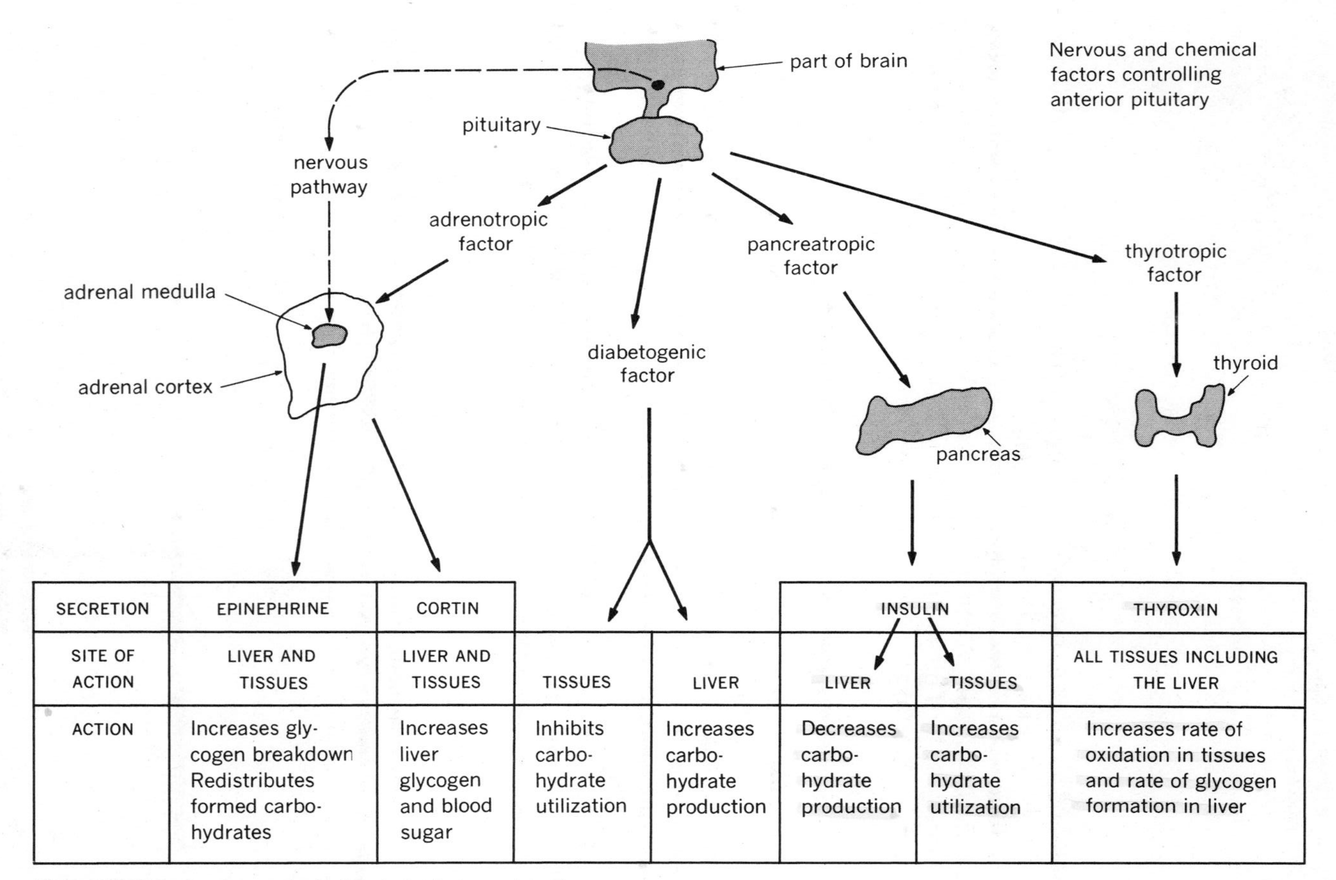

SECRETION	EPINEPHRINE	CORTIN			INSULIN		THYROXIN
SITE OF ACTION	LIVER AND TISSUES	LIVER AND TISSUES	TISSUES	LIVER	LIVER	TISSUES	ALL TISSUES INCLUDING THE LIVER
ACTION	Increases glycogen breakdown Redistributes formed carbohydrates	Increases liver glycogen and blood sugar	Inhibits carbohydrate utilization	Increases carbohydrate production	Decreases carbohydrate production	Increases carbohydrate utilization	Increases rate of oxidation in tissues and rate of glycogen formation in liver

Figure 17-7 Endocrine control of carbohydrate metabolism.

Therefore, when the insulin is nonfunctional or lacking, the blood sugar increases greatly due to the diabetogenic factor becoming dominant, and the urine usually registers a positive Benedict's test.

In a normal individual, these hormones play an important role in raising or lowering the blood sugar level, depending upon the needs of the body. The hormones from the adrenals and thyroid also govern the blood glucose level in similar ways.

Figure 17-7 summarizes the hormonal control of the carbohydrate metabolism.

Glucose and Energy Relationships

When glucose is completely oxidized, we obtain carbon dioxide and water.

$$C_6H_{12}O_6 + 6O_2 \longrightarrow 6CO_2 + 6H_2O + \text{approx. 670,000 small calories}$$

complete oxidation of glucose
(*aerobic*)

Here, energy is liberated, enabling us to work. The energy is stored in the glucose molecule by the radiant energy from the sun, as indicated in the photosynthesis equation.

$$\text{energy from sun} + 6CO_2 + 6H_2O \xrightarrow{\text{chlorophyll}} C_6H_{12}O_6 + 6O_2$$

photosynthesis equation

We refer to the complete oxidation of glucose as aerobic oxidation to indicate a sufficient supply of oxygen to accomplish this. If all the glucose were oxidized in an aerobic manner, a great quantity of energy would be liberated, perhaps more than needed, which would be wasteful.

In the body, where the oxygen supply is at first limited, a transformation called an anaerobic reaction occurs. We commonly refer to this reaction as glycolysis.

The important product of animal glycolysis is lactic acid.

$$C_6H_{12}O_6 \xrightarrow{\text{glycolysis}} 2CH_3\text{—}\overset{\displaystyle OH}{\underset{\displaystyle H}{\overset{|}{\underset{|}{C}}}}\text{—}COOH + \text{60,000 calories}$$

lactic acid

In the conversion of glucose to lactic acid, we do not go directly from the former to the latter. Apparently it is more economical for the body to proceed in a stepwise fashion that involves many compounds. We will discuss this conversion later in the chapter.

When it is caused by yeast, we commonly call this anaerobic reaction fermentation. The fermentation equation may be represented as follows:

$$\underset{\text{glucose}}{C_6H_{12}O_6} \longrightarrow \underset{\text{ethyl alcohol}}{2CH_3CH_2OH} + \underset{\text{carbon dioxide}}{2CO_2} + \text{energy}$$

fermentation reaction

Ethyl alcohol and carbon dioxide are the end products of this reaction. Here, also, the reactions proceed in a stepwise fashion similar to the animal anaerobic reaction of glucose.

In carbohydrate metabolism, many reactions occur, and, as in all biological systems, an enzyme is usually necessary for every step.

In many of these reactions, the starting compound and the product are of comparable energy levels. However, in some reactions, considerable energy may be liberated as the reaction proceeds. The muscles use the liberated energy to form an energy-rich compound, which enables them to contract.

For example, if A and B are of about the same energy level, within a few thousand small calories, going from A to B or from B to A would be similar to sliding across a level floor.

$$A \rightleftharpoons B$$

(A and B of comparable energy levels)

We could go in either direction without much effort or change in the energy content.

If, however, D is at a much lower energy level than C, we find that in going from C to D we liberate much energy. This is comparable to an object's falling from a position in the air to the ground. The liberated energy could be used by the muscles to make an energy-rich compound, which would enable them to contract.

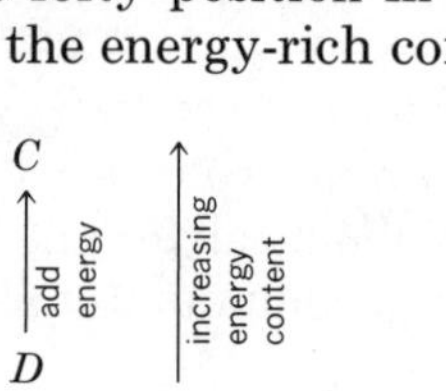

$$C \longrightarrow D + \text{energy}$$

(decreasing energy content ↓)

If we wish to go from D to C, we must furnish energy to cause this reaction to go. This is comparable to lifting an object from the ground to some lofty position in the air. To make reactions proceed uphill, nature uses the energy-rich compounds.

$$D \xrightarrow{\text{add energy}} C$$

(increasing energy content ↑)

The energy-rich compounds, available in carbohydrate metabolism, are the energy-rich phosphates.

THE ENERGY-RICH PHOSPHATE COMPOUNDS

Two energy-rich-type compounds of prime importance in the utilization of carbohydrates in the muscle and liver tissue are *adenosine phosphates* and *phosphocreatine*.

The adenosine phosphates:

increasing energy content ↑ / decreasing energy content ↓

$$\text{Adenine(NH}_2\text{)}-\underset{\text{H}}{\text{C}}-\underset{\text{H}}{\overset{\text{OH}}{\text{C}}}-\underset{\text{H}}{\overset{\text{OH}}{\text{C}}}-\underset{\text{H}}{\text{C}}-CH_2-O-\underset{\text{OH}}{\overset{\text{O}}{\text{P}}}-O-\underset{\text{OH}}{\overset{\text{O}}{\text{P}}}-O-\underset{\text{OH}}{\overset{\text{O}}{\text{P}}}-OH$$

adenosine triphosphate (*ATP*)

$+H_2O$ ↓ ↑ $-H_2O$

$$\text{Adenine(NH}_2\text{)}-\underset{\text{H}}{\text{C}}-\underset{\text{H}}{\overset{\text{OH}}{\text{C}}}-\underset{\text{H}}{\overset{\text{OH}}{\text{C}}}-\underset{\text{H}}{\text{C}}-CH_2-O-\underset{\text{OH}}{\overset{\text{O}}{\text{P}}}-O-\underset{\text{OH}}{\overset{\text{O}}{\text{P}}}-OH + H_3PO_4 + 10{,}000\ \text{calories}$$

adenosine diphosphate (*ADP*)

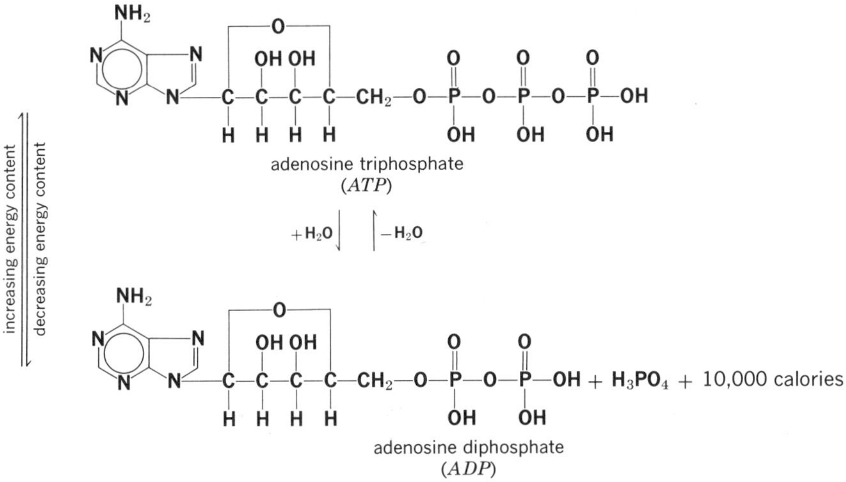

When adenosine triphosphate (ATP) is furnishing energy, a phosphate is split off to form adenosine diphosphate (ADP), and about 10,000 calories are liberated. ADP may be reconverted into ATP, but this requires reaction with phosphate and a boost of 10,000 calories to push it back up the energy scale.

Phosphocreatine (PC) is another energy-rich compound. It also liberates energy by the removal of the phosphate group.

Phosphocreatine:

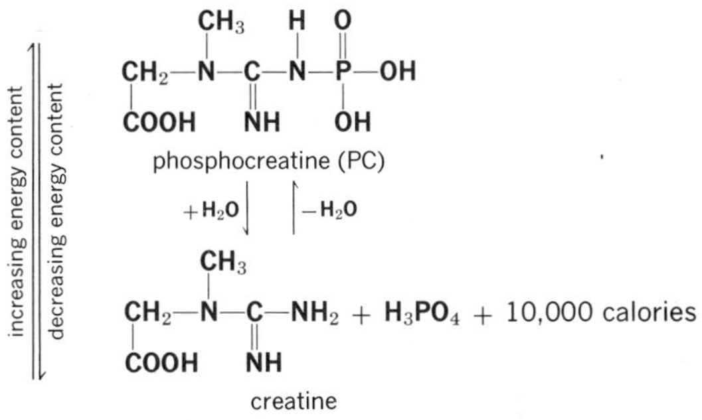

increasing energy content ↑ / decreasing energy content ↓

$$\underset{\text{COOH}}{CH_2}-\overset{\text{CH}_3}{N}-\underset{\text{NH}}{\overset{}{\underset{\|}{C}}}-\overset{\text{H}}{N}-\underset{\text{OH}}{\overset{\text{O}}{\text{P}}}-OH$$

phosphocreatine (PC)

$+H_2O$ ↓ ↑ $-H_2O$

$$\underset{\text{COOH}}{CH_2}-\overset{\text{CH}_3}{N}-\underset{\text{NH}}{\underset{\|}{C}}-NH_2 + H_3PO_4 + 10{,}000\ \text{calories}$$

creatine

We will discuss the function of PC at the end of the chapter. The reactions of these phosphates may be abbreviated as follows:

$$\text{ATP} \rightleftharpoons \text{ADP} + H_3PO_4 + \text{energy} \qquad \text{PC} \rightleftharpoons \text{C} + H_3PO_4 + \text{energy}$$

When ATP is changed into ADP and P, and when PC is changed into P and C, we are liberating energy, which may be used to perform work. To reconvert ADP into ATP and C into PC, we must add energy. Although ATP and PC may yield about 10,000 calories as a phosphate is split off, the energy may not be completely and most effectively utilized by the body. This is not unusual because most engines are not better than 50% efficient. Exactly what happens to the apparently wasted energy is not known, although it probably serves as a source of body heat.

It has been shown that the chemical reactions involving some of the conversions in carbohydrate metabolism and muscular contraction are undoubtedly interrelated with the energy-rich phosphates ATP and PC. We will discuss the mechanism of formation of the energy-rich phosphates later in the chapter.

The Interconversion of Glycogen and Glucose

As indicated in Chapter 10, glycogen is a very complex polysaccharide made up of many glucose units, bound together by α-linkages. With the aid of the enzyme phosphorylase and inorganic phosphate (not an energy-rich phosphate), the end glucose of the chain is split off, one at a time, as glucose-1-phosphate. It is comparable to the undoing of a chain, one link at a time, starting with the last link. Glucose-1-phosphate is then converted into glucose-6-phosphate.

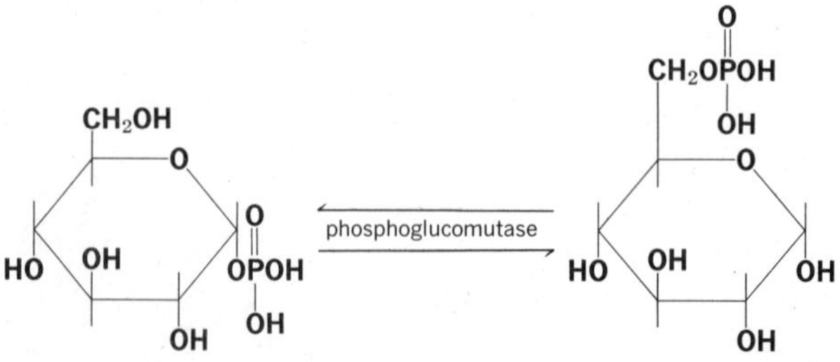

$$\text{glucose-1-phosphate} \xrightleftharpoons[\text{phosphoglucomutase}]{} \text{glucose-6-phosphate}$$

glucose-1-phosphate (ring: CH_2OH, O, HO, OH, OH, $O{-}\overset{O}{\overset{\|}{P}}OH$ with OH) — glucose-6-phosphate (ring: $CH_2O\overset{O}{\overset{\|}{P}}OH$ with OH, O, HO, OH, OH, OH)

The glucose-6-phosphate may be converted into *free glucose* if the enzyme *phosphatase* is present. This enzyme is found in the liver, but it is *usually absent in muscles.*

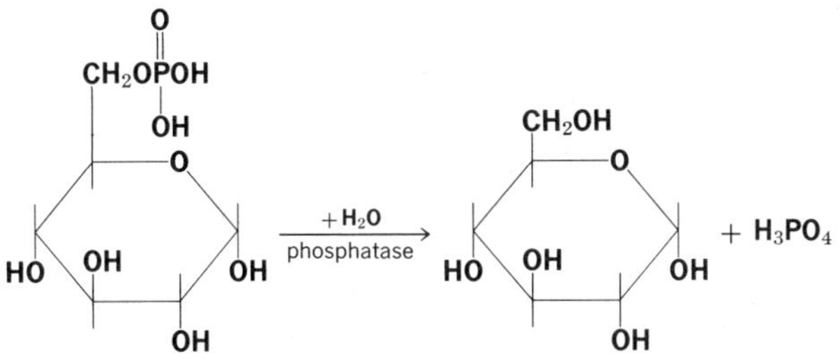

glucose-6-phosphate $\xrightarrow[\text{phosphatase}]{+H_2O}$ free glucose $+ H_3PO_4$

This means that the liver can convert glycogen into glucose (which it does) but that the muscles *cannot* readily perform this conversion because of insufficient phosphatase. Muscle glycogen, instead of being converted into glucose, as in the liver, is converted into lactic acid.

When free glucose is converted into glucose-6-phosphate, a definite amount of energy must be put into the system. ATP provides the energy boost. In this latter case, the enzyme hexokinase is a necessary catalyst.

$$\text{glucose} \xrightarrow[\text{(add energy)}]{\text{ATP + hexokinase}} \text{glucose-6-phosphate}$$

the conversion of glucose-6-phosphate into lactic acid (anaerobic carbohydrate metabolism)

The conversion of glucose-6-phosphate into lactic acid involves many intermediate compounds. Every one of these compounds has been isolated and identified, and most of the enzymes involved have been purified and characterized.

First, glucose-6-phosphate is isomerized to fructose-6-phosphate. This is a reversible reaction, catalyzed by the enzyme that is an *isomerase*. The two phosphates are of almost identical energy content. In this reaction we go from a six-membered oxygen-containing ring to a five-membered oxygen-containing ring.

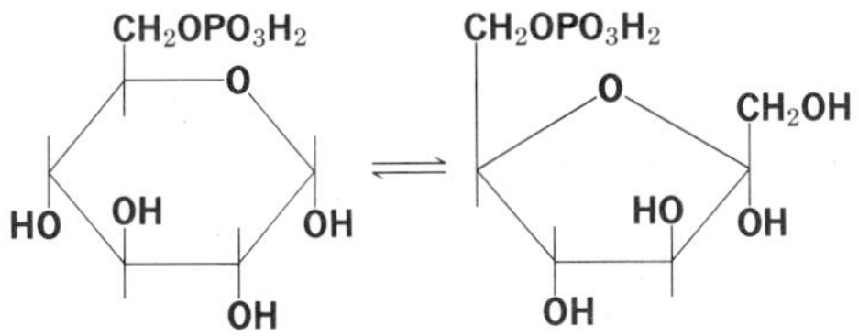

glucose-6-phosphate $\rightleftharpoons$ fructose-6-phosphate

Fructose-6-phosphate is next converted into fructose-1,6-diphosphate by the action of ATP. In this reaction we add about 3,000 calories.

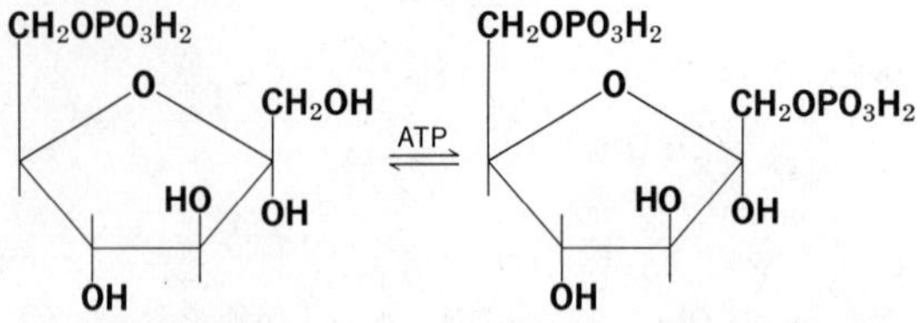

$CH_2OPO_3H_2$ … O … CH_2OH, HO, OH, OH $\xrightleftharpoons{ATP}$ $CH_2OPO_3H_2$ … O … $CH_2OPO_3H_2$, HO, OH, OH

fructose-6-phosphate fructose-1,6-diphosphate

The next reaction is particularly significant in that the fructose-1,6-diphosphate is broken down into *two three-carbon fragments* by the enzyme aldolase. The reaction is reversible, and, if the two three-carbon fragments react to re-form the fructose-1,6-diphosphate, this is an aldol condensation; hence, the name of the enzyme. Before the two three-carbon fragments are formed, the fructose-1,6-diphosphate is converted into the open-chain form.

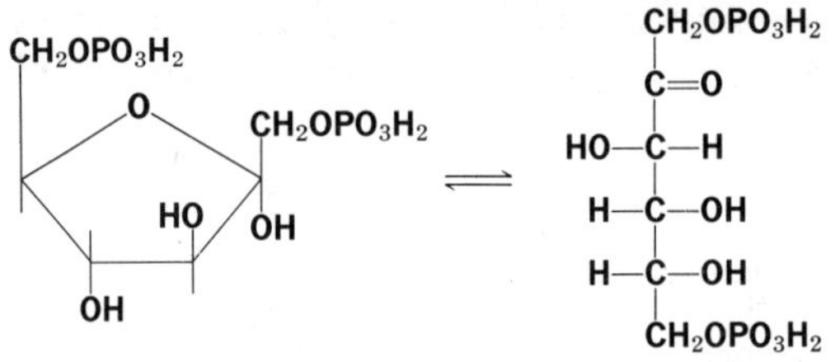

$CH_2OPO_3H_2$ … O … $CH_2OPO_3H_2$, HO, OH, OH $\rightleftharpoons$ $CH_2OPO_3H_2$—C=O—HO—C—H—H—C—OH—H—C—OH—$CH_2OPO_3H_2$

cyclic form of fructose-1,6-diphosphate open-chain form of fructose-1,6-diphosphate

Then

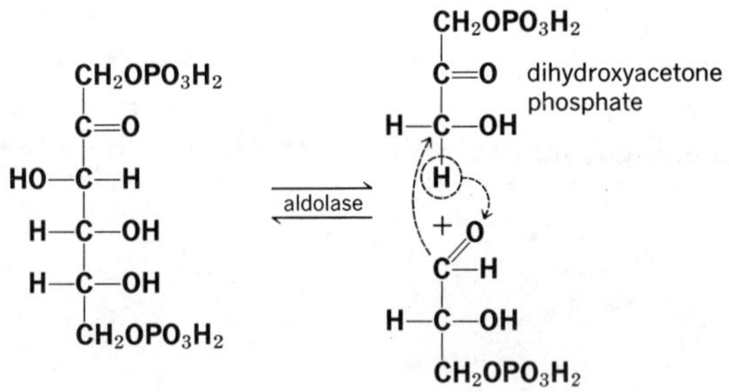

$CH_2OPO_3H_2$—C=O—HO—C—H—H—C—OH—H—C—OH—$CH_2OPO_3H_2$ $\xrightleftharpoons{aldolase}$ $CH_2OPO_3H_2$—C=O—H—C—OH (H) dihydroxyacetone phosphate + O=C—H—H—C—OH—$CH_2OPO_3H_2$

fructose-1,6-diphosphate glyceraldehyde-3-phosphate

The dotted lines indicate how the two fragments would react to re-form the fructose-1,6-diphosphate.

The two three-carbon fragments are themselves interconvertible by a specific isomerase enzyme and, in the pathway from glucose-6-phosphate to lactic acid, glyceraldehyde-3-phosphate persists.

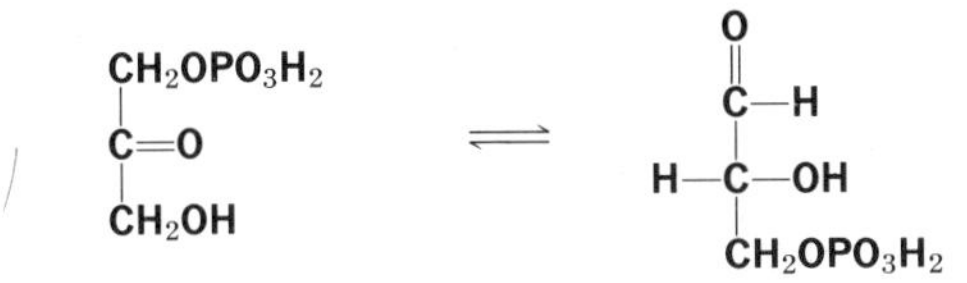

$$\underset{\text{dihydroxyacetone phosphate}}{\begin{array}{l} CH_2OPO_3H_2 \\ | \\ C{=}O \\ | \\ CH_2OH \end{array}} \rightleftharpoons \underset{\text{glyceraldehyde-3-phosphate}}{\begin{array}{c} O \\ \| \\ C{-}H \\ | \\ H{-}C{-}OH \\ | \\ CH_2OPO_3H_2 \end{array}}$$

Keep in mind, therefore, as the glycolysis proceeds, that at this stage we have *two moles of glyceraldehyde-3-phosphate* for every mole of fructose-1,6-diphosphate with which we started.

The aldehyde next reacts with inorganic phosphate as follows, and an oxidation occurs in which two hydrogens are also removed (hydrogens are circled).

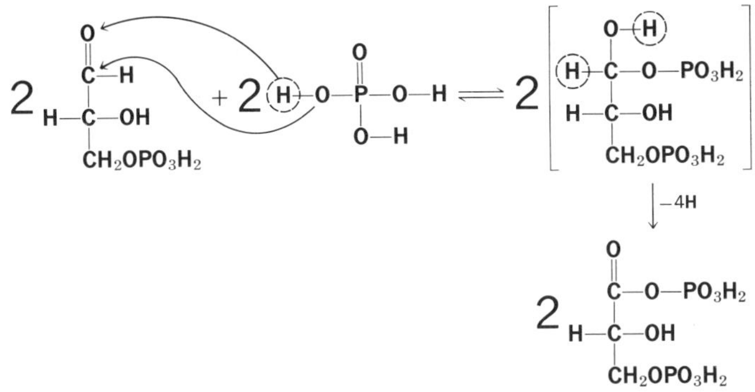

$$2\begin{array}{c} O \\ \| \\ C{-}H \\ | \\ H{-}C{-}OH \\ | \\ CH_2OPO_3H_2 \end{array} + 2\,(H){-}O{-}\overset{\overset{O}{\|}}{\underset{\underset{O-H}{|}}{P}}{-}O{-}H \rightleftharpoons 2\left[\begin{array}{c} O{-}(H) \\ | \\ (H){-}C{-}O{-}PO_3H_2 \\ | \\ H{-}C{-}OH \\ | \\ CH_2OPO_3H_2 \end{array}\right] \xrightarrow{-4H} 2\underset{\text{1,3-diphosphoglyceric acid}}{\begin{array}{c} O \\ \| \\ C{-}O{-}PO_3H_2 \\ | \\ H{-}C{-}OH \\ | \\ CH_2OPO_3H_2 \end{array}}$$

The net result of these reactions is that we have created some energy-rich bonds. The 1,3-diphosphoglyceric acid may readily lose energy by a reaction to break these energy-rich phosphate bonds. For example, two ATP's may be created in the following reaction:

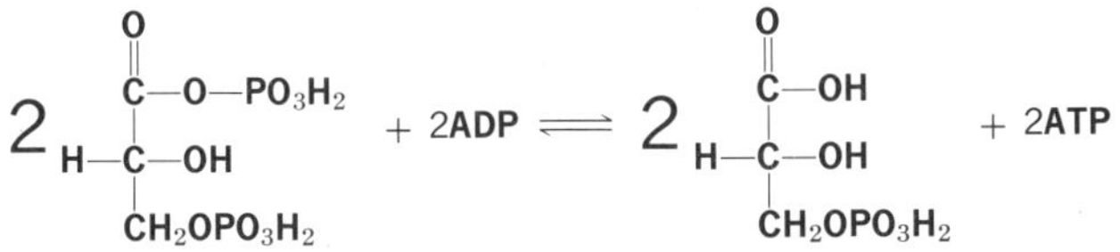

$$2\underset{\text{1,3-diphosphoglyceric acid}}{\begin{array}{c} O \\ \| \\ C{-}O{-}PO_3H_2 \\ | \\ H{-}C{-}OH \\ | \\ CH_2OPO_3H_2 \end{array}} + 2ADP \rightleftharpoons 2\underset{\text{3-phosphoglyceric acid}}{\begin{array}{c} O \\ \| \\ C{-}OH \\ | \\ H{-}C{-}OH \\ | \\ CH_2OPO_3H_2 \end{array}} + 2ATP$$

Approximately 30,000 calories are liberated in this reaction; approximately 20,000 are involved in creating two new ATP's, and the rest are presumably used to maintain body heat.

The 3-acid then readily isomerizes to the 2-acid.

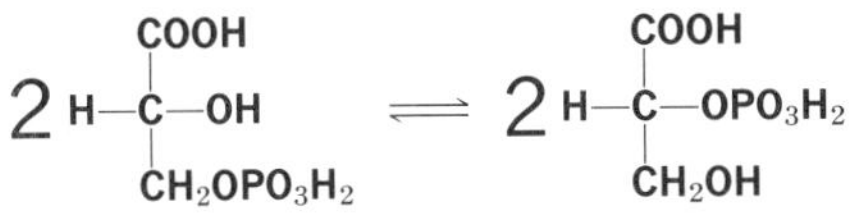

$$2\underset{\text{3-phosphoglyceric acid}}{\begin{array}{c} COOH \\ | \\ H{-}C{-}OH \\ | \\ CH_2OPO_3H_2 \end{array}} \rightleftharpoons 2\underset{\text{2-phosphoglyceric acid}}{\begin{array}{c} COOH \\ | \\ H{-}C{-}OPO_3H_2 \\ | \\ CH_2OH \end{array}}$$

The next step involves a dehydration, which leaves us with another high-energy phosphate bond.

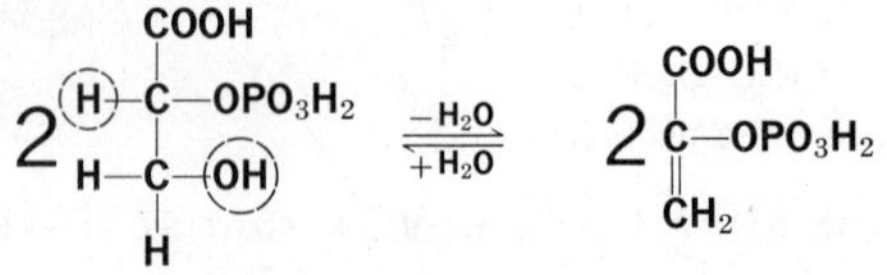

$$2\ \begin{array}{c} \mathrm{COOH} \\ | \\ \mathrm{(H)\!-\!C\!-\!OPO_3H_2} \\ | \\ \mathrm{H\!-\!C\!-\!(OH)} \\ | \\ \mathrm{H} \end{array} \underset{+H_2O}{\overset{-H_2O}{\rightleftharpoons}} 2\ \begin{array}{c} \mathrm{COOH} \\ | \\ \mathrm{C\!-\!OPO_3H_2} \\ \| \\ \mathrm{CH_2} \end{array}$$

2-phosphoglyceric acid — phospho-enol-pyruvic acid

The phosphate of this enol again liberates its energy by breaking the energy-rich phosphate bonds and creates more ATP.

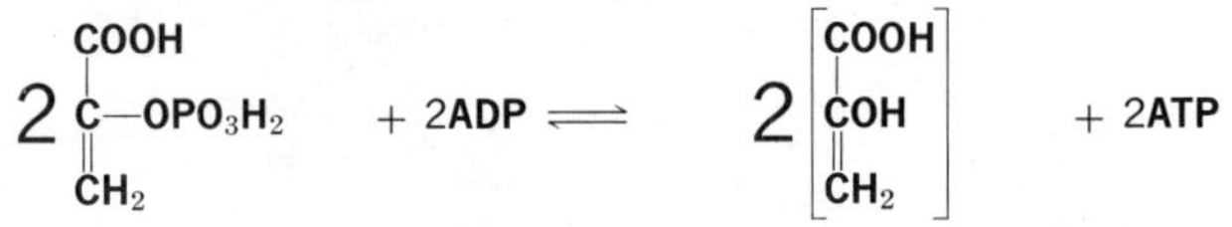

$$2\ \begin{array}{c} \mathrm{COOH} \\ | \\ \mathrm{C\!-\!OPO_3H_2} \\ \| \\ \mathrm{CH_2} \end{array} + 2\mathrm{ADP} \rightleftharpoons 2\left[\begin{array}{c} \mathrm{COOH} \\ | \\ \mathrm{COH} \\ \| \\ \mathrm{CH_2} \end{array}\right] + 2\mathrm{ATP}$$

phospho-enol-pyruvic acid — enol form of pyruvic acid

In this case also, approximately 30,000 calories are liberated; approximately 20,000 are used in creating two new ATP's, and the rest dissipates in body heat. The enol form readily converts into the keto form of the acid.

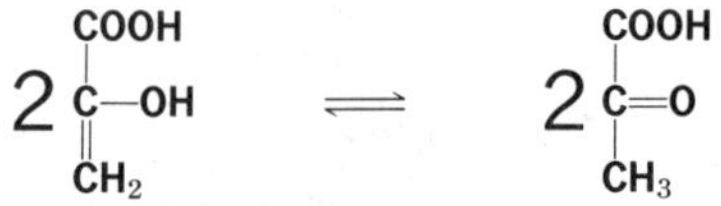

$$2\ \begin{array}{c} \mathrm{COOH} \\ | \\ \mathrm{C\!-\!OH} \\ \| \\ \mathrm{CH_2} \end{array} \rightleftharpoons 2\ \begin{array}{c} \mathrm{COOH} \\ | \\ \mathrm{C\!=\!O} \\ | \\ \mathrm{CH_3} \end{array}$$

enol form of pyruvic acid — keto form of pyruvic acid

In muscle tissue, the reduction of this acid is accomplished by *lactic dehydrogenase,* and

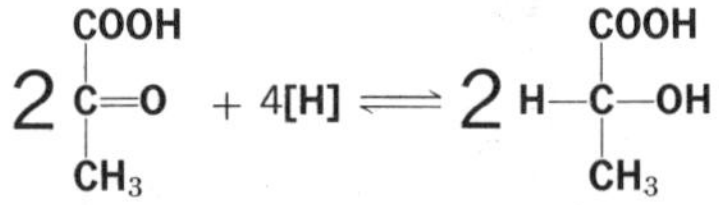

$$2\ \begin{array}{c} \mathrm{COOH} \\ | \\ \mathrm{C\!=\!O} \\ | \\ \mathrm{CH_3} \end{array} + 4[\mathrm{H}] \rightleftharpoons 2\ \begin{array}{c} \mathrm{COOH} \\ | \\ \mathrm{H\!-\!C\!-\!OH} \\ | \\ \mathrm{CH_3} \end{array}$$

pyruvic acid — lactic acid

the glycolysis finally comes to an end.

Organisms such as yeast, however, have a different enzyme, *pyruvic carboxylase,* which removes the CO_2 to yield acetaldehyde.

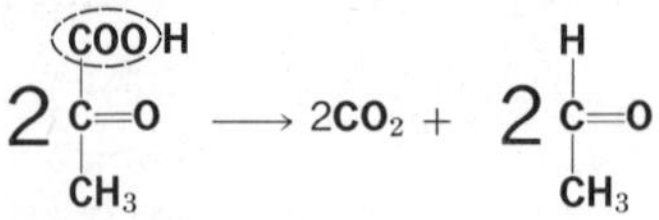

$$2\ \begin{array}{c} \mathrm{(COO)H} \\ | \\ \mathrm{C\!=\!O} \\ | \\ \mathrm{CH_3} \end{array} \longrightarrow 2\mathrm{CO_2} + 2\ \begin{array}{c} \mathrm{H} \\ | \\ \mathrm{C\!=\!O} \\ | \\ \mathrm{CH_3} \end{array}$$

pyruvic acid — acetaldehyde

Then, the final product of fermentation is formed, as the acetaldehyde is reduced.

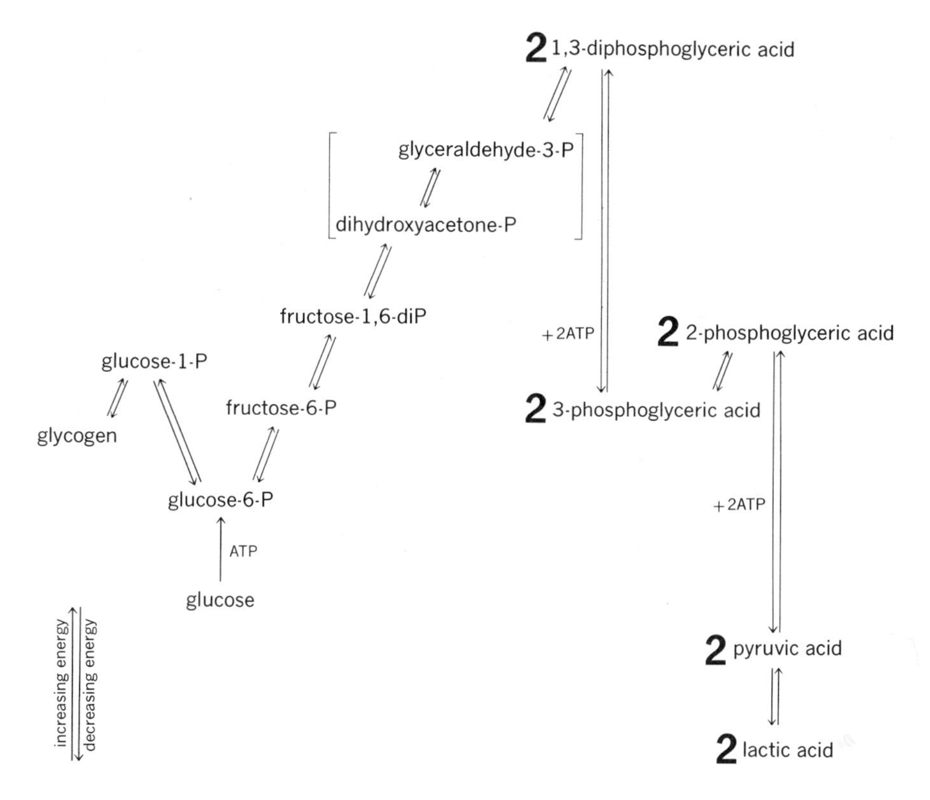

Figure 17-8 Anaerobic conversion of glucose to lactic acid.

$$2\ \underset{\text{acetaldehyde}}{H{-}C({=}O){-}CH_3} + 4[H] \rightleftharpoons 2\ \underset{\text{ethanol}}{CH_2OH{-}CH_3}$$

It is interesting that the fermentation reaction and the glycolysis reaction are identical to the pyruvic acid step, at which point they diverge: the muscles end up with lactic acid, and fermentation ends up with ethanol and carbon dioxide. See Figure 17-8.

Pyruvic acid is an important compound because it can form acetyl coenzyme A in a very complex series of reactions. In a simplified form, this reaction is an oxidative decarboxylation (i.e., carbon dioxide is lost, and essentially oxygen is added).

$$CH_3{-}\overset{O}{\overset{\|}{C}}{-}COOH + CoA \xrightarrow{\text{other factors}} CH_3{-}\overset{O}{\overset{\|}{C}}{-}S{-}CoA + CO_2$$

Acetyl coenzyme A is one of the most important chemicals in the body, because this compound is a link between carbohydrates and lipids and is also involved in many reactions in living systems.

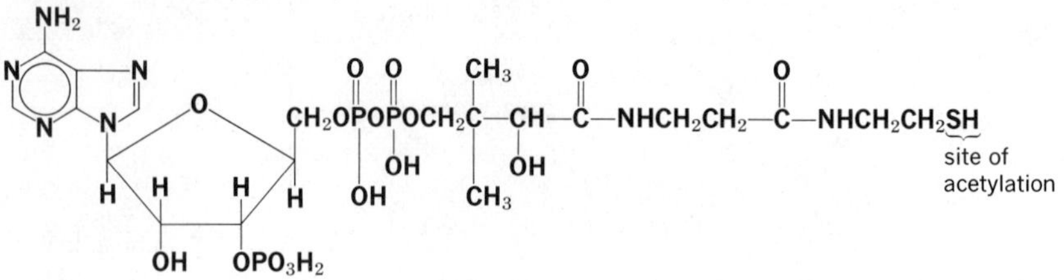

$$\text{adenine-ribose}(3'\text{-}OPO_3H_2)\text{-}CH_2OP(=O)(OH)OP(=O)(OH)OCH_2C(CH_3)_2\text{—}CH(OH)\text{—}C(=O)\text{—}NHCH_2CH_2\text{—}C(=O)\text{—}NHCH_2CH_2\underbrace{SH}_{\text{site of acetylation}}$$

coenzyme A

Coenzyme A was isolated and characterized by Lipmann. It contains adenine, ribose, and pantothenic acid (a B vitamin). Lynen showed that it is the —SH part of the molecule that is involved in acetyl coenzyme A formation; for simplicity, we shall draw it as follows:

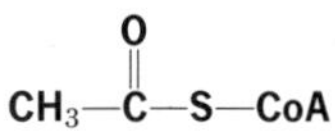

$$CH_3\text{—}\overset{\overset{\large O}{\|}}{C}\text{—}S\text{—}CoA$$

acetyl coenzyme A
(where CoA is the rest of the molecule)

The interrelationship of carbohydrates, lipids, and proteins is as follows:

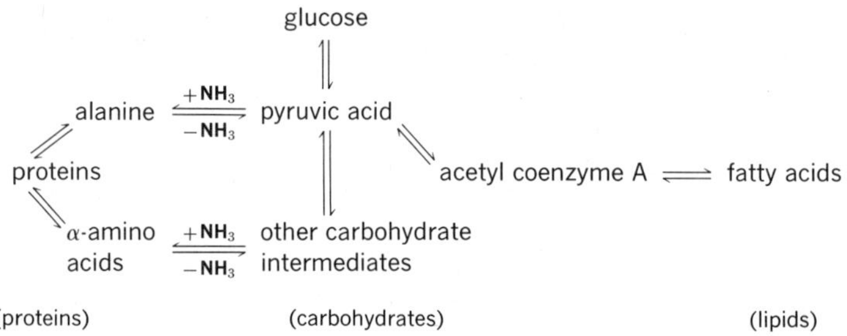

glucose
⇅
alanine $\underset{-NH_3}{\overset{+NH_3}{\rightleftharpoons}}$ pyruvic acid
proteins ⇌ alanine; proteins ⇌ α-amino acids
pyruvic acid ⇌ acetyl coenzyme A ⇌ fatty acids
⇅
α-amino acids $\underset{-NH_3}{\overset{+NH_3}{\rightleftharpoons}}$ other carbohydrate intermediates

(proteins) (carbohydrates) (lipids)

Fate of the Lactic Acid

As mentioned earlier in the chapter, when glycogen is converted into carbon dioxide and water in an aerobic process, about 670,000 calories are liberated per mole of glucose formed.

In the anaerobic process, or glycolytic process, glucose is converted into lactic acid, and only about 60,000 calories are liberated. This indicates that a considerable amount of energy remains in the lactic acid molecule.

There is no evidence that lactic acid or its oxidized product, pyruvic acid, accumulates in the muscle in normal circumstances. There seems to be no doubt that some of the lactic acid is oxidized and is indeed the source of probably all the carbon dioxide produced in the muscles. The oxidation of lactic acid is referred to as the aerobic phase, because it is here that the oxygen that is breathed in plays an important role. The inspired oxygen is carried by the blood stream (as oxyhemoglobin) to the tissues needing it. About 20–30% of the lactic acid formed in the glycolytic reaction is oxidized to carbon dioxide and water. This liberates a rather large amount of energy, which is used to convert ADP molecules into the very energy-rich ATP's. The ATP molecules then proceed to do work for us.

The 70–80% of the lactic acid that is *not* oxidized is converted back into glycogen, with the help of the energy furnished by the oxidation of the other 20–30%. There is some conversion of lactic acid to glycogen in the muscles, but the majority of lactic acid molecules are carried by the blood stream to the liver, where the conversion takes place (glycogenesis).

Figure 17-9 shows that the more work we do, the more lactic acid is formed; an increased rate of the breakdown of glycogen to lactic acid re-

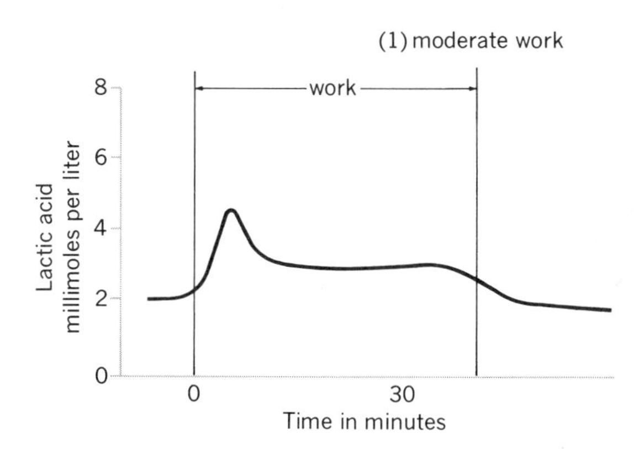

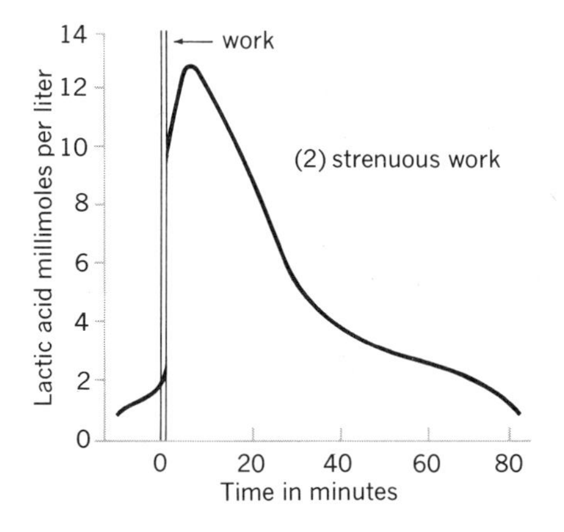

Figure 17-9 Changes in blood lactic acid (1) after moderate work and (2) after strenuous work.

sults in an increased rate of ATP formation so that we can continue to do the work.

Because lactic acid is an acid of appreciable strength, the appearance of large quantities of it in the blood stream would tend to reduce the alkaline reserve of the blood and cause an acidosis condition (the buffer systems try to prevent this). This is itself an automatic stimulus to increased breathing so that we can inspire more oxygen and oxidize the lactic acid faster. Also, the faster and harder we work, the faster we exhale to remove the excess carbon dioxide formed from the oxidation of 20–30% of the lactic acid. Here again, we see the body striving to maintain the blood pH within certain normal limits.

It stands to reason that the limit to how much work we can do is some function of our ability to breathe in enough oxygen to oxidize the lactic acid as quickly as it is formed (i.e., the limit is a function of the efficiency of the circulatory system). Prolonged strenuous exercise produces fatigue, whereby the lactic acid momentarily accumulates faster than the body can supply oxygen to oxidize it, resulting in a temporary acidosis and insufficiency of ATP to activate the muscle.

The Krebs Cycle, or Tricarboxylic Acid Cycle, or Citric Acid Cycle

The process whereby a portion of the lactic acid, formed in the glycolytic reaction, is oxidized has been proposed by Krebs and elaborated by Green and others. This is a cyclic process in that pyruvic acid keeps going into the cycle and three carbon dioxides keep coming out as energy is liberated.

We can illustrate the Krebs cycle as shown in Figure 17-10.

Pyruvic acid (3 carbons) undergoes oxidative decarboxylation to form acetyl coenzyme A, which reacts with oxaloacetic acid (4 carbons) to form citric acid (6 carbons).

The three tricarboxylic acids, citric, isocitric, and aconitic, are interrelated, and it has been shown that the isocitric acid is the one oxidized (two hydrogens removed) to form the oxalosuccinic acid, which then decarboxylates (loses CO_2) to form α-keto-glutaric acid.

The α-keto-glutaric acid undergoes oxidative decarboxylation (i.e., it loses CO_2 and essentially adds oxygen), and we end up with succinic acid, in the form of its coenzyme A complex.

The succinic acid is oxidized (i.e., two hydrogens are removed) to yield fumaric acid (the *trans* form). (It is interesting that the *cis* form, maleic acid, is poisonous and is not formed here.) The subsequent hydration of fumaric acid yields malic acid, which is oxidized (i.e., two hydrogens are removed) to give oxaloacetic acid, which is ready to react with more acetyl coenzyme A to repeat the cycle.

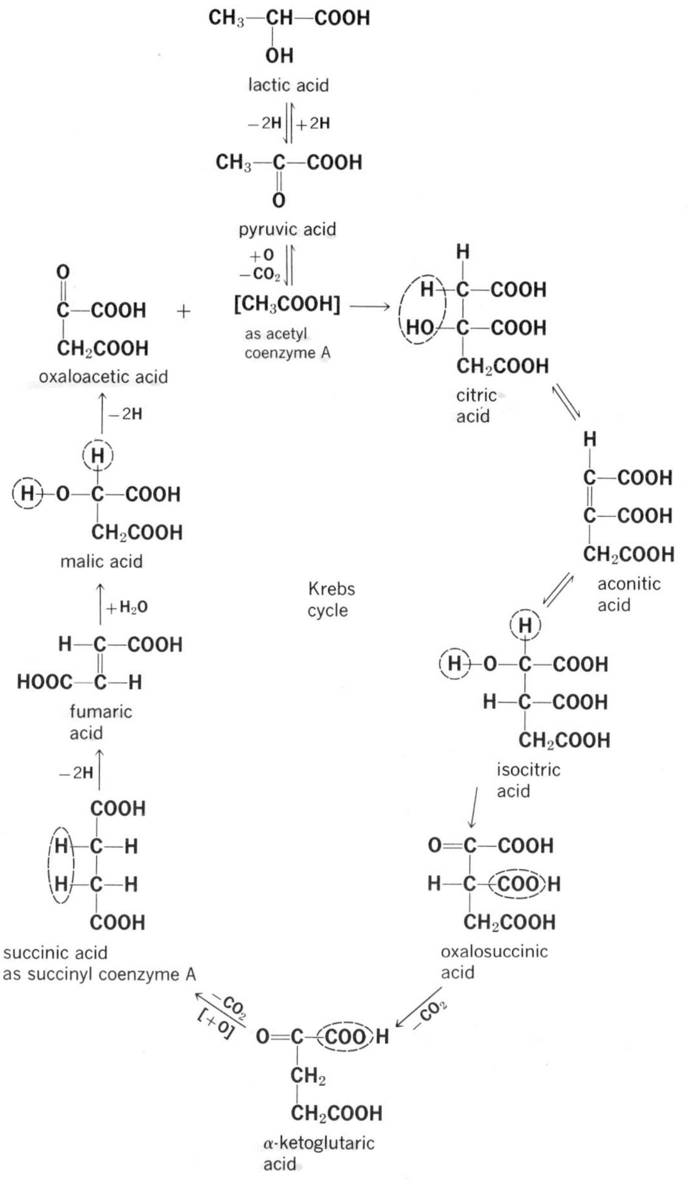

$CH_3—CH(OH)—COOH$

lactic acid

$-2H \rightleftharpoons +2H$

$CH_3—C(=O)—COOH$

pyruvic acid

$+O$, $-CO_2$

$[CH_3COOH]$ as acetyl coenzyme A

$O=C(COOH)—CH_2COOH$ + $[CH_3COOH]$ ⟶ citric acid

oxaloacetic acid

$HC(H)(COOH)—C(OH)(COOH)—CH_2COOH$

citric acid

$H—C(COOH)=C(COOH)—CH_2COOH$

aconitic acid

$H—O—C(H)(COOH)—H—C(COOH)—CH_2COOH$

isocitric acid

$O=C(COOH)—H—C(COOH)—CH_2COOH$

oxalosuccinic acid

$-CO_2$

$O=C(COOH)—CH_2—CH_2COOH$

α-ketoglutaric acid

$-CO_2$, $[+O]$

$COOH—CH_2—CH_2—COOH$

succinic acid as succinyl coenzyme A

$-2H$

$H—C—COOH \| HOOC—C—H$

fumaric acid

$+H_2O$

$H—O—C(H)(COOH)—CH_2COOH$

malic acid

$-2H$

Krebs cycle

If one adds up the net change in the lactic acid, we see that for each lactic acid that is converted into pyruvic, which then enters the cycle, three CO_2's and three H_2O's are formed. The balanced equation is

$$CH_3—C(H)(OH)—COOH + 3O_2 \longrightarrow 3CO_2 + 3H_2O + \text{energy}$$

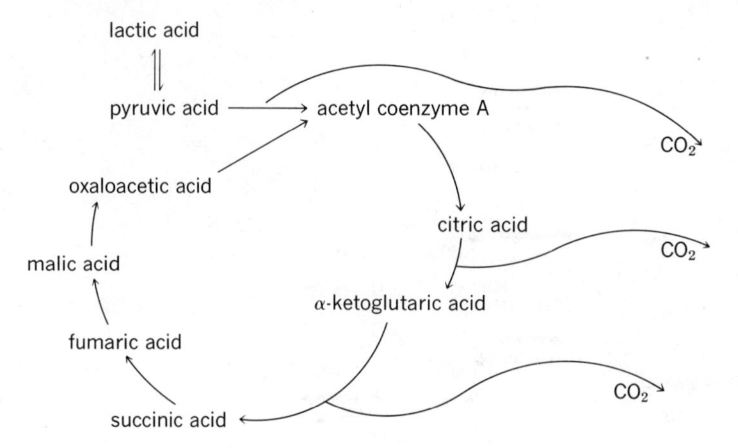

Figure 17-10 Krebs cycle.

Energetics of Carbohydrate Metabolism

In the conversion of glycogen to lactic acid, one ATP is used and four ATP's are formed. As a net result, three ATP's are created to do work for us.

If we consider going from glucose to lactic acid, we find that two ATP's are used and four ATP's are formed, resulting in a net increase of two ATP's.

If each lactic acid involved were completely oxidized to carbon dioxide and water, we would form about 24 new ATP molecules. Because two lactic acids are formed from each glucose molecule, the complete conversion of glucose to carbon dioxide and water would result in the formation of two ATP's in the glycolytic phase and 48 ATP's in the Krebs cycle, or a total of about 50 ATP's for the complete oxidation.

However, because only about 20–30% of the lactic acid is oxidized (the rest is converted back into glycogen), approximately 15 ATP's are actually formed in the aerobic process.

As we have indicated, the ATP molecules do the work for us. To insure a proper functioning of the body, the body must maintain a satisfactory supply of ATP or means of supply of ATP, because it and it alone is the final director of muscle action.

If certain enzyme poisons are present, the formation of lactic acid may be prevented(inhibition of glycolytic process). In this case, we have inhibited the formation of ATP from glycogen, and because we also have eliminated the Krebs cycle, ATP cannot be formed by carbohydrate oxidation. It has been found, in such a case, that the muscles will contract as long as a supply of phosphocreatine is available. The action of the PC is to "prime the pump," which means that the PC creates the necessary ATP. The reaction may be written as

$$PC + ADP \longrightarrow C + ATP$$

If the poisons persist when the PC is used up, the muscle will not contract, because all sources of ATP are gone. Therefore, an important function of PC seems to be to create ATP.

ATP is also involved in the various chemical syntheses in the body, for example, the synthesis of several coenzymes involved in tissue respiration.

The important role of ATP and its relation to other compounds may be summarized as shown in Figure 17-11.

ATP and Muscular Contraction

It has been shown experimentally that myosin (protein in muscles) preparations have the property of hydrolyzing an ATP to an ADP. Myosin, which is usually somewhat brittle, becomes easily contractible when ATP is introduced. This indicates that as the ATP changes to ADP, we affect the contraction of the muscle. We see that the energy stored in the ATP actually is transferred to the muscle and causes a change in the physical state of the muscle. In other words, the energy in the ATP is transferred to the actual protein in the muscles, causing them to change in shape and become smaller, which is the actual process involved in muscular contraction.

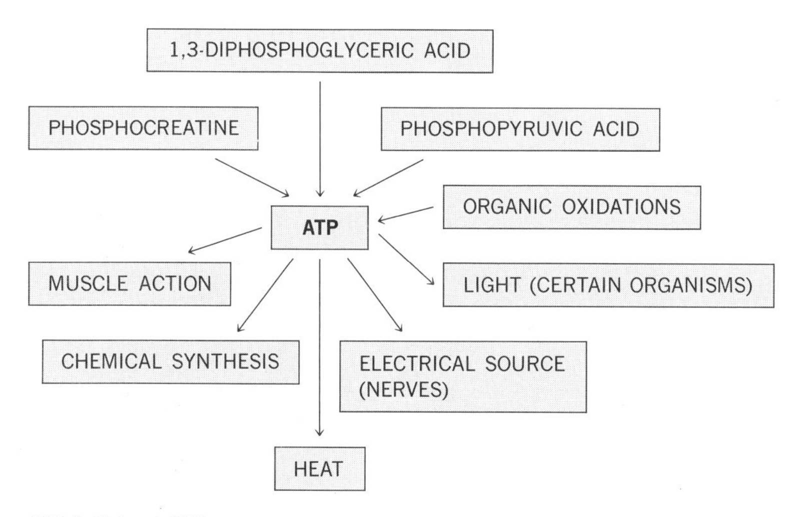

Figure 17-11 Role of ATP.

REVIEW QUESTIONS

1. Summarize the fate of glucose that has been absorbed in the intestine. Discuss the metabolism of glucose in muscle tissue from the standpoint of the availability of the glucose, production of lactic acid, and fate of the lactic acid.
2. What appears to be the main function of the adenosine triphosphate?
3. What is the overall equation for the complete combustion of glucose? How does this equation comply with the actual metabolism of glucose in the body?
4. Is the metabolism of carbohydrates and fats interrelated? How can this be shown?
5. Compare glycogenesis and glycogenolysis.
6. Which hormones influence the concentration of blood glucose? How?
7. What is meant by the renal threshold for glucose?
8. Write an equation illustrating the Benedict's test for glucose.
9. What is the function of phosphocreatine?
10. Discuss the Krebs cycle. Mention the compounds involved, the compounds entering the Krebs cycle, and the compounds leaving it.
11. Is more energy made available in the anaerobic or the aerobic oxidation phases of glucose?
12. Discuss the actual effect of adenosine triphosphate on muscle tissue.

18

absorption and metabolism of lipids

As indicated in Chapters 13–15, some lipid digestion occurs in the stomach, but most of the lipid digestion occurs in the intestines.

There appears to be a significant relationship between the melting point of a fat and its digestibility. A high melting point lowers the digestibility of a fat.

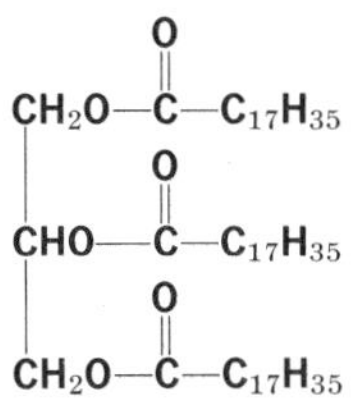

$$\begin{array}{l} CH_2O-\overset{\displaystyle O}{\overset{\|}{C}}-C_{17}H_{35} \\ | \\ CHO-\overset{\displaystyle O}{\overset{\|}{C}}-C_{17}H_{35} \\ | \\ CH_2O-\overset{\displaystyle O}{\overset{\|}{C}}-C_{17}H_{35} \end{array}$$

glyceryl tristearate
m.p. 73°C
(*about 40% digested*)

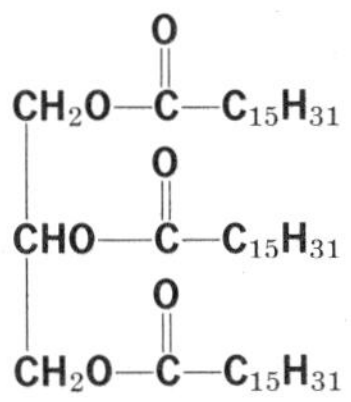

$$\begin{array}{l} CH_2O-\overset{\displaystyle O}{\overset{\|}{C}}-C_{15}H_{31} \\ | \\ CHO-\overset{\displaystyle O}{\overset{\|}{C}}-C_{15}H_{31} \\ | \\ CH_2O-\overset{\displaystyle O}{\overset{\|}{C}}-C_{15}H_{31} \end{array}$$

glyceryl tripalmitate
m.p. 65.5°C
(*about 73% digested*)

$$\begin{array}{ll}
CH_2\text{—}O\text{—}\overset{O}{\overset{\|}{C}}\text{—}C_{13}H_{27} & CH_2\text{—}O\text{—}\overset{O}{\overset{\|}{C}}\text{—}C_{11}H_{23} \\
| & | \\
CHO\text{—}\overset{O}{\overset{\|}{C}}\text{—}C_{13}H_{27} & CHO\text{—}\overset{O}{\overset{\|}{C}}\text{—}C_{11}H_{23} \\
| & | \\
CH_2O\text{—}\overset{O}{\overset{\|}{C}}\text{—}C_{13}H_{27} & CH_2O\text{—}\overset{O}{\overset{\|}{C}}\text{—}C_{11}H_{23}
\end{array}$$

glyceryl trimyristate
m.p. 56.5°C
(about 90% digested)

glyceryl trilaurate
m.p. 49°C
(about 97% digested)

The melting point–digestibility relationship probably involves the length of the saturated fatty acids. A long chain of carbon atoms of the saturated fatty acid lowers the digestibility. Unsaturated fatty acids are usually present in oils (liquid fats) and are essentially 100% digestible.

By the digestion process, lipids are converted into substances such as glycerol, phosphoric acid, and the fatty acids. The glycerol and phosphoric acid (usually in the form of a salt) are soluble in water and easily absorbed. The fatty acids, containing about 10 carbon atoms or more, are not very soluble, even as sodium salts. As stated in Chapter 11, the bile salts combine with the fatty acids and thus render them soluble and suitable for absorption.

Absorption

Various theories have been formulated about the nature of fat absorption. It appears most likely that the fatty acids are absorbed through the villi, and, as they pass through the intestinal mucosa they are converted into phospholipids before being resynthesized into simple glycerides. As is evident in the metabolism of carbohydrates, combination with phosphoric acid seems a necessary step before many reactions can occur. This phosphoric acid combination furnishes the necessary energy to make the reaction go.

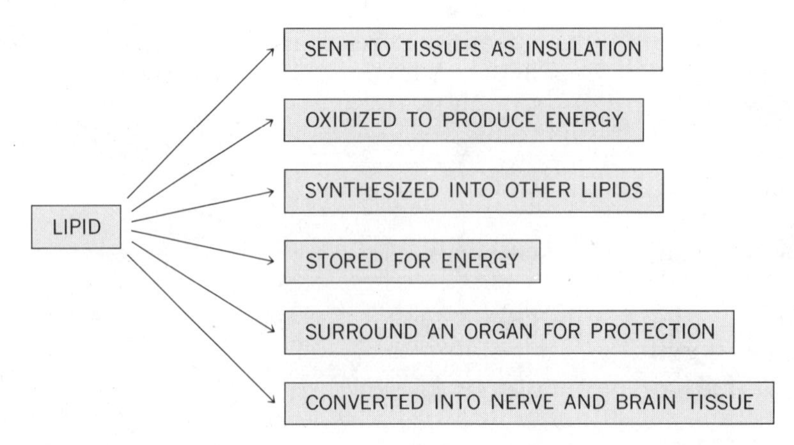

Figure 18-1 Fate of the lipid.

A small amount of the absorbed fat is sent directly to the liver via the blood stream. However, *most* of the absorbed fat passes into the lymphatic circulation. The fat in the lymphatic system finally enters the blood stream via the thoracic duct (located under the left shoulder) and may then make its way to the liver.

Chyle is the emulsion of fat in the circulation fluids. The chyle concentration increases enormously after the digestion of a fatty meal and then gradually decreases to normalcy after several hours.

Fate of the Lipid

Figure 18-1 indicates some of the things that can happen to the lipids.

Storage of Fat

Fat stored under the skin is known as adipose tissue (depot fat). In normal people, this tissue is widely distributed in the body. When too much fat is deposited, obesity results. In addition to being an energy storehouse, the fat tissue functions as an insulator.

If we compare a thin person and a fat person during the winter, the thin person has very little fat insulation, loses body heat rapidly, and is much colder than the fat person. During the hot summer, however, a fat person cannot lose body heat as rapidly as a thin person and thus is more uncomfortable.

Another important function of storage fat is to cushion and thus protect the body. All the organs are provided with some fat; the kidneys, in particular, are padded by a fat cushion. Certain individuals must purposely keep their body weight up to insure a proper fat cushion for the kidneys in order to prevent floating kidneys.

It has been shown that the fatty acids of the stored lipids are in a constant state of flux. The body can somewhat modify dietary fat by converting the fatty acids into other fatty acids, but the animal fat tends to resemble, to a great extent, the dietary fat.

Experiments using various tracers have shown that even depot fat is undergoing a relatively rapid chemical interchange. The changes usually involve a transformation of one fatty acid into another, even though the synthesized fatty acid may be abundantly supplied in the diet.

One of the most common of these transformations is the desaturation reaction, which is the conversion of a saturated fatty acid into an unsaturated fatty acid.

$$CH_3(CH_2)_7{-}CH_2{-}CH_2{-}(CH_2)_7COOH \quad \text{stearic acid}$$

$$+2H \uparrow \quad \downarrow -2H$$

$$CH_3{-}(CH_2)_7{-}CH{=}CH{-}(CH_2)_7COOH \quad \text{oleic acid}$$

an example of desaturation

These reactions usually occur in the presence of free oxygen, which aids in the removal of the two hydrogens. If oxygen is unavailable, there is another route for the conversion of a saturated fatty acid into a singly unsaturated fatty acid.

It has also been shown that in animal tissues, the unsaturated fatty acids, that is, oleic, (one double bond), linoleic (two double bonds), and linolenic (three double bonds), are *not* interconvertible. This means that oleic acid cannot form linoleic acid, and linoleic acid cannot form linolenic acid. However, *each particular unsaturated* fatty acid can become *more unsaturated* within its own family of *related acids*. In this latter sequence of reactions, a polyunsaturated fatty acid of *two additional* carbons is formed. For example,

$$CH_3(CH_2)_7CH{=}CH(CH_2)_7COOH$$
oleic acid ($C_{17}H_{33}COOH$)

does go (adds two carbons) ↓ — does not go ↓ (crossed)

$$CH_3(CH_2)_7(CH{=}CHCH_2)_3(CH_2)_2COOH$$
5,8,11-eicosatrienoic acid ($C_{19}H_{33}COOH$)

$$CH_3(CH_2)_4CH{=}CHCH_2CH{=}CH(CH_2)_7COOH$$
linoleic acid ($C_{17}H_{31}COOH$)

Another example is

$$CH_3(CH_2)_4CH{=}CHCH_2CH{=}CH(CH_2)_7COOH$$
linoleic acid ($C_{17}H_{31}COOH$)

does go (adds two carbon atoms) ↓ — does not go ↓ (crossed)

$$CH_3(CH_2)_4(CH{=}CHCH_2)_4(CH_2)_2COOH$$
arachidonic acid ($C_{19}H_{31}COOH$)

$$CH_3(CH_2)(CH{=}CHCH_2)_3(CH_2)_6COOH$$
linolenic acid ($C_{17}H_{29}COOH$)

From the foregoing we see that any *given unsaturated fatty acid* can form a specific polyunsaturated fatty acid, with two more carbons and with two or more nonconjugated double bonds. In each case, the additional double bonds appear *toward* the carboxyl group end of the molecule.

Because the animal system can indeed form polyunsaturated fatty acids but not specific ones such as linoleic and linolenic, it is obvious that the entire problem is the *location* of the double bonds. This is of special significance because fatty acids such as linoleic and linolenic appear to be essential for the maintenance of healthy skin. A deficiency of these unsaturated fatty acids may manifest itself in some skin disorder. In some cases, there has been a remarkable improvement in the eczematous condition of the skin by the inclusion of these fatty acids (as liquid neutral glycerides) in the diet. Acids such as linoleic and linolenic are sometimes referred to as "essential fatty acids," because they are apparently necessary for proper body function, cannot be readily synthesized in the body, and so must be in the diet.

However, a conversion of the following type (i.e., transformation of one saturated fatty acid into another saturated fatty acid) is quite common.

$$\underset{\text{stearic acid}}{CH_3(CH_2)_{16}COOH} \rightleftharpoons \underset{\text{palmitic acid}}{CH_3(CH_2)_{14}COOH} \rightleftharpoons \underset{\text{myristic acid}}{CH_3(CH_2)_{12}COOH}$$

Oxidation of Fatty Acids

Because carbohydrates and proteins yield about four calories per gram and fat yields about nine calories per gram, it is evident that fat is most ideal for the storage of energy.

Fat has more energy because it is more reduced than carbohydrates; that is, the ratio of hydrogen to carbon is greater in fats than in carbohydrates.

Most of the oxidation of fatty acids occurs in the liver. The fat that is already there or that has been sent there is first converted into a phospholipid, and the fatty acid is liberated.

There are several explanations of how fatty acids are broken down by oxidation. We shall illustrate only the β-oxidation theory, elaborated by Knoop. In this process, a β-keto acid is formed, and eventually the first two carbons are split off to leave a fatty acid with exactly two less carbons. This process is repeated, chopping off two carbons at a time, until the entire fatty acid is gone.

The following represents in a simplified fashion what happens in this so-called β-oxidation.

First, the fatty acid is converted into its activated form by coenzyme A in the presence of ATP.

$$R{-}CH_2{-}CH_2{-}\underset{|}{\overset{(H)}{C}}H{-}\underset{|}{\overset{(H)}{C}}H{-}\overset{O}{\overset{\|}{C}}{-}SCoA$$

fatty acid combination with coenzyme A

$$\downarrow -2H \quad \uparrow +2H$$

$$R{-}CH_2{-}CH_2{-}CH{=}CH{-}\overset{O}{\overset{\|}{C}}{-}SCoA$$

$$\downarrow +H_2O \quad \uparrow -H_2O$$

$$RCH_2{-}CH_2{-}\underset{O(H)}{\underset{|}{C(H)}}{-}CH_2{-}\overset{O}{\overset{\|}{C}}{-}S{-}CoA$$

$$\downarrow -2H \quad \uparrow +2H$$

$$R{-}CH_2{-}CH_2{-}\underset{O}{\underset{\|}{C}}\,\vdots\,CH_2{-}\overset{O}{\overset{\|}{C}}{-}SCoA$$

$$\downarrow HSCoA$$

$$R{-}CH_2{-}CH_2{-}\underset{O}{\underset{\|}{C}}SCoA \quad CH_3\underset{O}{\underset{\|}{C}}{-}SCoA$$

The compound

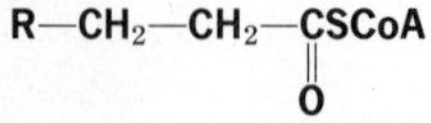

$$R—CH_2—CH_2—\underset{\underset{O}{\|}}{C}SCoA$$

repeats the entire process, chopping off two carbons at a time.

The ability of the body to oxidize acetoacetic acid is limited. If, for some reason, insufficient energy is available to accomplish this oxidation, we get the abnormal reactions shown below. Some of the acetoacetic acid is reduced to β-hydroxybutyric acid and some is decarboxylated (i.e., it loses carbon dioxide) to form acetone.

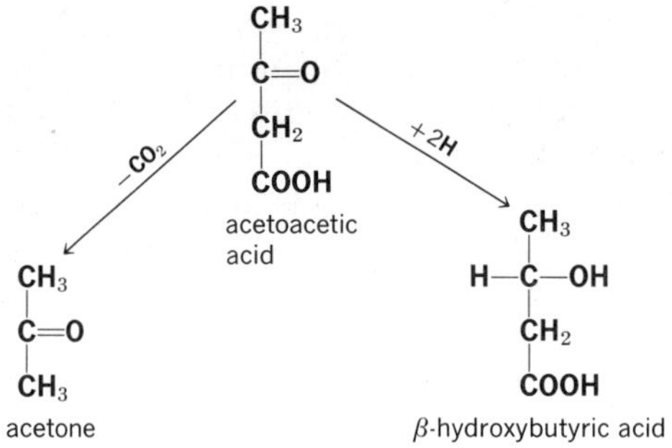

$$CH_3—C(=O)—CH_2—COOH \text{ (acetoacetic acid)}$$

$$\xrightarrow{-CO_2} CH_3—C(=O)—CH_3 \text{ (acetone)}$$

$$\xrightarrow{+2H} CH_3—CH(OH)—CH_2—COOH \text{ (β-hydroxybutyric acid)}$$

formation of ketone bodies

The compounds acetoacetic acid, β-hydroxybutyric acid, and acetone are known as acetone bodies or ketone bodies, and, when formed, they are eliminated in the urine. Since the two acids are reasonably strong, they greatly deplete the alkali reserve and cause a condition of acidosis. This acidosis is sometimes called ketosis because of the ketonic nature of two of the three acetone bodies. The formation of acetone bodies is commonly found in cases of diabetes and starvation because, in both cases, the body seems unable to completely oxidize the fatty acids.

Foods such as fats are called ketogenic because of the possibility of formation of acetone bodies. Foods such as carbohydrates are called anti-ketogenic because they furnish energy and so may prevent acetone body formation. A knowledge of the ketogenic and antiketogenic nature of foods is essential in dietetics.

If we begin with an even number of carbon atoms in the fatty acid, the oxidation works out well, because the number is divisible by two. (The β-oxidation reaction proceeds by chopping off two carbon atoms at a time.) It is significant, therefore, that the even-numbered carbon chains of fatty acids occur in nature in large amounts. The odd-numbered fatty acids do occur but are not so common. When a synthetic, artificial fatty acid containing an odd number of carbon atoms is fed to an animal, the body proceeds as usual by chopping off two carbon atoms at a time until it gets to the last three (propionic acid). Here the oxidation stops, because the body is not prepared to handle the situation, and the propionic acid is excreted.

It is known that acetyl coenzyme A, the active two carbon fragment, is used to make fatty acids in a multistep process, and it is rather interesting that most of these reactions *reverse the same sequence of steps as in β-oxidation of fatty acids,* except that one key step is not reversible. A key reactant in the synthesis of fatty acids is the activated *mono*-derivative of malonic acid, "malonyl coenzyme A."

$$HOOC-CH_2-COOH$$

malonic acid

$$HOOC-CH_2-C(=O)-SCoA$$

"malonyl coenzyme A"

The first step is

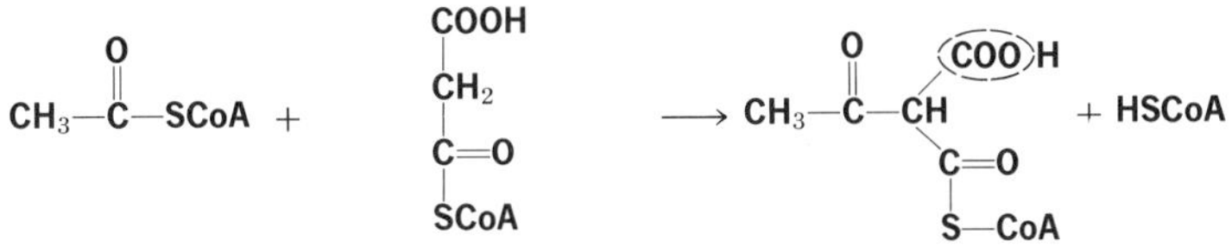

$$CH_3-\overset{O}{\overset{\|}{C}}-SCoA + HOOC-CH_2-C(=O)-SCoA \longrightarrow CH_3-\overset{O}{\overset{\|}{C}}-CH(COOH)-C(=O)-S-CoA + HSCoA$$

acetyl coenzyme A + "malonyl coenzyme A"

$$\downarrow$$

$$CH_3-\overset{O}{\overset{\|}{C}}-CH_2-\overset{O}{\overset{\|}{C}}-SCoA$$

acetoacetyl coenzyme A

The ketone group of acetoacetyl coenzyme A is reduced to an alcohol, the alcohol is dehydrated, and the double bond is reduced to give butyryl coenzyme A.

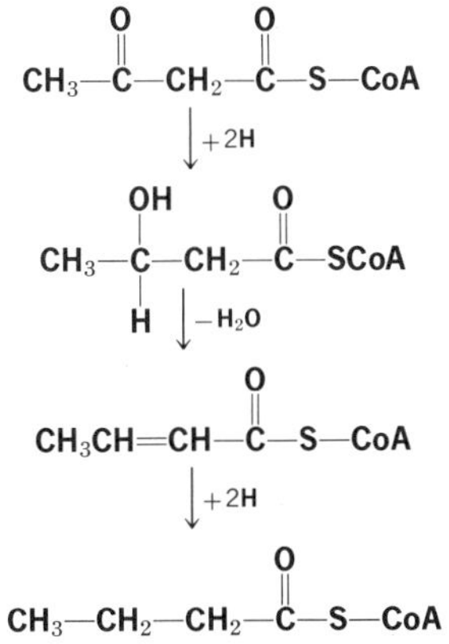

$$CH_3-\overset{O}{\overset{\|}{C}}-CH_2-\overset{O}{\overset{\|}{C}}-S-CoA$$

$$\downarrow +2H$$

$$CH_3-CH(OH)-CH_2-\overset{O}{\overset{\|}{C}}-SCoA$$

$$\downarrow -H_2O$$

$$CH_3CH=CH-\overset{O}{\overset{\|}{C}}-S-CoA$$

$$\downarrow +2H$$

$$CH_3-CH_2-CH_2-\overset{O}{\overset{\|}{C}}-S-CoA$$

butyryl coenzyme A

Butyryl coenzyme A then reacts with another "malonyl coenzyme A" and repeats the entire sequence of reactions above. In this manner, the fatty acids are synthesized, two carbons being added with each sequence of reactions, which are repeated, etc.

In *plants,* the conversion of fat into carbohydrate does indeed occur. In *animal tissues,* the key enzymes appear to be lacking, and the reaction does *not* occur.

The Isoprene Unit

One of the most significant repeating structural units in living systems, both plant and animal, is the isoprene unit. In Chapter 3, we discussed the natural polymer called rubber, which contains thousands of isoprene units.

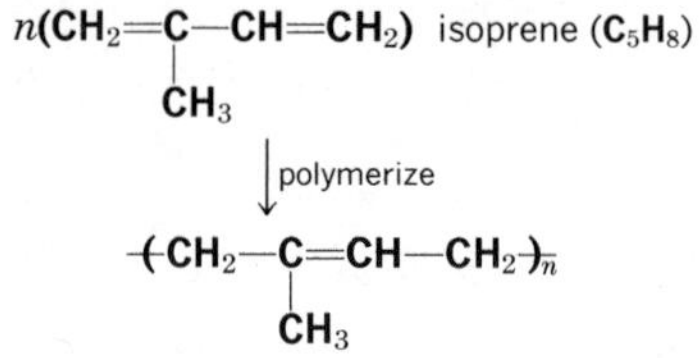

$$n(CH_2{=}\underset{\displaystyle CH_3}{\underset{|}{C}}{-}CH{=}CH_2) \text{ isoprene } (C_5H_8)$$

$$\downarrow \text{polymerize}$$

$$\text{-}\!\!(CH_2{-}\underset{\displaystyle CH_3}{\underset{|}{C}}{=}CH{-}CH_2)\!\!\text{-}_n$$

natural rubber

The terpenes are naturally occurring compounds that contain certain numbers of isoprene units.

terpenes	$(C_5H_8)_2$
sesquiterpenes	$(C_5H_8)_3$
diterpenes	$(C_5H_8)_4$
triterpenes	$(C_5H_8)_6$
etc.	

An interesting point concerning polymerizations is that the combination of units may follow several pathways. If we call one end of the molecule the *Head* (H) and the other end the *Tail* (T), two units may combine head to head (H–H), tail to tail (T–T), or head to tail (H–T). (Carbon skeletons are used.)

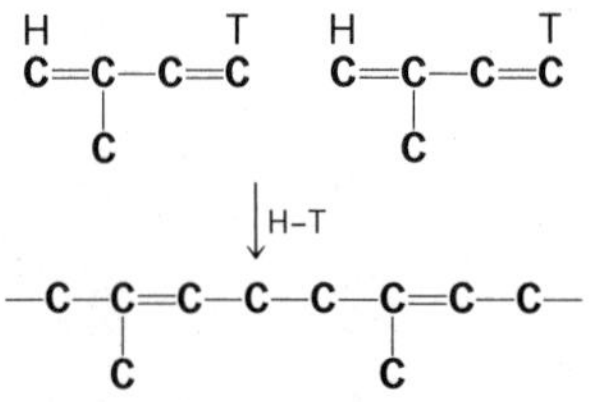

$$\overset{H}{C}{=}\underset{\displaystyle C}{\underset{|}{C}}{-}C{=}\overset{T}{C} \quad \overset{H}{C}{=}\underset{\displaystyle C}{\underset{|}{C}}{-}C{=}\overset{T}{C}$$

$$\downarrow \text{H–T}$$

$$-C{-}\underset{\displaystyle C}{\underset{|}{C}}{=}C{-}C{-}C{-}\underset{\displaystyle C}{\underset{|}{C}}{=}C{-}C-$$

Head to Tail

$$\overset{H}{C}{=}\underset{\displaystyle C}{\underset{|}{C}}{-}C{=}\overset{T}{C} \quad \overset{T}{C}{=}C{-}\underset{\displaystyle C}{\underset{|}{C}}{=}\overset{H}{C}$$

$$\downarrow \text{T–T}$$

$$-C{-}\underset{\displaystyle C}{\underset{|}{C}}{=}C{-}C{-}C{-}C{=}\underset{\displaystyle C}{\underset{|}{C}}{-}C-$$

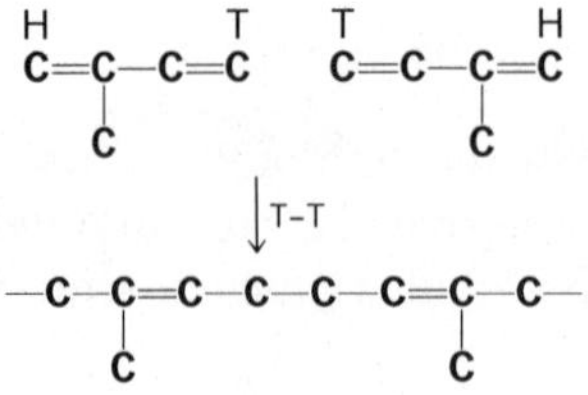

Tail to Tail

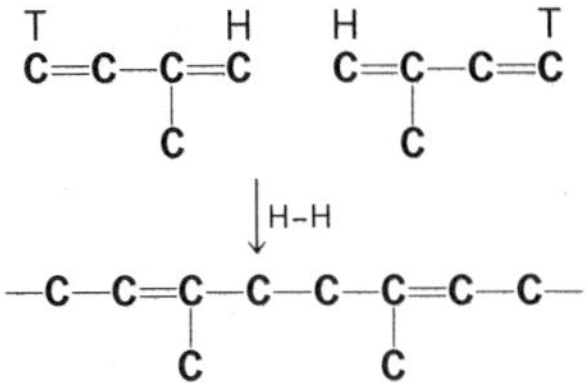

```
T        H    H        T
C=C—C=C    C=C—C=C
     |          |
     C          C

      ↓ H–H

—C—C=C—C—C—C=C—C—
       |       |
       C       C
```

Head to Head

In natural rubber, the polymerization is H–T. In terpene systems in nature, after the polymerization has occurred, reduction, hydration, oxidation, or subsequent internal reactions may then also occur.

If we redraw an H–T dimer of isoprene,

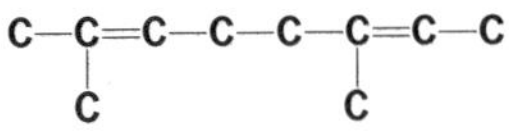

```
C—C=C—C—C—C=C—C
  |         |
  C         C
```

we obtain

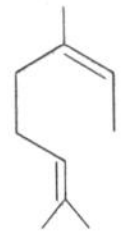

from which in nature we may isolate, for example,

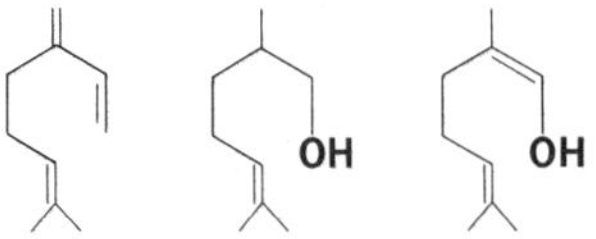

OH OH

myrcene citronellol geraniol

Myrcene, citronellol and geraniol are examples of open-chain terpenes.

If the open-chain structure closes the ring to form the common six-membered ring structure, we may get structures such as limonene or menthol,

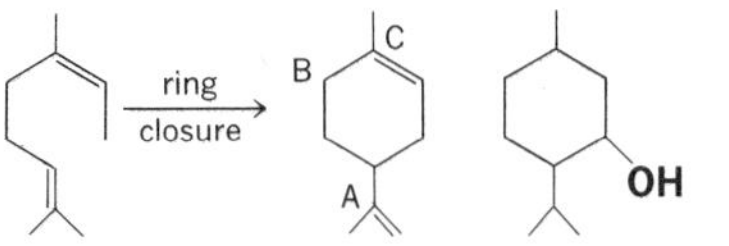

ring closure → C B A OH

limonene menthol

or the limonene-type structure may cyclize internally. If the cyclization is between points *A* and *B*, we get the pinene structure.

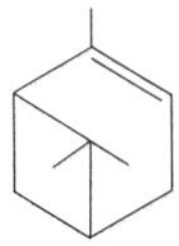

pinene, from oil of turpentine

If the cyclization is between points *A* and *C*, we get the camphane structure. Camphor is a well-known example.

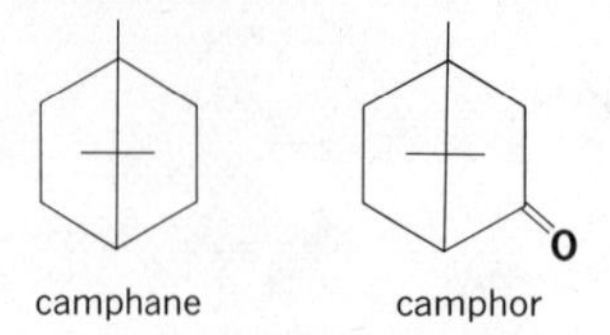

camphane camphor

In the many reactions of isoprene in natural systems, it has been shown that an important activated intermediate is the pyrophosphate of isoprene, called isopentenylpyrophosphate.

```
              O     O
              ‖     ‖
C=C—C—C—O—P—O—P—OH
  |           |     |
  C          OH    OH
```

isopentenyl pyrophosphate

Tracer and enzyme work has shown that isopentenylpyrophosphate is synthesized in the living system from the important, activated two carbon fragment, acetyl coenzyme A.

Biosynthesis of Steroids

The following sequence of reactions shows how cholesterol is prepared from isopentenylpyrophosphate. At first, the isopentenylpyrophosphate trimerizes; that is, three units combine head to tail in an orderly fashion. The dotted lines indicate the isoprene units. Carbon skeletons are used.

```
                O     O                                                     O O
                ‖     ‖                                                     ‖ ‖
3C=C—C—C—O—P—O—P—OH ⟶ C—C=C—C┆C—C=C—C┆C—C=C—C—OPOPOH
    |           |     |         |          |          |                 | |
    C          OH    OH         C          C          C                HO OH
```

farnesyl pyrophosphate

The farnesyl pyrophosphate then dimerizes (i.e., two units combine *tail to tail*), and, as the two ends combine, the pyrophosphates are eliminated.

2 farnesyl pyrophosphates

↓

```
C—C=C—C┆C—C=C—C┆C—C=C—C┆C—C=C—C┆C—C=C—C┆C—C=C—C
  |        |        |           |        |        |
  C        C        C           C        C        C
```

squalene

The clue to the steroid synthesis may be seen if we redraw squalene to show the arrangement of the atoms in the proper stereochemical pattern prior to the closing of the four rings.

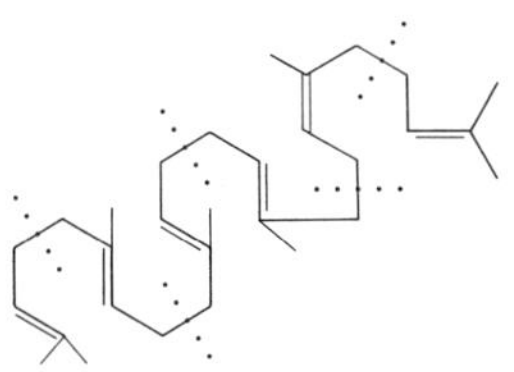

squalene, the dotted lines indicate the 6-isoprene units

Then, by a series of reactions that are not too clearly understood, the four rings close (dotted lines), one carbon rearranges (see arrow), and lanosterol is formed.

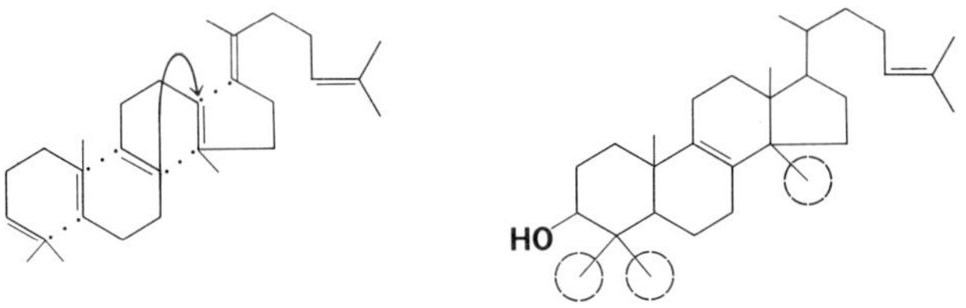

HO

lanosterol

In an additional series of reactions, again not clearly understood, the circled carbons are oxidized away; there is a rearrangement of several hydrogens, and cholesterol is finally formed.

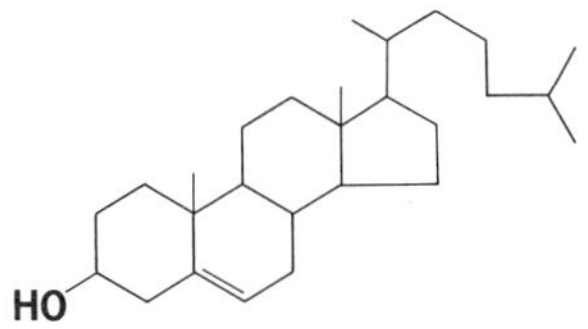

HO

cholesterol

Cholesterol is of major significance because of its relationship to the many physiologically active steroids, sex hormones, adrenal cortex hormones, bile salts, etc., which are in our bodies. Cholesterol is also significant because it has been often implicated as being involved in many aspects of high blood pressure. Cholesterol is a particularly insoluble substance and, along with other substances, tends to precipitate in and along the lining of the blood vessels, thereby restricting the flow.

Not only do we make our own cholesterol, as indicated above, but we also eat it in many foods. For these reasons, after a heart attack, for example, it is suggested that the dietary cholesterol intake be greatly lowered. Much work is also going on in the preparation of new chemicals, which may block the synthesis of cholesterol in our bodies, thus cutting down on that source of this highly insoluble substance.

Phospholipids and Glycolipids

The phospholipids are important structural materials of the brain, nerve, spinal cord tissue, and particularly cell membranes. There is much to be learned about them, but we do know they are involved in blood coagulation and form an integral part of the myelin sheath of nerve fibers. Because of their ionic nature, phospholipids are probably involved in nerve conduction and ionic transport in the body.

Glycolipids are involved in the structure of brain and spinal cord tissue and are apparently involved in some function, possibly in an insulating capacity.

Energetics of Lipid Oxidation

In the aerobic oxidation of the important two carbons fragment, CH_3COOH, a reasonable amount of energy is released; that is,

$$CH_3COOH + 2O_2 \longrightarrow 2CO_2 + 2H_2O + \text{about 200,000 cal/mole}$$

In this process, about 12 ATP's are formed, equivalent to about 120,000 calories per mole. This means about a 60% efficiency, with the rest of the energy being used for body heat, etc.

As we increase the length of the fatty acid chain by two carbons, we make available *much more* than another 200,000 calories, because the additional carbons are completely reduced and have a very large amount of energy stored in them. For example, palmitic acid, a C_{16} acid, which is C_2 + 14 carbons or $C_2 + 7C_2$'s, has more energy than 200,000 + 7(200,000) = 1,600,000 calories. The complete oxidation of palmitic acid probably yields in the neighborhood of 2.5 million calories per mole. Such a reaction is about 50% efficient and yields about 130 ATP's. Because most of the carbons in fat are completely reduced, it is quite clear that the oxidation of this type of structure would liberate the greatest amount of energy. It would be similar to the burning of gasoline in the engine of an automobile. Time-lapse photography of a living cell (greatly magnified) shows that fat globules are clearly visible as distinct insoluble circles in the cytoplasm. After a meal these globules increase in size as new fat comes into the cell; they later decrease in size as the cell burns up some of the fat to produce needed energy. The fat globules are in a constant flux.

Obesity, the Weight Problem, and Heart Disease

Obesity refers to a condition of excess deposition of fat in the tissues and beneath the skin. Some cases of obesity are due to endocrine disorders, that is, inactive thyroid, but the majority of obesity cases are due to overeating and improper diet.

Some individuals eat a lot of food but stay thin. These people either have endocrine irregularity, that is, overactive thyroid, do not digest the food, or do not absorb the digested food properly.

Thin people usually are more active than fat people. Thus, they oxidize the fat for the needed energy and the fat does not deposit. The intensity of the appetite may control the deposition of fat. People who are gaining weight usually have a greater appetite than those who are losing weight. No doubt many psychological factors are involved in obesity.

If you eat more carbohydrate than you can oxidize or store, the excess carbohydrate will probably be changed to fat, the economical way to store energy. Excess fat is stored as such. It is interesting that we can readily change carbohydrate into fat, but in our bodies the reverse may not take place. There is no doubt that fat may be changed into carbohydrate in plant systems, but we seem to lack the necessary enzymes for this conversion. Consequently, the only way to get rid of excess fat in our systems is to oxidize it. As long as there is an adequate amount of carbohydrate in the diet to be oxidized, the fat will probably not be used much. To use up the excess fat, the fat intake must be sharply curtailed and the carbohydrate intake limited.

People tend to put on weight as they grow older. This is due to many reasons: Older people exercise less, have more desk jobs, make more money, and can afford more luxurious food, which is often most fattening; older people metabolize less.

Desiccated thyroid gland contains the hormone that stimulates the metabolic rate, and this may help to burn off excess fat. This should be taken with great care and under steady medical supervision.

Most people who gain weight take in more calories than they need and as a result store these calories as fat, the most economical way to store energy. The most common way to reduce is to take in less calories than the body needs for its daily functions. In this way, the body must call on the reserve fat as a supply of energy; thus, the fat is oxidized and the body weight goes down.

Under dieting conditions, the subject may get discouraged by the apparent constancy of weight. Fat globules are temporarily replaced by water globules as the fat disappears. Because water weighs more than fat, the body weight does not change much during the initial days of dieting. Finally, when the water which acted as a temporary replacement (false fat cells), disappears, the body weight goes down rapidly.

Insurance tables tell us that fat people have a shorter life expectancy than thin people. In the folklore of our age, fat people are reported to be more jolly than thin people.

Food brought into the U.S. kitchens contains 44% fat, 13% protein, and 43% carbohydrate. These figures certainly indicate that we consume enough fat. However, authorities are worried not only about the amount of fat, but also about the kind of fat, because of its relationship to coronary heart disease.

The United States is a strong dairy-minded country, and we consume large quantities of milk, eggs, and cheeses, which contain rather significant quantities of cholesterol. Butter, lard, and beef fat contain large amounts of saturated fatty acids, whereas corn oil, peanut oil, and cottonseed oil contain significant amounts of unsaturated fats.

There has been and will be much more work done to determine *exactly* in what way fat in the diet is involved in heart disease and whether diet alone would have a pronounced effect on the incidence of coronaries in humans. The problem is very complicated indeed.

REVIEW QUESTIONS

1. Is there any correlation between the melting point of a fat and its digestibility? Discuss.
2. Summarize the fate of digested and absorbed lipids in the body.
3. What is chyle?
4. Discuss the function of adipose tissue.
5. What is β-oxidation? Give examples to show how this normally occurs.
6. What are the acetone bodies? Show how they may be formed.
7. What part do phospholipids play in fat metabolism?
8. Can carbohydrates be converted into fat? How? When does this happen? Discuss dieting.

19

absorption and metabolism of proteins

In the digestive process, proteins are hydrolyzed to α-amino acids. Phosphoric acid and nucleic acids (subject to further breakdown) may also be formed, but the α-amino acids are the primary units liberated.

The α-amino acids, which are soluble in water in the ionic form, are absorbed through the lumen of the small intestines and carried directly to the liver via the blood stream. In the liver, the necessary proteins can be synthesized from the α-amino acids and sent, via the blood stream, as plasma protein to whichever part of the body needs them. There is also evidence that α-amino acids circulate as such in the blood stream and may go in this simple form to the various tissues. By a process of rigid selection, the various parts of the body take or synthesize the proteins of particular shape and composition that they need and incorporate them as tissue.

Although their prime function is to build tissue, proteins undergo many important chemical transformations (see Figure 19-1).

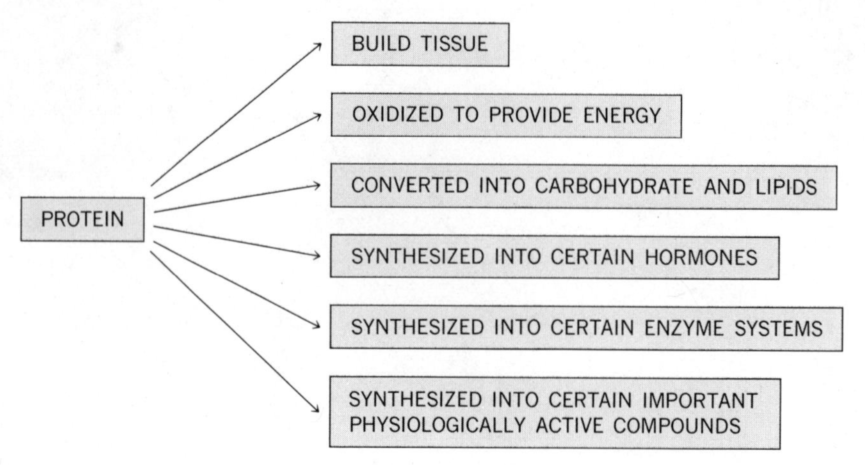

Figure 19-1 Fate of the protein.

Nitrogen equilibrium

One of the chief differences between carbohydrates, lipids, and proteins is that proteins are not stored in the body to any appreciable extent, whereas carbohydrates are stored as glycogen, and lipids are stored as fat tissue.

Within a few hours after a meal, almost all the nitrogen that has entered the body during the meal has left the body (mostly as urea in urine). For a normal adult, with reasonably constant weight, the nitrogen intake in food equals the nitrogen lost in urine, feces, and perspiration. Such a person is said to be in *nitrogen equilibrium.* It is not to be inferred that the actual nitrogen atoms entering the body in the food are the same nitrogen atoms leaving the body; this is not true. Apparently, the nitrogen atoms entering the body become incorporated in the body for a certain interval of time; the proteins already in the body break down, and their nitrogen is converted into urea, etc., and is excreted. In nitrogen equilibrium, we can say that the body is building up tissue and tearing it down at the same rate.

$$\underset{\text{entering body}}{\mathbf{N}} = \underset{\text{leaving body}}{\mathbf{N}}$$

nitrogen equilibrium

If the amount of nitrogen entering the body is greater than the amount of nitrogen leaving the body, we call this a *positive nitrogen balance.* This means that some nitrogen must be staying and accumulating in the body, presumably to build new tissue. This is a common occurrence in the growing child. The body in this case is building up tissue faster than breaking it down. In adults, this means that the body is not eliminating the nitrogen waste products properly.

N	$>$	N
entering body		leaving body

positive nitrogen balance

If the amount of nitrogen entering the body is less than the amount of nitrogen leaving the body, we call this a *negative nitrogen balance.* This means that the body is tearing itself down faster than body tissues are being built up. This condition would prevail during a wasting disease, starvation, or under conditions whereby the proper protein diet is lacking.

N	$<$	N
entering body		leaving body

negative nitrogen balance

From the foregoing it should be clear that a careful chemical investigation of the nitrogen equilibrium of a patient may give valuable evidence as to his health and chemical function and may give a clue to or confirm some serious body disorder.

The following figures give a clue to the amount of plasma protein in the human: Every 100 ml of blood plasma contains about 7% protein. The composition of this plasma is approximately as follows:

albumin	3.26 grams
α-globulins	1.01 grams
β-globulins	1.26 grams
γ-globulins	0.74 grams
fibrinogen	0.31 grams

Dynamic equilibrium

Research on the stability of proteins has shown that the tissues of the body are constantly broken down and the nitrogen eliminated, and the new tissues are resynthesized from the proteins in the plasma (dynamic equilibrium). This means that the body undergoes a complete protein overhaul every few months.

The fact that an animal kept on a *protein-free diet* will continue to eliminate nitrogen in urine and feces indicates that this breakdown process may continue even though *no new nitrogen compounds enter the body.* This means the body will continue to have plasma protein despite a protein-free diet. The plasma protein must come from easily expendible tissue. The location of this tissue is unknown. The tissue is of a reserve nature,

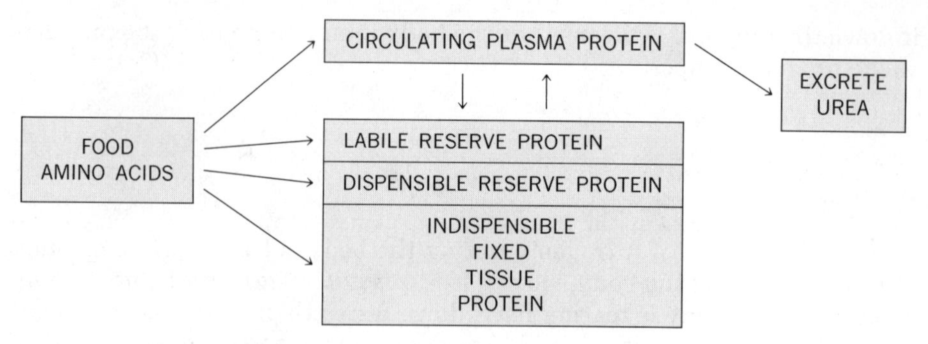

Figure 19-2 Protein equilibrium.

but it is not like glycogen or fat deposits, which are intracellular entities easily identified. This protein-expendable tissue may apparently be sacrificed without any serious effects. The reserve supply is not inexhaustible, but the body will continue to form plasma proteins for a rather long period of time (e.g., many days). When this supply is depleted, the plasma protein of an animal on a protein-free diet is then replenished very slowly and in small quantities, obviously from a supply that is reluctant to convert tissue into plasma protein. Even in this case, the animal may appear to be essentially normal. This process may last for a few days. Finally, we reach the stage at which indispensible fixed tissue begins to break down to furnish plasma protein. This is a slow process that causes great bodily harm and deterioration. This means the main structural tissues of the body are disintegrating. If a condition such as this continues, death soon results.

The relationships just discussed may be represented by Figure 19-2.

Proteins as a source of important compounds for the body

Many hormones, such as insulin, thyroglobulin, and adrenal-corticotrophic hormone (ACTH), are protein in nature. These proteins are synthesized by the endocrine glands. In a normal case, these glands can apparently obtain the proper α-amino acids in correct amounts from the plasma proteins and can prepare these special protein structures. If the endocrine glands are not furnished with a proper supply of starting α-amino acids, or if they are unable to synthesize a proper supply of the protein hormone, a serious endocrine deficiency may exist. Likewise, if the glands are overactive and synthesize too much protein hormone, the body may exhibit serious disorders.

Some other important compounds that are prepared by the body and contain nitrogen are epinephrine, creatine, etc. The body probably synthesizes these compounds from protein precursors.

Metabolic chemical reactions of α-amino acids

Deamination

Deamination is the process whereby the body removes the nitrogen from the α-amino acids to form an α-keto acid and ammonia. The ammonia can then react to form the many nitrogen-containing excreted products.

$$\text{H}-\underset{\text{COOH}}{\overset{\text{R}}{\text{C}}}-\text{NH}_2 \underset{+2\text{H}}{\overset{-2\text{H}}{\rightleftharpoons}} \underset{\text{COOH}}{\overset{\text{R}}{\text{C}}}=\text{NH} \underset{-\text{H}_2\text{O}}{\overset{+\text{H}_2\text{O}}{\rightleftharpoons}} \underset{\text{COOH}}{\overset{\text{R}}{\text{C}}}(\text{OH})(\text{NH}_2) \underset{+\text{NH}_3}{\overset{-\text{NH}_3}{\rightleftharpoons}} \underset{\text{COOH}}{\overset{\text{R}}{\text{C}}}=\text{O}$$

deamination

In some cases, the deamination process may be accompanied by an oxidation reaction. Such a combination is referred to as "oxidative deamination."

Transamination

Transamination involves the transfer of an amino group from one amino acid to a suitable acceptor, such as an α-keto acid.

$$\underset{\text{COOH}}{\overset{\text{R}}{\text{C}}}=\text{O} + \text{H}-\underset{\text{COOH}}{\overset{\text{R}'}{\text{C}}}-\text{NH}_2 \rightleftharpoons \text{H}-\underset{\text{COOH}}{\overset{\text{R}}{\text{C}}}-\text{NH}_2 + \underset{\text{COOH}}{\overset{\text{R}'}{\text{C}}}=\text{O}$$

transamination

In both transamination and deamination, the original α-amino acid is converted into an α-keto acid.

Note that many of the α-keto acids formed in these conversions are compounds involved in carbohydrate metabolism. This is precisely the way in which carbohydrates and proteins are interrelated.

Some specific examples are:

$$\text{HOOC}-\text{CH}_2-\text{CH}_2-\text{CH}(\text{NH}_2)-\text{COOH} + \text{CH}_3-\text{CO}-\text{COOH} \rightleftharpoons \text{HOOC}-\text{CH}_2-\text{CH}_2-\text{CO}-\text{COOH} + \text{CH}_3-\text{CH}(\text{NH}_2)-\text{COOH}$$

glutamic acid (*from proteins*) — pyruvic acid (*from carbohydrates*) — α-ketoglutaric acid (*carbohydrates*) — alanine (α-amino acid) (*protein*)

$$\begin{array}{c}COOH\\|\\CH_2\\|\\H-C-NH_2\\|\\COOH\end{array} + \begin{array}{c}CH_3\\|\\C=O\\|\\COOH\end{array} \rightleftharpoons \begin{array}{c}COOH\\|\\CH_2\\|\\C=O\\|\\COOH\end{array} + \begin{array}{c}CH_3\\|\\H-C-NH_2\\|\\COOH\end{array}$$

aspartic acid (*from proteins*) + pyruvic acid (*from carbohydrates*) ⇌ oxaloacetic acid (*carbohydrates*) + alanine (*proteins*)

Alpha-keto acids other than pyruvic acid may react with glutamic acid. Two such compounds are α-keto-butyric acid and oxaloacetic acid.

$$\begin{array}{c}CH_3\\|\\CH_2\\|\\C=O\\|\\COOH\end{array} + \begin{array}{c}COOH\\|\\CH_2\\|\\CH_2\\|\\H-C-NH_2\\|\\COOH\end{array} \rightleftharpoons \begin{array}{c}CH_3\\|\\CH_2\\|\\H-C-NH_2\\|\\COOH\end{array} + \begin{array}{c}COOH\\|\\CH_2\\|\\CH_2\\|\\C=O\\|\\COOH\end{array}$$

α-keto butyric acid + glutamic acid ⇌ α-amino butyric acid + α-keto glutaric acid

$$\begin{array}{c}COOH\\|\\CH_2\\|\\C=O\\|\\COOH\end{array} + \begin{array}{c}COOH\\|\\CH_2\\|\\CH_2\\|\\H-C-NH_2\\|\\COOH\end{array} \rightleftharpoons \begin{array}{c}COOH\\|\\CH_2\\|\\H-C-NH_2\\|\\COOH\end{array} + \begin{array}{c}COOH\\|\\CH_2\\|\\CH_2\\|\\C=O\\|\\COOH\end{array}$$

oxaloacetic acid + glutamic acid ⇌ aspartic acid + α-keto glutaric acid

Also, approximately sixteen different α-amino acids can react with α-keto glutaric acid to form glutamic acid.

16 different α-amino acids + α-keto glutaric acid ⇌ 16 different deaminated products (α-keto acids) + glutamic acid

Transmethylation

Transmethylation is the process whereby methyl groups are transferred from one compound to another. In this way, the body can synthesize some essential compounds. Methionine is an efficient supplier of methyl groups.

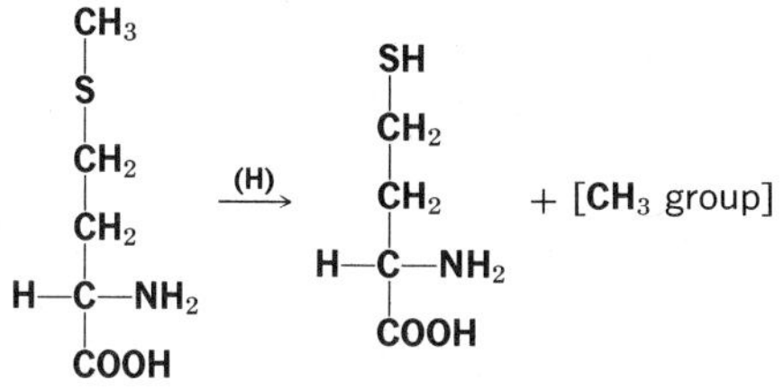

$$\underset{\text{methionine}}{\begin{array}{c} CH_3 \\ | \\ S \\ | \\ CH_2 \\ | \\ CH_2 \\ | \\ H-C-NH_2 \\ | \\ COOH \end{array}} \xrightarrow{(H)} \underset{\text{homocysteine}}{\begin{array}{c} SH \\ | \\ CH_2 \\ | \\ CH_2 \\ | \\ H-C-NH_2 \\ | \\ COOH \end{array}} + [CH_3 \text{ group}]$$

These methyl groups may be used to synthesize choline, creatine, and other important compounds needed by the body. For example,

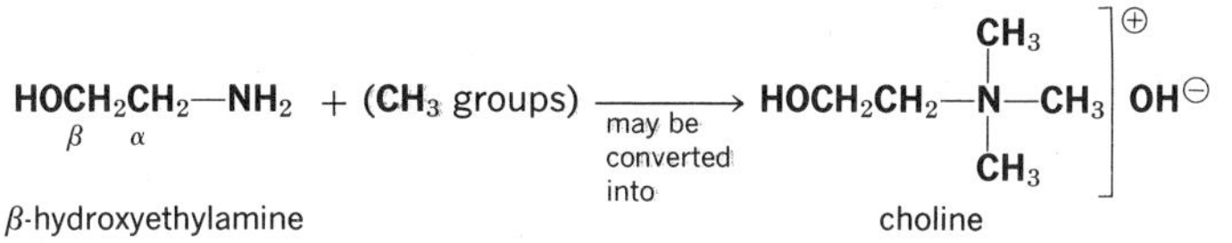

$$\underset{\beta\text{-hydroxyethylamine}}{\overset{}{\underset{\beta\ \ \alpha}{HOCH_2CH_2}-NH_2}} + (CH_3 \text{ groups}) \xrightarrow[\text{may be converted into}]{} \underset{\text{choline}}{\left[HOCH_2CH_2-\begin{array}{c} CH_3 \\ | \\ N \\ | \\ CH_3 \end{array}-CH_3 \right]^{\oplus}} OH^{\ominus}$$

FATE OF THE DEAMINATED α-AMINO ACID

The deaminated part can be converted into a carbohydrate, such as glucose, or oxidized to supply energy, or stored as glycogen. Once the deaminated part is converted into the carbohydrate metabolic pathway, the conversion may proceed further, and a lipid may be formed and stored as depot fat. The deaminated part may be reconverted into another α-amino acid (via carbohydrate pathways) and resynthesized into a particular protein. The various deaminated portions may also be decomposed further and excreted in several forms.

FATE OF THE NITROGEN

In the deamination process, nitrogen is removed.

Various things can happen to this nitrogen.

1. Formation of urea. The ammonia removed from the α-amino acid is eliminated mostly as urea. In a normal person, about 80–90% of the nitrogen in urine is in the form of urea. The actual urea content of urine varies daily and depends upon the protein intake (i.e., it is governed by nitrogen equilibrium).

A simple equation that represents the formation of urea is

$$2NH_3 + CO_2 \longrightarrow \underset{\text{urea}}{H_2N-\overset{\overset{\large O}{\|}}{C}-NH_2} + H_2O$$

However, it has been shown that, in the body, this equation is involved in the ornithine cycle. In this process, ornithine is converted into citrulline, which is converted into arginine, which is converted back into ornithine. Carbon dioxide and ammonia go into this cyclic process (see equations below), and urea comes out.

$$\underset{\text{ornithine}}{NH_2-CH_2-CH_2-CH_2-\underset{COOH}{CH}-NH_2} \xrightarrow[+NH_3]{+CO_2} \underset{\text{citrulline}}{NH_2-C(=O)-NH-CH_2-CH_2-CH_2-\underset{COOH}{CH}-NH_2} \xrightarrow{+NH_3} \underset{\text{arginine}}{NH_2-C(=NH)-NH-CH_2-CH_2-CH_2-\underset{COOH}{CH}-NH_2}$$

$$\text{arginine} \xrightarrow{+H_2O} \text{ornithine} + \underset{\text{urea}}{NH_2-C(=O)-NH_2}$$

ornithine cycle
(*formation of urea*)

2. *Formation of ammonium salts.* About 4–5% of the nitrogen excreted in urine is in the form of ammonium salts. The ammonium ion comes from the ammonia produced by the deamination of α-amino acids. Apparently, the body converts most of this into urea, but some is simply acidified to form NH_4^+.

$$NH_3 + H^+ \longrightarrow NH_4^{\oplus}$$

formation of ammonium ion

Creatine and creatinine are nitrogen-containing compounds present in urine. Creatine may be found in very small quantities, but creatinine is present in appreciable amounts. Creatinine is formed from creatine by dehydration.

$$\underset{\text{creatine}}{HN=C(NH_2)-N(CH_3)-CH_2-C(=O)OH} \xrightarrow{-H_2O} \underset{\text{creatinine}}{HN=C\text{—}N(CH_3)\text{—}CH_2\text{—}C(=O)\text{—}NH \text{ (ring)}}$$

creatine creatinine

FATE OF THE SULFUR

Amino acids such as cystine, methionine, and cysteine have an appreciable amount of sulfur in them. As discussed earlier, methionine is one of the eight essential amino acids. When the sulfur-containing amino acids are degraded by the body, deamination occurs. The sulfur is removed from the deaminated part and is usually oxidized to sulfates. These sulfates may be eliminated as inorganic sulfates, such as potassium sulfate (K_2SO_4), or as conjugated sulfates in the detoxication mechanism. Not all the sulfur is oxidized, and the rather small constant amount that is not oxidized is known as neutral sulfur. By neutral sulfur we mean such compounds as thiocyanates (SCN^-), mercaptans, sulfides, cystine, and taurine.

FATE OF THE NUCLEIC ACIDS

When the nucleic acid is completely hydrolyzed, we obtain phosphoric acid, a simple monosaccharide, and nitrogen bases, such as purines, pyrimidines, and pyridines.

The sugar may be involved in carbohydrate metabolism, and the phosphoric acid may be utilized in the synthesis of phospholipids or inorganic phosphates. Excess phosphoric acid is eliminated as inorganic phosphates.

The purines, such as adenine and guanine, are oxidized to uric acid and eliminated in the urine.

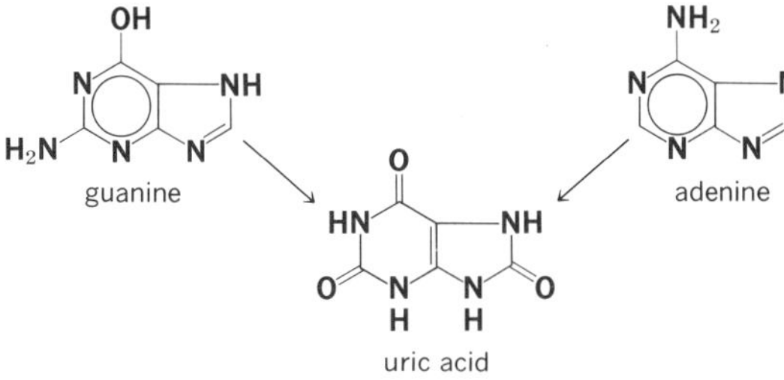

The metabolic fate of the pyrimidines is not completely known. Undoubtedly, some oxidation does occur; that is,

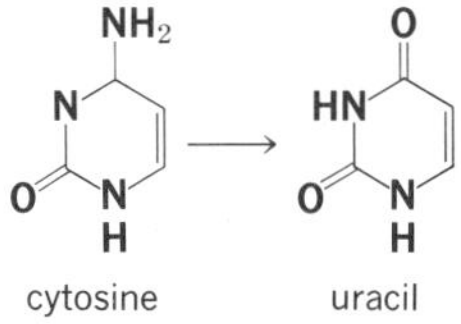

The uracil probably gets transformed into an intermediate of the Krebs Cycle and eventually gets completely oxidized.

Plasma proteins

Besides furnishing proteins for tissues, the plasma proteins are also important as agents to resist infection. The so-called gamma (γ)-globulin fraction of the blood plasma constitutes the antibodies. A diet deficient in protein may reduce the γ-globulin fraction of the plasma and, hence, reduce resistance to infection. A proper protein diet, therefore, from both a nutritional and a health-maintaining standpoint, is one that supplies not only the amino acids needed by the tissues, but also enough of the proper amino acids necessary to synthesize the proper quantities of γ-globulins.

Essential amino acids

There are approximately 20 α-amino acids composing proteins. These acids differ widely in chemical structure and in the functions they perform in the animal organism. The nutritional value of a protein is determined by the kind and amounts of its constituent amino acids.

From a nutritional standpoint, proteins that do not permit normal growth, reproduction, and other normal body functions are classified as *incomplete*. A *complete* protein presumably supplies all the amino acids necessary for maintenance of normal body function. See Table 19-1.

When speaking about incomplete or complete proteins, one must necessarily mention the percentage of such protein in the daily ration. Although a protein may contain all the necessary α-amino acids, some of these may be present in such small quantities that a deficiency may exist. For example, casein, the protein in milk, may be regarded as a complete protein. This is true if casein, which may be the only protein in the diet, is supplied in such quantities that it amounts to about 18% of the daily ration. If fed at a lower level, for example, 9% of daily ration, the diet becomes low in sulfur-containing α-amino acids. The completeness or incompleteness of a protein is unquestionably relative, depending upon the level at which the protein is fed.

Some elegant work by Rose has shown that, for the rat, the following α-amino acids had to be furnished in the diet.

lysine	isoleucine
valine	threonine
tryptophan	methionine
phenylalanine	histidine
leucine	arginine

If these acids were absent, normal maximum growth was impaired, and death resulted.

Rose also extended this work to humans. Healthy young men were fed a carefully prepared diet of starch, sucrose, centrifugated butter, inorganic salts, vitamins, and the different purified α-amino acids. This diet presumably contained all known ingredients necessary to maintain proper health and body function.

These men collected and saved all urine samples during the day and, by simple analytical procedures, could easily determine the total amount

Table 19-1

Protein	Source	Deficient in
SOME INCOMPLETE PROTEINS		
zein	corn	lysine and tryptophan
gliadin	wheat	lysine
gelatine	collagen	tyrosine, tryptophan and cystine
SOME COMPLETE PROTEINS		
casein	milk	
albumin	eggs	
proteins	lean meats, fish, and poultry	

of urea excreted during the day. Because the total amount of nitrogen entering the body was carefully controlled and measured, and the amount of nitrogen leaving the body was also easily measured, an accurate check of the nitrogen equilibrium was possible.

Because each of the amino acids was in a purified form, it was now possible to determine what would happen if one of them were removed from the diet. It was readily determined that if some α-amino acids were removed from the diet, nothing obvious or measurable happened. This simply means that, even if these amino acids are absent in the diet, they can be synthesized in the body *from certain other chemicals normally found in the body,* and so these acids are not really essential.

In some cases, if an α-amino acid was removed from the diet, the body soon exhibited negative nitrogen balance, meaning that the body could not synthesize the necessary proteins. Such an α-amino acid is called an *essential α-amino acid.* By the process of gradually decreasing the amount of such an α-amino acid, it was possible to determine at what level in the diet the body would respond by exhibiting negative nitrogen balance. In every case of this nature, as soon as the missing amino acid was then put back into the synthetic food mixture, the body returned to nitrogen equilibrium.

Whether or not an α-amino acid is essential depends on whether the proper carbon skeleton is available in the living system. If the carbon skeleton prerequisite *is available,* the reaction with ammonia (amination) or with another α-amino acid (transamination) can form the desired α-amino acid. For example, pyruvic acid can be converted into alanine.

$$\underset{\text{pyruvic acid}}{\begin{array}{c} CH_3 \\ | \\ C{=}O \\ | \\ COOH \end{array}} + NH_3 + [2H] \longrightarrow \underset{\text{alanine}}{\begin{array}{c} CH_3 \\ | \\ CHNH_2 \\ | \\ COOH \end{array}} + H_2O$$

amination

Because it is readily created from the plentiful pyruvic acid, alanine does not have to be present in the diet.

$$\underset{\text{oxaloacetic acid}}{O{=}C(CH_2COOH){-}COOH} + \underset{\text{alanine}}{CH_3{-}CHNH_2{-}COOH} \longrightarrow \underset{\text{aspartic acid}}{CH_2COOH{-}CH(NH_2){-}COOH} + \underset{\text{pyruvic acid}}{CH_3{-}C{=}O{-}COOH}$$

transamination

Because it is readily formed from oxaloacetic acid, aspartic acid does not have to be present in the diet.

On the other hand, phenylpyruvic acid, the precursor of phenylalanine, does not ordinarily occur in the body.

$$\underset{\text{phenylpyruvic acid}}{C_6H_5{-}CH_2{-}C{=}O{-}COOH} + \underset{\text{alanine}}{CH_3{-}CHNH_2{-}COOH} \longrightarrow \underset{\text{phenylalanine}}{C_6H_5{-}CH_2{-}C(H)(NH_2){-}COOH} + \underset{\text{pyruvic acid}}{CH_3{-}C{=}O{-}COOH}$$

Because this particular carbon arrangement is *not easily available in the body,* it must be supplied in the diet, and phenylalanine is an essential α-amino acid. It is interesting that if the synthetic phenylpyruvic acid *were* to be supplied in the diet, the body readily *could* convert it into phenylalanine.

Table 19-2 is based on the results so obtained, and lists eight α-amino acids judged essential to man and the recommendations made.

It should be realized that only one criterion (nitrogen balance) was used to judge the essential nature of these α-amino acids. One cannot say what effect a sustained diet of only these α-amino acids would have on all

Table 19-2 Minimum and recommended intakes for normal man

AMINO ACID	MINIMUM DAILY REQUIREMENT	RECOMMENDED DAILY INTAKE	NUMBER OF SUBJECTS TESTED
L-tryptophan	0.25 grams	0.5 grams	37[a]
L-phenylalanine	1.10	2.2	28
L-lysine	0.80	1.6	33
L-threonine	0.50	1.0	24
L-valine	0.80	1.6	29
L-methionine	1.10	2.2	19
L-leucine	1.10	2.2	14
L-isoleucine	0.70	1.4	14

[a] Of these subjects, 33 were kept in balance on 0.3 gram or less.

body functions. It has been claimed, for example, that a diet deficient in arginine may result in the atrophy of spermatogenic tissue. A diet lacking in certain supposedly nonessential α-amino acids may cause some body dysfunction, which may not be apparent for a long time. There are many problems still unanswered.

REVIEW QUESTIONS

1. In the normal adult, what percentage of nitrogen is excreted in proportion to the amount of nitrogen taken in as food?
2. In what chemical form is most of the nitrogen excreted?
3. What is known about the stability of tissue protein?
4. Define deamination. What can happen to the deaminated part? Define transamination.
5. Discuss urea formation.
6. Show how proteins can be converted into carbohydrates and fats.
7. Summarize what can happen to amino acids after they have been absorbed in the intestine.
8. Discuss positive and negative nitrogen balance.
9. List the essential amino acids.
10. What is meant by a complete protein? Give several sources of complete and incomplete proteins.
11. What is meant by transmethylation?
12. Discuss the fate of nucleoproteins in the metabolic process.
13. Does an expectant mother require more or less protein in her diet? Why?

20

blood

General Functions

Blood has been called the circulating tissue of the body because of the great number of cells and substances contained in its solution. Blood is a very important fluid whose prime function is to maintain the constancy of internal environment by continuously renewing the tissue fluid; in this manner it serves as a liaison between the tissue cells and the body's external surroundings. Although chemical substances are continuously entering and leaving the blood stream, the *overall* composition of the blood remains remarkably constant.

The respiratory function of the blood consists in bringing oxygen from the lungs to the tissues and carbon dioxide from the tissues to the lungs.

Digested food, which has been absorbed, is transported by the blood to the organs or tissues. There, the blood-borne food can be used to build and renew tissue, can be oxidized to provide energy, or can be stored in reserve depots.

Detoxified products and various end products of metabolism (e.g., CO_2, urea, etc.) are carried to the proper organs and eliminated. The blood also helps maintain the pH of the body by means of its buffer compounds. Water balance and fluid distribution are governed to a large extent by the inorganic salts and proteins present in the blood.

The white blood cells help destroy invading microorganisms.

Thus, we see that blood has many functions, all of which are essential to the maintenance of life.

Blood Volume

Although the volume of blood in men is subject to considerable variation, it appears that blood accounts for about 8% of the total body weight in a man. The volume is somewhat lower in women. This means that average adult males have approximately 6 quarts of blood.

The Formed Elements, Plasma, and Serum

It is possible to draw blood and to prevent its coagulation by the addition of an anticoagulant (see following section). Microscopically, one can then observe that certain forms are suspended in the liquid. These forms are called the *formed elements,* and the liquid is called *plasma.*

The formed elements are the *red cells* (i.e., erythrocytes), the *white cells* (i.e., leukocytes), and the *blood platelets.* The plasma contains the colloid proteins, salts, and various other products of digestive, metabolic, and hormonal activities. See Figure 20-1.

Ordinarily, when blood is let, coagulation occurs. This complex phenomenon may be initiated by the platelets. The formed elements are usually occluded in the jellylike confines of the clot. After the clot is formed, it usually undergoes contraction and leaves a pale yellow liquid known as *serum.* Serum is the liquid part of the blood after clotting has occurred, and plasma is the liquid part of the blood before clotting has occurred. The essential difference between the two fluids is that serum does not contain fibrinogen, which is removed in the clotting. Serum's color is due to the presence of porphyrins in the state of either synthesis or decomposition.

Defibrinated blood is blood that has been carefully coagulated so that most of the red cells are still suspended in the serum.

Laked blood is produced by suspending blood, whose coagulation has been prevented by some means, in a hypotonic solution. Under these conditions, the red cells swell and soon "burst," and the red coloring matter (hemoglobin) escapes into the surrounding fluid and thus forms a clear red solution.

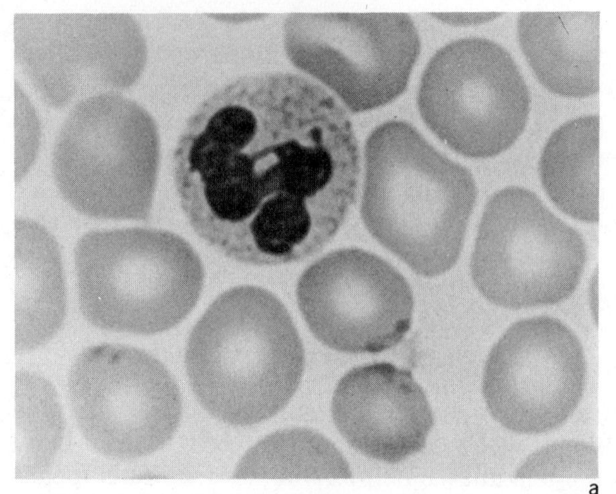
a

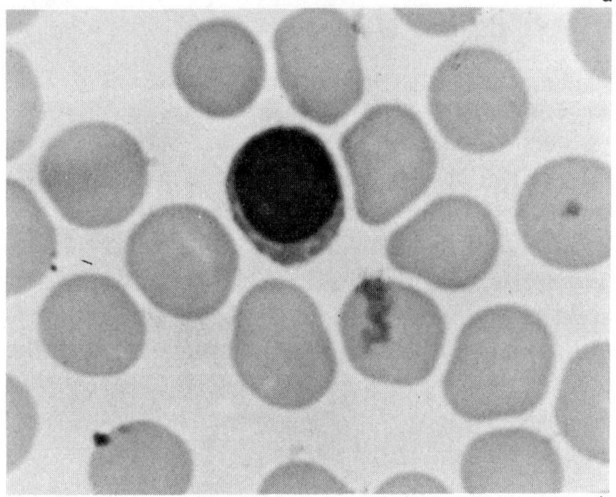
b

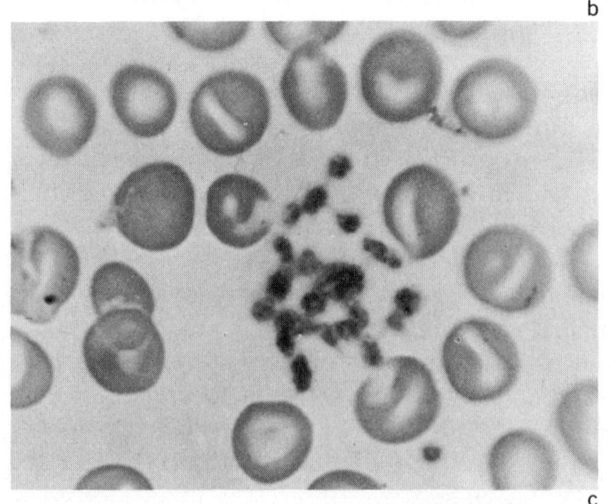
c

Figure 20-1 Photomicrographs of a stained film of human blood showing the major formed elements. A. (×1845) The large nucleated cell is a neutrophilic polymorphonuclear leukocyte. The nonnucleated cells are erythrocytes or red cells. B. (×1845) The nucleated cell is a lymphocyte. C. (×1920) A clump of platelets surrounded by red cells. (From *Life: An Introduction to Biology* Second Edition; by G. G. Simpson and W. S. Beck. © 1965 by Harcourt, Brace & World, Inc. Reprinted with permission.)

The Erythrocytes

The normal red cell in man is a biconcave, nonnucleated disc, with an average diameter of 6–9 microns. These erythrocytes are produced in the red marrow of bones.

The number of red blood cells (erythrocytes) is a variable figure, but the conventional "normal" red cell count is about 5,000,000 per cubic millimeter in women and about 5,500,000 per cubic millimeter in men. The determination is made by means of a standard hemacytometer, with which one microscopically counts the red cells in a certain aliquot portion of carefully diluted blood.

The red color of blood is due entirely to the hemoglobin in the red cells. Venous blood is purplish-red, and arterial blood is bright scarlet. The variation in color is due to the difference in amounts of oxygen absorbed by the hemoglobin in the two cases.

The amount of hemoglobin in 100 ml of blood of a normal person varies with sex, age, season of the year, and geographical location. The average normal hemoglobin content is about 15 g per 100 ml of blood. (Variations of 13.7 to 17.3 g are not uncommon.) Various instruments and a variety of apparatus (e.g., hemoglobinometers) are available for this determination.

The mean corpuscular volume (MCV) is a measure of the volume of packed cells per liter of blood. MCV is measured by means of a *hematocrit,* which is a small, graduated centrifuge tube. Oxalated blood is introduced into the hematocrit and centrifuged. The cells then sink to the bottom, and their volume can be read directly by the graduations. (A correction may be made for the oxalate.) Normally, the MCV averages 42% for females and 47% for males, and the red cells occupy nearly all the cell volume. Conditions in which the percentage of red cells is high (polycythemia), or low (anemia), or when the percentage of red cells is low and percentage of white cells is very high (leukemia) may be detected by the hematocrit technique.

Hemoglobin (Hb) is a crystalline protein with a total molecular weight of about 65,000. It is composed of *four* heme groups (i.e., red pigments that constitute 4% of the molecule) to each globulin part (i.e., a colorless globular protein). Hemoglobin readily combines with oxygen to form oxyhemoglobin (HbO_2). Oxyhemoglobin is bright red (arterial blood), whereas hemoglobin is purplish-red (venous blood). Oxyhemoglobin is a rather unstable compound, which readily gives up its oxygen to the tissues and forms hemoglobin again. The iron in the heme part is in the ferrous state (i.e., it has +2 valence). If the iron is oxidized to the +3 valence, ferric heme, which is brown, is produced (methemoglobin), and the oxygen-combining capacity is destroyed.

Hemoglobin can also readily combine with carbon monoxide to form carboxyhemoglobin (HbCO), which is much more stable than HbO_2. This accounts for the poisonous nature of carbon monoxide, because the HbCO

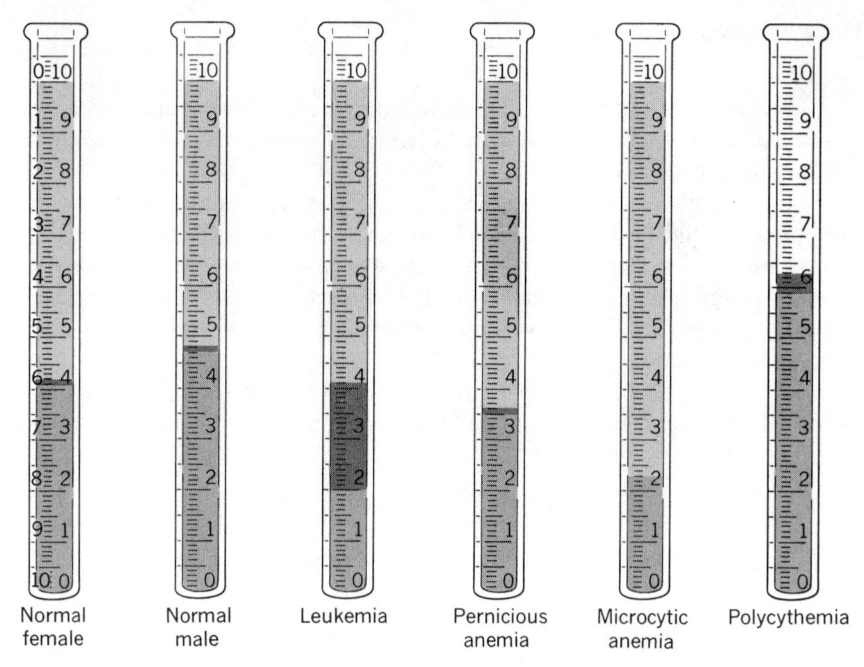

Figure 20-2 Typical normal and abnormal packed cell volumes as observed in Wintrobe hematrocrit tube.

decreases the amount of hemoglobin available to combine with the oxygen.

The isoelectric point of hemoglobin is 6.7. Since the pH of blood is about 7.3, this means that hemoglobin has a net overall negative charge and exists as a proteinate, very probably as the potassium salt.

The body is constantly creating new red cells and destroying old red cells. This means a constant destruction and synthesis of hemoglobin. The body reuses 85% of the iron. The heme part (minus the iron) is called the protoporphyrin part. The protoporphyrin is oxidized and reduced and is excreted as bile pigments (bilirubin, biliverdin, stercobilin) in the feces and urine. Apparently the body is capable of synthesizing the protein part of hemoglobin from the normal protein sources and the porphyrin part by its own means or by the help of porphyrins in the normal diet.

Because heme is a definite chemical compound of relatively low molecular weight, it is obvious that heme isolated from one species must be the same as heme obtained from other species. However, because hemoglobin contains heme and a *protein,* and the various species have characteristic proteins, hemoglobin from each species is different. For the same reason, oxyhemoglobin obtained from the various species is different. These differences may be conveniently detected by a simple microscopic inspection. See Figures 20-3 and 20-4.

Normally, blood will combine with oxygen in the ratio of 18.5 ml of

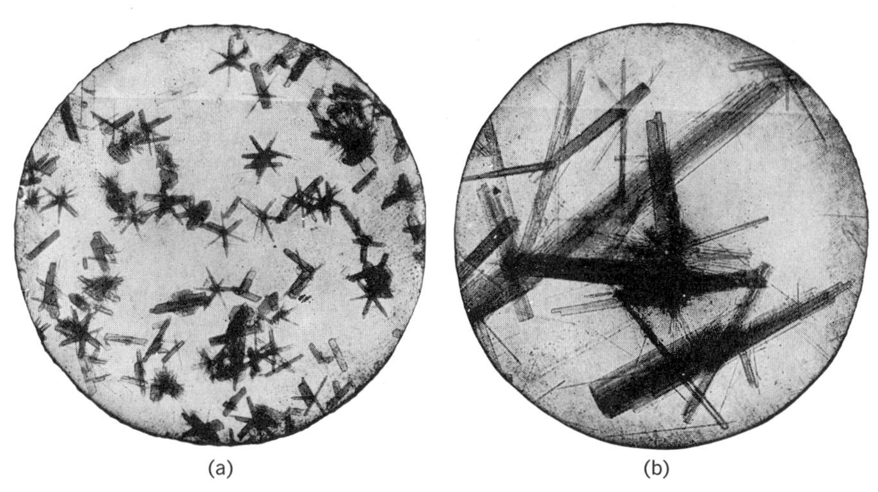

(a) (b)

Figure 20-3 (a) Oxyhemoglobin crystals from blood of the rat. (b) Oxyhemoglobin crystals from blood of the dog. (From *Hawk's A Physiological Chemistry*. Edited by Bernard L. Oser. 14th edition. McGraw-Hill Book Company, 1965.)

oxygen per 100 ml of blood. This blood circulates to the tissues that need oxygen, and the oxygen is given up; the blood then returns to the lungs. Blood returning to the lungs contains about 12 ml of oxygen per 100 ml of blood. This means that each 100 ml of blood supplies about 6.5 ml of oxygen to the tissues.

Oxyhemoglobin is unstable in the presence of carbonic acid (which is formed to some extent when carbon dioxide dissolves in water) and decomposes to liberate oxygen. The need of a tissue for oxygen is directly proportional to the concentration of carbon dioxide coming from the tissue.

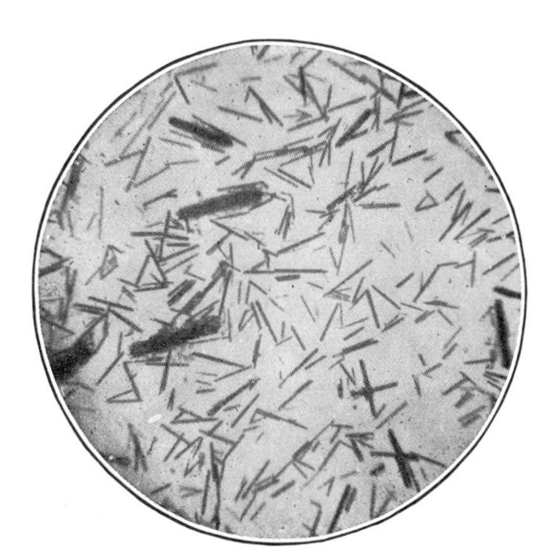

Figure 20-4 Carbon monoxide hemoglobin crystals from ox blood. (From *Hawk's A Physiological Chemistry*. Edited by Bernard L. Oser. 14th edition. McGraw-Hill Book Company, 1965.)

Also, an increase in the concentration of carbonic acid will increase the amount of oxygen released from the oxyhemoglobin.

The carbon dioxide that is liberated and carried away in the blood is essentially in three different forms: dissolved carbon dioxide (10%), sodium bicarbonate (about 70%), and carbamino hemoglobin HbNHCOOH (about 20%), a compound formed by the reaction of Hb with CO_2.

$$\text{Hb—N}\begin{matrix}\diagup \text{H} \\ \diagdown \text{COOH}\end{matrix}$$

carbamino hemoglobin

Blood entering the lungs may contain from 55–60 ml of CO_2 per 100 ml of blood, and blood leaving the lungs may contain about 50 ml of CO_2 per 100 ml of blood. This means that 5–10 ml of CO_2 are exhaled per passage of 100 ml of blood through the lungs. The exhaled CO_2 comes mostly from the dissolved carbon dioxide.

Diseases of the Red Blood Cells

These diseases may be divided into two classes: *anemia,* characterized by an abnormally low red cell count; and *polycythemia,* characterized by an abnormally high red cell count.

THE ANEMIAS

The anemic condition is characterized by a loss in red blood cells or by a change in cell size. Both of these conditions may occur at the same time. If the red blood cell is enlarged, the anemia is called *macrocytic* anemia. If the cell is reduced, the anemia is *microcytic.* If there is a decrease in the number of red blood cells, the resultant anemia is known as *normocytic* anemia.

Macrocytic anemia. This disease may result from intense activity of the bone marrow or, more commonly, from vitamin B_{12} or folic acid deficiencies. The red blood cells may be as large as 10 to 15 microns in diameter. The most common clinical syndrome is pernicious anemia, which is caused by the failure of the stomach mucosa to secrete a mucoprotein, the "intrinsic factor," needed for the absorption of vitamin B_{12}. The lack of vitamin B_{12} results in the failure of red blood cells to mature.

Sprue is a macrocytic anemic condition caused by lack of absorption of vitamin B_{12} even though the "intrinsic factor" is present.

Normocytic anemia. In this disease, the red blood cells may be of normal size, but they are decreased in number. The red cell count may be between two and four million and may fall to one million in certain cases.

Normocytic anemia may be due to a sudden loss of blood. In this case, the blood is diluted by tissue fluid, and the red cell count naturally goes down. Such anemia may occur after bleeding due to scurvy, hemophilia, or hemorrhage.

Lack of blood formation may also cause normocytic anemia. This may result from the presence of foreign chemicals (such as gold, arsenic, bismuth, mercury, and silver compounds) in the body. Exposure to radioactive substances may curtail blood formation, as do some infections and wasting diseases.

Normocytic anemia may also be caused by the destruction of blood (i.e., hemolysis), which results in a lowered cell count. This may be either acute or chronic. Acute hemolytic anemia may be due to the presence of hemolysins of incompatible blood, certain bacteria, or protozoa.

Chronic hemolytic anemia is found in the hereditary diseases of sickle cell anemia. This anemia almost always occurs in the Negro race. The red cells are bizarre in shape, being elongated and "sickled" in appearance, sometimes over 20 microns in length.

Simple microcytic anemia. In this disease, the red blood cells are smaller than usual, with an average diameter of about 6 microns with some as small as 4–5 microns. This condition is caused by imperfect formation of blood and is evident in some cases of subacute and chronic inflammatory diseases and chronic noninflammatory conditions. It may also be an inherited abnormality (e.g., familial microcytosis). Transfusions and treatment of the cause give the best results.

Hypochromic anemia. This condition is generally caused by an iron deficiency and results in a decrease in the number of red cells (values of 3 million or less are common), a decrease in the size of the red cells (average size is somewhat less than 7.2 microns), and a definite decrease in the hemoglobin content of the red cells.

This latter fact is easily verified by microscopic observation of the stained red cells, which reveal large pale centers. Some cells have so little hemoglobin that they look like rings.

This disease may be caused by an iron-deficient diet, by defective absorption of the iron in the digestive tract, by a continuous loss of blood, by excessive demands for iron (due to rapid growth or repeated pregnancies), or by Rh factor blood interactions.

POLYCYTHEMIA

This disease is characterized by a red blood cell count higher than normal; values of 7–15 million are not uncommon. It is associated with congenital heart disease or any other disease affecting oxygenation of the blood and often appears as an adaptation to high altitudes.

In *polycythemia vera* cases, the bone marrow is overactively producing red blood cells, causing an increase in the supply.

Table 20-1 Leukocytes

TYPE	PERCENTAGE
polymorphonuclear neutrophils	62
lymphocytes	30
monocytes	5.3
polymorphonuclear eosinophils	2.3
polymorphonuclear basophils	0.4

Leukocytes

The leukocytes are generally formed in the yellow marrow of the long bones and lymphoid tissue. The normal white cell count is about 7,000 per cubic millimeter, but it is subject to considerable variation. Table 20-1 lists the five types of leukocytes, and each type can be differentiated by proper staining and observation under the microscope.

The granulocytes, that is, those with granulations in the cytoplasm, are classified as *neutrophil, eosinophil, and basophil,* according to their staining reactions. Those leukocytes with no granulations are classified as *monocytes* and *lymphocytes.*

Leukocytes "crawl" like an amoeba and consequently move along surfaces. *Chemotaxis* is the term used to describe the direction of leukocyte motion with respect to external chemical stimuli. Positive chemotaxis is an attraction of the leukocytes, and negative chemotaxis is the repulsion of the leukocytes.

Phagocytosis is the process whereby certain leukocytes (e.g., neutrophils and monocytes) undergoing positive chemotaxis toward certain invading bacteria and other foreign agents approach and actively engulf these invaders. Protein-hydrolyzing enzymes are present in these leukocytes, and the foreign agents are usually proteins, which the neutrophil or monocyte then hydrolyzes.

As the number of foreign organisms increases, generally the white cell count goes up. The white cell count is frequently an excellent diagnostic aid in elucidating the nature of a disease and in following its course. The damaged or inactivated leukocytes accumulate in a cavity and are the chief form of *pus* cells.

The eosinophils are thought to detoxify proteins before they cause body damage. The role of the basophils is not clearly understood, but it is possible that they prevent coagulation of the blood cells during infection.

The lymphocytes have a potential for changing into monocytes and thus absorb foreign proteins. They may also be changed into other types of blood cells as the body requires them.

Diseases Involving the Leukocytes

In the course of many infectious diseases, the number of leukocytes normally increases as the disease progresses until a maximum is reached (crisis); then, the number of leukocytes returns to normal as the symptoms of the disease disappear. The numerical changes, however, are not as important as the qualitative changes.

LEUKOPENIA (AGRANULOCYTOSIS)

This condition represents a decrease in the number of leukocytes to below 5,000 per cubic millimeter. This might be due to chemical poisoning or excessive exposure to x rays or radioactive substances. Diseases that destroy the bone marrow may also cause leukopenia.

LEUKEMIA

This is a disease caused by a malignant tumor of the bone marrow or lymph nodes. This causes an overactive production of leukocytes. The varieties of leukemia depend on the type of cell affected; that is, if the myelocyte is affected, the disease is myeloid leukemia. In some leukemia cases, the white cell count may be as high as 100,000 and possibly 200,000 leukocytes per cubic millimeter. Leukemia may be classified as acute or chronic. There is as yet no cure for acute leukemia. Radioactive phosphorus (P^{32}) is useful in the treatment of chronic myeloid leukemia.

Blood Platelets

The blood platelets are formed from the megakaryocytes in the bone marrow, spleen, lungs, and possibly other sources. The platelets are about 2–4 microns in diameter, and there are usually about 250,000–400,000 platelets per cubic millimeter. Apparently, the chief function of the platelets is to share in the formation of blood clots.

Serotonin is a vasoconstrictor found in human sera. It appears to be liberated into the serum during dissolution of the platelets. Serotonin occurs as the complex creatinine sulfate salt, $C_{14}H_{21}N_5O_3 \cdot H_2SO_4$. When the creatinine sulfate is removed, serotonin can be isolated, and it has been proved to be 5-hydroxytryptamine.

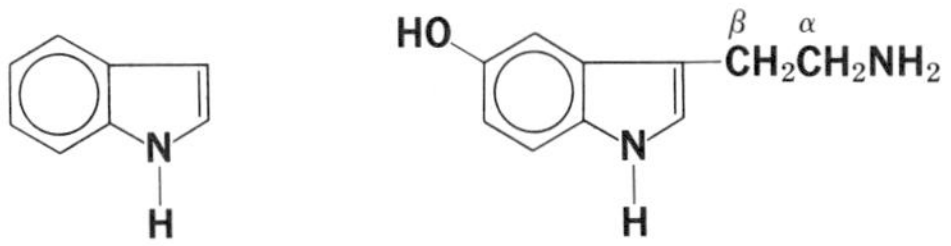

N–H

indole

HO, β α $CH_2CH_2NH_2$, N–H

serotonin

Note that serotonin is a substituted β-indolylethylamine. Epinephrine and related vasoconstrictors are β-phenylethylamines.

Lipids in the Blood

The major serum lipids that have been identified are neutral fats, fatty acids, cholesterol and its esters, phospholipids, and triglycerides. Lipid concentration is about 0.5% in the human body. After a meal containing much fat, the lipid content in the blood may be as high as 1 to 2%.

The blood contains an enzyme, *lipoprotein lipase,* which hydrolyzes the triglycerides attached to proteins. The free fatty acids may then be bound to a protein molecule and transported to other cells and tissues. Many body tissues also contain this enzyme and, thus, can hydrolyze these lipids.

The lipids may also be transported to the liver, where they are used for energy or converted into other lipids.

The blood also contains *lipoproteins,* which are combinations of lipids bound to proteins. These are of two types: α, which have a high concentration of triglycerides and a low concentration of protein, and β, which contain large amounts of protein and small amounts of the triglycerides. The function of these compounds is not well understood, but they are thought to be a means of lipid transport.

Experiments have shown that there is an excellent correlation between the amount of lipoproteins deposited in the blood vessels and the extent of atherosclerosis, one of the major vascular diseases. In the United States, atherosclerosis causes more than half of all human deaths. The disease involves the deposition of lipid material into the inner wall of the arteries, such that the wall thickens. As a result, the blood flow is impaired, the blood pressure rises, and the entire occlusion of the vessel may result.

Unfortunately, atherosclerosis is particularly prone to attack the vital coronary and cerebral arteries, causing heart attacks and cerebral hemorrhages.

A high fat diet, especially saturated fats, seems to increase the probability of developing atherosclerosis. A diet rich in cholesterol may predispose the disease, but not to the extent that the total fat diet does.

Blood Plasma

About 10% of blood plasma is dissolved solids, the greatest portion of which are the plasma proteins (7% of the plasma); the remaining solutes are inorganic salts, electrolytes (1% of the plasma), and organic compounds other than proteins, such as carbohydrates.

Table 20-2 Proteins in 100 ml of plasma

PROTEIN	GRAMS
albumins	3.26
α-globulins	1.01
β-globulins	1.26
γ-globulins	0.74
fibrinogen	0.31

Three types of plasma proteins are: fibrinogen, albumins, and globulins. The concentrations of these proteins in the blood plasma are given in Table 20-2.

There are several types of albumin proteins in the blood plasma. Their main function is to control the water balance between the blood and the tissues by regulating the osmotic pressure. If the albumin concentration is high, water enters the blood stream from surrounding tissues. If the albumin concentration is low, water tends to leave the blood stream. The concentration of salts in the blood has a larger effect on the osmotic pressure than does albumin.

Fibrinogen is important in the clotting of blood. The α- and β-globulins can react or combine with lipids and other compounds in the body and transport them from one section of the body to another.

The γ-globulins, and to a lesser extent the β-globulins, are important in the formation of antibodies and immunities.

The ions present in blood plasma are Na^+, H^+, K^+, Ca^{++}, Mg^{++}, OH^-, Cl^-, HCO_3^-, $H_2PO_4^-$, HPO_4^{--}, SO_4^{--}, and HSO_4^-. These electrolytes are a predominant factor in the governing of the passage of water in and out of the blood stream into cells and tissue. The concentration of ions in the plasma is about 0.3 equivalents per liter.

Use of Plasma

Because it does not contain red blood cells, plasma does not have to be typed or divided into various groups. Plasma from several donors is mixed together and stored either as a liquid at 4° C, as a solid, or in a dehydrated form .

In cases of severe hemorrhages, there is no substitute for whole blood, but in cases of shock, severe burns, and other conditions of blood loss, the transfusion of blood plasma is very effective.

Plasma Substitutes

When the amount of stored blood and plasma is not sufficient for the demands, for example, in war or a mass disaster, plasma extenders are used. These compounds do not replace the cells or proteins in the blood, but they do increase the volume. Blood plasma substitutes are usually very large molecules with molecular weights between 50,000 and 100,000. This means that they are approximately the same size as the blood proteins, and thus they do not pass through the blood vessels into the tissue. Plasma extenders are not normally metabolized and are not excreted through the kidneys.

There are several types of extenders: animal proteins, dextrans, and polyvinylpyrrolidone. Animal proteins are not widely used for this purpose, but they are appropriate compounds.

POLYVINYLPYRROLIDONE

Polyvinylpyrrolidone (PVP) was the first of the plasma extenders to be introduced (by Germany) during World War II. It is a synthetic substance.

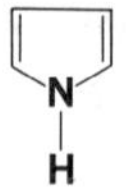

N—H
pyrrole

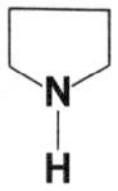

N—H
pyrrolidine

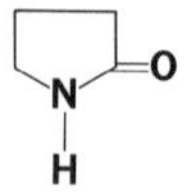

N—H, =O
pyrrolidone

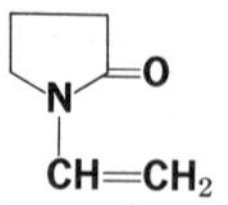

N—$CH{=}CH_2$, =O
vinylpyrrolidone

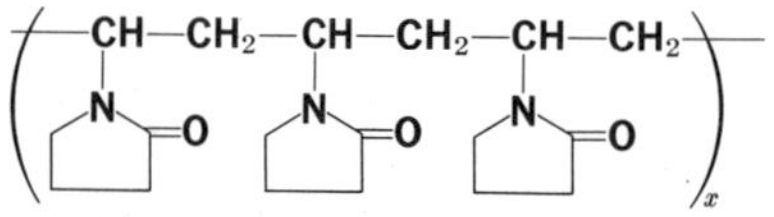

$(-CH-CH_2-CH-CH_2-CH-CH_2-)_x$ (each CH bearing a pyrrolidone ring through N)

polyvinylpyrrolidone

PVP is nonantigenic and stable in the dry form. PVP approximately equals the effectiveness of the plasma proteins in restoring diminished blood volume resulting from hemorrhage. However, duration of action is variable. PVP is rarely used in the United States.

DEXTRAN

Dextran is a blood extender related to glycogen. It is a polymer of glucose, prepared by fermentation of sucrose. For use as a plasma extender, very large native molecules with molecular weights of several million are partially broken down, usually by acid hydrolysis, to form molecules with the most effective molecular weights (i.e., around 75,000). Clinical dextrans, like all the plasma extenders, consist of molecules of widely differing size. A characteristic toxic reaction of allergic nature in humans has been reported with some dextran products.

A 6% solution is usually used as a plasma volume extender. Twenty-four hours after dextran is administered, 10 to 40% is excreted in the urine. Three-fourths (75%) is excreted after 14 days.

The Icterus Index

The Icterus Index is a means of describing the possible yellow color of blood plasma. This is done by comparing the sample color with that of a known standard (e.g., a solution of 0.1% of potassium dichromate, $K_2Cr_2O_7$). In cases of jaundice, there is an increase in the bilirubin content in the blood, which can be readily detected by this test.

Buffers in the Blood

Three buffer systems are effective in the blood: the bicarbonate pair, $NaHCO_3$ and H_2CO_3; the phosphate pair, NaH_2PO_4 and Na_2HPO_4; and the proteins. The bicarbonate and phosphate systems have already been discussed (Chapter 1).

Nearly all the proteins in the plasma have isoelectric points on the acid side. This means that in the plasma, with a pH of about 7.35, these proteins have a net overall negative charge. These proteins can take on extra hydrogens (in cases of acidosis) or give up hydrogen ions (in cases of alkalosis). By these simple reactions, the proteins may serve as excellent natural buffering agents over a wide pH range.

Lymph

As the lymph capillaries fill the tissue spaces, the lymph (interstitial fluid) may be regarded as the intermediary fluid between the blood plasma and the actual tissue cells. Lymph is the medium whereby nutritive materials, transported by the blood, are brought into contact with tissue cells. Lymph is also the medium that transports the end products of metabolism of the tissue cells to the blood stream. The lymph capillaries carry their fluid to larger and larger vessels, which finally unite at the thoracic duct, which empties into the subclavian vein. The fluid leaving the blood capillaries works its way through the lymph system and eventually gets back to the general blood circulation.

The lymph is formed by the filtration of the blood plasma from the blood capillaries to the lymph capillaries. As would be expected, under these circumstances the protein content of the lymphatics is always less than that of the blood plasma, because the plasma proteins cannot readily go through the blood capillary walls. Lymph is about the same chemically as blood plasma and contains mostly water and the various electrolytes.

Blood Tests

The *microscopic identification* of blood is a quick and often excellent way of detecting blood.

The Benzidine Test

This test is used to detect minute quantities of blood, specifically in urine and feces. It is a useful test for following the course of treatment of an ulcer patient. The solution, which may contain blood, is added to a solution of benzidine in glacial acetic acid; then hydrogen peroxide is added.

$H_2N-C_6H_4-C_6H_4-NH_2$

benzidine

A positive test is indicated by the formation of a blue color, reaching a maximum intensity within about 5 minutes. The test is very sensitive and presumably works by the blood catalyzing the decomposition of the hydrogen peroxide, which liberates oxygen. The free active oxygen then oxidizes the colorless benzidine to form a blue color. A negative test is more significant than a positive test.

Test for Iron

This may be done by igniting whole blood in a crucible until an ash is obtained. The ash is then taken up in dilute HNO_3 and filtered; the filtrate should contain the ferrous ion, Fe^{++}, which slowly oxidizes to the ferric ion, Fe^{+++}. When thiocyanate ion is added to Fe^{+++}, a deep red color is formed, due to the formation of ferric thiocyanate solution, $Fe(CNS)_3$ or $Fe(CNS)_6^{3-}$.

Removal of Proteins

Proteins are removed by treating the blood with dilute sulfuric acid, which effectively converts the negative net overall charge to a positive net overall charge. Sodium tungstate (Na_2WO_4) then precipitates the proteins as protein salt (i.e., protein tungstate). When this precipitation is complete and the precipitate has been removed by filtration or centrifugation, the filtrate should be free of all protein and should give a negative Biuret test.

In the protein-free filtrate, the *chloride ion* can be detected and precipitated as silver chloride, AgCl, by the addition of silver nitrate.

The *glucose,* present in the protein-free filtrate, can be detected by means of Benedict's Reagent.

Blood Typing

The red blood cells contain two substances capable of being precipitated or clumped, and they are referred to as the agglutinogens A and B. The agglutinogens are protein in nature and may be regarded as antigens. Serum contains two substances, anti-A agglutinin and anti-B agglutinin, capable of clumping the two agglutinogens A and B. The agglutinins may be regarded as antibodies or precipitins. Human blood is divided into four groups, based on the interaction of these four substances. See Figure 20-5.

According to Landsteiner's classification, the blood groups are A (39%), B (12%), AB (4%), and O (45%). (The percentages refer to the various blood groups as they occur in the population of the United States.) In blood transfusions, it is of major importance to know whether the blood will be compatible (i.e., will not clump or precipitate) with that of the recipient.

If red blood cells are mixed with anti-A agglutinin and separately with anti-B agglutinin and do not clump in either case, we designate such blood as in *group O*. If the red blood cells clump when mixed with anti-A agglutinin and with anti-B agglutinin, we designate such blood as in *group AB*.

If the red cells are clumped by anti-A agglutinin and not by anti-B agglutinin, we designate such blood as in *group A*. If the red cells are clumped by anti-B agglutinin and not by anti-A agglutinin, we refer to such blood as in *group B*.

Rh Factor

The red blood cells of about 85% of the white population also contain another antigen called the Rh factor or Rh substance. The term Rh is used because this antigen was first detected in Rhesus monkey red blood cells.

In general, human serum contains no Rh antibodies. If, however, antibodies *are* present in serum, it is obvious that if blood containing the Rh antigen is mixed with blood whose serum contains the Rh antibodies, the two would be incompatible, and death might result.

Rh positive blood contains the Rh factor (antigen). The Rh factor is inheritable and consequently presents a serious problem if the father is Rh positive and the mother is Rh negative, as the fetus may die of erythroblastosis.

Let us consider the classical case: The father is Rh positive and the mother is Rh negative. During the first pregnancy, the fetus contains the inherited Rh factor and causes the production of Rh antibodies in the mother. The first child is viable and normal. During the second pregnancy, the fetus is Rh positive and now the Rh antibodies in the mother enter the fetus and agglutinate the Rh positive red cells, which may result in the death

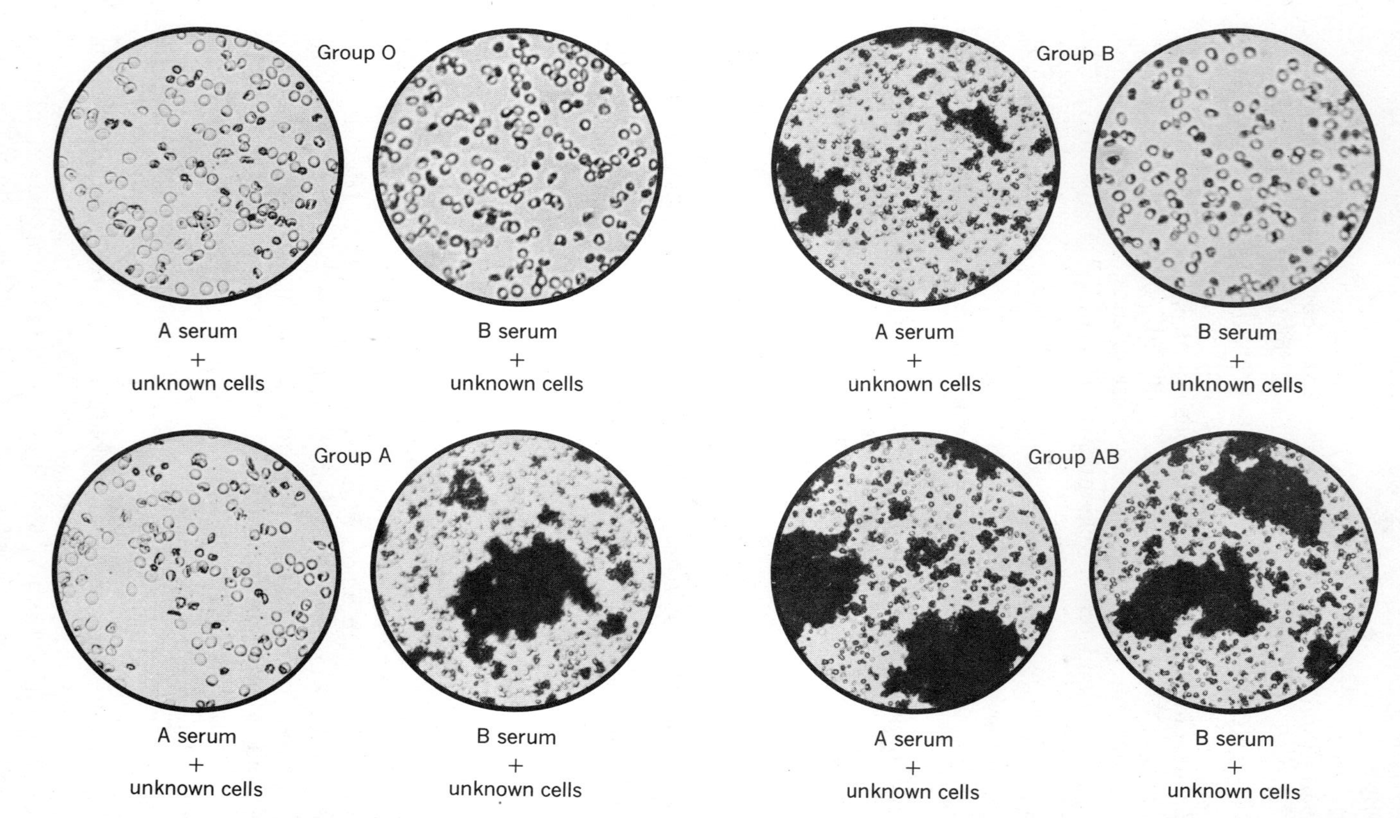

Figure 20-5 Appearance of preparations of unknown cells when mixed with A and B serums for determination of blood group according to Landsteiner or International classification. (Lester V. Bergman and Associates, Inc.)

of the fetus or the newborn child. Under certain circumstances, the death of the newborn baby may be avoided by a continuous transfusion (i.e., all the child's blood is replaced by some donor's blood).

Another situation could occur if an Rh negative female received a blood transfusion from an Rh positive individual. Such a transfusion would cause the formation of Rh antibodies in the female. If this person then carried an Rh positive fetus, the antibodies in the mother would agglutinate the red cells of the fetus and cause erythroblastosis in the fetus. The patient would also be in danger if she received a second transfusion of Rh positive blood.

From the foregoing it is apparent that an Rh factor test on blood in general is of great importance.

Our discussion of blood typing and the Rh factor may be oversimplified, because there are various subdivisions in blood typing and various divisions of Rh factor positivity. Because of these added factors, blood is usually crossmatched, that is, donor to recipient's blood, before a transfusion.

Blood Clotting

The exact mechanism of blood coagulation is not known. Many theories have been postulated to explain this process. All of these theories differ only in the exact details; they agree on the three main steps.

Blood coagulation is affected by as many as 30 factors. We will first consider several of these factors, and then we will discuss the mechanisms of coagulation.

Factors Affecting Coagulation

FIBRINOGEN

Fibrinogen is a high molecular weight protein found in the blood. When it is removed from blood, the remaining liquid is called serum. Most of the fibrinogen found in the blood is synthesized in the liver. Fibrinogen is converted to another protein, *fibrin,* which is mainly responsible for coagulation.

PROTHROMBIN

Prothrombin is a glycoprotein synthesized in the liver. Vitamin K is essential for prothrombin formation. Prothrombin is converted to *thrombin,* which is necessary for blood coagulation.

THE BLOOD PLATELETS

The platelets in the blood are not true cells but cell fragments formed in the bone marrow, lungs, liver, and spleen. Platelets tend to clump readily, cling to rough surfaces, and liberate thromboplastin.

THROMBOPLASTIN

This lipoprotein (i.e., phospholipid and protein) is found in blood platelets and tissue cells. Cephalin is very active in promoting clotting and is one of the phospholipids present in thromboplastin.

CALCIUM IONS

Unlike the other factors involved in blood clotting, calcium is an inorganic element. Calcium ions are necessary for blood coagulation and enter into the first and third steps of clotting.

A substance that will remove calcium ions from the blood will prevent blood coagulation. Oxalate and citrate will complex the Ca^{++} ions and keep them in solution. Citrated or oxalated blood will not coagulate unless thrombin is present or additional calcium is added.

GLOBULAR PROTEINS

Other factors that affect the coagulation of blood are globular proteins. Some globular proteins accelerate the conversion of prothrombin to thrombin; others, for example, antihemophilic factors, are necessary for clot formation.

Mechanism of Blood Coagulation

It is believed that blood coagulation begins with an injury to the blood vessel. The platelets accumulate at this point and thromboplastin is formed. Prothrombin is then converted to thrombin. This conversion requires calcium ions, thromboplastin, antihemophilic globulins, and other factors.

The thrombin that is released converts the fibrinogen into fibrin. Fibrin is a low molecular weight protein, which then polymerizes to form the clot. The characteristic appearance of the clot is due to red blood cells and platelets adhering to the fibrin clot. This can be represented schematically as follows:

$$\text{prothrombin} \xrightarrow[\text{thromboplastin, other factors}]{Ca^{++}} \text{thrombin}$$

$$\text{fibrinogen} \xrightarrow{\text{thrombin}} \text{fibrin}$$

$$\text{fibrin} \longrightarrow \text{blood clot}$$

After the blood clot has formed, it contracts; the yellow liquid that forms is called serum. After a few hours or days, the blood clot is dissolved. This solution of the clot is caused by fibrinolysins, hydrolytic enzymes.

Anticlotting Compounds

Heparin is sometimes called antiprothrombin. It is a very powerful anticoagulant and is a normal constituent of blood. Heparin is synthesized in the liver and acts to prevent the normal conversion of prothrombin to thrombin.

Dicumarol is another antiprothrombin and is found in sweet clover. Dicumarol acts on the site of formation of prothrombin in the liver and is counteracted by administration of vitamin K.

The Hemolytic Diseases

Hemophilia

Hemophilia is a hereditary disease due to the absence of certain blood clotting factors: antihemophilia agents or a plasma thromboplastin antecedent. This disease is transmitted by the female but usually attacks males. Hemophilic blood does not clot properly, and the patient usually dies at an early age. An effective treatment is blood transfusion, which will check the bleeding for several days.

Thrombocytopenia

Thrombocytopenia is characterized by a diminished supply of blood platelets. The bleeding time is prolonged. This disease is characterized by the failure of the blood clot to retract after formation.

In cases of advanced liver diseases, there is a decreased supply of plasma fibrinogen. The coagulation time is over 30 minutes, and the clot is thready.

A vitamin K deficiency results in an abnormally low supply of prothrombin. This decrease also causes a longer blood clotting time.

Immunochemistry

The microorganisms that cause disease are many and may be conveniently divided into three groups: (1) protozoa, (2) bacteria and fungi, and (3) viruses. Table 20-3 lists some diseases caused by these microorganisms.

The protozoal diseases are common in a tropical climate, and the bacterial diseases are most common in a temperate climate. The treatment of

Table 20-3 Diseases caused by microorganisms

PROTOZOA CAUSE	BACTERIA AND FUNGI CAUSE	VIRUSES CAUSE
malaria	diphtheria	influenza
sleeping sickness	cholera	poliomyelitis
amoebic dysentery	typhoid fever	small pox
and others	tuberculosis	common cold
	lockjaw	mumps
	anthrax	measles
	pneumonia	and others
	gonorrhea	
	scarlet fever	
	meningitis	
	syphilis	
	and others	

protozoal and bacterial infections has been much more successful than the treatment of virus infections.

True bacteria are divided into *Gram-positive* and *Gram-negative* groups, depending upon how they react to the Gram staining technique. Gram-positive organisms look dark after staining, whereas Gram-negative organisms look pale pink or colorless after staining.

The body defenses, such as skin over the body surface, protective mucous secretions in the nose and throat, acid in the stomach, and white cells in the blood stream, are so constituted as to prevent the invasion of dangerous microorganisms. The nose and throat, however, are most prone to attack. Despite the natural barriers, some disease-producing microorganisms occasionally make their way into the body and cause disease. We shall consider some ways of curbing the attack of these microscopic invaders.

Antibodies

When an antigen, such as a bacterium, virus, or some other foreign protein, enters the body, the defense forces in the body try to produce antibodies, specific for each antigen, to combat these antigens.

A very desirable situation occurs when the body is immune to the attack of a certain disease. By immune we may mean unsusceptible to the disease; this is *total immunity*. Total immunity may be evident when one species is not affected by disease organisms that ordinarily attack some other species. For example, it is known that the human is immune to some forms of chicken cholera. More generally, however, *by immunity we mean increased resistance to disease.*

Immunity may be further divided into various groups, such as *natural* or innate immunity, due to inherited factors; and *acquired* immunity, wherein one acquires antibodies by actually having the disease, by receiving them from the mother, or by immunization.

Artificially Acquired Immunity

This may be acquired in two ways: by *active immunization* (use of vaccine) or by *passive immunization* (use of immune sera).

USE OF VACCINE

Vaccines contain the dead or weakened organisms or the toxic products of the antigens. By suitably scaled injections, starting with a low level of concentration and building up to a high level of concentration, it is possible to stimulate the body to produce its own antibodies. When these injections are given, no disease is produced, for the microorganisms are too attenuated to cause the actual disease. Vaccinations are useful against scarlet fever, diphtheria, typhoid, tetanus, cholera, and rabies.

USE OF IMMUNE SERA

It is sometimes possible to produce antibodies in animals and to inject the sera of these immunized animals into the human. Under these circumstances, we are injecting the actual antibodies, and thus we are protecting the body from future attacks of the disease. Passive immunity may be acquired against smallpox, diphtheria, epidemic meningitis, and some types of pneumonia, and is of some value in treating or preventing tetanus, gas gangrene, botulism, measles, and some streptococcal infections.

Chemotherapy

Physicians and chemists have long sought certain chemicals, either natural or synthetic, which would cure or prevent disease. The treatment of diseases by definite chemical compounds is called chemotherapy.

Many chemicals would kill almost all microorganisms, but unfortunately they would also kill humans. The goal is to find a suitable chemical that will selectively kill the invading microorganisms but not the affected host.

Chemicals that could be effective in this regard are classified as either *bacteriostatic* or *bactericidal.* A bactericidal agent kills the organism by precipitating it directly or destroying it outright. A bacteriostatic agent affects the metabolism of the microorganism in such a way that its growth and reproduction are impaired, and the normal body defenses (white cells) destroy the invaders.

Before 1900, very few effective chemotherapeutic agents were known. Quinine was effective to some extent in preventing and curing malaria, and various heavy metal compounds, such as mercury, silver, and lead, had very limited application.

The first great triumph of chemotherapy came about 1910, when Ehrlich synthesized salvarsan. It was Ehrlich's idea to put the very poisonous arsenic into an organic compound and thereby mask the deadly properties of the arsenic to such an extent that it would not kill humans but would destroy smaller forms of living organisms, such as spirochetes. Salvarsan was a great step forward, but it was not a complete solution, since the compound was toxic.

With the advent of the sulfa drugs, an unusually selective agent that could preferentially destroy microorganisms was found. The antibiotics came next in ever-growing numbers.

The Sulfa Drugs

Domagk discovered that prontosil had an excellent curative effect on animals infected with streptococci.

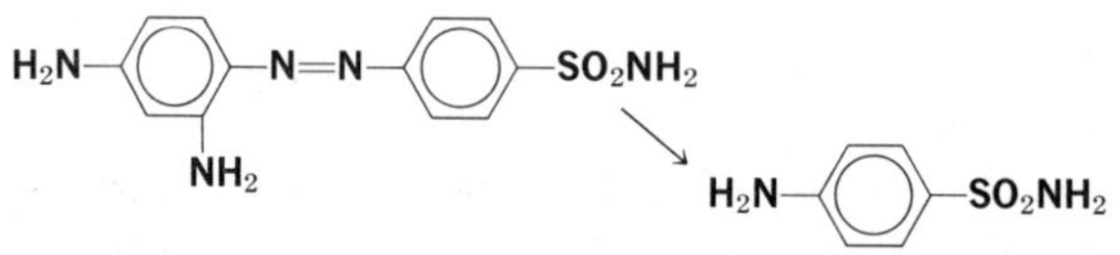

$$H_2N-C_6H_3(NH_2)-N{=}N-C_6H_4-SO_2NH_2 \rightarrow H_2N-C_6H_4-SO_2NH_2$$

prontosil sulfanilamide

It was later shown that, in the body, part of the prontosil molecule was converted into a well-known compound, sulfanilamide, and that the sulfanilamide was responsible for the remarkable effect of the drug. In the early 1930's, the success of the drug was phenomenal and gave rise to the expression the "wonder drug."

Further investigation showed that the essential part of the sulfanilamide structure was

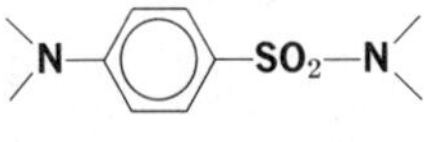

$$>N-C_6H_4-SO_2-N<$$

and that the four hydrogens attached to the two nitrogens could be replaced to produce, in some cases, a more active drug.

These experiments gave rise to the various sulfa drugs. Many were prepared and carefully tested. The following are among the most effective sulfa drugs:

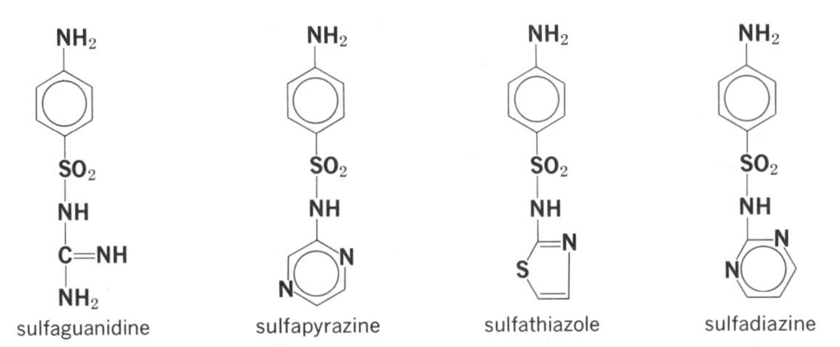

sulfaguanidine sulfapyrazine sulfathiazole sulfadiazine

Succinylsulfathiazole is used specifically to treat intestinal infections, as is phthalylsulfathiazole.

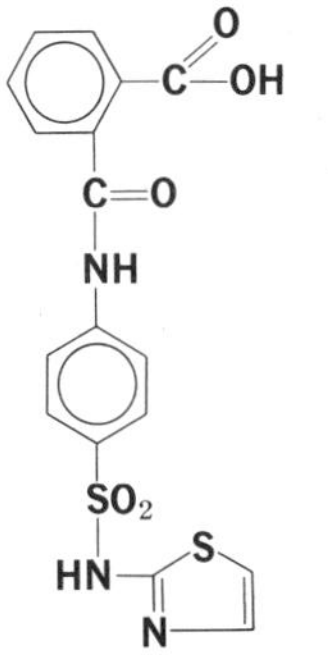

phthalylsulfathiazole 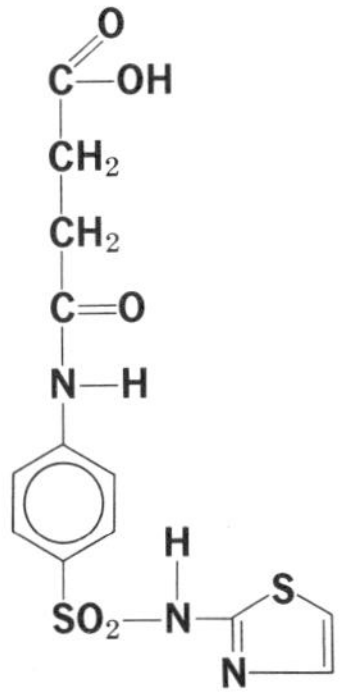 succinylsulfathiazole

The sulfa drugs belong to the class of compounds called *metabolite antagonists*. A metabolite antagonist generally resembles in structure the compound it inhibits.

Sulfanilamide resembles *p*-aminobenzoic acid (*p*-ABA) quite closely. Many microorganisms require *p*-ABA for proper growth and reproduction.

In the basic body fluids, *p*-ABA most likely exists as the negative ion. One of the various possible forms is illustrated below and compared with that of the sulfanilamide structure.

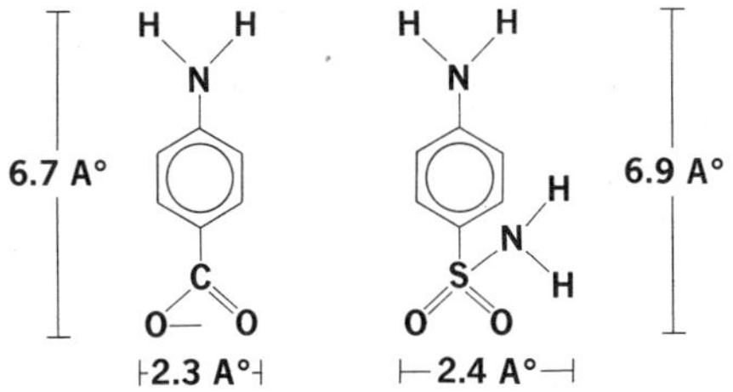

6.7 A° 6.9 A°

2.3 A° 2.4 A°

Clearly, the two structures are quite similar, and a microorganism that requires *p*-ABA may easily mistake the sulfa drugs (if they are also present) for the *p*-ABA and accidentally absorb the wrong one. The result is the formation of an enzyme system containing the sulfa drug and not the necessary *p*-ABA. Because this formation reaction is irreversible, the enzyme system does not function properly and the microorganism may not grow or reproduce and is destroyed more easily by the white cells of the body.

Some other examples of metabolite antagonists are: Desoxypyridoxin, which inhibits pyridoxin (vitamin B_6), and pyrithiamine, which inhibits thiamine (vitamin B_1). The structural similarity between the inhibitor and the metabolite is quite striking in both cases. Many other examples are known, and most antibiotics act as bacteriostatic agents.

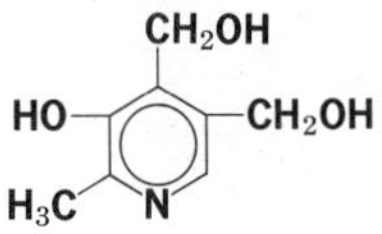

pyridoxin
(*vitamin* B_6)

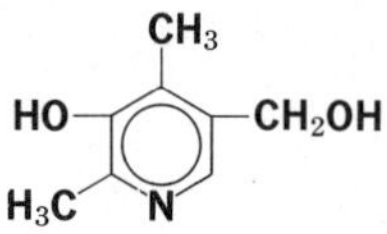

desoxypyridoxin
(*a* B_6*-inhibitor*)

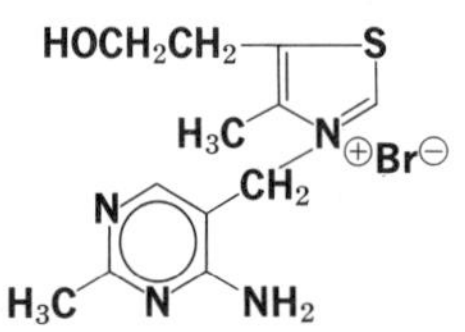

thiamine

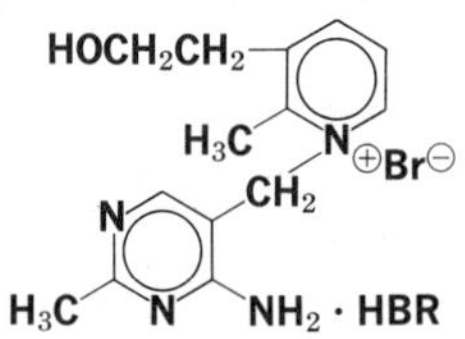

pyrithiamine

The sulfa drugs are administered by mouth and in rather large quantities (1 to 6 g) to insure a proper blood level. If the sulfa blood level is too high and the kidneys do not eliminate properly, some of the sulfa drug may crystallize out in the kidneys and may cause bleeding and kidney damage. Other reactions may be nausea, diarrhea, and skin lesions.

The sulfa drugs are amazingly effective against certain types of pneumonia, gonorrhea, blood poisoning, certain kidney infections, and many other diseases. Unfortunately, many diseases do not respond to sulfa drug treatment.

The sulfa drugs give toxic reactions in a small percentage of the people treated. The actual percentage of toxic reaction varies with the different sulfa structures. Another drawback in the use of sulfa drugs is that some microorganisms become resistant to the effect of the drug.

Antibiotics

An antibiotic may be defined as a compound that is synthesized by one living organism and that inhibits the growth of other organisms.

The antibiotics have had a profound effect on the public health and have greatly reduced the mortality rate for many diseases.

There is a tremendous research effort expended in attempts to discover more and better antibiotics.

According to Baron, to be clinically useful, an antibiotic

1. must have no lasting damaging action on body cells,
2. must be readily absorbed into the blood stream,
3. must be stable and effective in body fluids,
4. must have a low toxicity,
5. must not produce resistant strains of invading microorganisms, and
6. must not cause allergic reactions.

Actually, no one antibiotic fulfills all these requirements perfectly.

In general, the antibiotics are bacteriostatic, although some may also be bactericidal to some degree.

PENICILLIN

Probably the most widely used antibiotic is penicillin. It enjoys this position because of its wide range of application and because it is relatively nontoxic. Its discovery by Fleming in 1929 and the concentration and isolation studies by Florey and associates have been widely publicized and rewarded.

Fleming called the active principle penicillin because it was produced by the mold *Penicillium notatum.* Although the molecule has been well characterized and completely synthesized, the only practical method of production is by submerged aerobic fermentation of penicillin fungus.

All penicillins have the empirical formula $C_9H_{11}O_4SN_2 \cdot R$. Five penicillins have been isolated from natural media, and the only variation among them is in the structure of the R group. Table 20-4 lists these penicillins and the structures of their R groups.

Penicillin has the following structural formula.

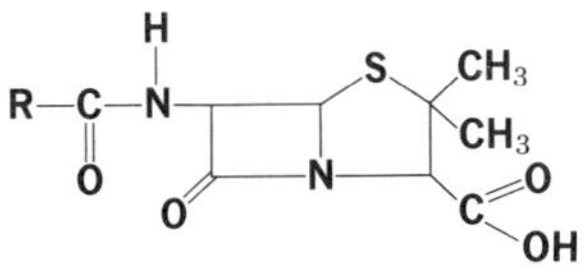

penicillin

Table 20-4 Natural penicillins

R	PENICILLIN TYPE	STRUCTURE OF THE R GROUP
2-pentenyl	penicillin F	$CH_3-CH_2-CH=CH-CH_2-$
n-amyl (pentyl)	penicillin dihydro F	$CH_3CH_2CH_2CH_2CH_2-$
benzyl	penicillin G	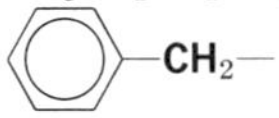 $C_6H_5-CH_2-$
n-heptyl	penicillin K	$CH_3CH_2CH_2CH_2CH_2CH_2CH_2-$
p-hydroxybenzyl	penicillin X	 $HO-C_6H_4-CH_2-$

By adding 2-phenoxyethanol to the cultures, penicillin V is isolated.

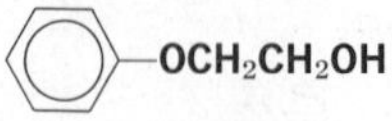

C_6H_5—OCH_2CH_2OH

2-phenoxyethanol

C_6H_5—O—CH_2—C(=O)—N(H)— [β-lactam fused to thiazolidine ring with S, N, O, CH_3, CH_3, COOH]

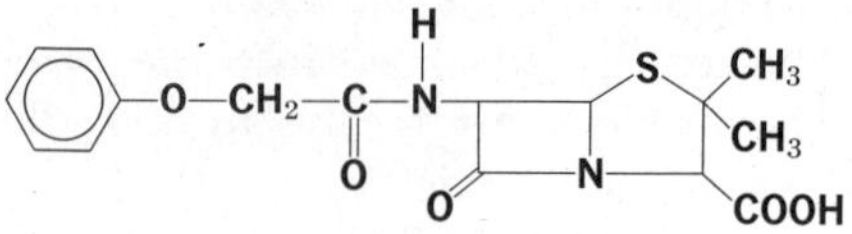

penicillin V

Penicillin V is a good oral penicillin because it is not readily digested by gastric juices.

Of the natural penicillins, penicillin G is the most widely used.

A wide variety of other penicillins are being synthesized; some show more promise than penicillin G.

The penicillins are all fairly strong acids and readily form salts, such as the sodium salt. Florey showed that the penicillins are not stable in strongly acidic or basic media, but they are stable in neutral media. For this reason, penicillin is usually available as the sodium salt, which in the dry state is quite stable.

Penicillin is effective when given parenterally, in very small doses, 10–100 mg. The sulfa drugs, in comparison, may require 2–4 g per dose. When penicillin is given orally, much of the activity is destroyed by the digestive juices. However, if the oral dose is increased to about 3 to 5 times the parenteral dose, in other words, to about 100–200 mg or possibly 300 mg, the oral dose will achieve an equivalent blood concentration of penicillin.

Penicillin is rapidly excreted (e.g., kidneys eliminate 60% within one hour), and originally large and repeated doses were necessary to maintain an adequate blood level. A recent improvement is to mix penicillin with something such as procaine to form procaine penicillin, a stable nontoxic crystalline salt. Procaine penicillin slowly liberates the penicillin in the blood stream and therefore is capable of maintaining a satisfactory blood level for longer periods. Other amine salts have also been used to prolong the action of penicillin for several weeks.

Penicillin generally is the drug of choice in the treatment of Gram-positive infections such as those causing tonsilitis, scarlet fever, anthrax, some types of pneumonia, diphtheria (in combination with antitoxins), and staphylococci and hemolytic streptococci. Some Gram-negative organisms, which cause syphilis and yaws, may be controlled with penicillin. Unfortunately, penicillin is ineffective against infections such as tuberculosis, malaria, and mumps.

Penicillin usage has several drawbacks. First, toxic reactions are not uncommon, and second, some people are very allergic to the drug. In addition, despite penicillin usage, many microorganisms mutate and become resistant to its action.

STREPTOMYCIN AND DIHYDROSTREPTOMYCIN

Streptomycin was one of the first antibiotics to be isolated from soil. In 1943–1944 Waksman and coworkers found that surface cultures of *Streptomyces griseus,* a microorganism found in soil, elaborated an antibiotic, which they isolated and called streptomycin.

This antibiotic is a complicated molecule $C_{21}H_{39}N_7O_{12}$, which contains three ring systems, connected by oxygen linkages.

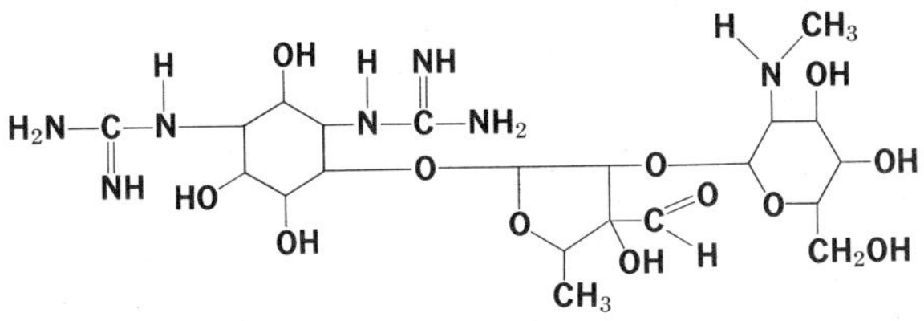

streptomycin

The antibiotic is available as the sulfate and as the triple salt, streptomycin $3HCl \cdot CaCl_2$.

In 1946, *dihydrostreptomycin,* $C_{21}H_{41}N_7O_{12}$, was developed synthetically from streptomycin by reduction of the aldehyde to the alcohol, and was reported to be less toxic in some respects but as effective as streptomycin itself. The dihydrostreptomycin is available as the sulfate.

Streptomycin and dihydrostreptomycin are used in the treatment of tularemia, peritonitis, and brucellosis, and in the management of tuberculosis and leprosy.

BACITRACIN

In 1943, seven-year-old Margaret Tracy suffered a compound fracture of her leg. There was contamination by dirt, and an infection soon appeared. Soon afterward, however, this infection suddenly disappeared. A strain of *Bacillus subtilis,* which had elaborated an antibiotic, was isolated from the wound. This antibiotic was called "Bacitracin" in honor of the young patient.

Bacitracin is a polypeptide, with a molecular weight of about 1,500. It yields amino acids on hydrolysis and contains carbon, hydrogen, oxygen, nitrogen, and sulfur.

The antibiotic properties of bacitracin are similar to those of penicillin. Bacitracin is predominately active against Gram-positive organisms. Bacteria do not seem to become resistant to this antibiotic, and allergic reactions are quite rare if the drug is given by any route other than injection. For this reason, bacitracin is useful to the dermatologist and is used effectively on carbuncles, styes, and impetigo, when applied topically.

Bacitracin is produced by a submerged aerobic fermentation process.

CHLORAMPHENICOL (CHLOROMYCETIN)

This antibiotic was first isolated from soil obtained near Caracas, Venezuela. The microorganism producing the antibiotic is called *Streptomyces venezuelae.*

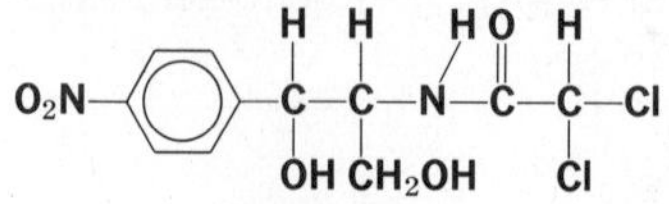

$$O_2N-C_6H_4-\underset{OH}{\overset{H}{C}}-\underset{CH_2OH}{\overset{H}{C}}-\overset{H}{N}-\overset{O}{\overset{\|}{C}}-\underset{Cl}{\overset{H}{C}}-Cl$$

chloramphenicol
(*chloromycetin*)

The antibiotic is produced both biologically, by an aerobic fermentation, and synthetically in several steps, starting with *p*-nitrobromoacetophenone.

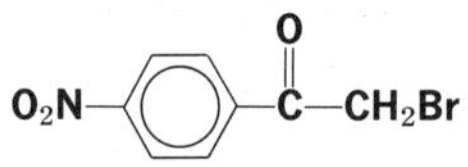

$$O_2N-C_6H_4-\overset{O}{\overset{\|}{C}}-CH_2Br$$

p-nitrobromoacetophenone

Chloramphenicol is one of the most stable antibiotics and is unaffected over a wide pH range and temperature range.

An outstanding property of chloramphenicol is that it has shown some activity against all the known rickettsia. Rickettsia are a group of minute bacterium-like, Gram-negative organisms believed to be transmitted by ticks, lice, mites, and fleas. The antibiotic has also proved valuable in the treatment of acute typhoid fever. Measles, mumps, urinary tract infection, dysentery, and many of the tropical diseases have responded to chloramphenicol treatment. Blood dyscrasias may be associated with intermittent or prolonged use. It is essential that adequate blood studies be made.

TYROTHRICIN

Tyrothricin was the name given by Dubos to an antibiotic produced by a sporulating bacillus isolated from the soil. It was later found that tyrothricin is a mixture of two crystalline compounds: one, a neutral molecule, *gramicidin,* and the other a basic compound, *tyrocidine.* Both gramicidin and tyrocidine are polypeptides.

Tyrothricin is exceptionally active against streptococci and pneumococci. Unfortunately, tyrothricin is very toxic and can only be used locally in a restricted manner. It is useful in the treatment of superficial ulcers, empyema, mastoiditis, and several wound infections.

TETRACYCLENES

Several antibiotics have four fused six-membered rings. These compounds are referred to as tetracyclenes. They have similar antibiotic properties.

Tetracycline is a general antibiotic useful against both Gram-positive and Gram-negative organisms and certain viruses. It is usually administered as the hydrochloride salt or as a phosphate complex.

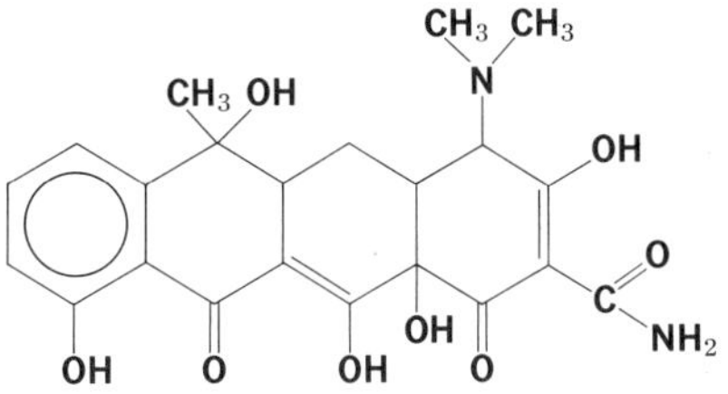

tetracycline

Terramycin was isolated from soil and is produced by the mold *Streptomyces rimosus*. The antibiotic is quite stable and exhibits amphoteric properties; that is, it can form both basic and acidic salts.

Because the antibiotic is relatively nontoxic and apparently does not cause the formation of resistant strains, it is valuable either alone or in combination with other antibiotics.

Terramycin has proved valuable against certain types of pneumonia, epidemic typhus fever (black plague), acute amoebic dysentery, infections of the urinary tract, whooping cough, malaria, and others. Its chemical formula is

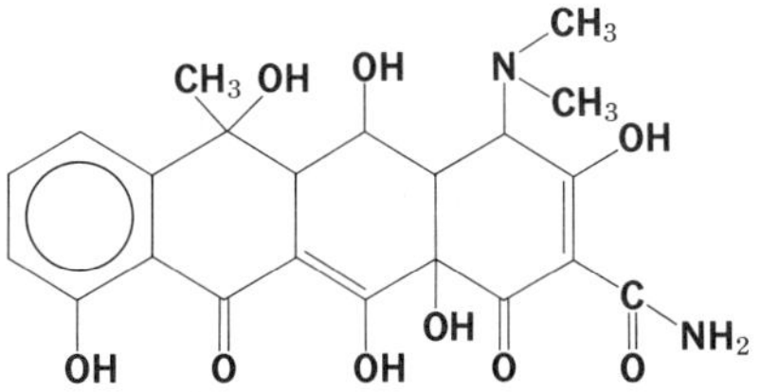

terramycin

Aureomycin was isolated from soil in 1948 and is elaborated by the mold from the *Actinomycete* group, *Streptomyces aureofaciens*. Its name is derived from the golden color of the crystalline product.

Aureomycin has proved effective against brucellosis, some rickettsial infections, tularemia, certain types of virus pneumonia, peritonitis, urinary tract infections, and gonorrhea.

Although aureomycin is relatively nontoxic, cases of nausea and diarrhea have been reported. The antibiotic is being produced by submerged aerobic fermentation.

Its chemical formula is

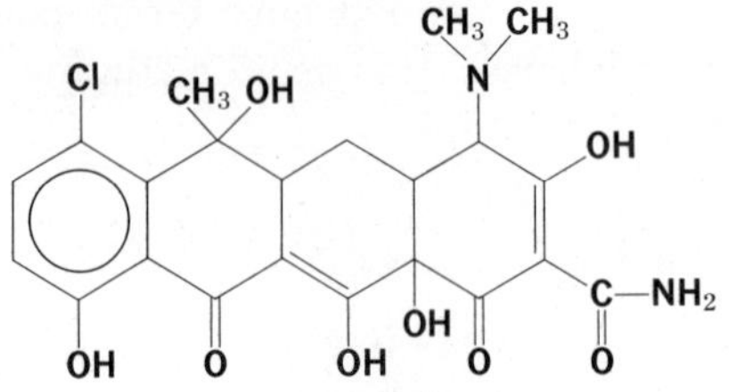

aureomycin

Erythromycin is an antibiotic used against penicillin-resistant staphylococci and in venereal diseases. It has few side effects. This drug is produced by a strain of *Streptomyces erythreus* found in the soil of the Philippine Archipelago.

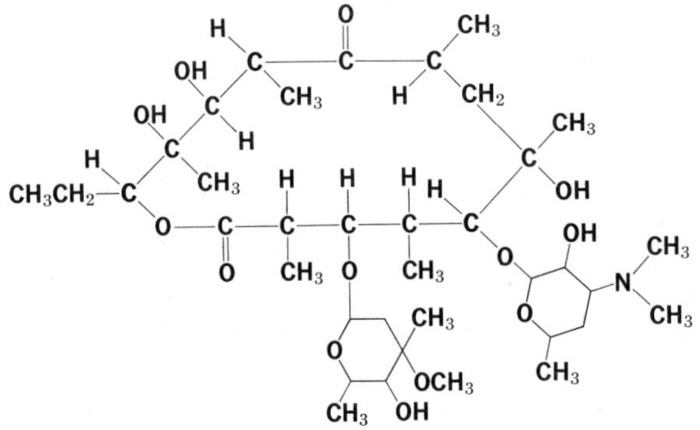

erythromycin

These are a few of the antibiotics presently in use. Many microorganisms are developing resistant strains to the antibiotics presently in use by mutation. For this reason, new antibiotics are constantly being discovered and tested.

REVIEW QUESTIONS

1. Discuss some of the general functions of blood. What are the formed elements? What are plasma and serum? How do they differ?
2. What is meant by defibrinated blood, laked blood, and oxalated blood?
3. Discuss the structure of hemoglobin. What is heme? Approximately how much iron is needed in the daily diet? Why is it needed?
4. What is the mean corpuscular volume? Of what use is a hematocrit?

5. Can iron be in the ferrous and the ferric states in hemoglobin?
6. Why is carbon monoxide poisonous?
7. What is the Icterus Index?
8. What is the relative amount of oxygen in the blood coming from and going to the lungs?
9. How is oxygen transported?
10. What is the relative amount of carbon dioxide coming from and going to the lungs? How is carbon dioxide transported?
11. Discuss the following: granulocyte, neutrophil, eosinophil, basophil, monocyte, and lymphocyte.
12. What is serotonin?
13. Discuss the composition of blood plasma.
14. What are the proteins in blood plasma, their properties, and their functions?
15. What are some electrolytes in plasma?
16. What is meant by plasma substitutes or plasma extender?
17. Why can plasma be pooled in a common bank indiscriminately, whereas whole blood cannot be pooled?
18. Discuss the formation, chemical composition, and circulation of lymph.
19. Discuss the chemistry of the benzidine test.
20. How would you test for iron, chloride ion, and sugar in the blood?
21. What is known about the lipids in blood serum and their relations to atherosclerosis?
22. What is meant by the blood groups A, B, AB, and O?
23. What is meant by Rh factor, and under what circumstances may death occur due to Rh incompatibility?
24. What are the normal concentrations of erythrocytes, leukocytes, and blood platelets in human blood?
25. What is meant by anemia? What are the various anemic conditions?
26. What is meant by polycythemia? What is meant by leukopenia and leukemia?
27. Discuss the substances involved in blood clotting.
28. How can blood clotting be prevented? List some of the hemolytic diseases.
29. List the three types of organisms that cause disease and some of the diseases they cause.
30. What is immunity? List several types of immunity and how they may be caused.
31. Define chemotherapy.
32. What is sulfanilamide? What is its relation to the sulfa drugs? What are some of the sulfa drugs?
33. Discuss the mode of action of the sulfa drugs.
34. What is an antibiotic? What would be some properties of an ideal antibiotic?
35. Discuss some of the antibiotics from the standpoint of chemical structure, source, method of production, toxicity, and mode of action.
36. Contrast the action of penicillin and sulfanilamide.
37. What is a tetracyclene?

21

vitamins

General discussion

Vitamins are *organic compounds,* which are essential nutrients even though necessary only in very small quantities. In most instances, these substances do not seem to be synthesized in the body in significant amounts; thus, we must obtain them in our diet to insure proper growth and maintenance of health and life. These organic compounds do not furnish energy, but they are responsible for the transformation of energy and for the regulation of the body metabolism. In the body, a vitamin may become part of a complex enzyme system, and it is these enzyme systems that catalyze many of the important chemical reactions of the body.

If some vitamins are absent from the diet, a body malfunction may occur. This may be remedied by the addition of the missing vitamin to the diet, provided that body deterioration has not been acute.

Pathological effects caused by insufficient amounts of vitamins in the diet are called *avitaminoses.*

History

Vitamin deficiencies may be traced back to the beginnings of history. Archeological and medical research on skeletons of prehistoric man indicate that rickets (due to vitamin D deficiency) and scurvy (due to vitamin C deficiency) were not uncommon.

Many physicians in the period before 1,000 A.D. described conditions that we now know were probably vitamin deficiencies. Until approximately 1,500 A.D., therapy was available only for night blindness (due to vitamin A deficiency). The cure, which consisted of eating goat liver, can be traced back to the Greek, Roman, and Arabian physicians. This treatment is also mentioned in the Bible.

In 1757, Lind, a surgeon in the British Navy, published the first account of the control of scurvy among sailors. He found that sailors could avoid scurvy during a long voyage by eating oranges, lemons, and limes. It was compulsory for the British sailors to eat limes during an ocean trip; therefore, they were nicknamed "limeys."

In the eighteenth century, several investigators suggested that certain diseases were due to faulty nutrition. However, it was not until 1897 that Eijkman showed that hens would develop a disease, similar to beriberi in man, when fed on milled rice instead of regular whole rice.

Eijkman also found that this experimental disease produced in hens could be prevented or cured by the addition of rice bran to the diet and that the substance responsible for the therapeutic effect could be extracted by water. In 1903, Grijns, a colleague of Eijkman, mentioned that this antiberiberi substance was effective, not because it counteracted an unknown

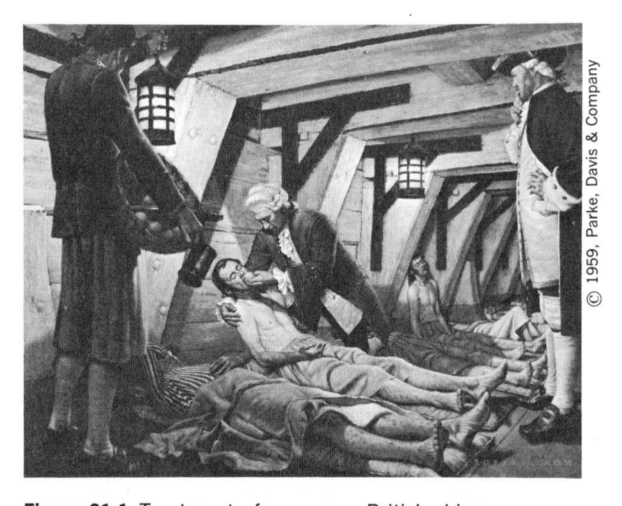

Figure 21-1 Treatment of scurvy on British ship.

producer of the disease, but because it supplied the diet with an essential constituent that had been lacking.

In 1907, Holst and Frolich produced experimental scurvy by using controlled diets. Interest in the field grew as many investigators began to correlate diet and certain diseases. In 1912, Funk tried to isolate the compound whose absence in the diet caused beriberi, and he succeeded in isolating a nitrogen-containing compound, nicotinic acid. We know now, however, that thiamine prevents beriberi. Because basic nitrogen organic compounds are amines, and because this substance seemed to be essential for the proper maintenance of life and health, Funk called it a *vitamine*. The term *vitamin* was later extended to cover the entire class of dietary essentials. We know now that not all vitamins contain nitrogen, but the name has persisted.

Because the chemical nature of these compounds was unknown, letters of the alphabet were used to designate the vitamins in the order in which they were identified. This led to the use of the terms vitamin A, vitamin B, vitamin C, vitamin D, and so on. As our knowledge of the vitamin field increased, certain difficulties arose. For example, it was found that "vitamin B" actually consisted of many vitamins, thus necessitating the use of the subscripts, for example, B_1, B_2, B_6, B_{12}, and we now refer to these as the "B complex." Other complications arose due to the fact that a particular vitamin may exist in more than one form, and all may be active, for example, the B_6 group: pyridoxin, pyridoxal, and pyridoxamine. In addition, some vitamins occur in nature in inactive forms and must be changed chemically to exhibit activity. These precursors to the vitamins are called provitamins.

Vitamins A, D, E, and K are soluble in various organic oils and insoluble in water, whereas the rest of the vitamins are generally soluble in water and insoluble in oil. Therefore, there is some validity in grouping the vitamins into two classes: fat-soluble and water-soluble. See Table 21-1.

Table 21-1 Classification of vitamins

FAT-SOLUBLE VITAMINS	WATER-SOLUBLE VITAMINS
vitamin A_1	vitamin C
vitamin A_2	the B vitamins
vitamin D_2	vitamin B_1 (thiamine)
vitamin D_3	vitamin B_2 (riboflavin)
vitamin E (tocopherol)	niacin (nicotinic acid)
vitamin K_1	vitamin B_6 (pyridoxin, pyridoxal, and pyridoxamine)
vitamin K_2	pantothenic acid
	biotin
	folic acid
	vitamin B_{12} (cyanocobalamin)
	inositol
	choline

The Fat-Soluble Vitamins

The vitamins A

Vitamin A_1

Vitamin A_1 is a highly unsaturated alcohol, $C_{20}H_{29}OH$. It is a yellow solid whose melting point is 64°C. It is insoluble in water and soluble in fat and fat solvents. Vitamin A_1 has five double bonds, all of which are conjugated. Its structure is

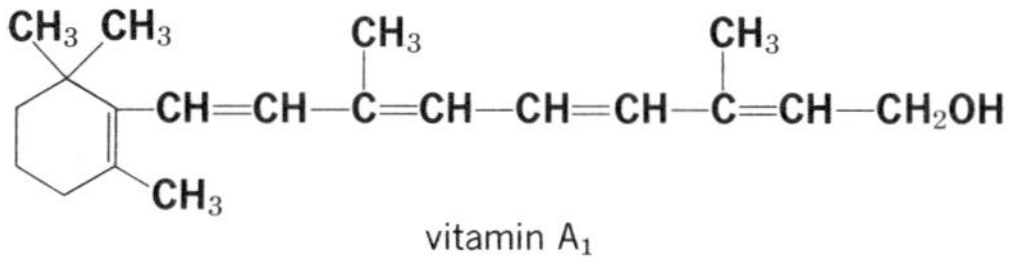

CH₃ CH₃ CH₃ CH₃
—CH=CH—C=CH—CH=CH—C=CH—CH₂OH
CH₃

vitamin A_1

We see that vitamin A_1 has an alicyclic ring (i.e., it contains a substituted cyclohexene ring). It is generally found in the *trans* form.

Other compounds in nature have vitamin A activity. These compounds are hydrocarbons of the carotenoid group. The carotenoids are compounds similar to carotene, the pigment of carrots, and are synthesized in the plant kingdom. Because the hydrolysis of these compounds yields vitamin A_1, these compounds are precursors of vitamin A_1 and are called provitamins A_1.

Carotene $C_{40}H_{56}$ is a common pigment found in carrots. Ordinary carotene was shown to consist of three isomers: α-carotene (15%), m.p. 184°C, β-carotene (85%), m.p. 184°C; and γ-carotene (trace), m.p. 177°C.

The structures of α- and β-carotene are

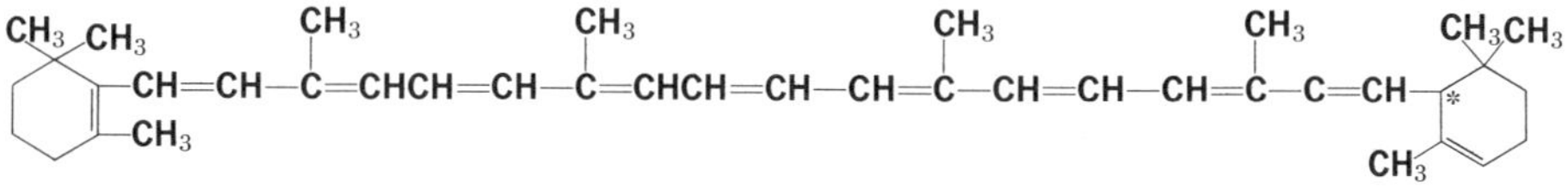

CH₃ CH₃ CH₃ CH₃ CH₃ CH₃ CH₃CH₃
—CH=CH—C=CHCH=CH—C=CHCH=CH—CH=C—CH=CH—CH=C—C=CH—*
CH₃ CH₃

α-carotene
[*indicates asymmetric carbon]

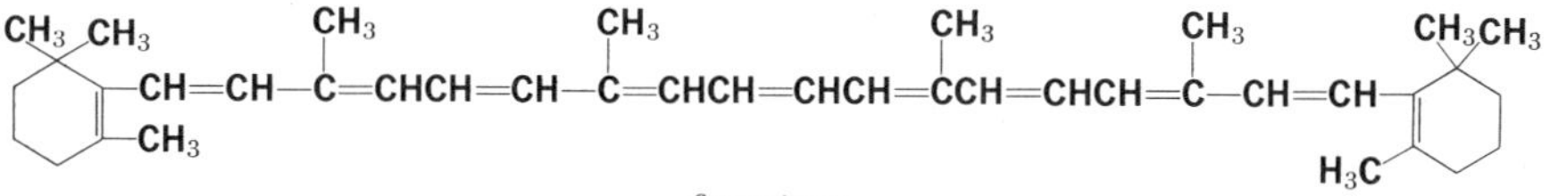

CH₃ CH₃ CH₃ CH₃ CH₃ CH₃ CH₃CH₃
—CH=CH—C=CHCH=CH—C=CHCH=CHCH=CCH=CHCH=C—CH=CH—
CH₃ H₃C

β-carotene

By the addition of two molecules of water to the central double bond of the carotene, the molecule may be split in half to form two alcohols, one or both of which may be vitamin A_1.

β-Carotene is the most active of the three carotenes. When hydrolyzed, β-carotene can yield two molecules of vitamin A_1; α-carotene and γ-carotene can yield, at most, only one vitamin A_1 molecule. α-Carotene is the only provitamin A with an asymmetric carbon atom, and it occurs naturally in an optically active form.

It was believed that the conversion of the provitamins into vitamin A_1 took place in the liver and also involved the pancreas. Present evidence indicates that the conversion takes place in the intestinal wall and that a normally functioning thyroid gland is necessary.

OCCURRENCE AND AVAILABILITY

The provitamins A occur in most plants. When chlorophyll is present, as in leafy vegetables, the presence of carotene is superficially masked. However, such foods are among the best sources of the provitamins A. Because animals seem able to hydrolyze the provitamins A, they do not accumulate in the body. However, traces of provitamins A are found in some of the fat depots of the body. For example, the corpus luteum is yellow due to the presence of the carotenoids. Vitamin A itself does not occur as such in plants.

From a practical point of view, the most important sources of vitamin A for man are the provitamins A found in all green and yellow vegetables. The most abundant source is fish liver oils (especially shark and halibut oils).

Vitamin A is stored in the liver as esters of the long-chain fatty acids. The body can not excrete vitamin A, so that which is absorbed by the body must be stored until it is used.

UNITS AND REQUIREMENTS

The U.S. Pharmacopeia organization provides a reference material for vitamin A in the form of cod liver oil that has been standardized in terms of International Units (I.U.). A group from the League of Nations prepared β-carotene as the reference material. One I.U. of vitamin A is equal in activity to 0.6 μg of crystalline β-carotene, or one gram of pure β-carotene equals 1,670,000 I.U. of vitamin A.

It is suggested that the *optimum amount* of vitamin A_1 for an adult is about 5,000 I.U. daily. Increased amounts are recommended for pregnant and nursing women and for adolescents.

DEFICIENCY

It is believed that a vitamin A deficiency is associated with a loss of weight and inhibition of growth in young animals. Xerophthalmia is a very characteristic eye disease caused by vitamin A deficiency. In this disease, the eyes become hemorrhagic, encrusted, and infected. This disease is somewhat rare in this country.

Nyctalopia (night blindness) may develop in the early stages of vitamin A deficiency. When one comes from the brightly illuminated outdoors into a dimly lighted room, such as a motion picture theater, it takes a definite amount of time (from 10 to 20 minutes) before one can distinguish objects clearly. In the absence of a sufficient amount of vitamin A, night blindness occurs, and an excessive amount of time may elapse before one can adapt from the light to the dark.

Recent investigation has shown that vitamin A is involved in the pigment of the eye.

Vitamin A_2 and others

In the retina of mammals, frogs, and *marine* fish, the eye pigment contains vitamin A_1. In the rods of certain *fresh water* fish, the eye pigments may contain another dietary factor known as vitamin A_2. Vitamin A_1 and A_2 are very closely related; vitamin A_2 has one more conjugated double bond.

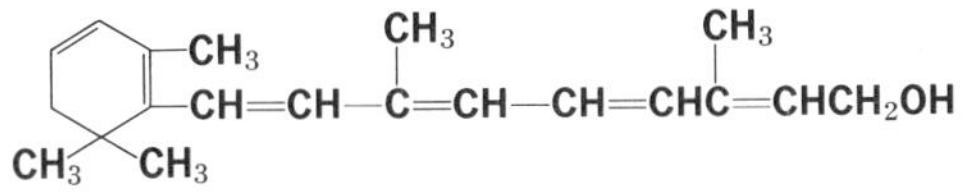

$$\text{(ring with } CH_3, CH_3, CH_3\text{)}-CH{=}CH-\underset{}{\overset{CH_3}{\overset{|}{C}}}{=}CH-CH{=}CH\overset{CH_3}{\overset{|}{C}}{=}CHCH_2OH$$

vitamin A_2

Migratory fish, which may be in both marine and fresh water, apparently contain mixtures of Vitamins A_1 and A_2 in their eye pigments.

THERAPY

Both provitamin A and vitamin A are preferably administered orally, but they may be given satisfactorily by intramuscular or subcutaneous injection. When given orally, they are usually dissolved in an oil solvent. The nature of the oil solvent is to some extent a function of the absorbability and consequent availability of the vitamin. Preferably, the oil is one that is readily absorbed in the intestines. Naturally, the presence in the diet of abnormal amounts of unabsorbable oils would tend to increase the body loss of all the fat-soluble vitamins.

There is also a trend toward the use of vitamin A in aqueous dispersions. The vitamin A is dissolved in oil and the oil dispersed or reduced to particles of colloidal dimensions in water solution. It appears that therapy is most effective under these circumstances.

The vitamins D

All the known pure vitamins D are colorless, odorless, crystalline alcohols possessing steroidlike structures. They are all soluble in fats and fatlike solvents and are insoluble in water. A decrease in potency is noted when the vitamins are exposed to increased temperatures, sunlight, or oxygen. These vitamins D, when present in the diet, prevent rickets.

Although, as early as 1882, Sniadecki suspected that sunlight might cure and prevent rickets, it was not until 1924 that Steenbock and Hess independently showed that certain foods (which possessed no vitamin D activity) could be induced to possess vitamin D activity when irradiated by ultraviolet light. A substance that can be converted into a vitamin D by irradiation is a provitamin D. The provitamins D are all steroids and are very sensitive to ultraviolet light.

Compounds possessing vitamin D activity occur only in the animal organism, but the provitamins D are widely distributed in the animal and plant kingdoms.

In the isolation of the first active material, vitamin D_1 was obtained. This turned out to be a mixture of at least two active substances. In 1932, Windaus, by the irradiation of ergosterol, isolated the first pure active substance, vitamin D_2. Vitamin D_3 was obtained later by the irradiation of 7-dehydrocholesterol.

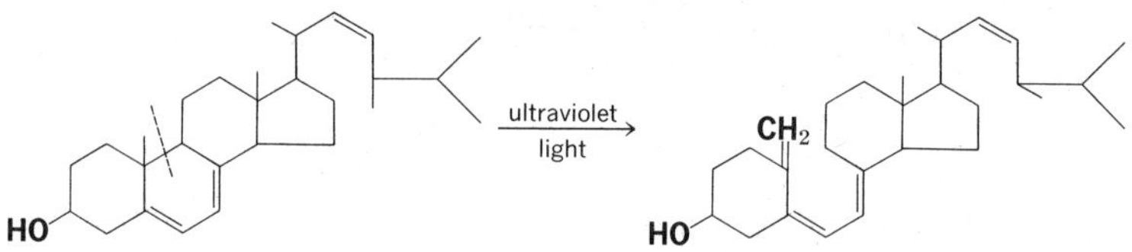

HO ergosterol —(ultraviolet light)→ HO, CH_2 vitamin D_2 ($C_{28}H_{43}OH$) (*calciferol*) m.p. 115–116°C

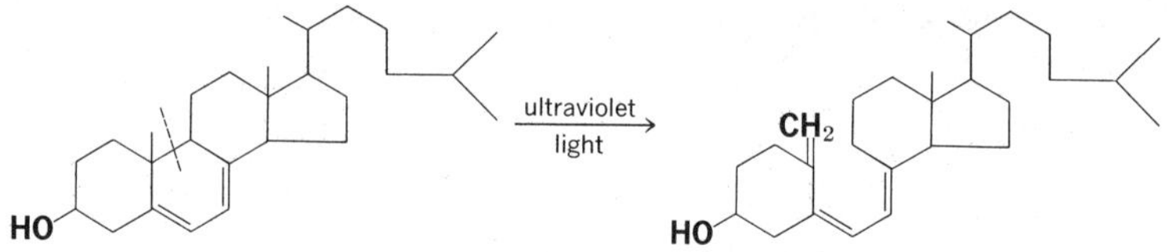

HO 7-dehydrocholesterol —(ultraviolet light)→ HO, CH_2 vitamin D_3 ($C_{27}H_{43}OH$) m.p. 81–82°C

Vitamin D_2 contains four double bonds, three of which are conjugated. Vitamin D_3 contains three double bonds, all of which are conjugated.

By the action of sunlight or ultraviolet light, the B ring, if it is the provitamin D type, becomes disrupted, with the resultant formation of one of the vitamins D.

OCCURRENCE AND AVAILABILITY

A large quantity of vitamin D is available in the form of irradiated fish oil concentrates (D_2). In addition, a fairly large quantity of irradiated 7-dehydrocholesterol (D_3) is made synthetically. The 7-dehydrocholesterol is made conveniently from the readily available cholesterol.

There appears to be a sufficient amount of provitamins D in our skin so that, by proper activation by sunlight (exposure of the skin to sunlight or ultraviolet lamp), a sufficient quantity of vitamins D is available to us.

Vitamin D is found in varying quantities in fish livers and in small quantities in other foods, such as eggs, steaks, and liver. Milk is generally fortified with vitamin D and thus becomes an ideal food for growing children, inasmuch as it already contains appreciable quantities of calcium and phosphorus.

UNITS AND REQUIREMENTS

The International Unit of vitamin D is defined as 0.00005 milligrams of pure crystalline vitamin D_2 (calciferol).

It is difficult to estimate human requirements, but it is suggested that an optimum amount of vitamins D for babies, children, adolescents, and pregnant and lactating women would be 400 I.U. daily, provided that a proper supply of calcium and phosphorus is available in the diet.

The daily requirement for animals varies to a great extent with the species, age, sex, and time of year and is a very important problem in animal husbandry.

VITAMIN D ACTIVITY AND DEFICIENCY

In discussing the activity of the vitamins D, one must necessarily discuss the intended use. Whereas vitamin D_2, prepared by the irradiation of ergosterol, is generally regarded as satisfactory for human therapy, vitamin D_2 is greatly *inferior* to vitamin D_3 in application to poultry husbandry.

The vitamins D are involved in the proper utilization of calcium and phosphorus and, consequently, are important in bone and teeth formation. When vitamins D are present in insufficient amounts or essentially absent in the diet, rickets in varying degrees of severity may develop.

In children, rickets is associated with knock-knees, bowlegs, and distorted joints. In general, in a rachitic patient, the ends of the bones show incomplete calcification. This can be easily seen by x-ray technique. As a corollary to bone malformation, in rickets, a relatively large quantity of calcium and phosphorus is lost in the feces, which indicates that vitamin D is essential in the utilization of calcium and phosphorus in bone deposition. It is not clear as yet how vitamin D accomplishes this.

TOXICITY

Although one should strive to furnish the body with an adequate supply of vitamin D, care should be taken that the body will not become overdosed with vitamin D, because decalcification of the bones may occur.

The vitamins E

The physiological effects of vitamin E are caused by a series of seven naturally occurring, closely related compounds. α-Tocopherol occurs most widely and has the greatest biological activity. The tocopherols are characteristically soluble in fat solvents and insoluble in water. They are colorless, noncrystallizing oils with the general structures of substituted chromanes.

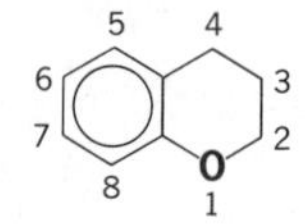

basic chromane structure

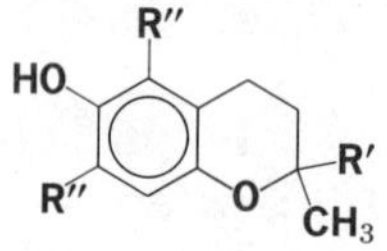

basic vitamin E structure
$R' = C_{16}H_{33}$
$R'' = CH_3$ or H

The structure of α-tocopherol is

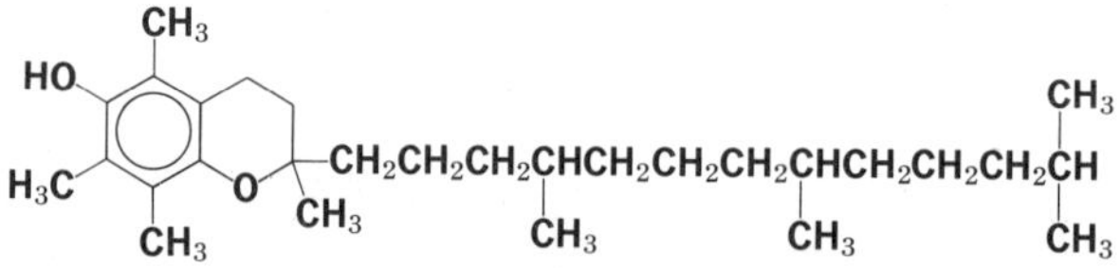

α-tocopherol

The remaining tocopherols differ from the α-form in the positions of the methyl groups. For example, β-tocopherol has methyl groups only on carbons 5 and 8.

OCCURRENCE AND AVAILABILITY

The group of vitamins E occur predominantly in plants. The animal organism contains only small amounts. Fish liver oils, which ordinarily are rich in vitamins A and D, are poor in vitamins E. Wheat germ oil is the best source of vitamins E. Other oils, such as rice germ oil and cottonseed oil, also contain large amounts. Not all oils are rich in vitamins E; olive oil and arachis oil are essentially devoid of vitamins E.

Although quite resistant to heat, acids, and bases, the vitamins E are, however, quite sensitive to oxidation, which destroys their activity. Although quite stable to ordinary light, the vitamins E are readily destroyed by ultraviolet light and rancid fat.

UNITS

One gram of naturally occurring α-tocopherol is equal to 1,000 International Units. For medical purposes, when the term vitamin E is used, the reference may be to α-tocopherol or the synthetic dl-α-tocopherol acetate.

DEFICIENCIES

In 1922, Evans and Bishop found that if a certain substance (originally called the "antisterility factor") was missing from the diet of rats, normal growth and reproduction did not occur. This substance was later called vitamin E. In the absence of the vitamin, the germinal epithelium of the testes of the rat is destroyed. In the female, ovulation and fertilization take place, but the fetus dies and is resorbed. The presence of vitamins E in the diet prevents this situation.

The earliest sign of a vitamin E deficiency in rats is that hematopoietic and mesodermal tissue growth is disturbed. The disturbances occur mainly in the gonads and neuromuscular systems and to a minor extent in the pituitary and thyroid glands.

Although a vitamin E deficiency can be demonstrated for mice, rats, rabbits, guinea pigs, dogs, chicks, and ducks, the significance of vitamin E in human nutrition is not clear. Apparently, it is useless in the treatment of sterility in humans. It does not prevent habitual abortions and does not cure toxemias in pregnancy.

The vitamins K

The vitamins K are two related compounds effective in preventing certain hemorrhages by causing the blood to coagulate. Dam, the discoverer, named the dietary factor vitamin K, from the German and Scandinavian term for coagulation: koagulations.

There are two naturally occurring substances, vitamins K_1 and K_2. A synthetic substance, known as menadione (see Figure 21-2), is as potent as the natural vitamin K_1. The three substances are substituted naphthoquinones. Many other substituted naphthoquinones exhibit varying degrees of activity, but we shall discuss only the above three.

The basic structures involved are

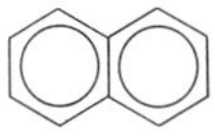

naphthalene

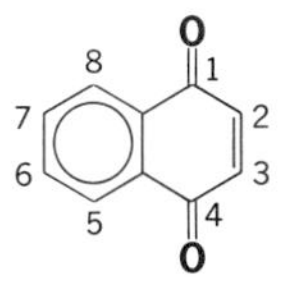

1,4-naphthoquinone

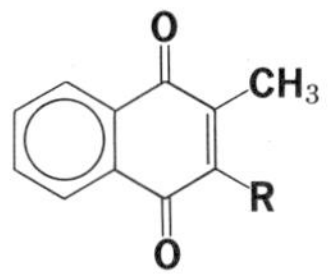

a 3-substituted-2-methyl-1,4-naphthoquinone

Figure 21-2 Photomicrograph of menadione crystals.

In the basic vitamin K structures, R = $C_{20}H_{39}$ (K_1), R = $C_{30}H_{49}$ (K_2), and R = H (menadione). The exact structures are as follows:

$$-CH_2CH{=}C(CH_3)-CH_2CH_2CH_2CH(CH_3)CH_2CH_2CH_2CH(CH_3)CH_2CH_2CH_2CH(CH_3)_2$$

vitamin K_1 ($C_{31}H_{46}O_2$)

$$-CH_2CH{=}C(CH_3)-CH_2CH_2\left(CH{=}C(CH_3)-CH_2CH_2\right)_2CH{=}C(CH_3)CH_2CH_2CH{=}C(CH_3)-CH_2CH_2CH{=}C(CH_3)_2$$

vitamin K_2 ($C_{41}H_{56}O_2$)

menadione ($C_{11}H_8O_2$)
(*vitamin K_3*)

We see that the side chain (R) in vitamin K_2 is larger and also contains more double bonds than the similar vitamin K_1.

OCCURRENCE AND AVAILABILITY

In general, vitamin K_1 occurs only in plant materials and vitamin K_2 only in microorganisms. The best sources of vitamin K_1 are the green leafy tissues, such as alfalfa, spinach, kale, cabbage, cauliflower, and chestnut, but vitamin K_1 is also found in soybean oil, tomatoes, and seaweed.

Vitamin K_2 occurs in many microorganisms, especially in microbacteria. Molds and yeast, however, contain essentially no vitamin K_2.

Although milk and eggs contain small amounts, hog's liver is the richest animal source of vitamin K. The liver of other species may contain small quantities.

PROPERTIES

The vitamins K are soluble in the common fat solvents and insoluble in water. They are quite stable at increased temperatures but are very sensitive to alkali and various light sources (ordinary and ultraviolet light).

Vitamin K_1 is a yellow oil at ordinary temperatures (m.p. $-20°C$). Vitamin K_2 is a yellow crystalline solid (m.p. 55°C). Menadione is a yellow crystalline solid (m.p. 104–106°C).

UNITS AND REQUIREMENTS

The reference standard for vitamin K is usually the synthetic menadione, and quantities are preferably expressed in terms of milligrams.

It is difficult to determine the amount of vitamin K needed by man because the intestinal flora provide the vitamins in the amounts required. A daily dose of 2 mg of menadione has been suggested for human therapy (0.5–1 mg for infants).

Vitamins K_1 and K_2 are nontoxic, and large doses may be taken without any apparent ill effects. No serious toxic reactions have been observed following the administration of menadione, but some severe dermatitis cases have been reported. In addition, menadione powder is irritating to the respiratory tract, and care should be observed in handling this drug.

DEFICIENCY AND USES

As mentioned in Chapter 20, vitamins K are responsible for the formation of prothrombin, a process that occurs in the liver. A deficiency of vitamins K may cause a deficiency of prothrombin in the circulating blood, a condition known as hypoprothrombinemia. The prothrombin level in normal healthy adults remains reasonably constant, and prothrombin is usually present in adequate quantities. The body will tolerate a drop in the prothrombin concentration to approximately one-fifth of normal. Serious hemorrhages do not occur until the prothrombin level is reduced below this one-fifth normal level.

It is generally recognized that during the first few days of an infant's life, there is a deficiency of prothrombin in the circulating blood (about 60% of adult prothrombin level). Premature infants are even more likely to have a low prothrombin level than normal infants. In certain severe cases of hemorrhages in the newborn, the prothrombin level may be as low as 5% of the adult value.

In many instances, it is strongly recommended, as a preventative measure, that vitamin K be given to the mother before delivery and to the newborn baby to prevent hypoprothrombinemia. Operative procedures on obstructive jaundice are usually deferred until the prothrombin level is raised to at least 60% of the normal value by the administration of bile salts and some vitamins-K-acting material.

In the presence of severe liver damage, the use of vitamin-K-acting material may be of no value, because the efficacy of this substance depends on an adequately functioning liver. In these cases, failure to respond to vitamin K therapy may in itself be indicative of extensive liver damage.

Vitamins K are of no value in hemophilic conditions. This is reasonable because the hemophilic patient is unable to make thromboplastin properly, and vitamins K are primarily concerned with the formation of prothrombin.

The vitamins K are also of no effect in treating scurvy and bleeding ulcers.

The Water-Soluble Vitamins

Vitamin C

Vitamin C ($C_6H_8O_6$) is known as ascorbic acid (see Figure 21-3) (scurvy preventing) and also as cevitamic acid. The vitamin is a colorless, odorless, crystalline material, melting at about 190–192°C. The acid is very soluble in water and quite insoluble in the fat solvents. The vitamin is a fairly strong acid whose aqueous solutions have a 2–3 pH range (depending upon the concentrations).

Ascorbic acid is closely related to the hexoses and is, in fact, conveniently synthesized from glucose.

Ascorbic acid is not a typical organic acid in that it has no free carboxyl group, COOH; actually, a lactone structure is present (a lactone is an inner ester of an alcohol and an acid group in the same molecule; see Chapter 8). The acidity is due to the active hydrogen in the *enediol* part.

Merck, Sharp & Dohme

Figure 21-3 Photomicrograph of ascorbic acid crystals.

Vitamin C readily forms salts of the type $C_6H_7O_6M$ (M = metal), indicating one very reactive hydrogen.

The structure may be written as I, but structure II is more indicative of the stereochemical relationships.

```
        O
        ‖
        C——┐
        |  |
  HO—C     O
        ‖  |
  HO—C     |
        |  |
   H—C——┘
        |
  HO—C—H
        |
       CH₂OH

        I
```

```
                          O—H O—H
                          |    |
         H  H—O   H   C═══C
         |    |     \ |    |
   H—O—C——C——C    C═O
         |    |        \  /
         H    H         O

                II
```

STABILITY

Ascorbic acid activity is destroyed by boiling or prolonged cooking. Drying, storing, and aging of food may also destroy the vitamin C activity.

The vitamin is very sensitive to light and air. Although vitamin C is reasonably stable in mild acid solutions, in alkaline solution there is a considerable loss of activity. Traces of certain metals, such as copper, accelerate the destruction of the vitamin. The natural vitamin is the L-form. The D-form and other stereoisomers may have activity but to a much lower degree. The natural L-ascorbic acid is the most potent vitamin C active material.

OCCURRENCE AND AVAILABILITY

Certain fruits and fresh vegetables are the most reliable sources of vitamin C. The citrus fruits, lemons, limes, and grapefruits, are excellent sources. Other good fruit dietary sources are raspberries, currants, gooseberries, and strawberries.

Among the good vegetable dietary sources are tomatoes and such green vegetables as kale, spinach, broccoli, cabbage, Brussels sprouts, and watercress.

Foods such as peas, bananas, potatoes, and apples are good sources of vitamin C, even though low in vitamin C content, because of the usually large quantities eaten. Considerable quantities of vitamin C are available from synthetic sources.

UNITS AND REQUIREMENTS

One International Unit equals 0.05 mg of pure L-ascorbic acid. The optimum amount required for adults is 75 mg daily. It is recommended that infants obtain about 30 mg daily and pregnant and lactating women 100–150 mg. Ascorbic acid is not toxic, and large doses may be taken without ill effects. The vitamin may be administered orally or parenterally. Because ascorbic acid is fairly strong, subcutaneous or intramuscular injections may be painful and irritating if not properly buffered. Parenteral injections are usually given in sterile, isotonic, phosphate-buffered solutions, buffered to a pH of about 6.8.

DEFICIENCY

Scurvy is the disease usually associated with a vitamin C deficiency. At the first signs of scurvy, there is a loss of weight and appetite, and pains develop in the joints and muscles. As the disease progresses, there is a swelling and tenderness of the legs and a swelling and bleeding of the gums. Finally, there is a great susceptibility to excessive bleeding from many parts of the body. Death may result from hemorrhage, shock, or some concurrent infection.

There are also many cases of subclinical scurvy, which are difficult to diagnose. Probably the most easily recognizable symptoms are those of gingivitis (i.e., an irritation of the gums surrounding the teeth).

BIOCHEMICAL RELATIONSHIPS

It is believed that ascorbic acid plays an important role in biological oxidation and reduction, because the molecule is easily oxidized and reduced again. However, the exact enzyme systems and exact chemical reactions involving ascorbic acid are still not too clear.

Considerable attention has been directed toward vitamin C because of its effect on the healing of wounds. In patients or experimental animals living on a vitamin-C-deficient diet, scar tissue has been found to be of low tensile strength. It appears that vitamin C is needed for the proper synthesis of collagen, the connective tissue protein.

The vitamins B

Historically, the term "vitamin B" was applied first to a water-soluble substance isolated from protein-free milk, wheat germ, and yeast, and found to be necessary (although only a very small amount was required) for the nutrition of young animals. At that time, vitamins C and A were recognized; hence, the term "vitamin B" to distinguish it from these two.

When it was later realized that many substances are included in this "vitamin B," subscripts were used to distinguish the various entities.

It is now known that the members of the vitamin B group are universally distributed in all living cells and are indispensable constituents of all living matter. The B vitamins form enzyme systems, many of which are well understood, and are very important in catalyzing many of the metabolic reactions in the body. We will discuss these B vitamins independently.

Thiamine Hydrochloride (vitamin B_1)

Thiamine hydrochloride, $C_{12}H_{18}Cl_2N_4OS$, is a white, crystalline solid with melting point at 248°C, with a faint yeast-like odor and a salty taste. Its aqueous solutions are acidic, the pH being 3–4, depending upon the concentration of the vitamin. See Figure 21-4.

Chemically, the vitamin is composed of two different heterocyclic nuclei: the pyrimidine and the thiazole rings.

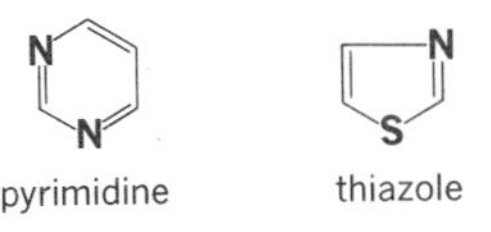

pyrimidine thiazole

In thiamine, two nitrogens have positive charges and are saltlike in character. Actually, one may consider the two nitrogens derived from the ammonium ion NH_4^+. In vitamin B_1, the two rings are connected by a methylene group —CH_2—. The pyrimidine ring contains a methyl group

Figure 21-4 Photomicrograph of Vitamin B_1 crystals.

CH_3— and an amino group —NH_2. The thiazole ring contains a methyl group and a hydroxyethyl group, —CH_2CH_2OH.

The two substituted rings in thiamine are

NH_2, N, N, CH_3 (pyrimidine ring) N, S, —CH_3, —CH_2CH_2OH (thiazole ring)

The actual structure of thiamine is

H—N(H)—$HCl^{\ominus}$ (N$^{\oplus}$), N, N, CH_3 —CH_2— N$^{\oplus}$ $Cl^{\ominus}$, S, CH_3, CH_2CH_2OH

thiamine hydrochloride
(*vitamin B_1*)

STABILITY

Thiamine hydrochloride is a vitamin of considerable stability. It is very stable in the dry state, even at a temperature of 100°C. In water solution, thiamine can be heated at a temperature of 120°C for 25 minutes without any significant decrease in potency. The acid is most stable at pH's around 3.5; as the pH reaches 6, the stability decreases. In basic or neutral solutions, the activity is lost. Sulfites destroy the activity. Vitamin B_1 is also quite sensitive to oxidation and reduction conditions.

OCCURRENCE AND AVAILABILITY

Vitamin B_1 is found in almost all plant and animal tissues although, in some cases, in exceedingly small amounts. Among the best sources are liver, heart, pork, kidney, cereal grains (soy, wheat, etc.), and nuts. Milk and eggs are fair sources. The legumes are good sources, but in the usual cooking procedure most of the vitamin may be lost in the cooking water. Some microorganisms can synthesize vitamin B_1; these microorganisms are usually found in the intestinal tract of animals. Vitamin B_1 is included in flour, bread, corn, and macaroni products (enriched foods). Vitamin B_2, niacin, and iron are also added to many of our foods.

In the body, apparently, vitamin B_1 is not stored in sufficient amounts to last more than a brief period. Therefore, for optimum nutrition, the body should receive a daily amount adequate for its needs.

Thiamine hydrochloride, although available naturally in adequate quantities in many foods, is also produced synthetically in very large quantities and is widely obtainable from many manufacturers.

UNITS AND REQUIREMENTS

One milligram of thiamine hydrochloride equals 333 International Units. Although an adult may fare well with a daily intake of 1 mg, it is recommended that the diet contain about 1.0–2.0 mg of vitamin B_1 daily, depending upon age and conditions. Children should obtain about 1 to 1.6 mg daily. Thiamine hydrochloride may be administered orally or parenterally. In certain advanced cases of vitamin B_1 deficiency, sometimes the vitamin is administered parenterally in 10–50 mg quantities. Care, however, must be taken in general to avoid very large doses, because some patients may exhibit shock symptoms.

DEFICIENCY

A vitamin B_1 deficiency may result as a consequence of (1) an improper regular diet, (2) a special diet followed because of some disease, such as peptic ulcer, diabetes, or renal disease, or (3) increased vitamin B_1 requirements, due to some condition such as pregnancy, lactation, extremely vigorous muscular exercise, or hyperthyroidism. Naturally, any condition, such as pernicious vomiting and severe diarrhea, that prevents proper assimilation of B_1 in the body tends to cause a vitamin B_1 deficiency.

A lack of vitamin B_1 may cause anorexia (lack of appetite) in minor cases or beriberi in major cases. In infants and children, a vitamin B_1 deficiency also may result in improper growth. *Beriberi* is the disease most commonly associated with the vitamin B_1 deficiency. Beriberi affects the peripheral nervous system, the gastrointestinal tract, and the cardiovascular system.

Among the early symptoms of a thiamine deficiency are lack of appetite, fatigue, and heaviness of the legs. As the disease progresses, an increasing neuritis manifests itself, causing the knee and ankle reflexes to be lost. Pain and tenderness develop in the leg muscles.

In the final stages, the calf muscles atrophy, the heart becomes enlarged and painful, and the pulse weakens. The body is usually edematous. The progression of the various symptoms varies with the individual.

Infantile beriberi is usually an acute disease. A sudden body rigidity is typical of this condition. Symptoms such as loss of appetite, constipation, diminished urinary excretion, general weakness, edema, and irregular pulse are characteristic.

It can be said that vitamin B_1 is essential for the maintenance of good appetite, normal digestion, and proper gastrointestinal activity. B_1 is necessary for proper growth, fertility, and lactation, and it is needed for the normal functioning of the nervous system.

The administration of vitamin B_1 either in the form of proper food or in the synthetic crystalline form to B_1 deficient patients usually elicits a dramatic response.

BIOCHEMICAL RELATIONSHIPS

The coenzyme containing B_1 is called *cocarboxylase* or *carboxylase;* it is an ester of B_1 and phosphoric acid. This coenzyme participates in all oxidative decarboxylations that lead to the formation of CO_2.

Riboflavin (vitamin B_2)

Riboflavin $C_{17}H_{20}N_4O_6$ is an orange-yellow crystalline solid, m.p. 280°C (see Figure 21-5). This vitamin is essentially odorless, but it has a bitter taste. Riboflavin is slightly soluble in water and insoluble in ether, chloroform, acetone, and benzene. The pH of a saturated water solution is about 6, indicating one weakly acidic hydrogen. The water solution of vitamin B_2 shows a yellow-green fluorescence.

Merck, Sharp & Dohme

Figure 21-5 Photomicrograph of riboflavin crystals.

Chemically, the vitamin contains three rings fused together and also a sugar alcohol derived from D-ribose. Two of the rings are nitrogen heterocycles, each containing two nitrogen atoms. The basic ring structure is isoalloxazine, and the sugar part is directly related to D-ribitol.

$$\begin{array}{c} CH_2OH \\ | \\ H-C-OH \\ | \\ H-C-OH \\ | \\ H-C-OH \\ | \\ CH_2OH \end{array}$$

isoalloxazine D-ribitol

In the vitamin itself, two methyl groups are on the ring system, and the sugar part is attached to one of the nitrogens in the middle ring. The structure of vitamin B_2 is

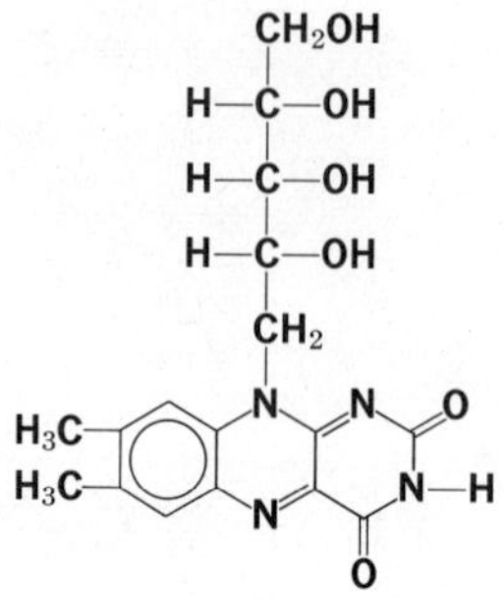

riboflavin
(vitamin B_2)

STABILITY

Riboflavin is quite stable to heat, air, and oxygen, but it is very sensitive to light. When irradiated with ultraviolet light or visible light, the molecule decomposes, and the activity is permanently lost. Riboflavin is very stable in strong acid solutions and may be maintained in solutions buffered at pH ranges of 5–6 without rapid decomposition. In alkaline solutions the activity is lost.

OCCURRENCE AND AVAILABILITY

Riboflavin is widely distributed in nature. Excellent sources among animal products are fresh liver, liver sausage, dry whole milk, heart, kidney, lean muscle meat, eggs, and cheese. Vegetables such as turnip tops, beet tops, kale, and mustard greens, and seeds such as wheat germ, rice polishings, peanuts, and soybeans are excellent sources of vitamin B_2. Fresh milk, peas, watercress, endives, lima beans, cauliflower, broccoli, carrots, beets, avocados, prunes, peaches, whole-grain wheat, and dried legumes are good sources of riboflavin.

Various foods, such as bread, flour, corn meal, and macaroni, are enriched with riboflavin.

Riboflavin has been prepared synthetically, but most of the materials available from pharmaceutical houses today is prepared by a yeast fermentation process. In such special fermentation, vitamin B_2 is produced in unusually large quantities, and the vitamin is then extracted from the solution and purified.

UNITS AND REQUIREMENTS

The optimum requirement for riboflavin for an adult is approximately 2 mg daily. Infants require about 1 mg daily. Pregnant and lactating women may need 2.5 mg daily. Riboflavin is conveniently administered by the oral route, but when gastric absorption is impaired, the vitamin is administered parenterally in sterile physiological saline solutions.

DEFICIENCY

A riboflavin deficiency (*ariboflavinosis*) may possibly be the most prevalent form of avitaminosis. Because many cases are at the subclinical level, and other cases may be complicated by other vitamin deficiencies, the exact extent of the deficiency in man is difficult to estimate.

Some signs and symptoms of ariboflavinosis are glossitis (inflammation of the tongue), seborrheic dermatitis (waxy accumulations in the skin), cheiloses (lesions of the lips with fissures in the angles of the mouth), corneal vascularization (ocular lesions), and keratitis (roughening of the skin at the mouth and nose).

BIOCHEMICAL RELATIONSHIPS

Warburg's yellow enzyme was shown to contain riboflavin attached to a phosphoric acid group, which is bound to a protein part. Riboflavin also forms another coenzyme called flavin adenine dinucleotide. This coenzyme is made from riboflavin, pyrophosphoric acid, ribose, and adenine.

The yellow enzymes containing riboflavin are effective hydrogen acceptors and are involved in oxidation-reduction reactions of metabolic nature in the body.

Niacin (the pellagra-preventing factors)

Nicotinic acid and its corresponding amide are two naturally occurring substances capable of preventing pellagra. The term nicotinic acid arises because when nicotine, a constituent of tobacco, is oxidized by vigorous chemical means, one can isolate the acid. Such a reaction however, does not occur when smoke is inhaled. The name *niacin* is used as a substitute for nicotinic acid, and the amide is called *niacinamide,* or *nicotinamide.* The two pellagra-preventing factors are exceedingly simple in structure in that they both contain the pyridine ring, with either a carboxy group or an acid amide group in the β-position.

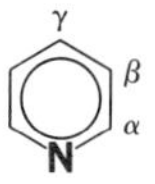

γ β α N — COOH N — O ‖ C—NH_2 N

pyridine 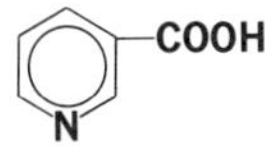 | niacin (*nicotinic acid*) | niacinamide (*nicotinamide*)

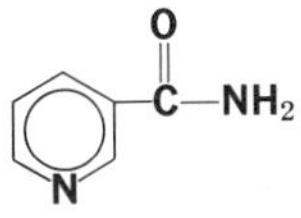

Niacin $C_6H_5NO_2$, m.p. 236–237°C, is a white, odorless, crystalline solid with an acidic tart taste (see Figure 21-6). It is quite soluble in water. The pH of a 1% water solution is about 3.

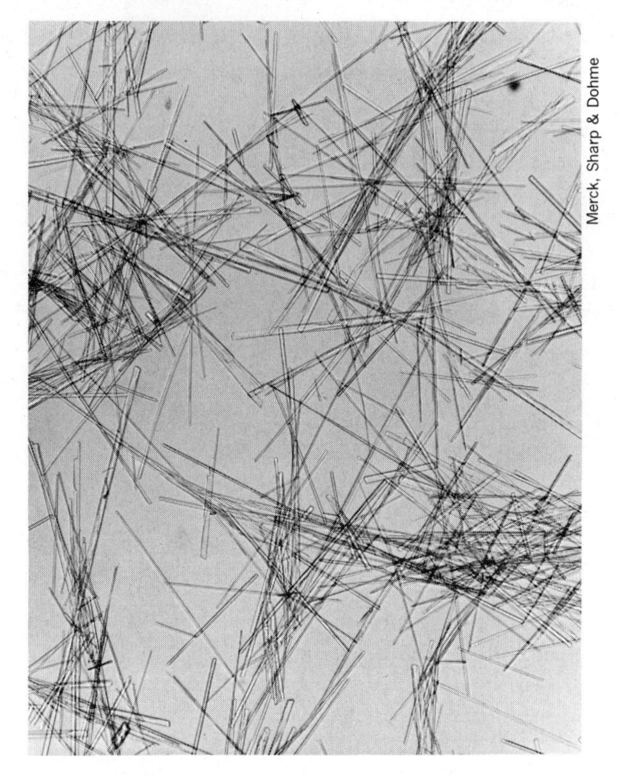

Figure 21-6 Photomicrograph of niacin crystals.

Niacinamide $C_6H_6N_2O$, m.p. 124–125°C, is a white, odorless, crystalline solid with a slightly bitter taste. It is very soluble in water. Niacinamide is only weakly acidic and a 1% aqueous solution has a pH of about 6.

STABILITY

Both niacin and niacinamide are very stable substances in that they are not inactivated by air, light, heat, acids, and alkali and are not destroyed in ordinary cooking processes.

OCCURRENCE AND AVAILABILITY

Niacin occurs in all living cells although sometimes in very small amounts. Excellent sources are liver, yeast, and wheat germ. Lean meats contain appreciable quantities. The pellagra-preventing factor, which usually occurs in tissues of living organisms, is niacinamide rather than the free acid.

Niacin and niacinamide are easily produced by synthetic means and are supplied by many pharmaceutical companies.

UNITS AND REQUIREMENTS

The units of the pellagra-preventing factors are commonly expressed in terms of milligrams. The optimum requirement of niacin has not been established for the normal adult, but a daily intake of about 15–20 mg has been estimated as sufficient. For serious pellagra cases, the daily dose of niacin may have to be maintained for over a week before considerable improvement occurs. A balanced diet should always be given in addition to niacin therapy.

The actions of niacin and niacinamide differ. The acid (not the amide) is a vasodilator and may produce aggravated headaches. Also, side reactions, such as irritations of the skin, localized heat flushes, and increased peristalses, may occur when the acid is used. Because niacinamide usually does not produce these side reactions, it is commonly preferred.

DEFICIENCY

Pellagra is a deficiency disease caused by insufficient niacin or niacinamide in the diet. This disease is common in areas where economically the people cannot afford a proper diet or where corn is a main staple. Pellagra is most frequent in the southern states.

The course of the symptoms of pellagra have been referred to as the four "D's," dermatitis, diarrhea, dementia, and death.

In the typical dermatitis, the skin exposed to the sunlight is most affected. Areas such as the hands, neck, and face become rough, swollen, and cracked and are easily differentiated from normal healthy skin. The lesions of the skin on the hands give rise to a typical "pellagra glove." Usually, the dermatitis is bilaterally symmetrical (i.e., equally distributed on both sides of the body) and occurring on both hands, elbows, knees and both sides of the neck.

Severe persistent diarrhea is most evident in the advanced cases of pellagra. The mental symptoms may be hallucinations, depression, and recessiveness. Patients may become excited, irritable, and sometimes dangerous maniacs.

BIOCHEMICAL RELATIONSHIPS

Nicotinamide is a part of two coenzymes that are composed of phosphoric acid, D-ribose, and adenine in different proportions.

Both of these coenzymes are hydrogen acceptors and participate in oxidation-reduction reactions. Each one is specific for certain reactions, and the two are not interchangeable.

Nicotinic acid can be synthesized biologically from tryptophan. This has been demonstrated by the fact that people on a nicotinic acid-deficient diet who obtain sufficient quantities of tryptophan do not exhibit pellagra symptoms.

Vitamin B_6

Although pyridoxin was at first thought to be "the vitamin B_6," it has since been shown that there are three naturally occurring substances, all of which are interconvertible in the body and effective in curing a deficiency due to vitamin B_6. The three are referred to as B_6. These three components are simple substituted pyridine derivatives. The only difference between them is the group in the γ-position, and this may be either a primary alcohol, an aldehyde, or a primary amine.

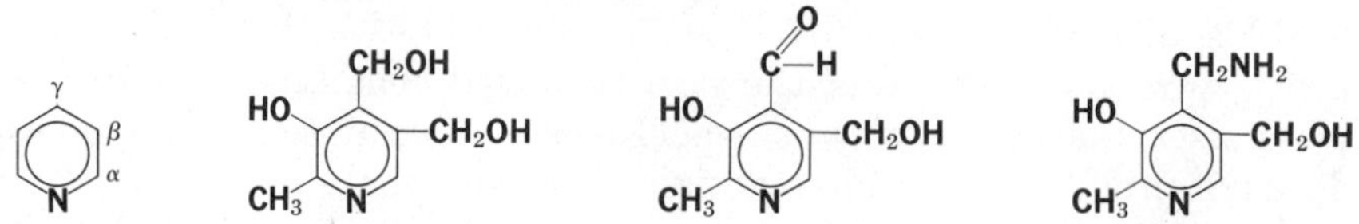

pyridine | pyridoxin | pyridoxal | pyridoxamine

Pyridoxin hydrochloride $C_8H_{11}NO_3 \cdot HCl$, the commonly available form, is a white, crystalline solid, m.p. 204–206°C. Pyridoxal hydrochloride $C_8H_9NO_3 \cdot HCl$ is a white, crystalline solid, m.p. 165°C. Pyridoxamine, $C_8H_{12}N_2O_2$, melts at 193°C, and its dihydrochloride, $C_8H_{12}N_2O_2 \cdot 2HCl$, melts at 227°C; both are white crystalline solids.

Pyridoxin was shown to be a necessary dietary factor for rats. If pyridoxin is missing in the diet of the rat, a characteristic dermatitis results (*acrodynia*), and a swelling and edema, particularly in the ear, nose, and digits of the paw, become evident.

STABILITY

The vitamins B_6 are quite stable to heat, acids, and alkali but are not stable in ultraviolet light, particularly in neutral or alkaline solutions.

OCCURRENCE AND AVAILABILITY

Good sources of pyridoxin are rice bran, liver, yeast, cereals, legumes, and bananas. The vitamins have been synthesized, and pyridoxin hydrochloride is conveniently supplied by many pharmaceutical companies as a purified white solid. Pyridoxin hydrochloride is readily soluble in water, and the pH of a dilute solution is about 3. The vitamin may be taken orally or parenterally.

UNITS AND REQUIREMENTS

Although the vitamin is essential for the rat, chick, dog, and pig, the human requirements have not been established. It has been suggested that 2 mg daily should be sufficient for a normal adult.

BIOCHEMICAL RELATIONSHIPS

Although the three vitamins B_6 are interconvertible in the body, pyridoxal is the important biologically active form. The coenzyme containing B_6 is pyridoxal phosphate:

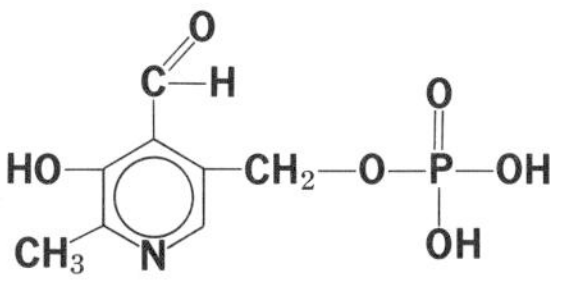

O
C—H
O
HO— —CH_2—O—P—OH
CH_3 N
OH

pyridoxal phosphate
(active coenzyme containing B_6)

Although the exact requirements of B_6 are not known, the reactions catalyzed by the enzyme system containing pyridoxal phosphate are well known. They are simple decarboxylations, transamination, and condensation reactions involving creation of new carbon-carbon bonds, or reactions involving the rupture of carbon-carbon bonds.

The primary function of the vitamins B_6 is the synthesis of certain amino acids and amines. Because these reactions are almost hopelessly complicated by other reactions, the vitamin B_6 requirement for humans may never be established.

It has been definitely established that the vitamins B_6 are involved in the metabolism of tryptophan, one of the essential α-amino acids. On a B_6-deficient diet, humans do not metabolize tryptophan properly, and a marked increase in xanthurenic acid is noted in the urine. This was one of the earliest symptoms of a B_6 deficiency in humans. The vitamins B_6 have also been useful in combating nausea and vomiting in early pregnancy.

Pantothenic Acid

Pantothenic acid (derived from the Greek *pantothen* meaning "from everywhere") seems to occur in all types of animal tissue and to be present in all protoplasm. The vitamin had been given many names before its chemistry and identity were completely established, and we shall use the accepted name exclusively.

Pantothenic acid $C_9H_{17}NO_5$ is an aliphatic compound, containing an amide linkage, a free acid group, and two free hydroxyl groups, one primary and the other secondary.

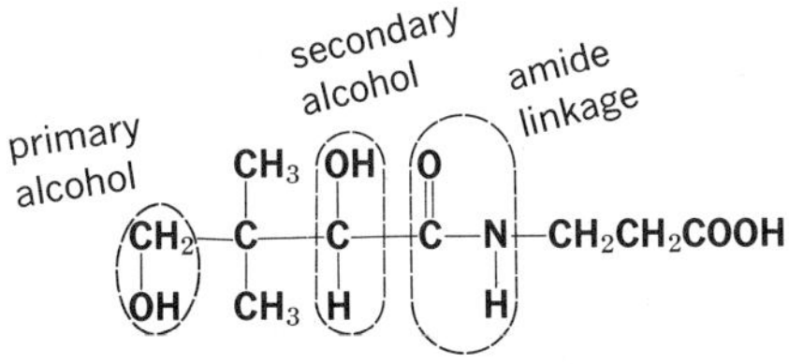

secondary alcohol
amide linkage
primary alcohol
CH_3 OH O
CH_2—C—C—C—N—CH_2CH_2COOH
OH CH_3 H H

pantothenic acid

The pure acid is a pale yellow viscous oil and is dextrorotatory (there is one asymmetric carbon atom). It is interesting to note the specificity of dextrorotatory pantothenic acid, because the levorotatory form (synthetic) has little biological activity.

STABILITY

The acid and its derivatives have been referred to as heat labile, in other words, unstable when heated. The calcium salt is not stable when treated with strong acids, alkali, and anything which would precipitate the calcium part.

OCCURRENCE AND AVAILABILITY

The best sources of pantothenic acid are the liver and kidneys; the heart, brain, and tongue are also good sources. Yeast, egg yolks, crude cane molasses, and cereal brans are other good sources. In animal tissues, the vitamin is usually found in enzyme systems and does not occur in the free state.

Pantothenic acid has been synthesized and is conveniently available as its calcium salt, $(C_9H_{16}NO_5)_2Ca$, also dextrorotatory. The calcium salt is a white crystalline material, odorless and sweet-tasting, which is very soluble in water. The pH of a 5% solution of the calcium salt is about 8.

UNITS AND REQUIREMENTS

The units of the calcium salt are usually referred to in terms of milligrams. The calcium salt may be conveniently taken orally.

The minimum requirements for man have not been established, and the deficiency disease has not been recognized. Pantothenic acid deficiency symptoms have been demonstrated for the mouse, rat, chick, fox, pig, dog, and some birds. Sheep and cattle require pantothenic acid, but they apparently obtain it from the bacterial action on food in the rumen.

DEFICIENCY

A pantothenic acid deficiency in the rat is recognized by poor growth, early aging, a graying of the hair, and a dermatitis.

BIOCHEMICAL RELATIONSHIPS

Coenzyme A (A for acetylation) contains about 27% pantothenic acid. This coenzyme system is responsible for various reactions occurring in the body, an important one being acetylation.

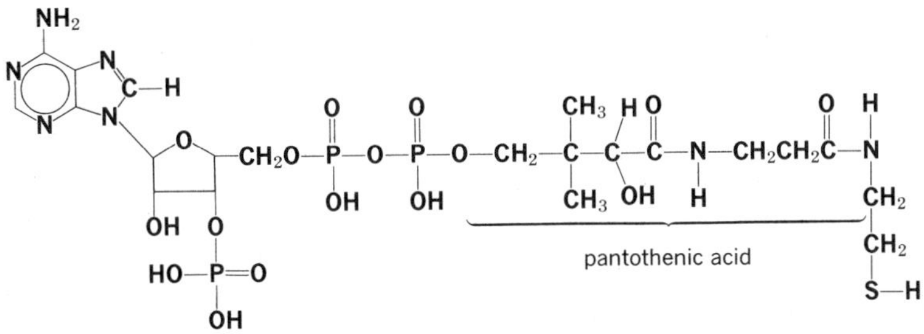

pantothenic acid

coenzyme A

Coenzyme A is also involved in carbohydrate metabolism in the Krebs cycle. In the presence of coenzyme A, citric acid is formed from pyruvic acid and oxaloacetic acid. Coenzyme A is a key enzyme in the interconversion of carbohydrates and fats. It is also known that coenzyme A is involved in the conversion of acetic acid into cholesterol.

Biotin

Biotin, $C_{10}H_{16}N_2O_3S$, is a complex substance containing a sulfur heterocyclic ring and a nitrogen heterocyclic ring, fused together. Its structure has been determined as

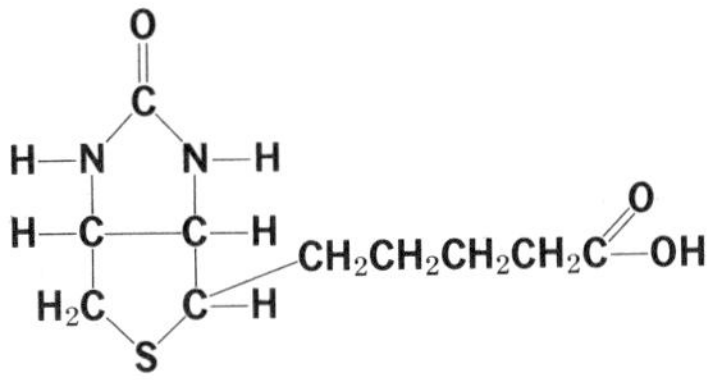

biotin

and has been verified by synthesis.

Biotin, m.p. 230–232°C, can be isolated as long, thin needles. The vitamin is sparingly soluble in water and insoluble in fat solvents. Biotin is reasonably stable toward dilute acids, alkali, and heat. Nitrous acid destroys the activity, and oxidizing agents affect the sulfur atom. Naturally occurring biotin is dextrorotatory.

OCCURRENCE AND AVAILABILITY

Biotin occurs in varying amounts in almost all animal tissue (the lens of the eye appears to be devoid of biotin). Good sources of biotin are liver, roasted peanuts, cauliflower, dried peas, chocolate, whole fresh eggs, and dried lima beans.

UNITS AND REQUIREMENTS

There is no generally accepted unit for biotin, and amounts are usually referred to in terms of weight, such as milligrams.

Biotin is required by all animals investigated so far. The vitamin is essential for rats, chicks, pigs, rabbits, monkeys, dogs, and man. The exact amount of biotin required by man has not been definitely established, although it has been reported that 0.5 mg daily should be ample.

DEFICIENCY

Biotin is synthesized by bacteria in the intestinal tract, which indicates that a spontaneous biotin deficiency in man would be highly unlikely.

The protein avidin, found in egg white, is known to combine readily with biotin to form a very stable complex, which is not easily broken down by digestion. This biotin-avidin complex is of such a nature that the biotin is not nutritionally available, and the vitamin is essentially inactivated. An artificial biotin deficiency may be produced by eating large amounts of egg white, thereby effectively removing all biotin from the digestive system. A substance that inhibits vitamin activity is known as an antivitamin. Avidin is a good example of an antivitamin.

Human volunteers, fed a 200 g dried egg white diet daily, developed a fine scaly dermatitis. In animals, a similar biotin deficiency may be produced, and seborrheic skin disorders, consisting of a generalized erythema, followed by scaling and alopecia (baldness), are characteristic. Rats on a biotin-deficient diet develop "spectacle eye" and, later, spasticity. Certain skin disorders in man have been corrected by the administration of biotin.

Because of the geometry and constitution of biotin, there are 8 optically active isomers, and all have been synthesized. The naturally occurring dextrorotatory isomer is much more active than the others. Biocytin is the chemical combination of biotin and L-lysine and may be regarded as the coenzyme containing biotin.

The Folic Acid Group

The evidence for the existence of folic acid, $C_{19}H_{19}N_7O_6$, was obtained concurrently from many sources. It has been called vitamin M, because it can prevent a nutritional anemia in monkeys; vitamin B_c because it can prevent nutritional anemia in chicks; factor U, when found essential for growth of chicks; and the *Lactobacillus casei* factor, because the vitamin is essential for the growth of that organism. We shall use the generally accepted term *folic acid* and refer to it and its derivatives as the folic acid group. Folic acid is associated with green leaves (folium); hence, its name.

It was found that the above-mentioned substances were either the same compound or very closely related compounds. Apparently the folic acid part (nonprotein part) is a constituent of the active coenzyme, which, when bound to a proper protein, forms the very effective total enzyme system. The active folic acid coenzyme seems to be much larger than folic acid.

Folic acid is also known as pteroyl glutamic acid. It is composed of an L-glutamic acid group, a *p*-aminobenzoic acid group, and a substituted pterin.

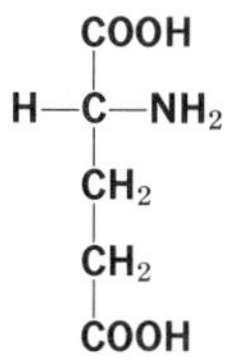

L-glutamic acid

p-aminobenzoic acid

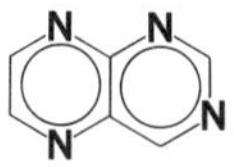

a pterin

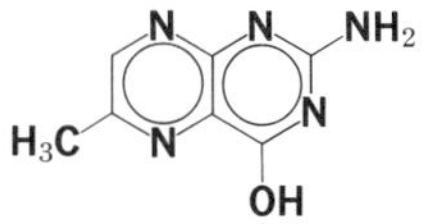

the substituted pterin found in folic acid

The combination of the substituted pterin and *p*-aminobenzoic acid is known as pteroic acid.

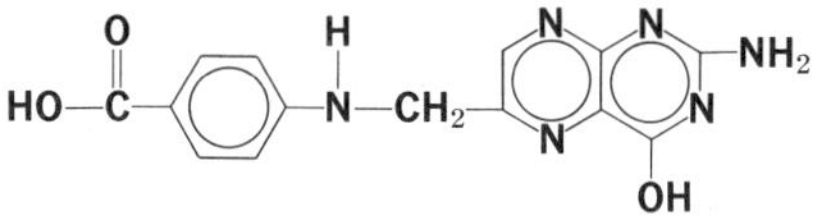

pteroic acid

The combination of pteroic acid and glutamic acid is known as pteroyl glutamic acid or folic acid.

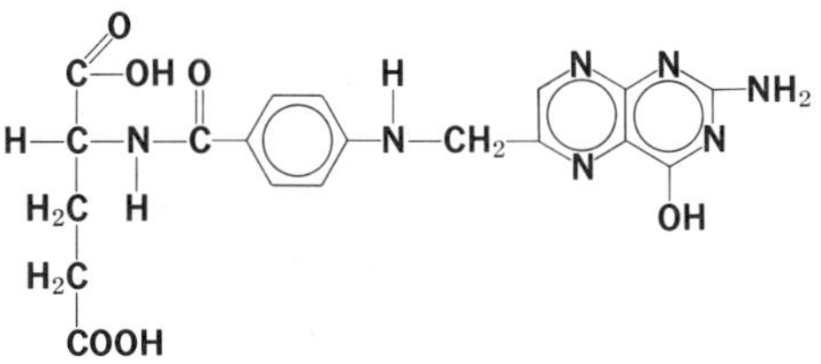

folic acid

The pterins are generally colored substances, and folic acid can be isolated as bright yellow needles. The vitamin is tasteless and only slightly soluble in water (0.2 g dissolve in 100 ml of water at 30°C). The sodium or potassium salt is much more soluble in water.

STABILITY

Folic acid is a sensitive compound and is destroyed (inactivated) by acid, base, sunlight, heat, oxidation, and reduction. Apparently there is an appreciable loss of folic acid potency in foods stored at room temperature for long periods of time and also in the ordinary cooking processes.

OCCURRENCE AND AVAILABILITY

The most potent sources of folic acid are liver, kidneys, and other animal organs. Yeast and salmon are excellent sources. Other good sources are wheat germ, spinach, dried lima beans, chicken, oysters, peanuts, and whole wheat.

UNITS AND REQUIREMENTS

The units of folic acid are generally expressed in terms of milligrams. About 20 mg daily are recommended as a therapeutic dose, and this may be taken orally or intramuscularly. The vitamin has been synthesized.

The daily requirements have not been established, but a daily quantity of about 0.1 mg should be ample, because most of it is synthesized by intestinal bacteria.

USES

The chief use today of folic acid is in the treatment of macrocytic anemia (increase in average size of red corpuscles) and sprue (a deficiency disease resulting from improper absorption of folic acid and possibly other factors).

There is evidence that folic acid is essential for the normal metabolism of all growing cells and tissues. Many animals, including man, generally do not exhibit a folic acid deficiency, because the vitamin is produced in sufficient quantities by the intestinal bacteria. A folic acid deficiency is easy to demonstrate on microorganisms such as *L. casei*.

It has been shown that folic acid is involved in the metabolism of tyrosine, one of the essential amino acids of the body. A folic-acid-deficient animal does not oxidize tyrosine properly, and the partially oxidized products are excreted in the urine. Folic acid has also been reported to increase the choline esterase content of the blood.

Vitamin B_{12}

Although in 1926 Minot and Murphy showed that pernicious anemia could be treated therapeutically with whole liver, it was not until 1948 that the active substance known as vitamin B_{12}, or the antipernicious anemia factor, isolated from liver, was purified and partially identified.

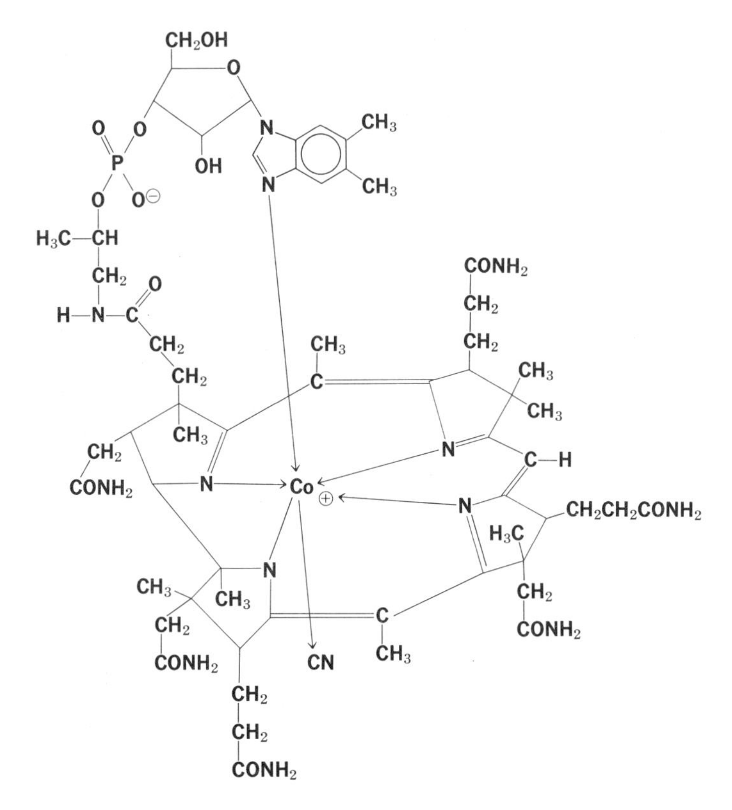

Figure 21-7

Vitamin B_{12} is a red crystalline solid with a highly complex structure (see Figure 21-7). The crystals decompose before the melting point is reached. Besides its distinctive color, vitamin B_{12} is also unique in that it contains cobalt, bound in the vitamin in a manner not too different from that of iron in heme and magnesium in chlorophyll. Vitamin B_{12} is active in amazingly small quantities. Doses of 0.0001 g daily are effective clinically in treating pernicious anemia when given in conjunction with an "intrinsic factor" of gastric juice. This "intrinsic factor" has not been identified, but it is known to be necessary for proper digestion of B_{12}.

B_{12} contains a dimethylbenzimidazole group along with other heterocyclic rings.

imidazole   benzimidazole   a dimethylbenzimidazole

There are various derived forms of B_{12}, such as hydroxycobalamin and nitrosocobalamin that have OH^- or NO_2^-, respectively, replacing the CN^-.

Because vitamin B_{12} is effective in such small quantities, it appears that it functions catalytically and probably as part of an enzyme system.

Vitamin B_{12} can be produced in high yields using members of the genus *Propionibacterium* to ferment solutions that contain skim milk or whey. Liver is an excellent source of B_{12}, and eggs and meat are good sources. Vitamin B_{12} participates in the isomerization reaction of dicarboxylic acids and in the conversion of dialcohols (e.g., 1,2-propandiol) to the corresponding aldehyde.

Inositol

There is considerable evidence that inositol, $C_6H_{12}O_6$, functions nutritionally for various experimental animals. The compound is relatively abundant in animal tissues (sometimes in amounts 100 to 1,000 times greater than that of the typical B vitamins).

Note that inositol is the first B vitamin we have discussed that does not possess nitrogen. Actually, the molecular formula is the same as that of glucose, and there is some evidence that it may, in a very limited way, be substituted for glucose in tissues. The structure of inositol is definitely different from that of glucose. Inositol is hexahydroxycyclohexane (i.e., a cyclohexane ring containing one —OH group on each carbon atom).

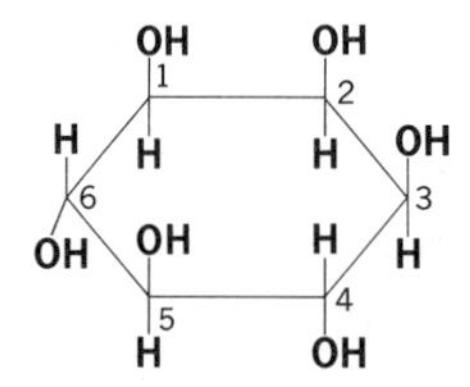

myo-inositol or *i*-inositol

The —OH groups on carbons 1, 2, 3, and 5 are above the plane of the ring, and the —OH groups on carbons 4 and 6 are below the plane of the ring. This is the only active form.

Inspection of the formula shows that nine geometric isomers are possible: seven optically inactive forms and one pair of optically active forms. Only the optically inactive myo- or *i*-form is nutritionally active.

Myo-inositol can be obtained as white crystals, m.p. 228°C, and is quite soluble in water. Inositol forms a dihydrate, $C_6H_{12}O_6 \cdot 2H_2O$, m.p. 216°C. Although inositol can be prepared synthetically, it occurs rather abundantly in nature in all plant and animal tissues and is easily available from natural sources.

In plants, the greatest amount of inositol is found in the leaves. Fruits (e.g., lemons, oranges, and grapefruits), cereal grains, yeast, molds and bacteria, dried peas, peanuts, wheat germ, and beef heart and brains are excellent sources of inositol.

Inositol deficiency in man is little understood. Possibly the only use for man is its effectiveness in preventing fatty livers caused by cholesterol feeding. Mice, rats, hamsters, pigs, chicks, turkeys, and certain fungi apparently require inositol for normal growth. It is hard to establish inositol deficiencies because of its rapid synthesis by microorganisms in the intestines. Inositol has been called the mouse antialopecia factor because mice, in which it is possible to demonstrate an inositol deficiency, exhibit the balding phenomenon. The mice, under these conditions, lose hair from the body, but not from the head, tail, or legs below the knees. Inositol has been shown to be necessary for the growth of some human cancer strains in tissue culture studies.

Choline

We have previously discussed choline in Chapter 11. Choline occurs principally in the chemically bound form in lecithins and sphingomyelins, and it is a structural part of a wide variety of naturally occurring compounds. Although acetylcholine is a very important compound from the standpoint of physiology, the amount of choline bound in this form is extremely small.

Choline, $C_5H_{15}NO_2$, is a colorless, viscous liquid, which is strongly alkaline. It is quite stable to heat and acids, but when heated with strong base, trimethylamine is liberated. Choline absorbs water and carbon dioxide from the air quite rapidly if exposed to the atmosphere. Choline is a typical base and forms salts readily with a variety of acids. This basic reaction is characteristic of a quaternary ammonium compound. Choline is readily soluble in water but insoluble in ether.

$$H_3C-N(CH_3)-CH_3$$

trimethylamine

$$\left[H-O-CH_2CH_2-N(CH_3)_2-CH_3\right]^+ OH^-$$

choline

The best source of choline is egg yolk. Other good sources are asparagus, soybeans, lamb kidneys, beef and pork liver, peas, spinach, and wheat germ.

Because choline occurs and functions in relatively large amounts in a living organism, there is some question as to whether choline should be included as a B vitamin. It obviously is in a different category from thiamine, riboflavin, and the others.

Since choline occurs in such a wide variety of naturally occurring materials, it is readily available. In any simple digestion process, choline is undoubtedly liberated from its many sources. It is, therefore, somewhat difficult at times to establish a true choline deficiency. To establish experimentally a choline deficiency, one must also limit the nutritional supply of serine and methionine, thereby decreasing the chance of synthesis of choline by the microorganisms in the intestinal tract.

REVIEW QUESTIONS

1. Define a vitamin.
2. List some fat-soluble vitamins. List some water-soluble vitamins.
3. Give other names for vitamins B_1, B_2, B_6, C, E, and D_2.
4. What vitamin is steroidal in nature? What vitamin is derived from a carbohydrate? What vitamin contains cobalt? What vitamin contains an aliphatic alcohol group? What vitamin contains a pyridine ring? What vitamin contains a lactone group?
5. What is meant by vitamin precursor, or provitamin? Name several provitamins and the vitamins to which they are related.
6. What is carotene?
7. List some vitamin deficiencies. The lack of which vitamins cause these disorders?
8. What is the relationship between nicotine and nicotinic acid?
9. Discuss the following terms: nyctalopia, rickets, scurvy, acrodynia, pellagra, alopecia, and coenzyme.
10. Discuss the history of the discovery of vitamins.
11. How did the term "limey" originate?

22

hormones

The body has many glands, most of which deliver their secretions through ducts. The salivary, gastric, and sweat glands are typical examples.

Another type of gland (the so-called ductless glands) has no external duct. These glands, called the endocrine glands, secrete their products directly into the blood stream (see Figure 22-1). These special chemical compounds produced by these glands are the *hormones*.

Hormones are compounds that influence the activity of the various organs of the body. They are sometimes called the "chemical messengers" of the body. Hormones regulate the rate at which certain organs function. The proper harmonious functioning of the endocrine glands makes for a healthy, normal individual. Excess functioning or lack of function of an endocrine gland may result in a serious physical disorder.

Chemically, the hormones may be divided into three classes:

1. protein hormones (e.g., insulin)
2. steroid hormones (e.g., sex hormones)
3. simple substances (neither protein nor steroid; e.g., epinephrine)

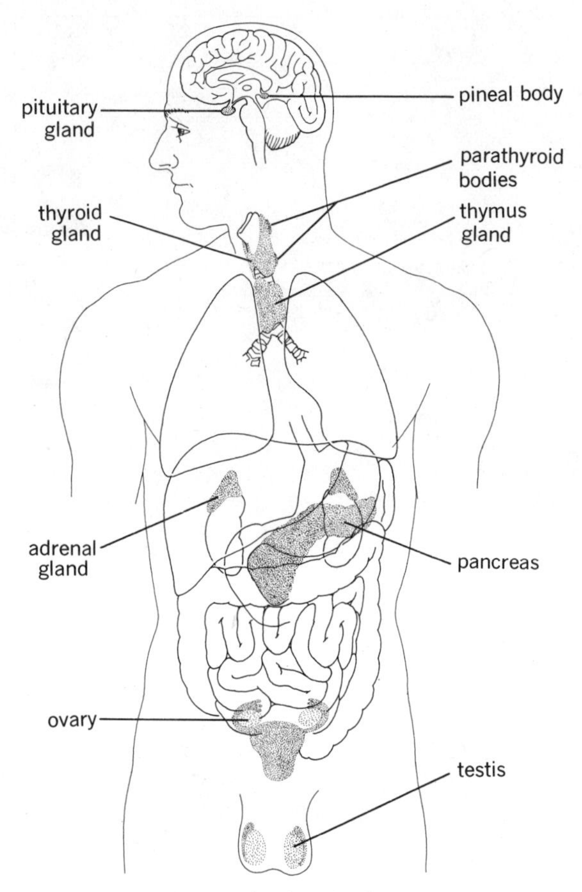

Figure 22-1 Location of the endocrine glands.

For convenience, the hormones are usually discussed in connection with the gland that secretes them.

The hypophysis (pituitary gland)

The hypophysis is perhaps the single most important endocrine gland in the body. It has been called the "master gland" because of the multiplicity of its functions, and because it controls many of the other endocrine glands.

The hypophysis is located directly beneath the brain and can be divided into three parts: the anterior portion (adenohypophysis), the posterior portion (neurohypophysis), and the pars intermedia. Although all are important, apparently the anterior portion of the pituitary is the most essential to life.

The anterior portion is characteristically glandular in nature, whereas the posterior is distinguished by its rich supply of nerves and may be called neural in character.

HYPOPHYSECTOMY

Hypophysectomy (i.e., the removal of the entire hypophysis) is a difficult operation; it was not until 1909 that Aschner perfected the techniques on dogs, and in 1926 Smith performed such operations on rats with great success. When the hypophysis is removed from a rat, the following effects may be noted:

1. The gonads in adults atrophy; in the young, the gonads fail to mature (sterility results).
2. The adrenal cortex atrophies, and the symptoms due to adrenal cortical insufficiency ensue.
3. The thyroid gland shrinks in size, producing a low metabolic rate and other manifestations of thyroid hormone insufficiency.
4. There is a failure of lactation if the hypophysectomy is performed late in pregnancy or after the young are born.
5. Growth ceases in the young of the species; there is a loss of body tissue in the adult and a tendency to revert to the juvenile form.
6. There is a complete alteration of the carbohydrate, lipid, and protein metabolism.
7. In some species, there are resultant pigmentation changes.

In man, a tumor or infarction of the pituitary, which is the clinical counterpart of a hypophysectomy, is called Simmond's disease.

The Hormones of the Anterior Pituitary

The anterior lobe secretes at least six different hormones, four of which are the trophic hormones. A trophic hormone stimulates some *other* endocrine organ to secrete its *own* hormones.

The trophic hormones are the two gonadotrophic hormones (which stimulate the gonads), the adrenocorticotrophic hormone (which stimulates the adrenal cortex), and the thyrotrophic hormone (which stimulates the thyroid gland). The lactogenic hormone (which stimulates lactation by the mammary glands) and the growth hormone are also secreted by the anterior lobe of the pituitary.

All the hormones of the anterior pituitary are protein in nature, and some have been isolated in very pure form.

We shall discuss these six hormones and their functions individually.

THE THYROTROPHIC HORMONE

This thyroid-stimulating hormone (TSH) is a protein of the globulin type. TSH has been isolated in a highly purified form and is a mixture of globulin proteins with an average molecular weight of about 30,000. It contains eight or nine cystine units per mole, along with mannose, glucosamine, and galactosamine.

When TSH is administered to normal animals, there is an increase in the iodine uptake of the thyroid, an increase in the metabolic rate, an increase in the heart beat, and an enlargement and hyperplasia of the thyroid. After a hypophysectomy, the total hormonal concentration of iodine in the blood decreases, as does the size of the thyroid gland.

THE LACTOGENIC HORMONE

This hormone, known as prolactin, stimulates the production of milk from the mammary glands. Prolactin has been isolated in a purified crystalline form from sheep and cattle. It appears to be a pure protein, with an isoelectric point of 5.7 and a molecular weight of about 30,000.

The growth of the mammary glands is due to stimulation from the normal growth and ovarian hormones, but prolactin from the pituitary initiates and maintains lactation. The adrenal cortical hormones and oxytocin may also act with prolactin to control lactation. Prolactin has not been uniformly successful in inducing milk in nonlactating mothers, but it is of value in some cases.

THE GROWTH HORMONE

This hormone is also known as somatotrophin (STH) or HGH (human growth hormone). HGH has been isolated in a highly purified state. In 1966, Li, Liu, and Dixon succeeded in identifying the α-amino acid sequence in this protein. The molecular weight is 21,500, and it has the structure of 188 amino acids shown in Figure 22-2.

The determination of the structure of the human growth hormone is truly a remarkable piece of experimental chemistry.

Excessive amounts of the growth hormone may produce gigantism or possibly acromegaly, which is a rare malady characterized by progressive enlargement of the ends of the long bones, thickening of the skull, lengthening of the jaw, and overgrowth of the skin. Presumably, an insufficiency of the growth hormone in children may result in dwarfism.

In discussing "growth" one must define the term carefully. By growth we mean the increase in tissue that has a constitution fairly similar to that of the original body. In other words, by growth we mean an increment in the amount of muscle tissue, bone structure, cartilage, etc., of the entire body. The pituitary growth hormone affects all of these and appears to be the hormone responsible for normal growth.

H — Phe — Pro — Thr — Ileu — Pro — Leu — Ser — Arg — Leu — Phe —
Asp — Asn — Ala — Met — Leu — Arg — Ileu — Leu — Ser — Leu — Glu —
Leu — Ileu — Ser — Try — Leu — Glu — Pro — Val — Glu — Phe — Ala — His —
Arg — Leu — His — Gln — Leu — Ala — Phe — Asp — Thr — Tyr — Glu — Glu —
Phe — Glu — Glu — Ala — Tyr — Ileu — Pro — Lys — Glu — Gln — Lys —
Tyr — Ser — Phe — Leu — Gln — Asp — Pro — Glu — Thr — Ser — Leu —
CyS — Phe — Ser — Ser — Ileu — Glu — Ser — (Asp,Pro,Pro,Thr) — Arg —
Glu — Glu — Thr — Gln — Lys — Ser — Asp — Leu — Glu — Leu — Leu —
Arg — Ser — Val — Phe — Ala — Asn — Ser — Leu — Val — Tyr — Gly —
Ala — Ser — Asn — Ser — Asp — Val — Tyr — Asp — Leu — Leu — Lys —
Asp — Leu — Glu — Glu — Gly — Ileu — Glu — Thr — Leu — Met — Gly —
Arg — Leu — Glu — Asp — Pro — Ser — Gly — Arg — Thr — Gly — Gln —
Ileu — Phe — Lys — Glu — Thr — Tyr — Ser — Lys — Phe — Asp — Thr —
Asn — Ser — His — Asn — Asp — Asp — Ala — Leu — Leu — Lys — Asp —
Tyr — Gly — Leu — Leu — Tyr — CyS — Phe — Arg — Lys — Asp — Met —
Asp — Lys — Val — Glu — Thr — Phe — Leu — Arg — Ileu — Val — Gln —
CyS — Arg — Ser — Val — Glu — Gly — Ser — CyS — Gly — Phe — OH

Figure 22-2 Somatotrophin.

However, somatotrophin regulates more than growth in the body; it is also important in carbohydrate, lipid, and protein metabolism. It has been demonstrated that the symptoms of diabetes in animals with a removed pancreas are increased when they are treated with growth hormone and are decreased with the removal of the pituitary. Somatotrophin has also been shown to increase the storage of glycogen in the skeletal and cardiac muscles and in the liver.

Somatotrophin affects lipid metabolism by raising the concentration of the unesterified fatty acids in the plasma. This effect may be retarded by the administration of insulin, food, or glucose. Fats are also mobilized and transported to the liver, and the formation of ketone bodies is increased. One of the more important effects of the growth hormone on the metabolic processes is an increase in the retention of nitrogen as protein in the tissues.

It is evident that the need for the growth hormone does not decrease with maturity; it is essential throughout life.

THE GONADOTROPHIC HORMONES

It was shown that after hypophysectomy the genital organs atrophy, and it was next demonstrated that pituitary extracts could cause enlargement of the ovaries. This led investigators to believe that there were some gonad-stimulating hormones in the pituitary.

Later experiments resulted in the isolation of two different fractions, which together could cause enlargement of the ovaries of hypophysectomized rats. These factors were characterized as the follicle-stimulating hormone (FSH) and as the luteinizing hormone (LH), or the interstitial cell-stimulating hormone (ICSH).

The follicle-stimulating hormone (FSH) is not a pure protein but apparently a combination of protein and polysaccharide. In the female, this hormone is concerned with the development of the ovarian follicle up to the point of ovulation; in the male, it is concerned with the development of the seminiferous (semen-carrying) tubules and the maintenance of spermatogenesis (production of sperm).

The luteinizing hormone is mainly protein, but it does contain some hexoses (carbohydrate). The molecular weight and isoelectric point vary considerably, depending upon the source. For example, the ICSH from the human has a molecular weight of 26,000 and an isoelectric point of 5.4, whereas the ICSH from swine has a molecular weight of 100,000 and an isoelectric point of 7.45.

In the female, the luteinizing hormone works with the FSH to help in the final development stages of the follicle and to produce ovulation. These two gonadotrophins are also responsible for the stimulation of the ovaries to produce estrogens (female sex hormones) and for the stimulation of the testes to produce androgens (male sex hormones).

The luteinizing hormone alone, however, induces luteinization of the ruptured follicle and stimulates the secretion of progesterone. In the male, the ICSH is involved in the development of the interstitial tissues of the testes.

Although the pituitary may be the prominent source of gonadotrophins, some of these gonad-stimulating hormones may be secreted by the placenta. When thus secreted, they are called the anterior pituitary-like hormones (APL), or the chorionic gonadotrophins. Although the APL are similar in action to the pituitary gonadotrophins, they are not identical and are separate, distinctly different proteins. The APL are found in relatively large quantities in the urine and blood of pregnant women. The common pregnancy tests are based on the identification of the presence of the chorionic gonadotrophins in urine.

Apparently, the placenta is also a production site for ACTH. It is known that pregnant women exhibit great remission in symptoms of asthma and other allergic signs during their pregnancy, but soon after delivery these symptoms return. ACTH has been found to alleviate greatly the asthmatic condition.

THE ADRENOCORTICOTROPHIC HORMONE (ACTH)

ACTH is a hormone secreted by the anterior lobe of the pituitary gland and is the true physiological stimulus to the adrenal cortex, thus causing the adrenal cortex to secrete all of its normal hormones at an increased rate.

Human ACTH was isolated in purified form by Li and his coworkers and by Bell and his associates. Bell determined the amino acid sequence of human ACTH to be that shown in Figure 22-3.

Ser — Tyr — Ser — Met — Glu — His — Phe — Arg — Tyr — Gly — Lys —
Pro — Val — Gly — Lys — Lys — Arg — Arg — Pro — Val — Lys — Val —
Tyr — Pro — Asp — Ala — Gly — Glu — Asp — Glu — Ser — Ala — Glu —
Ala — Phe — Pro — Leu — Glu — Phe $\quad$ NH_2 (on Glu)

Figure 22-3 ACTH.

Remember that ACTH stimulates the production of *all* the adrenal cortex hormones; thus, a wide variety of effects are observed. This also accounts for the large number of uses of ACTH.

ACTH is used as a nondisease specific. In other words, ACTH is used to stimulate the cortex to produce its own hormones, which enable the cells and tissues of the body to withstand stress or injury of almost any origin, whether from an external source (e.g., burns) or internal origin (e.g., emotional disorder or diseases associated with acute inflammatory reactions). Because it stimulates the adrenal cortex and allows the cells of the body to function in a relatively normal physiological manner in many situations, ACTH is used in the treatment of hypersensitivities and other inflammatory reactions.

ACTH finds use in the treatment of rheumatoid arthritis and acute rheumatic fever and in treating chronic and intractable cases of asthma, where epinephrine is no longer effective. Although useful in general in treating asthma, hay fever, and allergic manifestations, it is possible to treat these diseases, if they are not too acute, by other more simple means.

Acute psoriasis and other dermatitis conditions respond to ACTH. It is reported that the hormone is useful in the treatment of ulcerative colitis, alcoholism, and severe burns, and it is given as a therapeutic adjunct after operations involving skin grafting.

ACTH is a fast-acting substance that may be used continuously, if necessary. Side effects are variable. The drug may also be given in a tapering-off schedule. Excessive doses of the drug, however, can produce profound side effects, which may be reversible. In all cases, great care should be exercised in the usage of this powerful substance.

The Hormones of the Posterior Pituitary

Extracts from the posterior lobe of the pituitary exhibit three types of activity:

1. They cause pressor activity (i.e., they raise the blood pressure).
2. They cause strong contractions of the uterus and other smooth muscles (i.e., they have an oxytocic effect).
3. They affect the action in the loop of Henle in the kidneys and control diuresis (i.e., they exhibit the antidiuretic principle).

Kamm and his associates fractionated the extracts from the posterior lobe of the pituitary and isolated two substances. The pressor-active substance was called *pitressin* (vasopressin), and the oxytocic principle was called *pitocin* (oxytocin). They are both very low molecular weight proteins or, more correctly, polypeptides, with molecular weights in the 600–2,000 range. The oxytocic hormone has an isoelectric point of 8.5; the pressor-active substance has an isoelectric point of 10.8 and exists in at least two forms. Pitressin, in essence, stimulates the peripheral blood vessels (i.e., it contracts peripheral arterioles) and thus causes a rise in the blood pressure. The great use of pitressin is in combating the low blood pressure of shock, following surgery. Apparently, in some cases, pitressin is better than epinephrine, because pitressin acts more slowly, and, consequently, its effects are of longer duration. Pitressin also exhibits antidiuretic properties. In cases of *diabetes insipidus,* one observes an elimination of rather large quantities of urine. The antidiuretic principle, pitressin, is of value in the therapy of such cases.

Pitocin has its greatest effect on the uterine muscles and a lesser effect upon the other smooth muscles. It finds its greatest use in obstetrics to facilitate deliveries.

The Pars Intermedia

There is evidence that a hormone called melanotropin is secreted by this pituitary tissue, which connects the posterior and anterior portions of the pituitary. Melanotropin has been isolated in a pure form by Li and his associates. It is responsible for the darkening of the skin of amphibians, but its biological significance in man is unclear.

The thyroid gland

The thyroid gland consists of two lobes that lie close together on either side of the trachea and are joined by thin connective tissue. The thyroid gland in an adult male weighs between 25 and 40 grams, but it varies widely in size. The thyroid gland is larger in females than in males and may enlarge still more in pregnancy. The flow of blood to the thyroid gland is most profuse.

The hormone produced by the thyroid gland is called thyroglobulin. This hormone is a very large molecule with a molecular weight of about 675,000, and it is characterized by containing 0.5 to 1% of iodine by weight. Kendall showed that thyroglobulin consists of a protein globulin and a simple unit called thyroxine, which contains 65% of iodine by weight.

The hormone circulating in the plasma is thyroxine, tightly bound to the α-globulin fractions of the serum proteins and slightly bound to the albumin fraction. Thyroglobulin in the thyroid gland is the storage form of the hormone. In normal adults, the blood serum may contain 1 part of iodine per 20 million parts of serum. In hypothyroid cases, the value may be 1 part in 100 million; in hyperthyroid cases, the iodine may be present to the extent of 1 part in 1 million parts of serum.

Iodine in the diet, such as in the form of iodides (e.g., sodium iodide NaI), is rapidly taken up by the thyroid gland and incorporated as organic iodine. It is postulated that the iodine is made to iodinate tyrosine to form diiodotyrosine

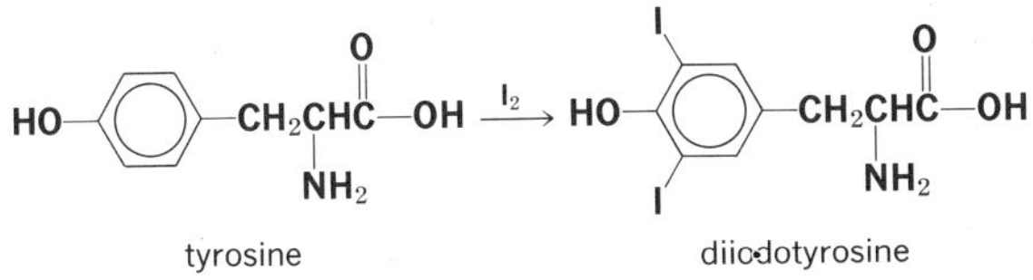

$$HO-C_6H_4-CH_2CH(NH_2)C(=O)-OH \xrightarrow{I_2} HO-C_6H_2I_2-CH_2CH(NH_2)C(=O)-OH$$

tyrosine diiodotyrosine

and that two molecules of diiodotyrosine combine, with the elimination of alanine, to form thyroxine.

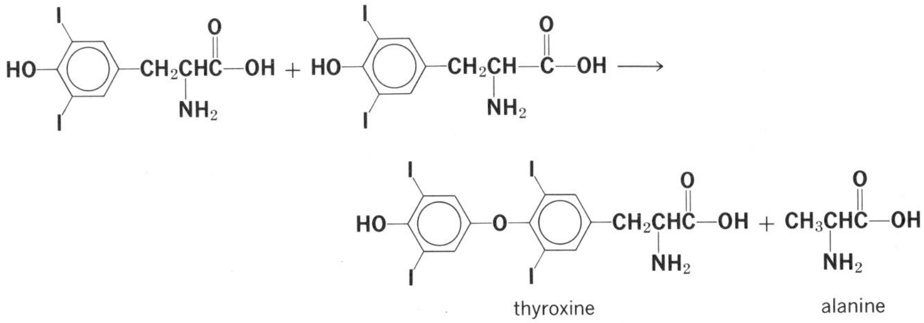

$$HO-C_6H_2I_2-CH_2CH(NH_2)C(=O)-OH + HO-C_6H_2I_2-CH_2CH(NH_2)-C(=O)-OH \longrightarrow$$

$$HO-C_6H_2I_2-O-C_6H_2I_2-CH_2CH(NH_2)C(=O)-OH + CH_3CH(NH_2)C(=O)-OH$$

thyroxine alanine

HYPOFUNCTION OF THE THYROID GLAND

Hypothyroidism may be caused by a deficiency of the hormone or a thyroidectomy (i.e., removal of the thyroid gland).

In cases of hypofunction of the thyroid, one characteristically finds a lowering (about 20–30%) of the basal metabolism rate in warm-blooded animals. In the young of the species, a thyroid deficiency may cause cretinism, which is an inhibition of the physical and mental growth of the individual. In cretinism we encounter dwarfism, serious mental deficiencies, and a peculiar infantile facial expression.

Hypothyroidism also causes a decrease in the sensitivity to stimulus of the peripheral neuromuscular system, and some changes in the intermediary metabolism are evident. The serum cholesterol level is high, and anemia is quite common.

In adults, a condition of myxedema may be evident in these cases. Myxedema is characterized by a peculiar thickening and puffiness of the skin and subcutaneous tissue, particularly of the face and extremities.

A hypothyroid condition is treated with small daily doses of the thyroid hormone. Recovery may be slow, but in many cases all the symptoms may be removed and the deficiency remedied.

HYPERTHYROIDISM

Hyperthyroidism is caused by an excess of the thyroid hormone. Under these circumstances, we may find an increased metabolic rate, perhaps even double the normal rate. Perhaps the most drastic effects are on the nervous system: Reflex sensitivity is increased; sweating, flushing, rapid respiration, palpitation, and increased gastrointestinal activity can be noticed. The heart is also affected, because the cardiac output is increased.

Spontaneous hyperthyroidism is known as Grave's disease. Goiter is a condition caused by the enlargement of the thyroid gland, and in some cases this may cause the eyeballs to bulge out (i.e., exophthalmus). Goiter may be due to an excessive stimulation from the pituitary or, more likely, from an inadequate supply of iodine in the diet, which causes the gland to overwork.

Goiter may be cured by surgery (i.e., thyroidectomy) or perhaps better by "chemical surgery," which consists in the use of radioactive iodine (in sodium iodide). In "chemical surgery," the radioactive iodine is incorporated in the thyroid tissue along with the normal iodine. The radiation from the radioactive iodine causes a destruction of some of the excessive thyroid tissue, and, because it soon loses its activity, the radioactive material is not a threat to the life of the patient.

To prevent goiter, the dietary iodine intake should be about 0.1 mg daily. It is possible to buy iodized salt containing a sufficient supply of nutritionally available iodine.

The parathyroid glands

The parathyroid glands are small paired bodies attached to the thyroid gland. The glands are very small; the combined weight of parathyroid tissue in man is about 0.1 g. The hormone of the parathyroid glands has been called "parathormone." It has not been isolated in the pure state, but it appears to be a protein with a molecular weight of about 20,000. The protein is very sensitive to changes in pH, and action of acids and bases inactivates the hormone. This indicates a protein structure. Other physical evidence indicates the presence of tyrosine, phenylalanine, and tryptophan.

Parathormone is concerned with the metabolism of calcium and phosphorus in the body. (It should be recalled that the body is normally rich in calcium and phosphorus: About 2% of the body weight is calcium and about 1% is phosphorus.) Calcium is in the bones and teeth, and 90% of the phosphorus (as phosphates) is in the skeleton.

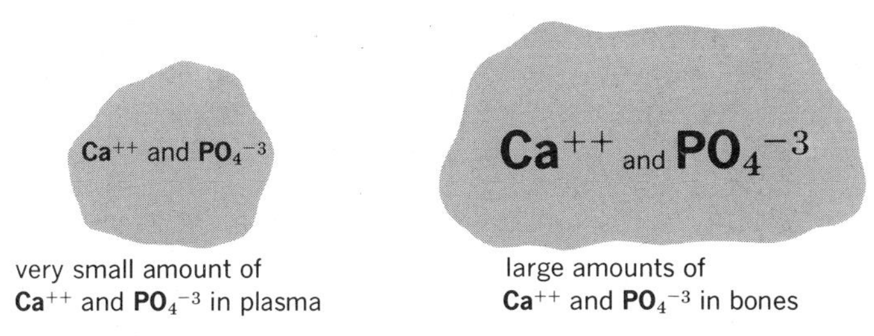

Figure 22-4 Concentrations of Ca and PO_4 in plasma and bones.

The plasma, however, contains a very low concentration of calcium and phosphorus. In essence, the calcium and phosphorus supply in the bones is enormously greater than that which circulates in the plasma, and there is indeed an equilibrium between the two, governed by several factors, such as the diet, excretion, vitamins, and hormones.

HYPOPARATHYROIDISM

Removal of the parathyroid glands (i.e., parathyroidectomy) or, rarely, nonfunctioning of the glands, may cause tetany. Tetany is a hyperirritability of the nervous system, which may be characterized by a twitching of the muscles and spasms of the body. Under these conditions, the calcium ion level in the blood decreases, and the phosphate level increases. Treatment of hypoparathyroidism is accomplished by adjustment of the calcium and phosphate intake in the diet; that is, add 1% calcium gluconate or lactate to the diet and decrease the phosphate supply. Another useful therapeutic device is to administer rather large quantities of vitamin D, in amounts far in excess of that necessary to prevent rickets. This favorably affects the calcium and phosphate relationship between the plasma and the skeleton in tetany. Of course, in cases of hypoparathyroidism, the administration of parathyroid extracts containing parathormone counteracts the parathyroid deficiency by increasing the phosphate excretion (decreasing the phosphate plasma level) and the blood calcium level.

HYPERPARATHYROIDISM

Hyperparathyroidism is a condition caused by excess activity of the parathyroid glands. This condition is characterized by a depletion of the minerals of the bones. Under these conditions, the calcium and phosphate levels in serum are very high, causing kidney stones and other abnormal calcifications in the body.

There has not yet been demonstrated any direct connection between the pituitary and parathyroids. Under normal circumstances, it seems that the principal regulatory factor governing the secretion of the parathyroid glands is the calcium level of the blood.

The pancreas

The function of the pancreas as an organ producing a digestive fluid has already been discussed in Chapter 15.

Because a pancreatectomy (removal of the pancreas) results in an excretion of glucose in urine (similar to diabetes mellitus) and other metabolic changes, and because ligation (tying) of the pancreatic duct does not produce diabetes, it was assumed that the pancreas produces some internal secretion of the hormonal type, and this hormone was called insulin.

In 1869, Langerhans noted that there were small islets or nests of cells in the pancreas that differed histologically from the rest of the pancreas tissue. These were called the islets or islands of Langerhans; the total volume amounted to 1–3% of that of the whole pancreas. It was found that these islets were not connected to the duct system through which the digestive pancreatic juice flows.

Staining studies showed that the islet cells are of two kinds, the α- and the β-cells, and apparently the β-cells produce insulin.

Banting, Best, and, later, Collip were successful in preparing active extracts of cattle pancreas. Later workers were able to prepare the pure crystalline hormone. Insulin was the first hormone to be identified as a protein and has been very extensively studied. The molecular weight is about 6,000. Not only have all the α-amino acids in insulin been identified, but the exact sequence of the acids has been elucidated by Sanger (see Figure 22-5). In 1966, Chinese chemists reported the successful synthesis of bovine insulin.

Insulin is commonly precipitated with zinc, but it can be obtained free of zinc. It is interesting to note that the pancreas is relatively rich in zinc, a metal that may be regarded as a trace element.

Because insulin is a protein, it is deactivated by the digestive (proteo-

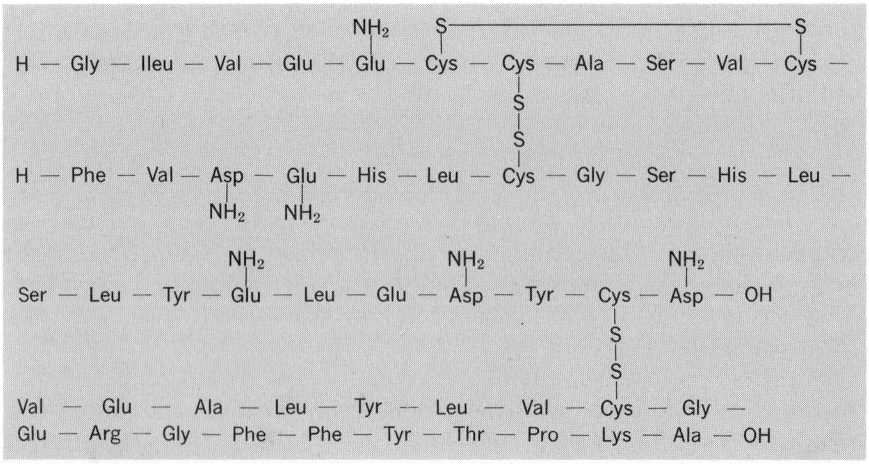

H — Gly — Ileu — Val — Glu — Glu(NH_2) — Cys(S) — Cys — Ala — Ser — Val — Cys(S) —
(S–S bridge between the first Cys and the last Cys of this chain; Cys at position 7 linked by S–S to Cys of the chain below)

H — Phe — Val — Asp(NH_2) — Glu(NH_2) — His — Leu — Cys — Gly — Ser — His — Leu —

Ser — Leu — Tyr — Glu(NH_2) — Leu — Glu — Asp(NH_2) — Tyr — Cys — Asp(NH_2) — OH
(Cys linked by S–S to Cys of the chain below)

Val — Glu — Ala — Leu — Tyr — Leu — Val — Cys — Gly —
Glu — Arg — Gly — Phe — Phe — Tyr — Thr — Pro — Lys — Ala — OH

Figure 22-5 Insulin.

lytic) enzymes and must be given parenterally. Insulin plays an important role in carbohydrate metabolism.

The effect of an insulin injection is almost immediate; the blood sugar level decreases rapidly, reaches a minimum in about 1–2 hours, and then gradually (in about 7–8 hours) returns to the original value. This means that a patient receiving insulin requires about three injections daily. A great improvement in insulin therapy was the combination of insulin with the protein protamine to form the relatively insoluble protamine insulin complex. This complex takes longer to act, but its effects are prolonged over many hours, and, consequently, a patient may require only one injection a day.

INSULIN DEFICIENCY

As mentioned before, insulin is concerned with carbohydrate metabolism. If insulin is not produced or if it is produced in insufficient amounts, diabetes mellitus may result. The following signs are characteristic of diabetes mellitus:

1. Hyperglycemia (i.e., high blood sugar level) is evident. Glycosuria (i.e., sugar in urine) is common.
2. Diuresis (i.e., increased flow of urine) is evident.
3. The body seems to have a decreased ability to oxidize glucose.
4. Liver glycogen levels may be below normal; muscle glycogen in general may be about normal, and the heart muscle glycogen level is much above normal.
5. The conversion of carbohydrates into fat is reduced.
6. Because the oxidizing power of the body is decreased, fats cannot be completely oxidized, and the ketone bodies (i.e., acetone, acetoacetic acid, and β-hydroxybutyric acid) are produced in abnormal quantities. The acidic substances decrease the alkaline reserve of the blood and tissue fluids and cause an acidosis condition.
7. A negative nitrogen balance is common (i.e., there is more nitrogen leaving than entering the body).
8. The formation of glucose from noncarbohydrate sources (mostly protein) is increased.

In cases of an excess secretion or the administration of excessive amounts of insulin, the blood sugar may decrease to a low level (insulin shock), and serious symptoms may ensue: weakness, sweating, dizziness, and finally unconsciousness.

In cases of insulin shock (i.e., low blood sugar level), the body is cold and clammy, and there is no tell-tale odor on the breath. In cases of diabetic coma (i.e., too high blood sugar level), the body is warm and perspiring, and there is a fruity odor on the breath.

In normal individuals, the control of insulin secretion seems to be the concentration of glucose in the blood.

Note that a substance known as alloxan

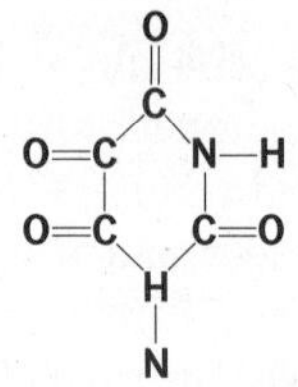

alloxan ($C_4H_2N_2O_4$)

is capable of producing diabetes in experimental animals. It was found that alloxan exerts a specific necrotic action only upon the β-cells of the islets of Langerhans and not on the α-cells. Under these circumstances, the normal supply of insulin for the body is curtailed and essentially eliminated.

Under normal circumstances, glucose in the blood is reabsorbed in the cells of the renal tubules of the kidney, and the glucose is not found in urine. By the administration of the drug phlorhizin, this reabsorption process is prevented, and sugar will be found in the urine. This is a case of experimental glucosuria or false diabetes.

Phlorhizin is a natural product obtained from the bark of certain trees and is composed of glucose, phloroglucinol, and *p*-hydroxyhydratropic acid.

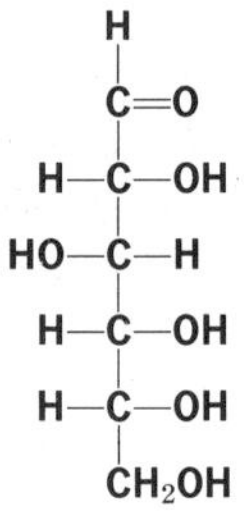

D-glucose ($C_6H_{12}O_6$)

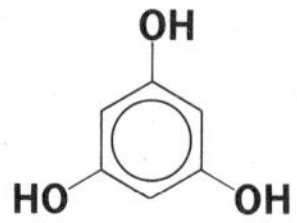

phloroglucinol ($C_6H_6O_3$)

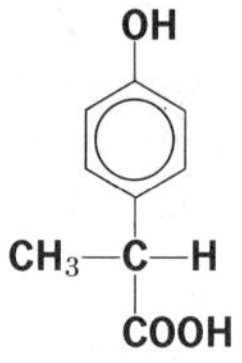

p-hydroxyhydratropic acid ($C_9H_{10}O_3$)

The α-cells produce a hormone, glucagon, which has a molecular weight of 3,485 and an isoelectric point of 8.0. Glucagon has the structure shown in Figure 22-6.

Glucagon accelerates glycogenolysis in the liver and inhibits the synthesis of fatty acids.

His — Ser — Glu(NH_2) — Gly — Thr — Phe — Thr — Ser — Asp — Tyr — Ser —
Lys — Tyr — Leu — Asp — Ser — Arg — Arg — Ala — Glu(NH_2) — Asp — Phe —
Val — Glu(NH_2) — Try — Leu — Met — Asp(NH_2) — Thr

Figure 22-6 Glucagon.

The adrenal glands

The adrenal glands are two glands, each located above a kidney. These glands are rather small in man, with a weight of about 3 g each. They are essentially double organs, composed of two distinct kinds of tissue with different functions.

In mammals, a glandular portion of the adrenals, called the adrenal cortex, surrounds the central part, called the medulla. The adrenal cortex tissue more closely resembles other glandular tissue, whereas the adrenal medulla tissue resembles neural tissue.

We shall discuss the two types of tissue and their secreted hormones separately.

The Adrenal Medulla

In 1895 it was observed that extracts of adrenal tissue, when given intravenously to animals, showed powerful vasopressor activity (i.e., increased blood pressure). The active principle was isolated in 1901 and was called epinephrine. This was the first hormone to be obtained in a pure form. It has been shown that the adrenal extracts from natural sources also contain a compound closely related to epinephrine, called norepinephrine or noradrenaline. This substance differs from epinephrine in that the methyl group on the nitrogen is lacking.

$$HO-C_6H_3(OH)-CH(OH)-CH_2-NH(CH_3)$$

epinephrine

$$HO-C_6H_3(OH)-CH(OH)-CH_2-NH_2$$

norepinephrine

Both of these hormones contain an asymmetric carbon atom, and both naturally occur as D isomers. D(−)Epinephrine is about 15 times more potent than the synthetic L(+)isomer; D(−)norepinephrine is 20 times more potent than its synthetic mirror image.

Normally, epinephrine occurs in five to ten times the concentration of norepinephrine in the adrenal medulla. Epinephrine is readily oxidized to inactive material both in living organisms and in the laboratory. Because it is readily destroyed, the drug cannot be taken orally; it must be administered by injection. When given intravenously, the hormone action is immediate. Substances similar to epinephrine in pharmacological activity are known as sympathomimetic agents.

Of the two types of tissue in the adrenals, it is known that the adrenal cortex is the most important, and it is essential for life. Removal of the adrenal medullae (adrenal demedullation), however, shows no obvious ill effects on the health, vigor, and reproductive ability of the experimental animals. The present theory is that epinephrine may be secreted by other tissue in the body. These other bodies, similar to the adrenal medullae, are called paraganglia and are found adjacent to the chain of sympathetic ganglia.

Epinephrine has been known as the emergency hormone, in that its secretion is proportional to the stimulus through the central nervous system.

Under the conditions of stimulus, such as cold, heat, drugs, and emotional excitement, the secretion of epinephrine is greatly increased. In circumstances of great stress, strain, and emotional upheaval, the body requires additional energy in a hurry. Epinephrine accordingly increases the conversion of glycogen to glucose and thus provides quickly available energy. Because it also increases the blood flow, the available glucose may quickly go where it is needed.

ACTION OF EPINEPHRINE

Epinephrine is a powerful vasoconstrictor; it affects the cardiac and smooth muscles, and it is also important in regulating carbohydrate metabolism. Epinephrine increases both the force and the frequency of the contraction of the heart muscles, resulting in rise in blood pressure, rise in pulse rate, and rise in cardiac output. It is used as a heart stimulant in acute emergencies.

Epinephrine also shows a strong bronchodilating effect and is used in the treatment of asthma and other allergic conditions.

Epinephrine affects the carbohydrate metabolism by increasing the rate of conversion of glycogen into glucose, which then may be rushed to the muscles to form ATP, which is used to perform work.

Epinephrine has been shown to stimulate secretions of some of the hormones of the anterior pituitary, such as adrenotrophin, thyrotrophin, and gonadotrophin.

NOREPINEPHRINE

This hormone has little activity in regulating carbohydrate metabolism and is not a vasodilator; it is a powerful excitor.

THE ADRENAL CORTEX

The adrenal cortex consists of large granular cells particularly rich in lipids, such as cholesterol. Removal of the adrenal glands (adrenalectomy) of the rat, dog, cat, or rabbit leads to death within several days. Because an extract of the adrenal cortex, called cortin, was capable of prolonging the lives of the adrenalectomized animals, it was realized that this extract possessed hormone activity.

Extensive investigations resulted in the isolation of at least *30 different* crystalline compounds, and at least 10 others not yet characterized, from the adrenal cortex. These compounds are a series of closely related steroids, and seven of these are well known (see below) and cause specific body functions.

These seven adrenal cortical hormones are

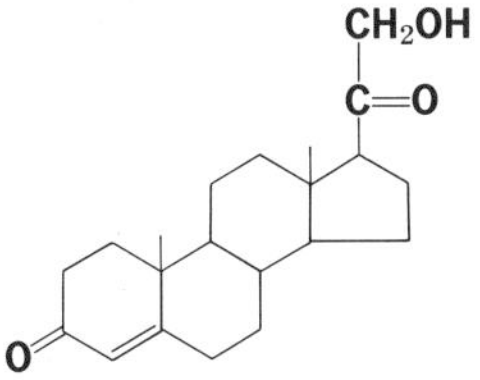

CH_2OH
C=O
O

desoxycorticosterone (Q)

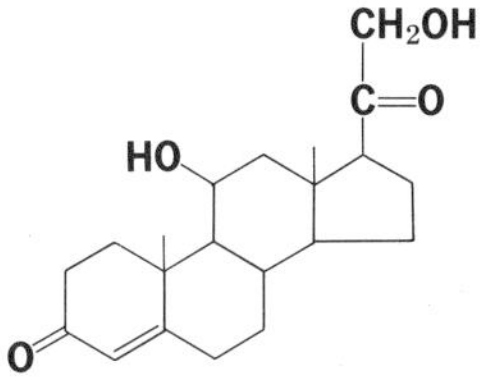

CH_2OH
C=O
HO
O

corticosterone (H)

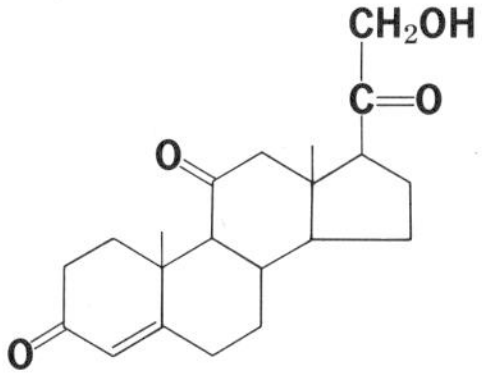

CH_2OH
C=O
O
O

11-dehydrocorticosterone (A)

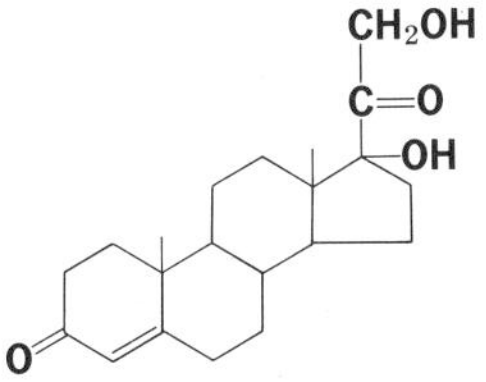

CH_2OH
C=O
OH
O

17-hydroxydesoxycorticosterone (S)

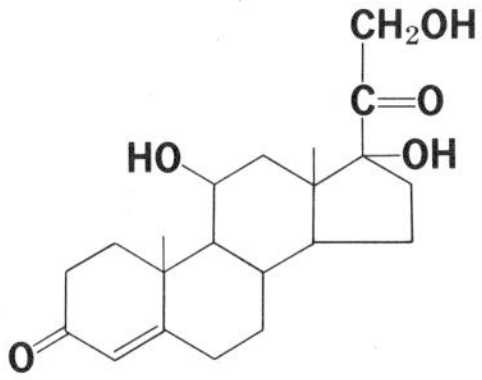

CH_2OH
C=O
HO
OH
O

17-hydroxycorticosterone (F)

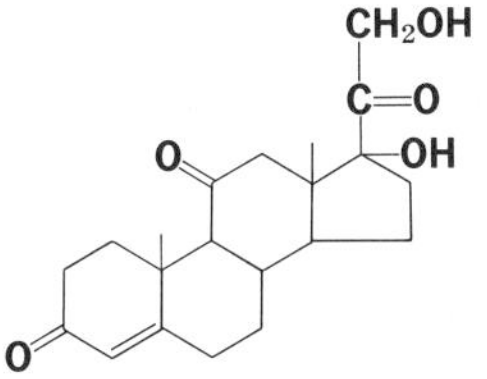

CH_2OH
C=O
O
OH
O

17-hydroxy-11-dehydrocorticosterone
(*cortisone*)

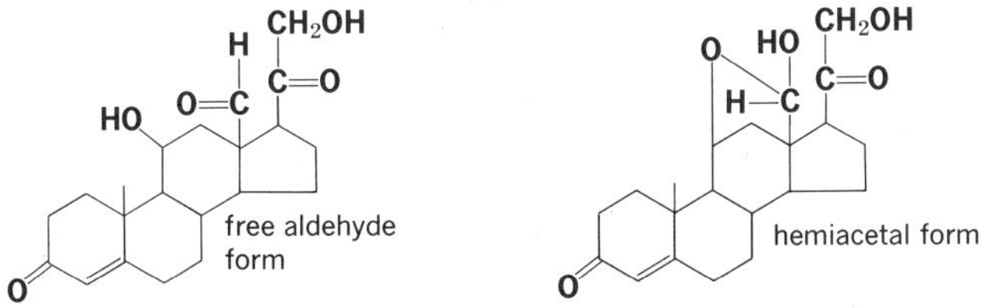

H
CH_2OH
C=O
O=C
HO
O

free aldehyde
form

O
HO
CH_2OH
C=O
H—C
O

hemiacetal form

aldosterone

aldosterone exists in solution both as the
free aldehyde and as the hemiacetal

As each compound was isolated by the various investigators, it was first designated by a letter of the alphabet, and it sometimes took several years before the exact structure was certain. In some cases, the same compound was given different letters by the different investigators. Aldosterone was not isolated until 1955 and was previously known only as an active substance in the amorphous (noncrystalline) residue of the adrenal cortex extracts.

PHYSIOLOGICAL ACTIVITY

If the adrenals are removed and the animal survives, within a few days the following symptoms are noticed: loss of appetite, nausea, diarrhea, asthenia (i.e., lack of strength), lowering of the blood sugar level, decrease in blood pressure, and renal failure.

In man, chronic adrenal insufficiency is known as Addison's disease. A patient suffering from adrenal insufficiency is particularly susceptible to external stress and shock and to infection. In man, there is a unique pigmentation (e.g., bronzing of the skin) or depigmentation in naturally pigmented areas. The excretion of abnormally large amounts of sodium chloride and, thus, a lowering of the salt content of the blood plasma, are also observed. Correspondingly, there is an increase retention of potassium ions resulting in the movement of water into the cells, which causes a diminution of the volume of extracellular fluid. This causes hypotension, reduced circulation through the kidneys, and renal failure, followed by an increase in blood urea.

Usually under these circumstances a condition of hypoglycemia is evident, accompanied by the depletion of the liver glycogen supply. Also, because the body is not excreting a normal amount of nitrogen, it is believed that the body cannot draw on the normal protein sources.

The hormones with the strongest effect on the potassium and sodium balance in the body are aldosterone and desoxycorticosterone. Aldosterone is about 25 times more effective in this respect than desoxycorticosterone. It was also found that synthetic 9-halogenated cortisone compounds help to maintain the electrolyte balance in the body.

The control of carbohydrate, fat, and protein metabolisms is largely affected by the 11-oxygenated steroids, that is, 17-hydroxycorticosterone, corticosterone, 11-dehydrocorticosterone, and cortisone.

All seven of these active adrenal cortical hormones are important in controlling the sodium and potassium balance, the water metabolism, and the carbohydrate, fat, and protein metabolisms of the body, but those mentioned exhibit the greatest effects.

CORTISONE

Although cortisone was isolated in small quantities by Kendall in 1936, it was not until 1946 that Sarett succeeded in synthesizing enough cortisone so that its effects could be observed clinically.

The clinical trials showed that cortisone had a phenomenal success in curing rheumatoid arthritis. It was noted, however, that the hormone generally would have to be given continuously, for if it were discontinued, the symptoms would often reappear.

Because the partial synthesis of Sarett was exceedingly complicated and the starting material (bile acids) was limited, attempts were made to obtain cortisone by a more convenient and cheaper route. The search culminated in 1951 in the announcement of several different partial syntheses, showing that cortisone could be made relatively cheaply from such available starting substances as cholesterol (from animal brains and spinal cords), stigmasterol (from soybean oil), ergosterol (from yeast), and diosgenin (from Mexican yams).

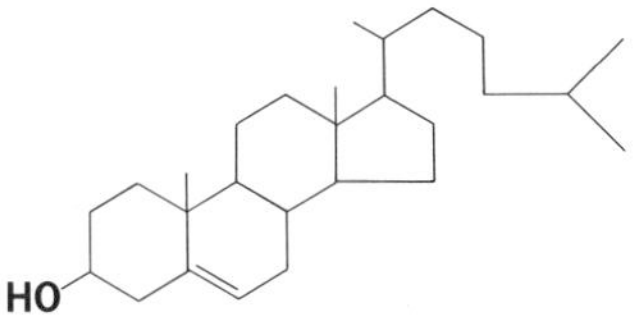

cholesterol ($C_{27}H_{46}O$)

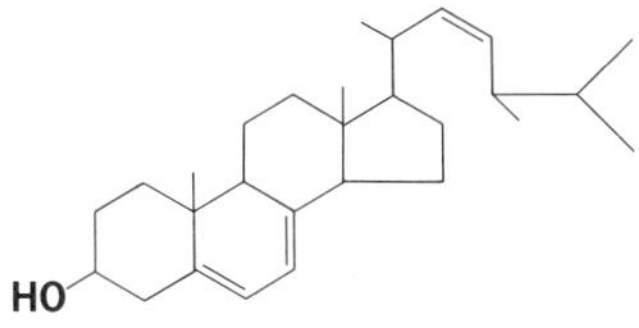

ergosterol ($C_{28}H_{44}O$)

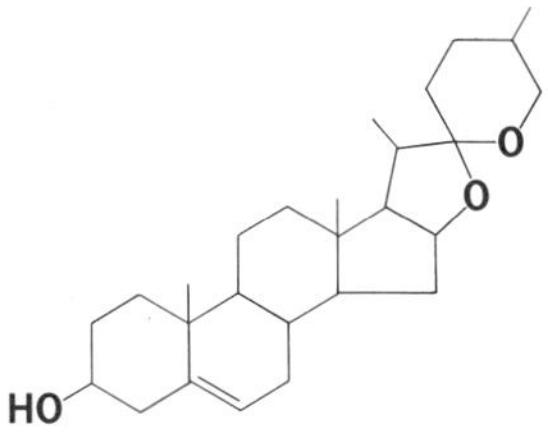

diosgenin ($C_{27}H_{42}O_3$)

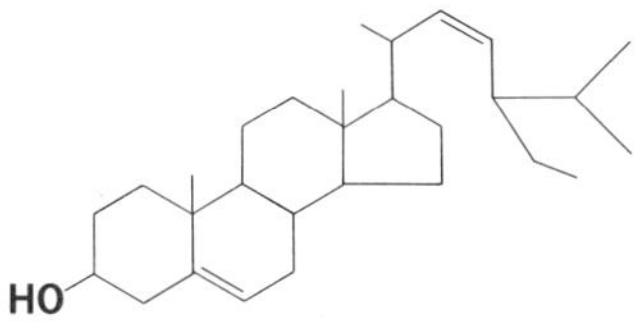

stigmasterol ($C_{29}H_{48}O$)

In addition, a total synthesis of cortisone, a truly remarkable masterpiece of chemical ingenuity, was reported by Woodward in 1951. This might possibly compete with the partial synthesis.

Sweat reported that he could convert compound S (17-hydroxydesoxycorticosterone) into compound E (cortisone) by enzyme action. Although not of importance commercially, this is of great significance from a theoretical point of view, because it is an example of the formation of a hormone by an enzyme.

Also of great interest was the report in 1952 that the mold *Rhizopus arrhizus* could convert progesterone into 11-hydroxyprogesterone, which is then convertible into cortisone.

CORTISONE ACTIVITY

Although the predominant physiological effects of cortisone are related to the metabolisms of carbohydrates (it increases blood sugar level) and proteins (it causes a negative balance), an important effect of cortisone is in increasing the resistance of the body to stress.

The electrolyte (Na^+ and K^+) balance is affected to a varying degree, and usually it is recommended that the sodium ion intake be restricted or that diuretics be administered.

Cortisone is beneficial and often dramatic in the treatment of cases of rheumatoid arthritis, rheumatic fever, Still's disease, Addison's disease, inflammatory eye diseases, and psoriasis. It is effective in the treatment of various allergies, when epinephrine is no longer of use and when other simpler treatments have failed.

Cortisone's success has led to its use in the treatment of many diseases, and time must elapse before we can give a more critical evaluation of its possible therapeutic future and power.

Li and Reinhardt have proposed that too much growth hormone produced by the pituitary apparently causes rheumatoid arthritis. They found that pure growth hormone would produce classic arthritis symptoms occasionally in normal rats and in all rats with adrenal glands and ovaries removed. Tenderness, painful swelling of the joints, and other signs of arthritis were relieved when hydrocortisone was given. The explanation is that during youth, the growth hormone is primarily concerned with the growth of the body. In most cases, even an excessive flow of the hormone is not damaging, because the cortisone produced by the adrenal glands combats the action of the growth hormone. However, as people grow older and the body reaches maturity, the pituitary keeps on producing growth hormone at a significant rate; at the same time, the adrenals produce less cortisone. Then, the growth hormone has no place to go. It cannot go into normal body growth because normal growth is completed. Thus, the growth hormone starts making the joints grow with the end results of deformed fingers and painful, enlarged hips, knees, or elbows. When cortisone is injected into the arthritis victim, the action of the growth hormone is once again checked, and the patient gets better.

OTHER ADRENAL CORTICAL HORMONES

Two other substances are capable of prolonging the lives of adrenalectomized animals: progesterone and 21-acetoxypregnenolone.

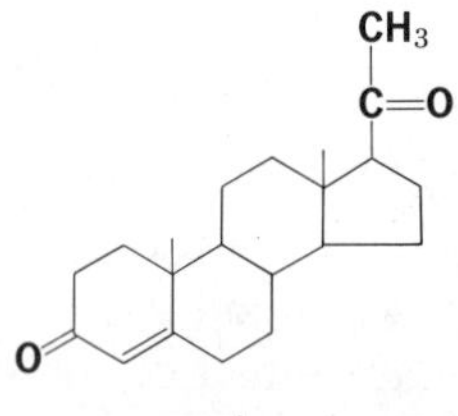

progesterone

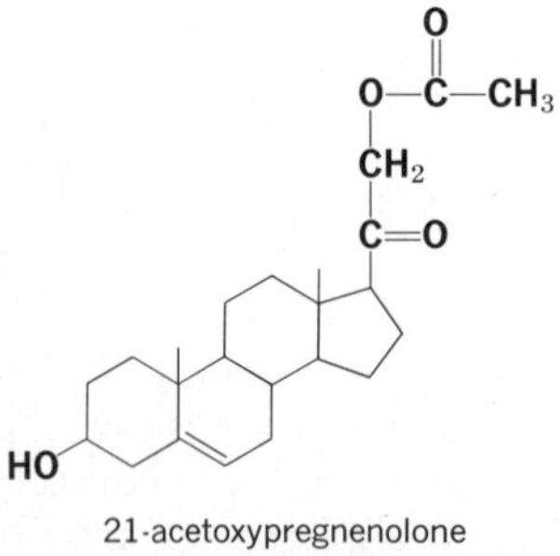

21-acetoxypregnenolone

These substances are sex (progestational) hormones, but, as can be seen, they are closely related structurally and chemically to the cortical hormones. In the body, these two substances are probably readily converted to the cortical hormones. The cortical activity of these progestational hormones probably accounts for the fact that pregnant animals survive adrenalectomy.

ORIGIN OF THE CORTICAL HORMONES

Tracer studies with radioactive elements and with nonradioactive isotopes have shown conclusively that the cortical hormones are synthesized in the body from cholesterol.

The function of the adrenal cortex is mainly controlled by the adrenalcorticotrophic hormone (ACTH) from the anterior pituitary, but other hormones probably act in conjunction with it. Aldosterone alone is not controlled by ACTH; the production of aldosterone is not stimulated by injection of ACTH or decreased with the removal of ACTH. The exact method of control of this hormone is not yet clear, but the mechanisms involved appear to be different from the ones involved in the control of the other adrenal cortical hormones. One possible explanation is that it is controlled by the electrolyte balance of the body.

THE RELATIONSHIP OF THE ADRENALS AND SEX

It has been found that the adrenals also produce sex hormones, both male and female. Whether these are by-products of cortical hormone synthesis, or made by the body as supplementary sex hormones in addition to those produced in the gonads, is not clear. However, they can markedly affect the sex characteristics.

In a disturbance of the adrenal cortex, which may involve excessive activity of the gland, such as in cortex tumors, an excessive amount of sex hormone is produced, and this may produce sex disorders.

Females may assume male secondary sex characteristics, such as excessive hair on the body, and normal female characteristics may be repressed. Normal males may become exceptionally virile or young individuals may exhibit precocious maturity. This is due to excessive sex hormone production.

There are cases of feminization of males, but this is less common. Although the adrenals may produce both female sex hormones and androgens (male sex hormones), apparently the androgens are the most potent sex hormones produced by these glands. It is significant that the urine of castrated males and of ovariectomized females still shows the presence of androgens.

The Sex Hormones

The most important feature differentiating the animate from the inanimate is that the former can reproduce itself.

The male sex possesses the property of producing the seeds (spermatozoa) and the female sex the eggs (ova). It has been shown that certain hormones are responsible for the growth and maintenance of the testes (where the spermatozoa are produced) and for the growth and activities of the ovaries (where the ova are formed).

There is a multiplicity of hormones involved in the formation and activities of both pairs of sex glands. Although much is known about these hormones, the complete function and interrelationships among them are as yet incompletely understood.

THE MALE SEX HORMONES

The male reproductive system is concerned with the production of spermatozoa in the testes and with their delivery for fertilization of the ovum in the female. The testes are also responsible for the maintenance of the masculine secondary sex and body characteristics.

The various hormones responsible for these effects are the gonadotrophins from the anterior lobe of the pituitary and the androgens (male-characteristic producing hormones) from the testes.

As mentioned before, the follicle-stimulating hormone (FSH) is responsible for the development of the seminiferous tubules and for the maintenance of spermatogenesis; the interstitial cell stimulating hormone (ICSH) develops the interstitial tissue of the testes and stimulates the production of the androgens.

In the absence of FSH and ICSH, the testes can produce neither spermatozoa nor androgens. Actually, some estrogens (female sex hormones) are also produced in the testes, due to stimulation from the pituitary. The exact site of estrogen production in the testes is not known.

THE ANDROGENS

The most important and potent androgen is testosterone, found in the testes. Somewhat less potent androgens, which are also found in the testes, are androstanedione and dehydroandrosterone. Androsterone, also a fairly strong androgen, second in activity to testosterone, is found in male urine. (*Cis-trans* isomers are not indicated in these structures.)

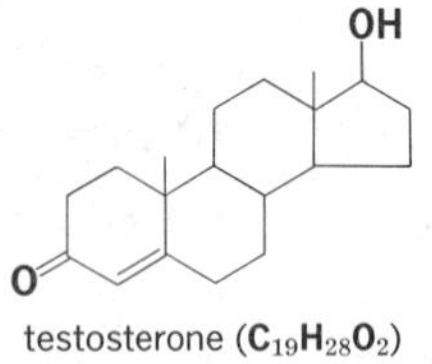

testosterone ($C_{19}H_{28}O_2$)

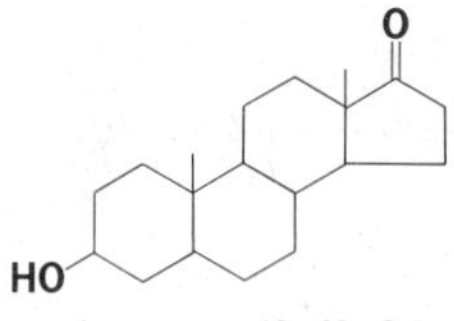

androsterone ($C_{19}H_{30}O_2$)

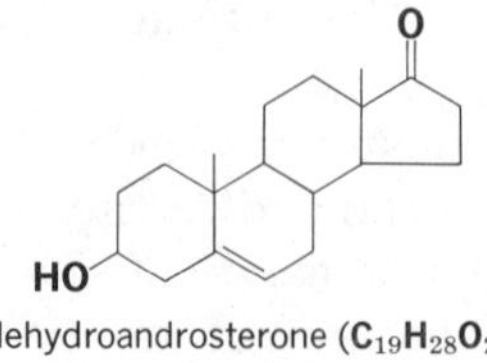

dehydroandrosterone ($C_{19}H_{28}O_2$)

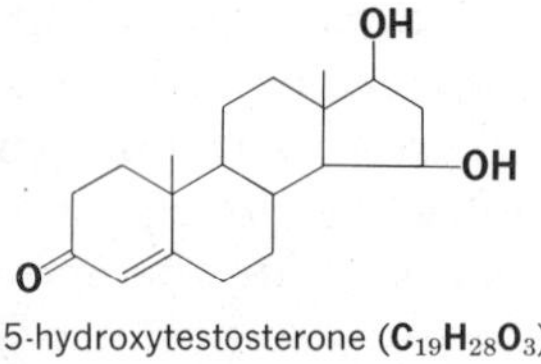

15-hydroxytestosterone ($C_{19}H_{28}O_3$)

As can be seen, the structures are all very similar. Testosterone is considered the parent substance; androsterone and several other androgens found in male urine are considered metabolic products that are excreted. Consequently, male urine exhibits a rather high degree of androgenic activity. Some estrogens are also found in male urine.

Because the urine of eunuchs (i.e., castrated males) and ovariectomized women still contains androgens and estrogens, it appears that these substances are produced in small quantities in the adrenal cortex.

As can be seen from the formulas, the chemistry of these compounds is quite complicated. It was not until the early 1930's that these structures were completely elucidated. Although these substances may be isolated from urine, a great deal of testosterone, for example, is produced synthetically by the various pharmaceutical and hormone production companies.

Clinically, the favored androgen is testosterone in the form of its propionate ester.

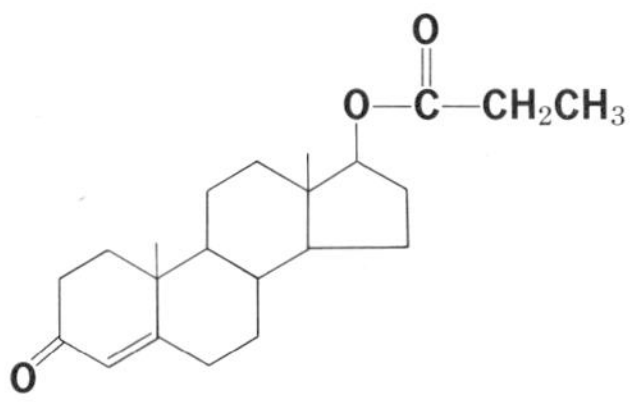

$O-\overset{\overset{O}{\|}}{C}-CH_2CH_3$

testosterone propionate

In this form, the androgen is slowly absorbed and its effects are of longer duration. The potency of the male sex hormones is conveniently tested on the capon (i.e., castrated rooster) or hen. The capon or hen fails to grow adequate wattles, comb, and ear lobes. When an androgen is given to a capon or hen, a pronounced growth of these atrophied tissues is evidenced.

SPERMATOGENESIS

The activity of the testes is dependent upon three types of cells: germ cells, interstitial cells of Leydig, and Sertoli cells. Until puberty, the testes are more or less nondifferentiated from those of early infancy. The seminiferous tubules are small, the germ cells are very few, and Sertoli cells and interstitial cells are undeveloped or not yet formed. The physiological and morphological changes produced at puberty are due to the stimulus of the gonadotrophic hormones from the pituitary.

At puberty, the interstitial cells develop and begin active production of androgens, and the seminiferous tubules develop. When the child becomes 12 or 13 years old, the interstitial cells and Sertoli cells are essentially differentiated, and the germ cells are active: Spermatogenesis is an active process. During the next two or three years, the differentiation is completed, and the testes assume the complete adult pattern.

In spermatogenesis, the germ cells undergo the complicated process of cell division—the various cell changes and stages and the splitting of the chromosomes—and the resultant cell is a spermatozoon. Apparently, at this stage, the Sertoli cells aid in some way the further development of the spermatozoa, which then go down the seminiferous tubules, the efferent ductules, and to the epididymis. In the epididymis (a coiled tube about 18 feet long), the spermatozoa further mature and increase in motility and fertility to complete activity.

ACTION OF THE ANDROGENS

Although there is some argument on this point, it still appears that the androgens are not required for the stimulus of spermatogenesis. The formation of sperm is apparently due to the stimulus from the gonadotrophic hormones from the pituitary. The androgens are responsible for the secondary sex characteristics.

The androgens affect:

1. *The genital organs.* The androgens are responsible for the normal growth of the penis, scrotum, prostate gland, and the other portions of the genital tract.

2. *Hair.* The growth and distribution of body hair, one of the most conspicuous of the secondary sex characteristics, is caused by the androgens. Castrates have sparse pubic hair, but this is probably due to the small amount of androgens produced in the adrenals.

3. *Voice.* The androgens are responsible for the depth of voice which differentiates men from boys. It is interesting to note that androgens cause the same deepening of voice in women as that in men.

4. *Muscle.* The androgens are presumably responsible for the muscular strength of males as compared to that of females.

5. *Subcutaneous fat.* It appears that the distribution of subcutaneous fat is influenced by androgens. The pattern for the distribution of fat in men is quite different from that in women.

6. *Skeleton.* It seems that the androgens affect skeletal growth, but there are some inconsistencies; that is, prepubertal castrates are frequently quite tall.

7. *Color and texture of the skin.* Castrates have skin that is furrowed, soft, and pale in color. Castrates have little or no ability to tan. The administration of androgens to castrates makes the skin normal, that is, firm, ruddy, and of a darker color (flesh color), and it then may tan on exposure to sunlight.

8. *Metabolism.* There are indications that the nitrogen, sodium, potassium, inorganic phosphorus, and chloride ion metabolisms are dependent upon androgens.

9. *Sebaceous glands.* The androgens increase the secretions of the

sebaceous glands. Acne vulgaris is an inflammation of the sebaceous glands, and the androgens seem to be acnegenic.

THERAPY

The androgens may be given in cases of underproduction of the male sex hormones, hypogonadism. Injections appear to be more effective than oral doses, partly because androgens undergo metabolism in the liver.

THE FEMALE SEX HORMONES

The natural female sex hormones are steroids. They are of two types: the estrogens and the progestational hormones. These two types of hormones, in conjunction with the follicle-stimulating hormone and the luteinizing hormone from the anterior pituitary, are responsible for the secondary sex characteristics in the female, govern the complete menstrual cycle, and are involved in the maintenance of the fetus during pregnancy.

THE ESTROGENS (*estrus producing hormones*)

The principal naturally occurring estrogens are estradiol, estrone, and estratriol.

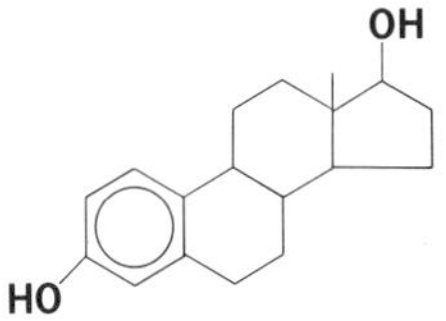

OH O OH OH

HO HO HO

estradiol ($C_{18}H_{24}O_2$) 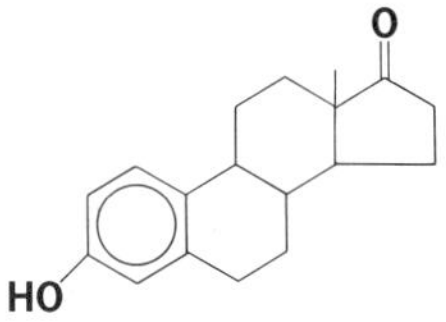 estrone ($C_{18}H_{22}O_2$) 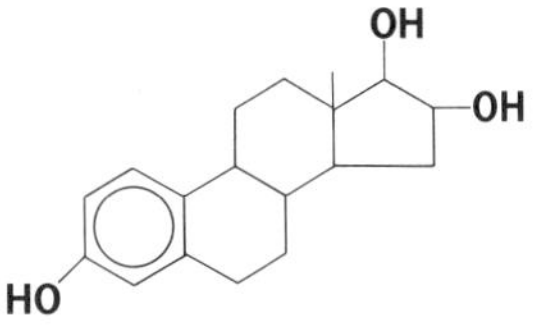 estratriol ($C_{18}H_{24}O_3$)

The estrogens are produced by the ovaries, in part by the adrenals, and also by the placenta in pregnant females. The estrogens are found in varying amounts in the blood and urine, and the concentrations depend upon the time of the menstrual cycle or pregnancy. As the term of pregnancy increases, the amount of estrogens excreted in the urine rises markedly and reaches a very high level before parturition, after which the level decreases rapidly to a normal value. Just before ovulation, the estrogens reach a maximum concentration in the blood.

The term "estrus" was originally used to denote the time when female animals are in "heat" or sexually excited. This generally coincides with the time of ovulation. In the human species, ovulation also causes a slight elevation of the body temperature.

It is surprising that in one species, the equine (e.g., horses, zebra, etc.), the male contains and excretes more estrogen than the female. The urine of the stallion is very rich in the estrogenic hormones, and the estrone used medicinally may come from this source. Today, however, most of the estrone is prepared by partial synthesis.

The estrogens are the primary female sex hormones and are responsible for the development of all the female secondary sex characteristics. By secondary sex characteristics we mean the growth of pubic and axillary hair and the development of the accessory reproductive organs (the uterus and vagina) and the mammary glands. The estrogens are also responsible for the proliferation of the endometrium during the menstrual cycle.

Some other estrogens have been isolated from the urine of pregnant mares. They are equilin ($C_{18}H_{20}O_2$), hippulin ($C_{18}H_{20}O_2$), and equilenin ($C_{18}H_{18}O_2$). They are all steroids.

Many other compounds have been synthesized that exhibit estrogenic activity, and many of these active compounds are not steroids. It has not been possible to account for the hormonal activity of some of the compounds, but in others it appears that the active synthetic material resembles the structure of the natural estrogens.

A well-known and very active synthetic estrogen is stilbestrol. Stilbestrol is a derivative of stilbene. If we write the stilbestrol structure, however, in a certain way, the relationship between it and the steroids becomes quite apparent. Note that stilbestrol has the same molecular formula as equilenin ($C_{18}H_{18}O_2$).

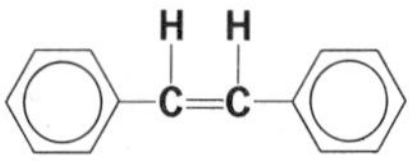

stilbene

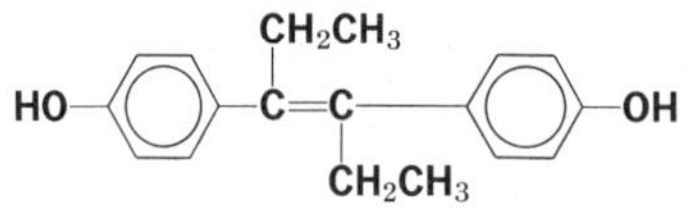

stilbestrol ($C_{18}H_{20}O_2$)

If we write stilbestrol in another way, it more closely resembles equilenin or estradiol. Stilbestrol is about five times more active than estrone.

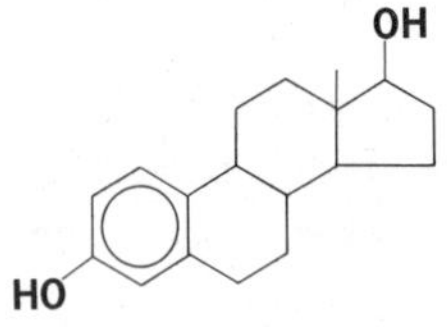

estradiol

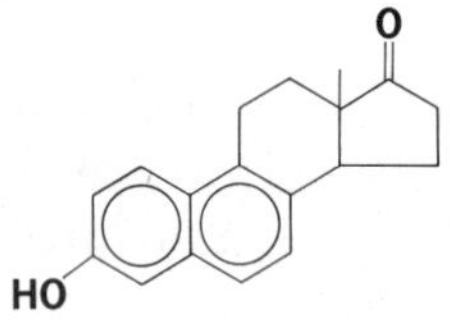

equilenin

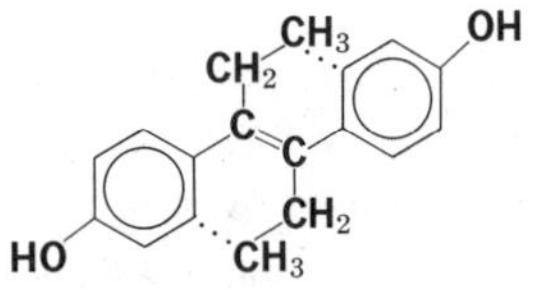

stilbestrol (*the dotted lines are indicated to stress the resemblance*)

THE PROGESTATIONAL HORMONES

The primary progestational hormone appears to be progesterone, $C_{21}H_{30}O_2$, although a naturally occurring product, $C_{21}H_{28}O_2$, described by Wettstein, is reported to be three times as active as progesterone.

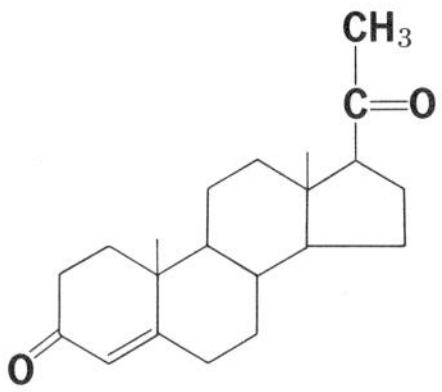

progesterone ($C_{21}H_{30}O_2$) 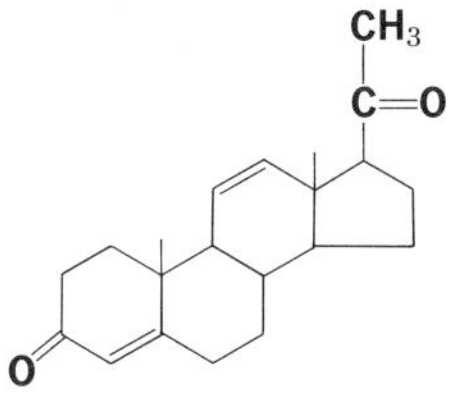 $C_{21}H_{28}O_2$ 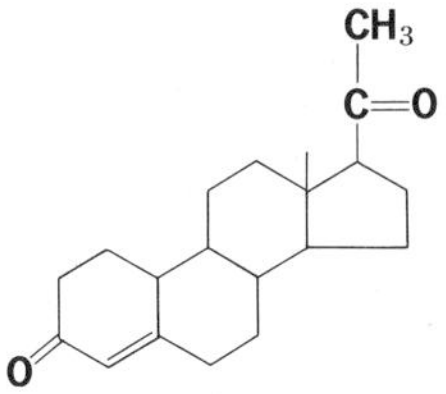 19-norprogesterone ($C_{20}H_{28}O_2$)

Note that a synthetic product, 19-norprogesterone, prepared by Djerasi, is reported to be five times as active as progesterone. Progesterone is produced synthetically by partial synthesis and is the cheapest of the synthetic hormones.

BIOLOGICAL PRODUCTION OF PROGESTERONE

Progesterone is produced by the corpus luteum, by the adrenal cortex, and by the placenta. The progesterone level in the blood begins to rise just before ovulation and reaches a maximum about the twentieth day of the menstrual cycle. It then declines to its preovulatory level.

Progesterone apparently causes relatively little growth of the endometrium during the normal menstrual cycle, and its main functions are related to other phenomena, such as the secretory activity of the uterine glands, the stimulation of the hypophysis, and the making of the uterus relatively quiescent (progestational activity). Under the influence of estrogen, the uterus is relatively motile and contractile. Progesterone is also important in maintaining the fetus during pregnancy.

In pregnant women, the progesterone level slowly rises. In the period of 90 to 120 days of pregnancy, the level begins to rise rapidly; it reaches a maximum just before parturition and then decreases rapidly to a very low value.

In 1960, oral contraceptives, which act on the body to simulate pregnancy, were introduced. These suppress ovulation and produce many of the effects of pregnancy. Many of these synthetic compounds lack the methyl group at carbon 19 and are referred to as 19-norsteroids. (The term *nor* means that a carbon is missing.) Some of these compounds are

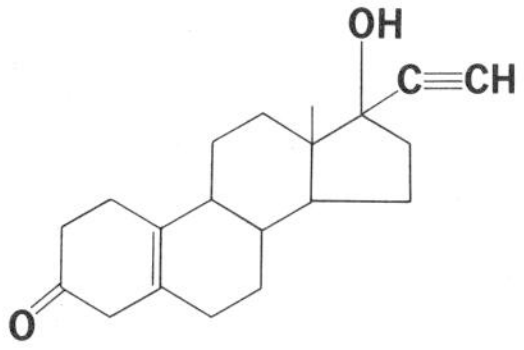

norethynodrel 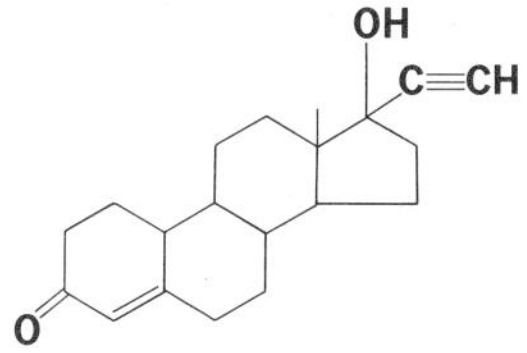 norethindrone 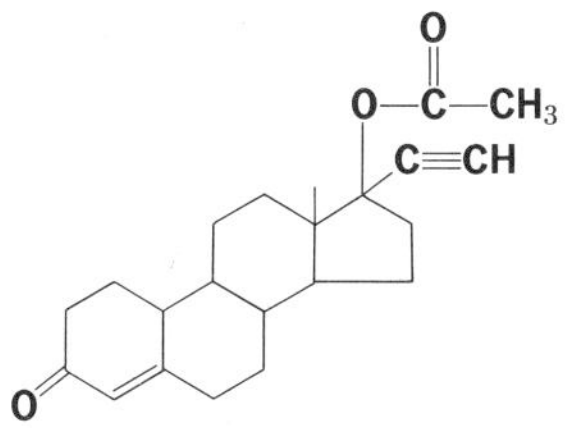 norethindrone acetate

some 19-norsteroids effective as oral contraceptives

Some regular steroids (carbon 19 methyl group present) are also effective as oral contraceptives.

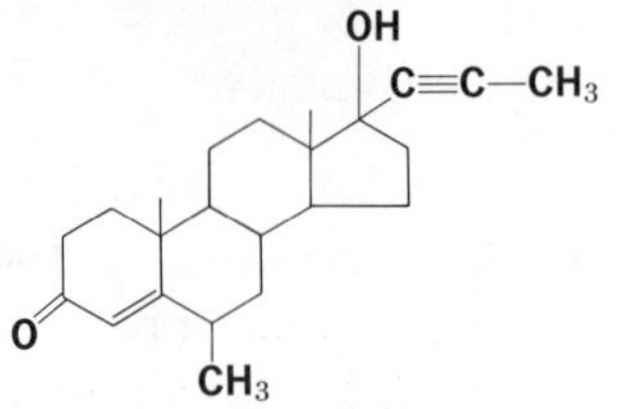

dimethisterone

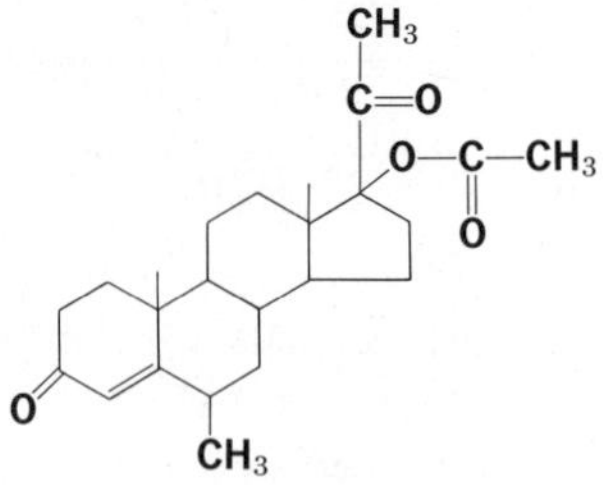

medroxyprogesterone acetate

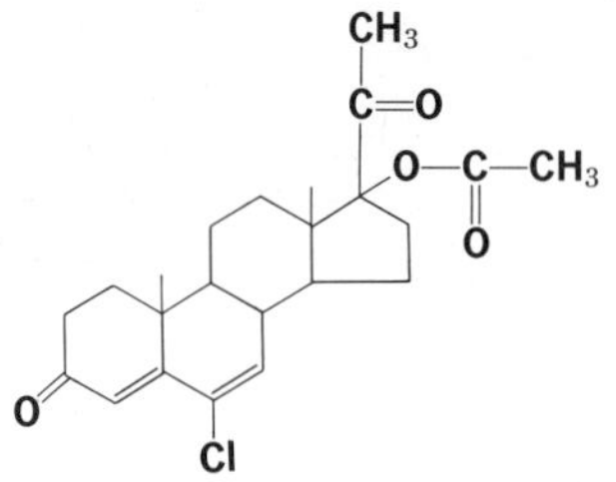

chlormadinone acetate

The contraceptives involve taking small amounts of synthetic progestins or estrogens together or in sequence.

The gastrointestinal hormones

These hormones have been mentioned in Chapters 13–15, but we shall briefly discuss them again. These hormones originate from the gastrointestinal system, are involved in the digestive processes, and are usually concerned with the flow of the various digestive juices.

Gastrin is the hormone in the pyloric mucosa that stimulates secretion of the gastric digestive juice and also causes contractions of the stomach walls. Although some believe it to be identical or similar to histamine, this has not been unequivocally established. Some physiologists believe it to be a proteinlike hormone.

In the duodenal mucosa, there is a hormone known as pancreatic *secretin,* which stimulates the flow of pancreatic juice. In the duodenal tissue (not mucosa), there is another hormone called *pancreozymin,* which stimulates the flow of enzymes from the pancreas. The hormones secretin and pancreozymin work together: one causes the pancreatic juice to be formed, and the other stimulates its flow into the duodenal canal to aid in the digestive process. Secretin has been characterized as a polypeptide, whereas pancreozymin is not yet well characterized.

Cholecystokinin is a gastrointestinal hormone liberated into the blood stream when food enters the duodenum. Cholecystokinin causes the gall bladder to contract: it thus forces bile juice through the ducts into the duodenum, so that the digestive process may be facilitated.

Enterogastrone is a hormone that inhibits gastric secretion. Apparently this hormone inhibits pepsin production more than hydrochloric acid production. This hormone may be regarded, in part, as a regulator of the emptying time of the stomach. The more enterogastrone, the less the gastric juice and, consequently, the longer the digestion in the stomach and the longer the emptying time. *Urogastrone,* a substance isolated from urine, is also a gastric depressant. Urogastrone may be a metabolic product of enterogastrone.

Enterocrinin is a hormone isolated by Nasset from both the small and large intestinal mucosa. It appears to be a protein in nature. Enterocrinin seems to affect the production as well as the secretion of intestinal juice.

REVIEW QUESTIONS

1. Define a hormone. What are the endocrine glands? Name several endocrine glands and one hormone each gland produces. List some steroid hormones. What are some protein hormones? What hormone is neither steroid nor protein? Name a synthetic female sex hormone.
2. Why is the pituitary gland sometimes called the "master gland"?
3. What is meant by trophic hormone?
4. What is ACTH? Of what use is ACTH?
5. What is meant by pressor activity?
6. What is meant by oxytocic effect?
7. What hormone contains iodine?
8. Of what use is radioactive sodium iodide in medicine?
9. What hormone is concerned with the metabolism of calcium and phosphorus in the body?
10. What hormone contains zinc? Why cannot insulin be taken orally? Compare the effect of a protamine insulin complex with insulin itself.
11. What is cortin? What is cortisone? What are some of the active hormones isolated from the adrenal cortex?
12. What are the gonads? What is an androgen? What is an estrogen? Define the term progestational hormone.
13. List some gastrointestinal hormones and their physiological effects.

1

appendix

Radioactivity

With the advent of the atomic bomb, the topic of radioactivity has become very important. In addition, the availability of radioactive isotopes for research, made possible by the Atomic Energy Commission, has contributed much to our fundamental knowledge and has helped create new therapeutic methods in medicine.

In ordinary chemical reactions, changes occur in the *orbital electron configuration.* In radioactive reactions, changes occur in the atomic *nucleus.* Removing one electron from the outermost shell simply changes the neutral sodium atom into the positive sodium ion, but removing one electron from the atomic nucleus is a profound change that results in the *conversion of one element into another.*

Radioactivity is concerned with the emission of certain particles from the nucleus of an unstable atom. Certain elements found in nature emit particles of their own accord and are referred to as *naturally radioactive.*

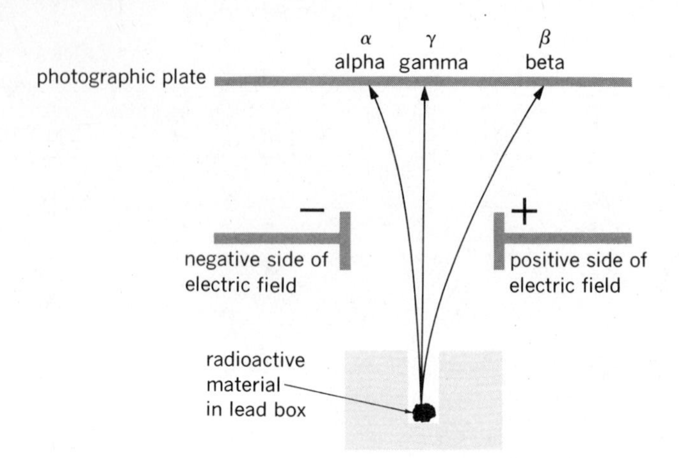

Figure A-1 Alpha, beta, and gamma rays in an electric field.

Some relatively stable elements can be bombarded with various particles and converted into unstable elements; hence, they are radioactive; we refer to this as *artificial or induced radioactivity.*

The nucleus of a naturally radioactive atom may emit three main particles: alpha (α), beta (β), and gamma (γ). Although other particles may be emitted, we shall not consider them here.

An *alpha particle* is a helium nucleus consisting of two protons and two neutrons.

2 p
2 n

If an element loses an α particle, it loses four units in atomic weight and two units in atomic number, because we determine atomic weight by the protons and neutrons in the nucleus and the atomic number by the protons in the nucleus.

Atoms can be conveniently designated as $^{1}_{1}H$, $^{9}_{4}Be$, $^{7}_{3}Li$, $^{238}_{92}U$, $^{23}_{11}Na$, etc., where the subscript designates atomic number and the superscript designates atomic weight. In the past, we have written *atomic* or *molecular equations,* such as

$$HCl + NaOH \longrightarrow NaCl + H_2O$$

In discussing radioactivity, we can write *nuclear equations,* such as

$$^{238}_{92}U - ^{4}_{2}He \longrightarrow ^{234}_{90}Th$$

or

$$^{238}_{92}U \longrightarrow ^{4}_{2}He + ^{234}_{90}Th$$

or

$$\text{(92 p, 146 n)} \longrightarrow \text{(2 p, 2 n)} + \text{(90 p, 144 n)}$$

These three equations all say the same thing. We can consider these equations *balanced* because the algebraic sum of the weights and numbers on one side equals the algebraic sum of the weights and numbers on the other side. These equations indicate that when uranium (at. no. 92, at. wt. 238) loses an α particle, it becomes a different element, thorium (at. no. 90, at. wt. 234). Naturally occurring thorium has atomic number 90 and atomic weight 232; therefore, the thorium produced from uranium in the above equation is an isotope of the naturally occurring substance.

The *beta particle* is an electron. The electron does not significantly influence the weight of an atom; therefore, its loss does not change the atomic weight. Beta elimination can be pictured as a neutron in the nucleus splitting into a proton and an electron. The electron, then, comes off as a β particle, leaving the proton in the nucleus. The gain of a proton thereby increases the atomic number of the element.

In an oversimplified way we can say that when a β particle is emitted from the nucleus, a neutron is changed into a proton.

$$\underset{\text{neutron}}{(\pm)} \longrightarrow \underset{\text{proton}}{(+)} + \underset{\text{electron}}{(-)}$$

or

$$\underset{\text{neutron}}{(\pm)} \longrightarrow \underset{\text{proton}}{(+)} + \underset{\text{beta particle}}{\beta}$$

If thorium of atomic number 90 and atomic weight 234 loses a β particle, it becomes protactinium Pa (at. no. 91, at. wt. 234).

$${}^{234}_{90}\mathrm{Th} \longrightarrow \beta + {}^{234}_{91}\mathrm{Pa}$$

or

$$\text{(90 p, 144 n)} \longrightarrow \beta + \text{(91 p, 143 n)}$$

or[1]

$${}^{234}_{90}\mathrm{Th} \longrightarrow {}^{0}_{-1}e + {}^{234}_{91}\mathrm{Pa}$$

[1] The beta particle, which is an electron, is designated as ${}^{0}_{-1}e$. The superscript zero is easy to understand because the electron carries essentially no weight. The subscript indicates the atomic number, or the charge on the nucleus, or the number of protons in the nucleus. An electron, naturally, has no protons, but, more important, as an electron is emitted from the nucleus, an additional proton appears in the remaining nucleus. To make the nuclear equation balanced algebraically, the subscript is thus indicated as -1.

From these equations, we see that the loss of a β particle gives a different element of the *same* atomic weight, but *one higher atomic number.*

The *gamma rays,* which are similar to x rays, do not affect the atomic weight or the atomic number and may be considered excess energy radiated from the nucleus due to the other nuclear transformations. The emission of either α or β particles is generally accompanied by simultaneous emission of gamma rays.

Properties of the emitted particles

Alpha particles, because they are the heaviest of the three types of radiation, move the slowest (about 30,000 km/sec) and have the lowest penetrating power (α particles travel about 3 to 7 cm in ordinary air). Because they are doubly positively charged, α particles have the highest ionizing power (as they travel through gas, they strip electrons from the gas, forming neutral helium atoms, and leave behind charged gas molecules).

The β particle, being quite small, has a high speed, varying between 100,000 and 300,000 km/sec (the speed of light). The β particles are smaller and move faster than α particles; thus, their penetrating power is about 10–100 times greater than that of α particles. The ionizing power of β particles is about $\frac{1}{100}$ to $\frac{1}{200}$ that of α particles.

Gamma rays are electromagnetic waves traveling with the velocity of light. Because they have no mass, γ rays have the greatest penetrating power, about 20 times greater than that of β particles. The ionizing power of γ rays approximately equals that of β particles, but, because the γ rays travel greater distances than β particles, the amount of *ionization per unit distance* is smaller than in the case of β particles.

Table A-1 Rays emitted from radioactive substances[a]

RAY	CHARACTER	CHARGE[b]	MASS[c]	VELOCITY	PENETRATION
α	He^{++}	+2	4.0026	about 0.1 speed of light	stopped by paper or human skin
β	electron	−1	0.000548	up to 0.9 speed of light	several mm in human tissue
γ	short X rays	0	0	speed of light[d]	human body or several feet of concrete

[a] Adapted from L. P. Eblin, *Elements of Chemistry.* New York: Harcourt, Brace & World, 1965, p. 361.

[b] The unit of charge employed here is the amount of charge of the electron itself.

[c] The mass is expressed on the atomic-weight scale, defined as $C^{12} = 12$ exactly.

[d] The velocity of light in a vacuum is 3.00×10^{10} cm per second.

Our discussion here has been necessarily limited. We should mention that the speed, penetrating power, ionizing power, etc., of the particles actually depends on the source of these particles and, consequently, on the initial energy.

Methods of detecting radioactivity

The number of ionizing particles at a given place can be conveniently measured by a Geiger counter. A Geiger counter consists of a glass tube containing a metal cylinder with a metallic wire through its center (Figure A-2). The air has been removed and some inert gas introduced (i.e., argon and some alcohol). The passage of some ionizing radiation through the tube causes a breakdown of electrical potential between the wire and the cylinder. This discharge can be amplified and recorded or registered in many ways. A common method is to amplify electronically the pulses coming from the counter in order to produce a click at each discharge. In many experiments, the discharges are automatically recorded by a counting device.

Workers who may be exposed to harmful radiation often wear detection instruments. The pocket ionization chamber is widely used. This indicating mechanism is so small that it resembles a fountain pen and can be conveniently clipped in one's pocket. By measuring the electrical potential at the start of the day and the residual charge at the end of the day, it is easy to determine how much radiation has entered the chamber. The greater the residual charge, the less the exposure to radiation, and the less the residual charge, the greater the exposure to radiation.

The film badge is also used and may be conveniently clipped on one's pocket. By examining the photographic film in the badge after a certain unit of time, the radiation to which the body has been exposed can be determined.

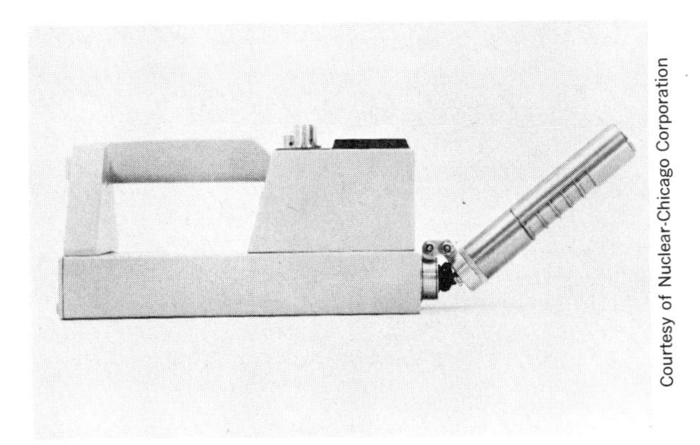

Courtesy of Nuclear-Chicago Corporation

Figure A-2 Beta-gamma count meter.

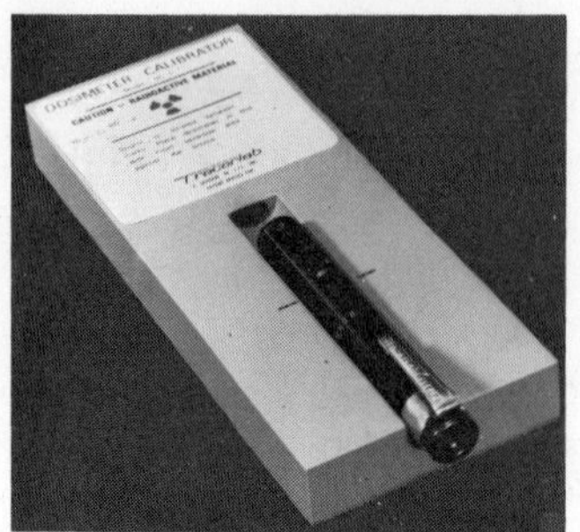

Courtesy of Tracerlab, Inc. **Figure A-3** Pocket ionization chamber.

Natural radioactivity

Most elements with atomic numbers less than 84 usually have at least one stable isotope, although other isotopes of the same element may be radioactive. All the isotopes of elements higher than 83 are radioactive, and most of these radioactive isotopes are found in nature. Radioactive elements disintegrate or decay at different rates, and this disintegration rate is often very useful. The half-life is a convenient way to characterize a radioactive element's instability. The *half-life* of an element is the time interval in which half the radioactive atoms in a sample disintegrate; the half-life remains constant, regardless of the number of atoms in the sample. For every specified unit of time, half the radioactive atoms disintegrate. The units of time may be years, days, hours, minutes, seconds, etc. For example, suppose a radioactive isotope had a half-life of one week, and suppose we had two grams of that isotope. In this case, after one week, we would be left with 1 gram, in another week $\frac{1}{2}$ gram, another week only $\frac{1}{4}$ gram would remain; at the end of four weeks, only $\frac{1}{8}$ gram of the starting isotope would remain.

Courtesy of Tracerlab, Inc. **Figure A-4** Film badges.

Table A-2 Some half lives

LONG-LIVED (YR)	MODERATELY LONG-LIVED (YR)	SHORT-LIVED
$^{238}_{92}$**U** 5,000,000,000	$^{226}_{88}$**Ra** 1,580	$^{131}_{53}$**I** 8 days
$^{234}_{92}$**U** 1,000,000	$^{14}_{6}$**C** 5,100	$^{32}_{15}$**P** 14.3 days
$^{99}_{43}$**Te** 500,000	$^{241}_{95}$**Am** 458	$^{24}_{11}$**Na** 14.8 hr
$^{59}_{28}$**Ni** 50,000		$^{42}_{19}$**K** 12.4 hr
$^{36}_{17}$**Cl** 1,000,000		$^{214}_{82}$**Pb** 27 min

In Table A-2, we divide the stability of radioactive elements into three categories: long-lived (much more than thousands of years), moderately long-lived (about several thousand years), and short-lived (ranging from years and days to fractions of a second). From our observations of radioactive elements, it appears that there are four well-defined series. In a radioactive series, the original unstable element emits a particle and changes into another unstable element, which emits its characteristic particle and changes into another unstable element; this process continues until a stable nonradioactive element is formed. The particle written over the arrow is emitted spontaneously from the element to its left.

Uranium Series

$$^{238}_{92}\mathrm{U} \xrightarrow{\alpha} {}^{234}_{90}\mathrm{Th} \xrightarrow{\beta} {}^{234}_{91}\mathrm{Pa} \xrightarrow{\beta} {}^{234}_{92}\mathrm{U} \xrightarrow{\alpha} {}^{230}_{90}\mathrm{Th} \xrightarrow{\alpha} {}^{226}_{88}\mathrm{Ra} \xrightarrow{\alpha} {}^{222}_{86}\mathrm{Rn}$$

$$\downarrow \alpha$$

$$^{210}_{84}\mathrm{Po} \xleftarrow{\beta} {}^{210}_{83}\mathrm{Bi} \xleftarrow{\beta} {}^{210}_{82}\mathrm{Pb} \xleftarrow{\alpha} {}^{214}_{84}\mathrm{Po} \xleftarrow{\beta} {}^{214}_{83}\mathrm{Bi} \xleftarrow{\beta} {}^{214}_{82}\mathrm{Pb} \xleftarrow{\alpha} {}^{218}_{84}\mathrm{Po}$$

$$\downarrow \alpha$$

$$^{206}_{82}\mathrm{Pb}$$

stable

In the uranium series, we see that as unstable $^{238}_{92}U$ changes into the stable $^{206}_{82}Pb$, a total of 8 α and 6 β particles are emitted.

Actinium Series

$$^{231}_{90}\mathrm{Th} \xrightarrow{\beta} {}^{231}_{91}\mathrm{Pa} \xrightarrow{\alpha} {}^{227}_{89}\mathrm{Ac} \xrightarrow{\beta} {}^{227}_{90}\mathrm{Th} \xrightarrow{\alpha} {}^{223}_{88}\mathrm{Ra}$$

$$\downarrow \alpha$$

$$^{211}_{84}\mathrm{Po} \xleftarrow{\beta} {}^{211}_{83}\mathrm{Bi} \xleftarrow{\beta} {}^{211}_{82}\mathrm{Pb} \xleftarrow{\alpha} {}^{215}_{84}\mathrm{Po} \xleftarrow{\alpha} {}^{219}_{86}\mathrm{Rn}$$

$$\downarrow \alpha$$

$$^{207}_{82}\mathrm{Pb}$$

stable

In the actinium series, unstable $^{231}_{90}Th$ changes into stable $^{207}_{82}Pb$, and a total of 6 α and 4 β particles are emitted.

Thorium Series

$$^{232}_{90}\text{Th} \xrightarrow{\alpha} {}^{228}_{88}\text{Ra} \xrightarrow{\beta} {}^{228}_{89}\text{Ac} \xrightarrow{\beta} {}^{228}_{90}\text{Th} \xrightarrow{\alpha} {}^{224}_{88}\text{Ra} \xrightarrow{\alpha} {}^{220}_{86}\text{Rn}$$

$$^{220}_{86}\text{Rn} \xrightarrow{\alpha} {}^{216}_{84}\text{Po} \xrightarrow{\alpha} {}^{212}_{82}\text{Pb} \xrightarrow{\beta} {}^{212}_{83}\text{Bi} \xrightarrow{\beta} {}^{212}_{84}\text{Po} \xrightarrow{\alpha} {}^{208}_{82}\text{Pb}$$

$^{208}_{82}\text{Pb}$
stable

In the thorium series, unstable $^{232}_{90}\text{Th}$ changes into stable $^{208}_{82}\text{Pb}$, and a total of 6 α and 4 β particles are emitted.

Neptunium Series

$$^{241}_{94}\text{Pu} \xrightarrow{\beta} {}^{241}_{95}\text{Am} \xrightarrow{\alpha} {}^{237}_{93}\text{Np} \xrightarrow{\alpha} {}^{233}_{91}\text{Pa} \xrightarrow{\beta} {}^{233}_{92}\text{U} \xrightarrow{\alpha} {}^{229}_{90}\text{Th}$$

$$^{229}_{90}\text{Th} \xrightarrow{\alpha} {}^{225}_{88}\text{Ra} \xrightarrow{\beta} {}^{225}_{89}\text{Ac} \xrightarrow{\alpha} {}^{221}_{87}\text{Fr} \xrightarrow{\alpha} {}^{217}_{85}\text{At} \xrightarrow{\alpha} {}^{213}_{83}\text{Bi}$$

$$^{213}_{83}\text{Bi} \xrightarrow{\beta} {}^{213}_{84}\text{Po} \xrightarrow{\alpha} {}^{209}_{82}\text{Pb} \xrightarrow{\beta} {}^{209}_{83}\text{Bi}$$

stable

In the neptunium series, unstable $^{241}_{94}\text{Pu}$ changes into stable $^{209}_{83}\text{Bi}$, and a total of 8 α and 5 β particles are emitted.

The uranium, actinium, and thorium series have been known for some time, because the elements in these series can be detected, by one means or another, on the earth today. Closer examination of the neptunium series shows that it contains many elements unknown to man before 1942. There had been considerable speculation as to why the neptunium series did not occur naturally, and we can now say that the half-lives of many of the neptunium series are so short, in comparison to geological time, that in the twentieth century, the entire series had disappeared from the earth, leaving only the stable end product. Only by recreating the precursors to $^{209}_{83}\text{Bi}$ could we follow in detail the steps of the neptunium series.

A very interesting use of radioactive elements is in the determination of the age of a specimen. Anyone or anything that has been "alive" has been exchanging its carbon atoms with the carbon atoms of the atmosphere (as carbon dioxide). The process stops with the death of the person, or animal, or tree, etc. Examination of the carbon atoms in the specimen today, coupled with the knowledge of the carbon atom composition of the atmosphere, has enabled us to readily calculate the age of the specimen. This method is quite useful for dating many wood, rug, mummy, bone, etc., specimens. For samples older than 20,000 years, the method is not very useful.

By examination of rock specimens and careful determination of the amount of stable lead and radioactive uranium concentrations, it is possible to estimate the age of the earth. Such calculations indicate that the earth is approximately six billion years old. By using other radioactive isotopes as indicators, careful dating of rocks has furnished much useful and fascinating information about the past geologic upheavals and changes.

Artificial radioactivity

Experiments performed as early as 1919 showed that it was possible to transmute elements by bombarding their nuclei with fast-moving particles. These subatomic projectiles would either dislodge pieces from the nucleus, and thus change it, or add parts to the nucleus and also change it, or transmute the element.

Alpha particles, protons, and deuterons are some of the particles used in the bombardment. For example,

$$^{14}_{7}N + ^{4}_{2}He \longrightarrow ^{17}_{8}O + ^{1}_{1}H$$

nitrogen, alpha particle, isotope of oxygen, proton

$$^{9}_{4}Be + ^{4}_{2}He \longrightarrow ^{12}_{6}C + ^{1}_{0}n$$

beryllium, alpha particle, carbon, neutron

$$^{12}_{6}C + ^{1}_{1}H \longrightarrow ^{13}_{7}N$$

carbon, proton, nitrogen isotope

$$^{32}_{16}S + ^{2}_{1}H \longrightarrow ^{30}_{15}P + ^{4}_{2}He$$

sulfur, hydrogen isotope[2], phosphorus isotope, alpha particle

$$^{23}_{11}Na + ^{2}_{1}H \longrightarrow ^{24}_{11}Na + ^{1}_{1}H$$

sodium, hydrogen isotope, sodium isotope, proton

Because of their positive charge, α particles, protons, and deuterons have some limitations. You would expect that a positive projectile's approach to a positively charged nucleus would create electrical repulsive forces, because *like charges repel.* This is indeed true; consequently, in order to overcome these repulsive forces, particles must be hurled with tremendous speed and energy at the nucleus. The cyclotron and the linear accelerator are two man-made devices used to hurl small charged particles at nuclei.

The cyclotron works on the principle of the sling shot. A positive particle is caught in an electric field and hurled around in the field ("cycled"; hence, the name cyclotron) faster and faster until sufficient speed is attained; then the particle is released and hurled at the target atoms. The linear accelerator is not very useful for positively charged particles but is exceed-

[2] Hydrogen, with an atomic weight of 2, is often called heavy hydrogen or deuterium, and this nucleus is sometimes written as D or ^{2}H and called a deuteron.

Courtesy of Argonne National Laboratory

Figure A-5 Beam of deuterons coming from Argonne National Laboratory's 60″ cyclotron.

ingly useful for accelerating electrons. The linear accelerator moves electrons in a straight line (linear manner) from one end of the machine to another. As the particles move through the machine, they accelerate; when they achieve the desired speed and have sufficient energy, they are released at the appropriate moment and position and hurled at the target atoms. Since the electron is so small, it must be hurled at fantastic speeds at a target nucleus to accomplish the desired nuclear change.

A very convenient projectile that circumvents the difficulties of both positively and negatively charged particles is the *neutron.* The neutron is neutral and also has an effective mass for bombarding the nucleus. Our only source of neutrons are nuclear reactions. This may sound self-contradictory, because to cause a certain type of nuclear reaction, we must have

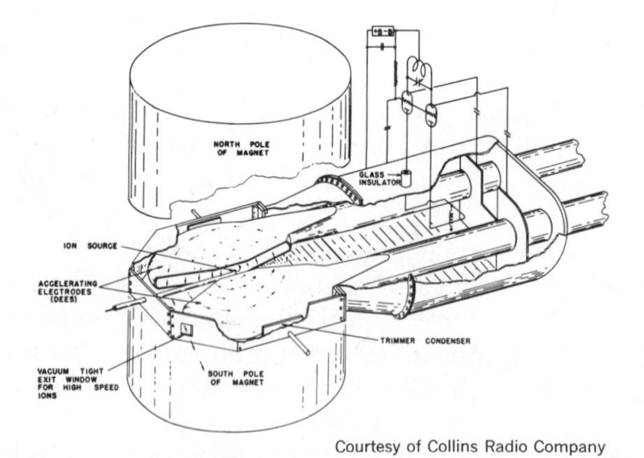

Courtesy of Collins Radio Company

Figure A-6 Schematic diagram of a conventional cyclotron.

Courtesy of Argonne National Laboratory

Figure A-7 A section of the ring magnet of Argonne National Laboratory's Zero Gradient Synchrotron as it appeared while under construction. The magnet coil had just been installed. The vacuum chamber, through which the protons pass, was fitted between the coil housings. Another set of magnet blocks, similar to those already in place, was installed on top of the vacuum chamber and coil. The ZGS has a design energy of 12.5 BeV. It has been in operation since August, 1963.

a nuclear reaction with which to begin. However, a naturally occurring α-particle emitter (i.e., radium) is easily combined with a light element (usually beryllium) to furnish neutrons conveniently.

$${}^{9}_{4}\mathbf{Be} + {}^{4}_{2}\mathbf{He} \longrightarrow {}^{12}_{6}\mathbf{C} + {}^{1}_{0}\mathbf{N}$$

A most prolific source of neutrons is the *nuclear chain reactor* or *pile*. A pile is an assembly of fissionable[3] material so arranged that after the first neutron has struck a nucleus, one or more neutrons are emitted, which in turn strike other nuclei, causing them to emit neutrons, and so on. This is called a *chain reaction,* and we see that once started, it is self-perpetuating; therefore, the convenient chain of reactions remains intact. Thus, the pile is an effective neutron producer, and, in addition, the number of available neutrons can be conveniently *controlled*. By using graphite or heavy water

[3] By fissionable material, we refer to certain isotopes, such as ${}^{235}_{92}\mathrm{U}$, ${}^{233}_{92}\mathrm{U}$, and ${}^{239}_{94}\mathrm{Pu}$. In fission, the entire nucleus is broken apart, not necessarily in equal parts, but in certain large fragments, by an atomic projectile such as the neutron. In this process of fission, a tremendous amount of energy is liberated (atomic energy). Whereas the atomic pile is a *controlled* nuclear chain reaction, the atomic bomb explosion is an *uncontrolled* nuclear chain reaction.

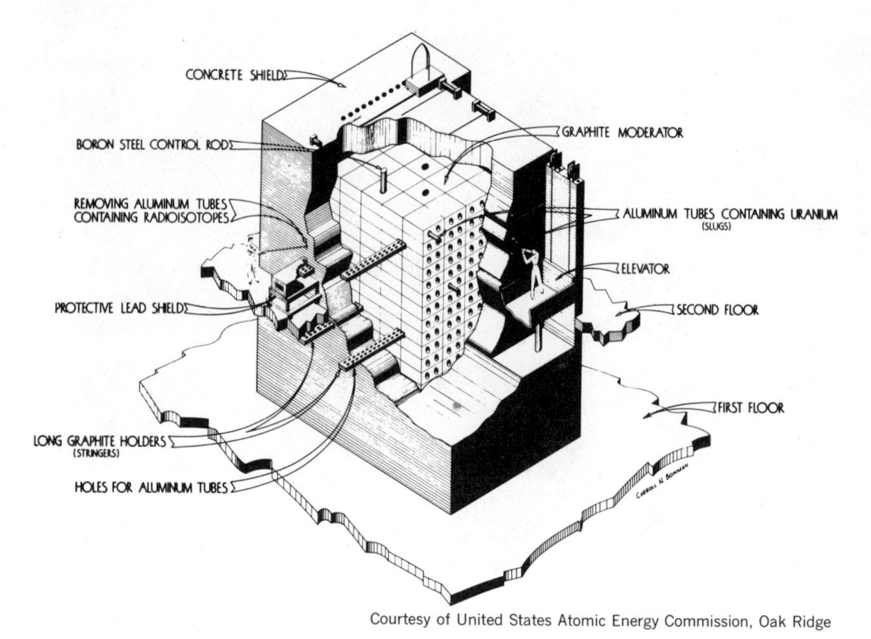

Courtesy of United States Atomic Energy Commission, Oak Ridge

Figure A-8 Simplified schematic of a uranium reactor. Heat produced in a reactor such as this would need to reach a turbo-generator via a steam boiler in order to produce electricity.

to slow down the neutrons, and by using cadmium or boron rods to absorb any excess neutrons, one can regulate the speed and the amount of neutrons being produced.

Some radioactive elements of interest

In administering radioactive isotopes to humans, we have certain limitations. We cannot use a radioactive isotope with a moderately long half-life, which might accumulate in the body and be damaging to our system. Also, we cannot take internally isotopes that give out radiations so powerful that they would cause serious damage to a major portion of the body. It is most convenient to use isotopes that disintegrate into harmless species in a relatively short time. Note also that to use certain radioactive isotopes, we require proper measuring instruments and properly trained personnel.

${}^{14}_{6}C$

Carbon-14 can be produced by bombarding the stable isotope, carbon-13, with neutrons, but it is preferable to make it from stable nitrogen. A nitrate salt is irradiated with neutrons. Carbon dioxide and carbon monoxide are formed, and the product is isolated as $Ba^{14}CO_3$ (barium carbonate containing carbon-14). The $Ba^{14}CO_3$ can be acidified to yield $^{14}CO_2$, which, in turn, can be used to make many valuable tracer compounds.

$$\mathbf{Ba^{14}CO_3 + H_2SO_4 \longrightarrow BaSO_4 + H_2O + \underset{\text{gas}}{^{14}CO_2}}$$

As carbon-14 decays, it gives off very low-energy β particles. The radiation is so low in energy that it cannot penetrate the walls of a glass container. Therefore, if ^{14}C is kept in ordinary closed glass containers, there is little danger in handling it. The true danger lies in its ingestion or absorption into the body. Under these circumstances, some radioactive carbon makes its way into bone tissue and may remain for a very long time. The accumulation of dangerous quantities of carbon-14 in bone tissue may result in the destruction of this tissue and eventual death. Carbon-14, therefore, must be used with extreme caution on human subjects, and the amount of radioactive carbon-14 atoms is exceedingly small. Carbon-14, however, is employed in experiments on animals and is used in many organic compounds as tracers. The availability of organic compounds containing

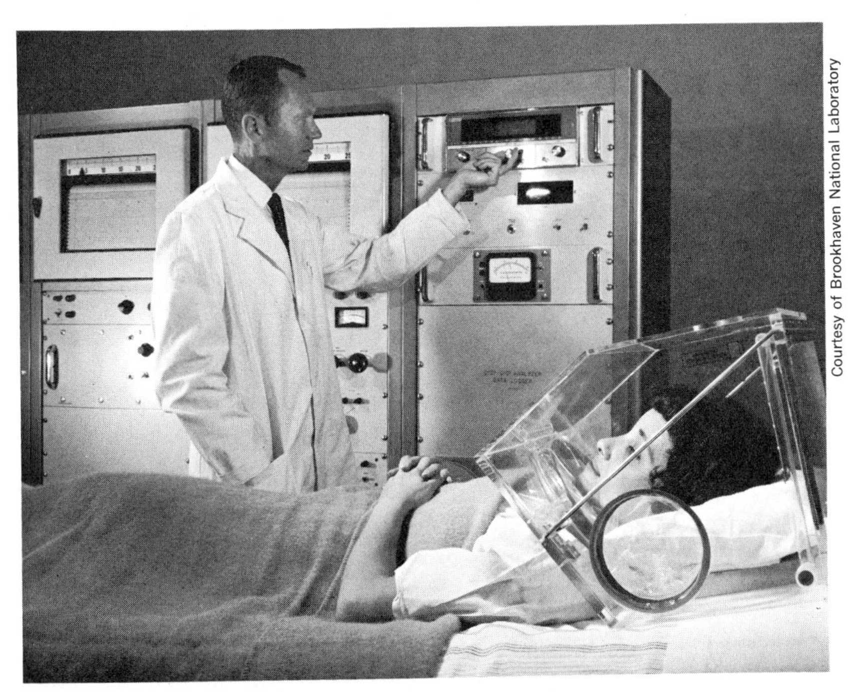

Courtesy of Brookhaven National Laboratory

Figure A-9 Collection of breath from a patient for the continuous analysis of radioactive carbon-14 in expired carbon dioxide, in studies of patient metabolism. The patient has been given sugar labeled with carbon-14 and as the sugar is used by the body, the carbon-14 is released and is expelled in the breath, where it can be detected by means of the radioactivity.

Courtesy of Union Carbide Corporation

Figure A-10 The thickness of a sheet of plastic film is being checked automatically by a radioactive gauge.

carbon-14 has opened up vast fields of research. This has enabled us to get precise data concerning some of the fundamental body processes. Since carbon-14 is moderately long-lived, its storage and shipment is not a serious problem.

USE

Suppose we have a box containing a large number of small white balls, all the same size. If we remove one ball, then put it back, and shake the box vigorously to mix the balls, we would not know which ball was originally removed because they are all alike. However, if we paint one ball black and then mix the balls by shaking the box, it would not be too difficult to find the painted ball. We say that the painted ball has been "tagged" or "labeled." The color difference enables us to "trace" the black ball.

If we feed an animal food that contains ordinary carbon atoms, we cannot tell whether these ingested atoms remain in its body or leave its body, because all the carbon atoms entering and leaving the body are alike. If we label the carbon atoms by using radioactive carbon-14, we can now identify these atoms quite readily, because these tagged atoms give off radiation that ordinary carbon atoms do not. We can tell not only if the tagged atoms remain in the body, but also where they are. By moving a device, which detects radioactivity, all over the body, we can discover the areas giving the greatest intensity of radiation and thus locate the radioactive atoms. We can also tell how long a compound remains in certain areas, what happens to it, and in what form it is excreted in urine and feces.

$^{131}_{53}I$

Radioactive iodine-131 can be made by bombarding tellurium with neutrons to form radioactive tellurium, which decays into radioactive iodine-131.

$$^{130}_{52}Te + ^{1}_{0}n \longrightarrow ^{131}_{52}Te$$

$$^{131}_{52}Te \longrightarrow ^{131}_{53}I + \beta \text{ particle}$$

At first, this method was widely used, but now most of the radioactive iodine-131 is obtained from extraction of the fission products of uranium. One of the fission products formed in this process is $^{131}_{52}Te$, which then gives off its β particle to form iodine-131. Radioactive iodine-131 emits strong γ rays, which easily penetrate the entire body. Iodine-131 is also a β-particle emitter. The glass vial containing the sample is usually kept in a stainless steel cylinder, which in turn is placed in a thick-walled lead container. Since the half-life of iodine-131 is about 8 days, the manufacture, storage, and shipment are very important considerations.

USE

In administering radioactive iodine in the form of sodium iodide (NaI) to the body, the radioactive iodine atoms usually form thyroxine and diiodotyrosine, two important iodine-containing compounds in the body. These iodine-containing compounds are found in the thyroid gland, and consequently the greatest radioactivity is found there. When a patient has an overactive thyroid gland, the tissues grow and the gland greatly increases in size (hyperthyroidism). Because of their radiation, the presence of some compounds containing radioactive iodine in the thyroid would tend to destroy some of the tissue and thus avoid surgery. This then is the great use of radioactive iodine. One must limit the dosage, however, because too much radioactivity in one area may cause the development of cancerous tissue. In certain actual cases of thyroid gland cancer, radioactive iodine treatment has been successful because it also appears able to destroy cancer tissue. A patient with cancer of the thyroid gland often suffers from hypothyroidism (insufficient activity of the thyroid), which means that the gland does not tend to take up a normal amount of iodine. Under these circumstances, the big problem is to give sufficient radioactive iodine so that enough will accumulate in the gland to destroy the cancer tissue there.

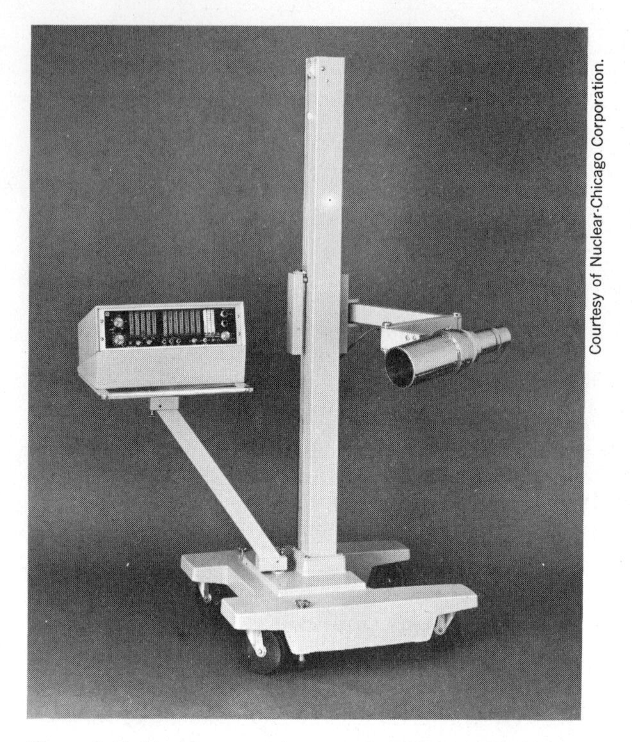

Courtesy of Nuclear-Chicago Corporation.

Figure A-11 Machine used for evaluation of thyroid function.

Radioactive iodine is also used in medicine as an aid in locating brain tumors. Diiodofluorescein, containing iodine-131, selectively locates itself in tumor tissue in the brain. This helps solve a difficult problem for the brain surgeon: the exact location of the tumor. By a Geiger counter, which is placed in various positions about the head, and by simple geometry, one can estimate the exact source of the radiation and the site of the tumor. This has proved effective in more than 90% of cases tested.

$^{32}_{15}P$

Phosphorus-32 is produced by bombarding sulfur of atomic weight 32 with neutrons.

$$^{32}_{16}\mathbf{S} + ^{1}_{0}n \longrightarrow ^{32}_{15}\mathbf{P} + ^{1}_{1}\mathbf{H}$$

Radioactive phosphorus-32 is a strong β ray emitter but apparently does not emit a significant amount of gamma radiation. Since the half-life of phosphorus-32 is 14.3 days, production, shipment, and quick usage are important considerations.

USE

Radioactive phosphorus, in the form of sodium phosphate, has been used very successfully in the treatment of polycythemia vera, a condition in which the formation of the red blood cells is abnormally rapid. In this disease, phosphorus-32 is the drug of choice. Almost all of the disease symptoms are destroyed by proper dosage of the radioactive isotope. Phosphorus-32 is of no value in acute leukemia, but it is somewhat successful in treatment of cases of chronic myelogenous leukemia.

$^{198}_{79}Au$

Radioactive gold is made by irradiating stable gold-197 by means of neutrons in a pile. The radioactive isotope-198, whose half life is 2.8 days, is employed in medicine most frequently in the form of colloidal gold.

$$^{197}_{79}\mathbf{Au} + ^{1}_{0}n \longrightarrow ^{198}_{79}\mathbf{Au}$$

This isotope is very strongly radioactive. It gives off a powerful β particle as it changes into a stable mercury isotope. Gold-198 emits powerful gamma radiation, similar to radium. Actually, colloidal gold-198 is more powerful than radium; 64 mg of gold-198 is equivalent to 330 mg of radium. For this reason, radioactive gold will tend to displace radium from many radiological techniques. The short half-life of gold-198 may pose certain problems, although it has been shipped by air mail from this country to Europe and used successfully there. Even if half the radiation is gone in several days, the material was originally so powerful that the remaining half is still very potent.

USE

Radioactive gold-198 may find increasing use in treatment of certain cases of lymphosarcoma. The colloidal material is injected directly into tumor tissue in carefully controlled amounts. In some cases, amazing destruction of the cancer has resulted. One objection is the staining of the tissue due to the presence of the colloidal metal. This may not be a sure cure for certain cancer cases, but it may help in greatly prolonging the life of afflicted patients. One of the big problems always will be the extent of breakdown of cancer tissue and subsequent distribution throughout the body (metastases). If cancer is localized, this treatment may be of great value, but if the cancer tissues have formed in various places of the body, the destruction of cancer tissue in one area is of limited value in prolonging the life of the patient.

$^{24}_{11}Na$

Radioactive sodium-24 is made by irradiating the stable sodium atom with neutrons.

$$^{23}_{11}\mathbf{Na} + ^{1}_{0}n \longrightarrow ^{24}_{11}\mathbf{Na}$$

Sodium-24 has a half-life of 14.8 hours. The radioactive isotope emits an extremely powerful β particle as it decays, and it simultaneously gives off a γ ray of such intensity that it easily penetrates throughout the entire body. The very short half-life of this radioactive isotope poses a difficult problem in production and transportation.

USE

Sodium-24 has found limited use in experimental work in tracing blood circulation in the body, and in the discovery of blocked blood vessels.

$^{90}_{38}Sr$

Strontium-90 is one of the products of atomic fallout. Because of the similarity of the chemistry of calcium and strontium, the body cannot readily distinguish between the two elements; strontium is then incorporated into the body tissue, along with the calcium, where it decays. As more and more radioactive isotopes, such as strontium-90, accumulate in our bodies, considerable controversy has arisen concerning the effect of these radioactive isotopes on our offspring and, in fact, on the future of the human race. This matter has been, and still is, of international importance and has resulted in treaties banning the use of atomic explosions in which the atomic fallout represents a hazard to all living people.

Other isotopes that offer great promise are: K-42, Mn-52, Cu-64, Zn-72, Kr-91, Sr-91, Ag-106 and 111, Cd-115, Sb-121 and 127, Xe-133, W-187, Bi-206, Co-60, and Fe-55.

Dangers in the Use of Radioactive Substances

A radioactive substance may enter the human system in three principal ways: ingestion, inhalation, and incision (or puncture). Part of the radioactive substance remains in the body, where it is distributed by the blood stream; the remainder is eliminated in the exhaled air, in expectoration, in perspiration, in the feces, or in the urine. Some of the radioactivity in the human system is reduced considerably by natural radioactive decay. Consequently, in hospitals, for instance, where radioactive materials are eliminated by patients, proper care should be taken in handling urine, feces, etc.

2

appendix

IUPAC nomenclature rules

Preferential and Nonpreferential Groups

In naming organic compounds, certain groups (called preferential groups) have preference for the lowest number.

The following groups are listed in descending order of preference:

1.	—COOH	carboxyl (highest preference)
2.	>C=O	ketone
3.	—CHO	aldehyde
4.	—OH	alcohol
5.	—C≡C—	triple bond
6.	$-\overset{}{\underset{|}{C}}=\underset{|}{C}-$	double bond

Some nonpreferential groups are $-NH_2$ (amine); —X (halogen); —OR (ether); —R (alkyl); —Ar (aryl).

If there are two or more preferential groups in a molecule, the most preferential (see list) gets the choice for the lowest number. For example,

```
4     3   2       1
CH3—C—CH2—COOH
γ     ‖β  α
      O
```

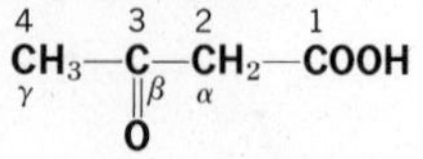

β-ketobutyric acid
3-oxobutanoic acid

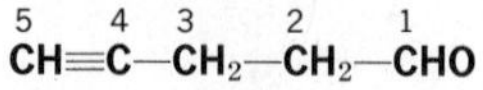

```
5     4    3       2       1
CH≡C—CH2—CH2—CHO
```

4-pentyne-1-al

```
5       4       3       2  1
CH2═CH—CH2—C≡CH
```

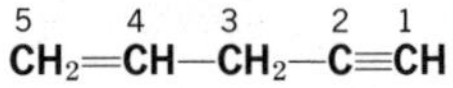

4-pentene-1-yne

If a preferential and a nonpreferential group are in the same molecule, obviously the preferential group is assigned the lowest number. For example,

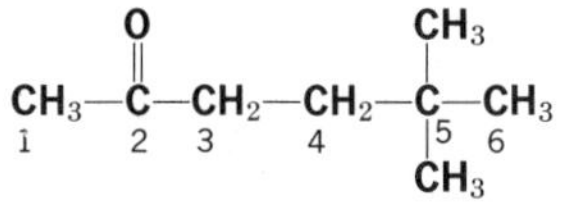

```
       O                      CH3
       ‖                      |
CH3—C—CH2—CH2—C—CH3
1      2   3       4      |5   6
                            CH3
```

5,5-dimethyl-2-hexanone

```
       Cl  Cl
       |   |    6       5       4       3       2       1
CH3—C—C—CH2—CH2—CH2—CH2—CH2—COOH
9      |8  |7
       Cl  Cl
```

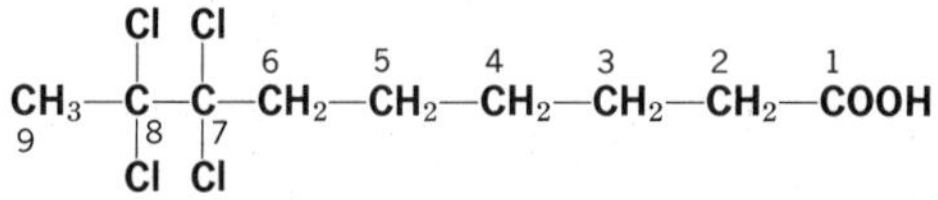

7,7,8,8-tetrachlorononanoic acid

If a molecule contains only nonpreferential groups, the numbering preference is to select the first occurring lowest number. For example,

```
        CH3                   CH3
1       |2    3      4        |5    6      7
CH3—C——CH—CH2—C——CH—CH3
7       |6    |5     4        |3  2|       1
        CH3  CH3             CH3  CH3
```

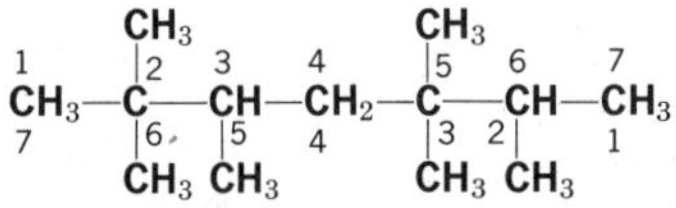

If we number from the left, the name is

(a) 2,2,3,5,5,6-hexamethylheptane.

If we number from the right, the name is

(b) 2,3,3,5,6,6-hexamethylheptane.

In both (a) and (b) we began the name with 2. In sequence (a) the second number is 2, whereas in (b) the second number is 3; thus, sequence (a) is correct.

Groups with No Common Name

To name a group that has no common name, we simply utilize the existing rules as follows:

```
 1     2     3     4     5    6     7     8     9     10    11
CH3—CH2—CH2—CH2—CH—CH2—CH2—CH2—CH2—CH2—CH3
                    |1
               CH3—C—CH3
                   2|
                    CH2
                   3|
                    CH3
```

5-(1,1-dimethylpropyl)undecane

```
1  2  3  4  5  6  7  8  9  10  11  12  13
CH2CH2CH2CH2CH2CHCH2CH2CH2CH2CH2CH2CH3
                1|
                 CH · CH3
                2|
      CH3—CH2—C—CH3
                3|
                 CH2
                4|
                 CH3
```

6-(1,2-dimethyl-2-ethylbutyl)tridecane

Structures of Equal Chain Lengths

If there is a choice between two structures of equal chain lengths, select the one with the greatest number of branches. Let us consider two ways to name the following compound:

```
 4     3    2  1                          2  1
CH3—CH—C=CH2                    CH3—CH—C=CH2
      |    |                           |  3|
     CH3  CH2                         CH3  CH2
           |                              4|
          CH3                              CH3
```

(a) 2-ethyl-3-methyl-1-butene (b) 2-isopropyl-1-butene

Structure (a) has two branches (one at carbon 2 and one at carbon 3) and (b) has only one branch, namely, that at carbon 2. Therefore, structure (a) is correct.

Appendix 3 Logarithms

Natural numbers	0	1	2	3	4	5	6	7	8	9	*Proportional parts*								
											1	2	3	4	5	6	7	8	9
10	0000	0043	0086	0128	0170	0212	0253	0294	0334	0374	4	8	12	17	21	25	29	33	37
11	0414	0453	0492	0531	0569	0607	0645	0682	0719	0755	4	8	11	15	19	23	26	30	34
12	0792	0828	0864	0899	0934	0969	1004	1038	1072	1106	3	7	10	14	17	21	24	28	31
13	1139	1173	1206	1239	1271	1303	1335	1367	1399	1430	3	6	10	13	16	19	23	26	29
14	1461	1492	1523	1553	1584	1614	1644	1673	1703	1732	3	6	9	12	15	18	21	24	27
15	1761	1790	1818	1847	1875	1903	1931	1959	1987	2014	3	6	8	11	14	17	20	22	25
16	2041	2068	2095	2122	2148	2175	2201	2227	2253	2279	3	5	8	11	13	16	18	21	24
17	2304	2330	2355	2380	2405	2430	2455	2480	2504	2529	2	5	7	10	12	15	17	20	22
18	2553	2577	2601	2625	2648	2672	2695	2718	2742	2765	2	5	7	9	12	14	16	19	21
19	2788	2810	2833	2856	2878	2900	2923	2945	2967	2989	2	4	7	9	11	13	16	18	20
20	3010	3032	3054	3075	3096	3118	3139	3160	3181	3201	2	4	6	8	11	13	15	17	19
21	3222	3243	3263	3284	3304	3324	3345	3365	3385	3404	2	4	6	8	10	12	14	16	18
22	3424	3444	3464	3483	3502	3522	3541	3560	3579	3598	2	4	6	8	10	12	14	15	17
23	3617	3636	3655	3674	3692	3711	3729	3747	3766	3784	2	4	6	7	9	11	13	15	17
24	3802	3820	3838	3856	3874	3892	3909	3927	3945	3962	2	4	5	7	9	11	12	14	16
25	3979	3997	4014	4031	4048	4065	4082	4099	4116	4133	2	3	5	7	9	10	12	14	15
26	4150	4166	4183	4200	4216	4232	4249	4265	4281	4298	2	3	5	7	8	10	11	13	15
27	4314	4330	4346	4362	4378	4393	4409	4425	4440	4456	2	3	5	6	8	9	11	13	14
28	4472	4487	4502	4518	4533	4548	4564	4579	4594	4609	2	3	5	6	8	9	11	12	14
29	4624	4639	4654	4669	4683	4698	4713	4728	4742	4757	1	3	4	6	7	9	10	12	13
30	4771	4786	4800	4814	4829	4843	4857	4871	4886	4900	1	3	4	6	7	9	10	11	13
31	4914	4928	4942	4955	4969	4983	4997	5011	5024	5038	1	3	4	6	7	8	10	11	12
32	5051	5065	5079	5092	5105	5119	5132	5145	5159	5172	1	3	4	5	7	8	9	11	12
33	5185	5198	5211	5224	5237	5250	5263	5276	5289	5302	1	3	4	5	6	8	9	10	12
34	5315	5328	5340	5353	5366	5378	5391	5403	5416	5428	1	3	4	5	6	8	9	10	11
35	5441	5453	5465	5478	5490	5502	5514	5527	5539	5551	1	2	4	5	6	7	9	10	11
36	5563	5575	5587	5599	5611	5623	5635	5647	5658	5670	1	2	4	5	6	7	8	10	11
37	5682	5694	5705	5717	5729	5740	5752	5763	5775	5786	1	2	3	5	6	7	8	9	10
38	5798	5809	5821	5832	5843	5855	5866	5877	5888	5899	1	2	3	5	6	7	8	9	10
39	5911	5922	5933	5944	5955	5966	5977	5988	5999	6010	1	2	3	4	5	7	8	9	10
40	6021	6031	6042	6053	6064	6075	6085	6096	6107	6117	1	2	3	4	5	6	8	9	10
41	6128	6138	6149	6160	6170	6180	6191	6201	6212	6222	1	2	3	4	5	6	7	8	9
42	6232	6243	6253	6263	6274	6284	6294	6304	6314	6325	1	2	3	4	5	6	7	8	9
43	6335	6345	6355	6365	6375	6385	6395	6405	6415	6425	1	2	3	4	5	6	7	8	9
44	6435	6444	6454	6464	6474	6484	6493	6503	6513	6522	1	2	3	4	5	6	7	8	9
45	6532	6542	6551	6561	6571	6580	6590	6599	6609	6618	1	2	3	4	5	6	7	8	9
46	6628	6637	6646	6656	6665	6675	6684	6693	6702	6712	1	2	3	4	5	6	7	7	8
47	6721	6730	6739	6749	6758	6767	6776	6785	6794	6803	1	2	3	4	5	5	6	7	8
48	6812	6821	6830	6839	6848	6857	6866	6875	6884	6893	1	2	3	4	4	5	6	7	8
49	6902	6911	6920	6928	6937	6946	6955	6964	6972	6981	1	2	3	4	4	5	6	7	8
50	6990	6998	7007	7016	7024	7033	7042	7050	7059	7067	1	2	3	3	4	5	6	7	8
51	7076	7084	7093	7101	7110	7118	7126	7135	7143	7152	1	2	3	3	4	5	6	7	8
52	7160	7168	7177	7185	7193	7202	7210	7218	7226	7235	1	2	2	3	4	5	6	7	7
53	7243	7251	7259	7267	7275	7284	7292	7300	7308	7316	1	2	2	3	4	5	6	6	7
54	7324	7332	7340	7348	7456	7364	7372	7380	7388	7396	1	2	2	3	4	5	6	6	7

(Continued)

Appendix 3 (Continued)

Natural numbers	0	1	2	3	4	5	6	7	8	9	*Proportional parts*								
											1	2	3	4	5	6	7	8	9
55	7404	7412	7419	7427	7435	7443	7451	7459	7466	7474	1	2	2	3	4	5	5	6	7
56	7482	7490	7497	7505	7513	7520	7528	7536	7543	7551	1	2	2	3	4	5	5	6	7
57	7559	7566	7574	7582	7589	7597	7604	7612	7619	7627	1	2	2	3	4	5	5	6	7
58	7634	7642	7649	7657	7664	7672	7679	7686	7694	7701	1	1	2	3	4	4	5	6	7
59	7709	7716	7723	7731	7738	7745	7752	7760	7767	7774	1	1	2	3	4	4	5	6	7
60	7782	7789	7796	7803	7810	7818	7825	7832	7839	7846	1	1	2	3	4	4	5	6	6
61	7853	7860	7868	7875	7882	7889	7896	7903	7910	7917	1	1	2	3	4	4	5	6	6
62	7924	7931	7938	7945	7952	7959	7966	7973	7980	7987	1	1	2	3	3	4	5	6	6
63	7993	8000	8007	8014	8021	8028	8035	8041	8048	8055	1	1	2	3	3	4	5	5	6
64	8062	8069	8075	8082	8089	8096	8102	8109	8116	8122	1	1	2	3	3	4	5	5	6
65	8129	8136	8142	8149	8156	8162	8169	8176	8182	8189	1	1	2	3	3	4	5	5	6
66	8195	8202	8209	8215	8222	8228	8235	8241	8248	8254	1	1	2	3	3	4	5	5	6
67	8261	8267	8274	8280	8287	8293	8299	8306	8312	8319	1	1	2	3	3	4	5	5	6
68	8325	8331	8338	8344	8351	8357	8363	8370	8376	8382	1	1	2	3	3	4	4	5	6
69	8388	8395	8401	8407	8414	8420	8426	8432	8439	8445	1	1	2	2	3	4	4	5	6
70	8451	8457	8463	8470	8476	8482	8488	8494	8500	8506	1	1	2	2	3	4	4	5	6
71	8513	8519	8525	8531	8537	8543	8549	8555	8561	8567	1	1	2	2	3	4	4	5	5
72	8573	8579	8585	8591	8597	8603	8609	8615	8621	8627	1	1	2	2	3	4	4	5	5
73	8633	8639	8645	8651	8657	8663	8669	8675	8681	8686	1	1	2	2	3	4	4	5	5
74	8692	8698	8704	8710	8716	8722	8727	8733	8739	8745	1	1	2	2	3	4	4	5	5
75	8751	8756	8762	8768	8774	8779	8785	8791	8797	8802	1	1	2	2	3	3	4	5	5
76	8808	8814	8820	8825	8831	8837	8842	8848	8854	8859	1	1	2	2	3	3	4	5	5
77	8865	8871	8876	8882	8887	8893	8899	8904	8910	8915	1	1	2	2	3	3	4	4	5
78	8921	8927	8932	8938	8943	8949	8954	8960	8965	8971	1	1	2	2	3	3	4	4	5
79	8976	8982	8987	8993	8998	9004	9009	9015	9020	9026	1	1	2	2	3	3	4	4	5
80	9031	9036	9042	9047	9053	9058	9063	9069	9074	9079	1	1	2	2	3	3	4	4	5
81	9085	9090	9096	9101	9106	9112	9117	9122	9128	9133	1	1	2	2	3	3	4	4	5
82	9138	9143	9149	9154	9159	9165	9170	9175	9180	9186	1	1	2	2	3	3	4	4	5
83	9191	9196	9201	9206	9212	9217	9222	9227	9232	9238	1	1	2	2	3	3	4	4	5
84	9243	9248	9253	9258	9263	9269	9274	9279	9284	9289	1	1	2	2	3	3	4	4	5
85	9294	9299	9304	9309	9315	9320	9325	9330	9335	9340	1	1	2	2	3	3	4	4	5
86	9345	9350	9355	9360	9365	9370	9375	9380	9385	9390	1	1	2	2	3	3	4	4	5
87	9395	9400	9405	9410	9415	9420	9425	9430	9435	9440	0	1	1	2	2	3	3	4	4
88	9445	9450	9455	9460	9465	9469	9474	9479	9484	9489	0	1	1	2	2	3	3	4	4
89	9494	9499	9504	9509	9513	9518	9523	9528	9533	9538	0	1	1	2	2	3	3	4	4
90	9542	9547	9552	9557	9562	9566	9571	9576	9581	9586	0	1	1	2	2	3	3	4	4
91	9590	9595	9600	9605	9609	9614	9619	9624	9628	9633	0	1	1	2	2	3	3	4	4
92	9638	9643	9647	9652	9657	9661	9666	9671	9675	9680	0	1	1	2	2	3	3	4	4
93	9685	9689	9694	9699	9703	9708	9713	9717	9722	9727	0	1	1	2	2	3	3	4	4
94	9731	9736	9741	9745	9750	9754	9759	9763	9768	9773	0	1	1	2	2	3	3	4	4
95	9777	9782	9786	9791	9795	9800	9805	9809	9814	9818	0	1	1	2	2	3	3	4	4
96	9823	9827	9832	9836	9841	9845	9850	9854	9859	9863	0	1	1	2	2	3	3	4	4
97	9868	9872	9877	9881	9886	9890	9894	9899	9903	9908	0	1	1	2	2	3	3	4	4
98	9912	9917	9921	9926	9930	9934	9939	9943	9948	9952	0	1	1	2	2	3	3	4	4
99	9956	9961	9965	9969	9974	9978	9983	9987	9991	9996	0	1	1	2	2	3	3	3	4

index

Page numbers followed by *t* indicate references to tables.

table of atomic weights (based on carbon-12)

ELEMENT	SYMBOL	ATOMIC NUMBER	ATOMIC WEIGHT
Actinium	Ac	89	(227) *
Aluminum	Al	13	26.9815
Americium	Am	95	(243)
Antimony	Sb	51	121.75
Argon	Ar	18	39.948
Arsenic	As	33	74.9216
Astatine	At	85	(210)
Barium	Ba	56	137.34
Berkelium	Bk	97	(247)
Beryllium	Be	4	9.0122
Bismuth	Bi	83	208.980
Boron	B	5	10.811
Bromine	Br	35	79.909
Cadmium	Cd	48	112.40
Calcium	Ca	20	40.08
Californium	Cf	98	(249)
Carbon	C	6	12.01115
Cerium	Ce	58	140.12
Cesium	Cs	55	132.905
Chlorine	Cl	17	35.453
Chromium	Cr	24	51.996
Cobalt	Co	27	58.9332
Copper	Cu	29	63.54
Curium	Cm	96	(247)
Dysprosium	Dy	66	162.50
Einsteinium	Es	99	(254)
Erbium	Er	68	167.26
Europium	Eu	63	151.96
Fermium	Fm	100	(253)
Fluorine	F	9	18.9984
Francium	Fr	87	(223)
Gadolinium	Gd	64	157.25
Gallium	Ga	31	69.72
Germanium	Ge	32	72.59
Gold	Au	79	196.967
Hafnium	Hf	72	178.49
Helium	He	2	4.0026
Holmium	Ho	67	164.930
Hydrogen	H	1	1.00797
Indium	In	49	114.82
Iodine	I	53	126.9044
Iridium	Ir	77	192.2
Iron	Fe	26	55.847
Krypton	Kr	36	83.80
Lanthanum	La	57	138.91
Lawrencium	Lw	103	(257)
Lead	Pb	82	207.19
Lithium	Li	3	6.939
Lutetium	Lu	71	174.97
Magnesium	Mg	12	24.312
Manganese	Mn	25	54.9380
Mendelevium	Md	101	(256)

* ( ) indicates the most stable or best-known nuclide, all nuclides of the element being radioactive.